ENVIRONMENT and PEOPLE

An Integrated Course for A and AS Geography

General Editor
Michael Witherick

David Elcome
Norman Law
Roger Robinson
Murray Thomas
Sue Warn
Judith Woodfield

STANLEY THORNES

Stanley Thornes (Publishers) Ltd

First published in 1995 by:
Stanley Thornes (Publishers) Ltd
Ellenborough House
Wellington Street
CHELTENHAM GL50 1YW
England

Reprinted 1995 (twice)

A catalogue record for this book is available from the British Library.

ISBN 0 7487 2120 7

Printed and bound in Singapore by Craft Print.

Managing editor: John Day
Editor: Katherine James
Picture researcher: Anne Lyons
Designed and produced by Gecko Limited

Acknowledgements
Photograph credits
The authors and publisher thank the following for permission to reproduce their photographs in this book. Reference is by figure number and the abbreviations are BC Bruce Coleman, FLPA Frank Lane Picture Agency, OSF Oxford Scientific Films, PP Panos Pictures, SPL Science Photo Library:

Aerofilms 23.15, Heather Angel 17.4, BC/ M P L Fogden 2.6r, BC/Bob and Clara Calhoun 8.10, BC/Leonard Lee Rue 16.5, BC/Frances Furlong 19.6, Colorsport 22.11c, DRIK/Dr Shahidul Alam 34.9tr, Ecoscene/Sally Morgan 3.5, Ecoscene/Mark Tweedie 4.2, Ecoscene/Nick Hawkes 5.15, Edifice 24.30, David Elcome 13.1, 13.9, 14.2, 14.8, 14.18, 14.19, 17.6, 18.2, 18.5, 18.8, 18.9, 18.15, 18.16, 19.3l, 19.9, 19.19, Mary Evans Picture Library 19.15, Eye Ubiquitous/Dorothy Burrows 7.10, Eye Ubiquitous/V C Sievey 24.16, FLPA/W Broadhurst 5.6, FLPA/E and D Hosking 14.6, FLPA/W Wisniewski 15.2, 15.9, 17.7, FLPA/Silvestris 16.2t, FLPA/Steve McCutcheon 16.6, FLPA/C Carvalho 16.7, FLPA/D P Wilson 17.1, FLPA/P Harding 18.4, FLPA/Roger Tidman 19.5, FLPA/Fritz Polking 19.14, Leslie Garland Picture Library/John Morrison 19.12, Geonex 31.6, GeoScience Features 2.6l, 5.6, Haverfordwest Library 12.1t, Grant Heilman Photography 15.8, © Paul Huffman 11.22, Anthony King 18.19, Josephine Law 22.13, Magnum/Sebastiao Salgado 15.13, Magnum/Gilles Peress 22.2(c), NHPA/John Shaw 16.1, NHPA/David Woodfall 18.1, 18.10, Network/Justin Leighton 22.12, Network/C Pillitz 32.13, Peter Newark's Pictures 24.5, 35.11, Orion Press, Tokyo 2.13, OSF/Michael Pitts 6.2, OSF/Ronald Toms 10.13(a, b, c), OSF Earth Scenes/R F Head 10.13(d) OSF/Martyn Chillmaid 10.13(e), OSF/Warren Faidly 11.18, OSF/Jim Hallet 13.6, OSF/D J Saunders 14.10, OSF/M Wendler 14.16, OSF/David Cayles 15.4, OSF/Eyal Bartov 15.7l, OSF/Doug Allen 16.3, OSF/Waina Chang 17.2, OSF/Howard Hall 17.18, OSF/Peter Parks 17.20, OSF/Terry Heathcote 19.4, PP/Trygve Bolstad 14.21, PP/J Hartley 15.5, PP/Ron Gilling 20.14r, PP/J Holmes 20.14l, 35.9, PP/B Klass 34.9br, PP/J Young 22.2(b), PP/Sean Sprague 22.2(d), 24.2, 34.12, PP/Chris Toidai 24.8, PP/Tom Learmouth 34.9tl, PP/Chris Stowers, 36.9, Planet Earth/Dr Pete Gasson 18.18, Rex Features 18.7, 29.12, Roger Robinson 31.1, 31.3, 32.7, 32.15, 32.17, 32.19, 32.20, 33.2, 33.11, Scope Features 22.11br, Skyscan Balloon Photography 31.2, 35.2, Ken Smith 14.17, 18.21, 18.22, South American Pictures/Bill Leimbach 32.1, SPL/David Leah 2.12, SPL/Simon Fraser 7.2, SPL/Sinclair Stammers 7.13, SPL/NRSC Ltd 9.3, SPL/NOAA 11.20, SPL/Nasa 12.16, SPL/Earth Satellite Corporation 14.22, SPL/Restec, Japan 17.4, 31.9, SPL/Novosti 18.25, SPL/National Snow and Ice Data Center 20.4, Frank Spooner/Chip Hires 4.21, Frank Spooner/Stephen Ferry 15.12, Still Pictures/Nigel Dickinson 14.15, Still Pictures/Mark Edwards 36.8, Murray Thomas 12.1b, Topham 22.11bl, Topham/PA/John Giles 22.11t, TRIP/Helene Rogers 6.10, 21.14, Trocaire 34.15, University of Dundee 11.10, John Watney 3.2, 17.10, 17.12, Zefa/Kurt Scholz 15.7, Zefa-DAMM 22.2(e), Zefa/Orion Press 22.2(a), 35.11b.

Other Credits
The authors and publisher are also grateful to the following for permission to reproduce their copyright materials either in their original form or in a form adapted for the purposes of this book:

Amnesty International 36.6; BBC Enterprises Ltd 35.6; B.J.L. Berry, *The Human Consequences of Urbanisation*, Macmillan 36.17; Birmingham City Council/*Annual Report 1992–93* 35.6, *Labour Market Bulletin* 33.8; Birmingham Economic Information Unit/*Employment Trends in Birmingham* Jun 1993 35.8; L. Bourne, *Urban Systems*, OUP 36.18; 'The geography of agriculture' in I.R. Bowker (ed), *D.M. Economics*, Longman 26.4; British Geology Survey 3.7; British Petroleum 27.2, 27.3, 27.6; D. Bull, *The Geography of Rural Sources*, Oliver & Boyd 36.17; A. Champion, *Counterurbanisation*, Arnold 35.20; L. Chatterjee, 'Women working in Third World cities' in R. Peet and N. Thrift (eds), *New Models in Geography* vol 2, Unwin Hyman 36.10; W. Carter, *Urban and Rural Settlements*, Longman 32.3, 33.16; S. Cumming, 'Post-colonial urban residential change in Harare' in L. Zinyama et al (eds), *Harare: View of Zimbabwe*, University of Harare 34.4, 34.5; P.W. Daniels, *Service Industries Growth and Location*, CUP 29.6, 29.7; J. Edwards, 'The UK heritage coasts – an assessment of the ecological impacts of tourism', *Annals of Tourism Research* no. 1, 1987 29.16; Financial Times Group 20.3, 20.6, 23.8; G. Giles et al, 'Trends in skin cancer in Australia', *Trans Menzies Foundation* 15, 1989 12.18; G. Gappert, 'A management perspective on cities' in R.V. Knight and G. Gappert (eds), *Cities in a Global Society*, Sage 35.18; H. Girardet, 'The metabolism of cities' in D. Cadman and G. Payne (eds), *The Living City*, Routledge 36.3; J. Gottman, 'Centres of what?' in R.V. Knight and G. Gappert (eds), *ibid* 33.3; Guardian Newspapers Ltd 27.7, 28.4; R. Gunter von Wahl and W. Kerst, 'Fusarium and didymeth – neglected spores in the air', *Aerobiologia* 7, 1991 8.14; O. Hare, *Soils and Ecosystems*, Oliver & Boyd 26.1; D. Herbert and C.J. Thomas, *Urban Geography*, Wiley 33.18; Hillier Parker 29.11; D. Horsfall, *Agriculture*, Blackwell 26.9; Institute of African Studies, *City of Kumasi Handbook* 34.16; *Japanese Education Journal* no. 41, 1989 28.15; Joint Matriculation Board 22.7, 22.8, 22.9; P. Jones, *Hydrology*, Blackwell 4.3; K. Lemberg, 'The need for autonomy; improving local democracy' in R.V. Knight and G. Gappert (eds), *ibid* 36.20; R.E. Lew et al, 'Epidemiology of cutaneous melanoma, *Symposium on Melanoma and Pigmental Lesions* 12.17; J.P. Lewis and V. Kallab (eds), *US Foreign Policy and the Third World*, Agenda 1983, Praeger 30.4; J. Logan et al 'Poverty and income equality' in S. Fainstein et al (eds), *Divided Cities*, Blackwell 36.12; P. McCullagh, *Modern Concepts in Geomorphology*, OUP 3.10, 3.11, 3.12; Midland Weekly Newspapers 35.6, 36.5, 36.6, 36.8; Mieczkowski, *A Community Approach*, Methuen 29.13; N. Myers (ed), *The Gaia Atlas of Planet Management*, Pan Books 20.2, 20.18; National Landslide Data Bank 3.8; National Trust of Northern Ireland Region 17.15; Network Migration Services 22.2; *New Internationalist* 21.11, 21.13, 21.15, 21.16; Newspaper Publishing plc 22.15, 23.12, 24.15, 24.21; OPCS 20.5; Oxfam 26.15; Pardon Services Canada 22.2; C. Park, *Environmental Hazards*, Macmillan Education 1.9; B.K. Paul, 'Female activity space in rural Bangladesh', *Geographical Review* 1, 1992 32.12; R. Prud'homme, 'New trends in cities of the world' in R.V. Knight and G. Gappart (eds), *ibid* 35.19; R. Quayle and F. Dearing, 'Heat stress', *Weatherwise* Jun 1981 8.11, 8.12; R. Robinson and I. Jackson, *People on Earth*, Longman 32.11, 33.4, 33.5, 34.3; W. Rollinson, *A History of Man in the Lake District*, Dent 32.8; *Scientific American* Sep 1989 27.5; Shell Oil 27.9, 27.10; J. Small and M. Witherick, *A Modern Dictionary of Geography*, Arnold 33.14; R.J. Small, *Geomorphology and Hydrology*, Longman 2.2, 2.3; R.J. Small, *The Study of Landforms*; CUP 3.6; C. Starr and R. Taggart, *Biology: The Unity and Diversity of Life*, Wadsworth 14.1, 15.1; Dr R.I. Thomas, Brisbane 12.15; K. Thomson (ed), *Agenda 21*, UNEP-UK 36.19; Tourism Concern 29.17; G.T. Trewartha et al, *Elements of Geography*, McGraw-Hill 9.9; 'Feeding the World' in *Understanding Global Issues*, 3–93, European School Books Collection 26.18; D. Waugh, *Geography*, Nelson 3.1, 3.4, 4.6, 33.17; D. Weyman, *Tectonic Processes*, Allen & Unwin 2.1; J.W.R. Whitehead, 'Development cycles and urban landscapes', *Geography* Jan 1994 34.2, 35.3; M. Witherick, *Population Geography*, Longman 20.1, 21.17, 23.7; M. Witherick and M. Carr, *The Changing Face of Japan*, Hodder & Stoughton 32.23, 35.12.

Information was also obtained and used from the following sources, to which the authors and publishers acknowledge their indebtedness:

Atmospheric Environment Service, Canada 10.3; 'Mortality from fog in London', *BMJ* Mar 1956; Bureau of Census, US Department of Commerce 31.11; CSO 28.2c; DoE/*Employment Gazette* 28.8ab; DTI 28.7; European Monitoring and Evaluation Programme Data/ACID Sep 1989 8.17; IAEA 27.13b; GATT/*International Trade 1988–89* 29.2; Meteorological Service, Singapore 10.3, 10.19, 10.20; New Zealand Meteorological Services 9.8; OPCS 21.21, 22.20, 23.9, 23.10, 23.16, 23.17, 24.29; Statisches Bundesamt 23.11; Tokyo Metropolitan Government 35.14; UN 30.14, *World Development Report 1992* 31.7; UNDP/*Human Development Report 1993* 28.1; UNFPA 24.3; UNIDO 28.10, 28.11; Weather Office, Sharjah Airport, UEA 10.3; World Bank 30.15, *World Development Report 1993* 21.19; World Meteorological Organisation 9.2; World Tourist Organisation 29.14; Worldwatch Institute 27.13ac.

Every effort has been made to contact copyright holders to obtain permission to reproduce copyright materials. If any have been overlooked, the publishers will make the appropriate arrangements at the first opportunity.

Contents

UNIT C Ecosystems
David Elcome

UNIT D Population
Norman Law

UNIT E Economic Activity
Sue Warn

Introduction

A new textbook to mark a unique event

This book has been especially prepared and published to coincide with a major landmark in the teaching of geography at the Advanced and Advanced Supplementary levels in the General Certificate of Education. A whole suite of new syllabuses has been introduced for first examination in June 1997. The preparation of revised syllabuses is nothing unusual in such a dynamic subject as geography. What is new – indeed unique – is that all eight GCE Boards will be launching their new syllabuses at the same time. Furthermore, all those syllabuses have been designed to accommodate clear guidelines laid down by the Secretary of State for Education in two key documents – the *Code of Practice for A/AS Examinations* and the *Subject Core for A/AS Geography*. The latter has been particularly significant, for it insists that all syllabuses should, as a basic minimum, encourage the acquisition of knowledge, understanding and skills in broadly specified areas of the subject.

The inevitable outcome of adherence to this guidance from the Secretary of State for Education are syllabuses that bear much stronger similarities than was the case with their forebears. Indeed, one might claim that spatial differences in the content, emphases and directions of geography teaching and examination throughout England, Wales and Northern Ireland have been greatly reduced. Never has there been such a closeness of focus between the GCE Boards and their syllabuses.

In this new scenario of syllabus convergence, a unique opportunity has arisen to prepare a single textbook that meets the basic requirements of all syllabuses. This was never possible in the past. Not only does *Environment and People* seize this opportunity, it also acknowledges another unique ingredient in the present situation: namely that those candidates sitting the early examinations of these new syllabuses will be students who have made a pioneering way through the National Curriculum. Truly, they represent a new 'breed' of student. Equally, they deserve a new 'breed' of textbook that recognises and builds on the particular traits of their training up to Key Stage 4 or its equivalent.

The case for a new textbook is further strengthened by the very nature of geography. A widely accepted definition of geography as 'the study of the Earth's surface as the environment in which people live' fails to underline two distinct dynamic aspects of the subject. First, the relationships between these two key ingredients of the **environment** and **people** are constantly changing over both space and time. Secondly, whilst there is this focus on the interaction of physical and human processes, the perceptions, priorities and emphases of geographers themselves also change over time in harmony with the mood-swings of economy and society. At the end of the 20th century, the world is slowly recovering from probably its worst-ever economic recession. This prolonged downturn has thwarted development and frustrated human progress. In this global scenario, the mix of topics and issues rising towards the top of the agenda are those at the interface between environment and people. They include popular concern for the environment, sustainable development, health and well-being, leisure and recreation. *Environment and People* seeks to embrace these and other contemporary concerns and to integrate them into a geographical analysis of a world caught in unending transition.

A message for teachers

Three particular aspects of *Environment and People* need to be brought to your attention.

The contributors

Preparation of this book has involved seven contributors, all of whom have considerable experience of teaching and examining geography at this level. For example, three of them share over 30 years of service as Chief Examiners for three GCE Boards and a fourth has served for 25 years as an Assistant Examiner. Two of these are part-time consultants to the Schools Curriculum and Assessment Authority. As for 'chalkface' experience, two are currently teaching geography and two have recently retired from university appointments in geography and education. One of them is now employed by a Development Education Centre. Supplementing this wealth and diversity of educational experience, three members of the team are engaged in work outside the classroom. One is applying geography on an everyday basis as a marketing consultant, whilst two others work for the Royal Society for the Protection of Birds, using their geographical knowledge and understanding in the promotion of conservation and environmental management.

Achieving an integrated approach

Environment and People makes a concerted effort to reconcile the dichotomy created by another demand placed on the designers of the new-generation syllabuses: namely to produce structures that can be delivered and examined in a modular manner. Learning and assessment on the instalment plan do not fit easily with the holistic and integrative nature of geography. This problem is not a new one, for it has long been the tradition to divide the subject into systematic components. Subdivisions such as 'Landforms and Water', 'Weather and Climate', 'Population' and 'Settlement' have a familiar and reassuring ring. Although the descriptors may have changed, they are still there in spirit in most of the new syllabuses. How else can you teach the basics of the subject other than in convenient, discrete parts? Such a natural tendency has been reinforced, of course, by the widespread introduction of modular syllabuses. In counteracting this disaggregation, the crucial art is to weave and integrate, and progressively establish those interrelationships between phenomena that are such a vital part of geography.

A number of new textbooks claim to pursue an integrated approach to the subject. In the case of *Environment and People*, integration is pursued at four distinct levels:

- The first links are those that prevail within each of the six systematic units, as for example the important process–form relationships that are formative influences on the environment.

- Then there are those links of content and concept that bind two or more branches of the subject. This might be illustrated by the connection in physical geography between climate change and landforms; in human geography, between the location of economic activity and the land-use patterns of settlements; and at the interface between physical and human geography by the pressure of population on ecosystems.

- It is possible to identify a small number of major topics that reach across the breadth of the subject, particularly across the physical–human interface. Although they may not be entirely freestanding, they are sufficiently overarching as to command great power as potential bonding agents. Systems and natural hazards constitute two such integrating themes.

- Finally, there is the obvious geographical integration that flows from a multifaceted study of a particular place. The definition of *place* can range in scale from the global to the local, but the crucial thing is the coming together of all the different strands and perspectives of geography in a single location.

It is in these last two levels of integration that this book breaks new ground. Eight **integrating themes** have been defined and each is picked up and pursued to varying degrees in all of the six units. Each is launched in the most appropriate unit. The matrix that follows identifies the themes, their key ideas and where they are taken up; relevant text and illustrative materials are also flagged *in situ* accordingly.

Matrix 1: Integrating themes (ITs)

| 1.1 | decimal numbers refer to sections of the book | p. | page number |
| CS | case study | **IT1** | flag identifying reference to an integrating theme |

Integrating Theme Key Ideas	Unit A	Unit B	Unit C	Unit D	Unit E	Unit F
IT1 Systems A system is a set of interrelated parts or objects connected together to form a working unit or unified whole. Given its stress on interrelationships, the adoption of a systems approach is particularly appropriate and helpful in geography.	1.1 1.2 1.6 3.5 4.1 5.0 5.4 5.5 5.6 7.3 7.7	8.3 12.7	13.1 13.2 13.5 13.6	21.1	25.1 25.2 26.1 26.3 28.1 28.2 28.3	36.2 36.8

Integrating Theme Key Ideas	Unit A	Unit B	Unit C	Unit D	Unit E	Unit F
IT2 Natural Hazards The world is a hazardous place. There is a whole range of natural events that threaten people in some way or another. People themselves can both trigger and intensify hazards. Perception plays an important part in the evaluation of risk and in hazard adjustment.	1.3 1.4 1.5 1.6 2.3 CS p.16 2.4 CS p.18 CS p.19 2.5 3.3 CS p.26 4.7 CS p.46 CS p.60 6.1 6.5 CS p.71 CS p.79 7.7	CS p.93 8.5 10.5 10.8 11.6 CS p.142 11.7 CS p.148 12.1 12.7	CS p.190 CS p.194 15.1 CS p.210	22.1	26.6 27.6 CS p.364	36.8
IT3 Pollution Pollution is the release of energy and substances into the environment by a range of human actions in such quantities as to harm living things and to impair environmental amenity. Pollution is a major threat; reducing it is an urgent challenge.	3.1 CS p.23	8.1 CS p.87 CS p.89 CS p.100 CS p.152 12.6	CS p.185 17.6 CS p.226	24.3	26.6 27.1 27.4 CS p.364 28.7	36.2 36.8
IT4 Sustainability Sustainability is to achieve, through the wise use of resources and appropriate technology, a mode of development that meets the needs of today without compromising the ability of future generations to meet their needs. Reconciling the conflicts between development and conservation.	CS p.19	8.1 CS p.93 12.6	13.8 14.3 CS p.192 15.1 CS p.203 17.3 Cs p.236 19.2 19.4	24.1 24.2 24.3	25.2 25.3 26.5 CS p.344 26.7 27.5 Cs p.362 27.7 CS p.368 27.8 29.7 30.1 30.5 30.7	32.6 CS p.489 36.4 36.8
IT5 Health & Well-being These are key aspects of quality of life and are good indicators of level of development, service provision and social justice. Equally, they provide irrefutable evidence of the spatial inequalities that characterise today's global society,	1.3 1.5 CS p.16 CS p.18	CS p.87 CS p.89 8.4 CS p.98 8.5	19.8	20.3 21.3 21.4 CS p.275 21.5	25.4 26.6 26.7 27.1	CS p.462 CS p.463 CS p.477 CS p.479 CS p.481

Integrating Theme Key Ideas	Unit A	Unit B	Unit C	Unit D	Unit E	Unit F
from inner-city deprivation and suburban affluence to the North–South divide.		12.6 12.7 CS p.162		CS p.304 24.4 24.5 24.6 CS p.321 CS p.323	27.6 28.7 30.1 30.2 30.3 30.5 30.7	34.4 CS p.491 36.3 36.5 36.7 36.8
IT6 Leisure & Recreation The growth of leisure and recreation represents a major development of the 20th century. They are of increasing consequence in terms of the economy, the environment and well-being. Whilst demand is largely rooted in the developed world, the supply side is more evenly distributed.	CS p.80	12.7	15.1 16.3 CS p.234 19.5 19.7	CS p.304	29.7	CS p.460 36.8
IT7 Competition & Conflict Modern society is marked by competition between different interest groups for space and resources. As in all competitive situations, there is discrimination between winners and losers, as well as the generation of conflict. Both processes are key triggers of change and development.	CS p.60 5.6 CS p.80	CS p.93	14.3 CS p.190 14.4 16.3 CS p.217 CS p.218 CS p.220 CS p.222 17.5 18.3 CS p.233 CS p.234 19.1 19.7	22.5 CS p.290 CS p.292 CS p.295 CS p.307	CS p.356 CS p.374 CS p.378 CS p.382 CS p.385 29.5 29.7 30.3 30.6	CS p.459 CS p.461 33.3 33.4 CS p.479 CS p.489 CS p.491 35.4 36.4 36.6 36.7 36.8 36.9
IT8 Environmental Change Environments change over a wide range of time scales, in different ways and to varying degrees. Change may be the result of natural processes. However, it is increasingly the outcome, both deliberate and accidental, of human activities largely to do with resource exploitation and settlement.	CS p.46 5.5 CS p.60 5.6 6.5 CS p.71 6.6 7.7	CS p.109 12.1 12.2 12.3 12.4 CS p.152 12.5 CS p.155 12.6 12.7	13.7 13.8 14.1 CS p.179 14.2 14.3 CS p.184 15.1 CS p.202 CS p.203 CS p.206 CS p.207 CS p.210 CS p.220 17.6 18.2 CS p.231 CS p.238 19.7	21.6	26.6 27.4 CS p.362 29.7 30.7	31.3 32.5 CS p.453 34.1 35.1 35.2 35.4 35.6 36.8

Similarly, two **integrating places** of contrasting scale, environment and development level have been defined. In a sense, there is nothing special or exclusive about our choice of Tokyo and Japan, or India and its neighbouring states. No doubt there are as good, if not more rewarding, parts of the globe that merit particular attention, and you are encouraged to find your own 'regional' exemplars. The vital point concerns the bene-fits to be gained from regularly touching base with the same areas, as one works through the systematic and thematic range of the subject. The first is a heightened awareness of spatial interrelationships, and the second is an 'earthing' of study to the real world. As with the integrating themes, the matrix below indicates where there is sustained reference to either place, and again relevant text and illustrations are flagged *in situ*.

Matrix 2: Integrating places (IPs)

Integrating Place Basic data	Unit A	Unit B	Unit C	Unit D	Unit E	Unit F
IP1 Tokyo & Japan Area ('000 km^2) – Tokyo 2 – Japan 378 Population (millions) – Tokyo 12 – Japan 125	CS p.19	CS p.89	CS p.220	Activity 22 p.269 23.1	CS p.374 CS p.378 29.4	31.3 31.4 CS p.453 CS p.461 CS p.491
IP2 India & neighbouring states Area ('000 km^2) – India 3288 – Bangladesh 144 – Nepal 141 – Pakistan 796 Population (millions) – India 800 – Bangladesh – Nepal 18 – Pakistan 105	CS p.46	9.3	14.4 CS p.194 CS p.207 CS p.233	21.3 CS p.275	CS p.344 CS p.362	31.4 31.6 31.7 32.2 32.3 CS p.449 33.1 CS p.460 34.1 CS p.477

Case studies

Also helping to keep this book in touch with the real world are the case studies, which are to be found in almost all of the chapters. Their prime aim is to support and exemplify, but because of constraints set by the publishers on the overall dimensions of this book, we would be the first to admit that there is considerable scope for:

■ extracting more from them in a classroom context, and

■ introducing case studies of your own to reinforce the themes and other subject areas.

A message for students

Making the most of this book

There are a number of features of this book designed to help you make the fullest use of its contents, as well as to help you with your course:

■ All chapters are punctuated by what we call 'Activities'. These take various forms (questions, assignments, data-response exercises, etc.) and are intended to consolidate your understanding of the subject matter in hand. Don't be surprised if your teacher latches on to these!

■ As explained earlier, we have been keen to stress the integrative nature of geography. To this end, there are eight different **themes** which run as threads through the six units and two **places** which surface recurrently in the text. The two matrices set out on pages vi–ix signpost where you may pick up these linking themes and places.

■ There is increasing emphasis nowadays on the acquisition of life skills. That's a rather frightening way of saying that you need to learn things that will be useful to you when you have left college, particularly in the workplace. In this context, instruction is given, at appropriate points, in the use of some statistical and cartographic **techniques** that have quite wide application. We make no claims to provide comprehensive cover of the techniques utilised at this level; those set out in the matrix below merely represent a selection of the more commonly used techniques. Encouragement is also given in some of the Activities for you to develop your more basic communication skills of literacy and oracy.

Matrix 3: Techniques

Technique	Unit A	Unit B	Unit C	Unit D	Unit E	Unit F
Rose diagram	7.5	Activity 14, p.146				
Isopleths		8.6				
Descriptive statistics		9.3				
Histogram		Activity 15, p.146				
Investigating soils & vegetation			13.9			
Measuring vegetation change			14.5			
EIA & SEA			19.9			
Measuring population density & distribution				CS p.259		
Population mapping				20.4		
Preparing an examination answer				20.5		
Frequency distributions				24.5		
Location quotient					28.4	
Nearest-neighbour analysis						31.7
Personal investigative work						36.1 36.8

■ One key requirement of your A or AS Geography course is to undertake a piece of personal investigative work. This could account for up to 20 per cent of your final assessment. It is in the completion of this task that you are expected to demonstrate your command of the sorts of skills and techniques mentioned above. In this book, often in the Activities boxes, suggestions are made as to suitable topics, and advice is given on how to go about such a task (see Chapter 36, for example).

Making the grade

Finally, a word of encouragement, particularly so far as examinations are concerned. Success is the name of the game (would that exams were a sport!) or to put it more precisely, success is realising your potential and achieving the grade you really deserve. No one can guarantee that this happens, but certain steps can be taken to minimise the risk of disappointing results. Vitally important are your motivation, your organisational powers and your input of time and effort during the course. Imaginative and supportive teaching helps, of course, as do sensible revision and sound examination technique. But there is also no substitute for a good textbook that imparts the knowledge and understanding prescribed by your syllabus in an interesting and digestible manner, and which facilitates self-paced learning. *Environment and People* strives to do just that and at the same time to give you a sound feel for modern geography – its principles, concepts and current priorities.

All we can do now is to leave you with this book. We hope you find it stimulating and challenging. May it help you make the grade you deserve.

Michael Witherick

Landforms & Water

1.1 **A systems view of the world**

IT1

The world in which we live can be considered under two headings: the living (**biotic**) and the non-living (**abiotic**). Though complex, the world is orderly and may be seen as being made up of biotic and abiotic objects linked together by flows of energy and matter. Such a view of the world is the essence of what geographers call the **systems approach**, a **system** being defined as any set of inter-related components or objects which are connected together to form a working unit or unified whole.

Systems exist and may be defined at a range of scales and at many levels of complexity. Geographers are primarily interested in the medium scale which fills the range between the extreme microscale (for example the atom) and the extreme macroscale (for example the universe). At the global level, the basic systems which help to explain how the physical world works are those of (**1.1**):

- the **biosphere** (the zone of the Earth in which life is found)

- the **hydrosphere** (the total 'free' water of the Earth's surface)

- the **atmosphere** (the layer of gases surrrounding the Earth)

- the **lithosphere** (the rocks of the Earth's crust).

These large systems are at the top of the global hierarchy, the vital point being that each system, no matter what its scale, is part of a larger system – that is, systems 'nest' within systems. Thus a 'bottom-up' view sees the Earth as part of the solar system. Equally, the small mountain stream system is but a minuscule cell in the hydrosphere, being linked to it by drainage systems of increasing scale. Conversely, a 'top-down' view of systems sees each major landform as breaking down into a series of smaller but relatively simple slope systems.

IT1

Although it is often difficult to define the precise boundaries of a particular system, there is no doubt that in geography the systems approach provides opportunities for investigating, at varying spatial scales, both the processes at work and their resulting structures. If we define **geography** as being the study of the Earth's surface, particularly the space within which the human population lives, then it is possible to see the subject as being concerned with the structure and interaction of two major systems – the **ecological system** that links people to their environment, and the **spatial system** that links one part of the Earth's surface with another. Given those two major focuses of modern geography, it is clear that a systems approach has a vital part to play in promoting our knowledge and understanding. Hopefully, this will become more evident as you work through the book, the vital point being that it is not only in the context of this first unit – the study of landforms and water – that the systems concept applies. Systems provide one of the seven integrating themes of this book, and will be much in evidence in all six units:

- Unit A – the slope; the hydrological cycle; the drainage basin; the glacier

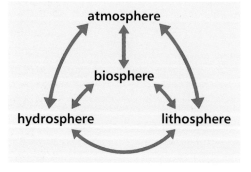

atmosphere

biosphere

hydrosphere   lithosphere

■ **1.1** Global systems

■ Unit B – the atmosphere; a depression
■ Unit C – the ecosystem; the soil; the nutrient cycle
■ Unit D – the population of an area; migration
■ Unit E – the farm; the manufacturing firm
■ Unit F – the settlement network; the city

1.2 Types of system and how they work

In general, systems show three or four distinct operational stages. Energy and/or matter enters the system (as **input**), is retained (as **store**) or passes through it (as **throughput**) and leaves (as **output**). Viewed in this way, a system is a set of operations acting upon one or more inputs and producing one or more outputs. The connecting throughput process either sustains or transforms the operational structure of the system. All this may be illustrated by the drainage basin. As a system, the drainage basin receives input in the form of precipitation which then assumes various through-put forms (as runoff, throughflow or as a stream) or is held as stores (as lakes and groundwater) and eventually out-puts as water and sediment discharged into the sea or as moisture lost to the atmosphere through evapotranspiration (see section 4.1).

The natural systems studied by physical geographers may be classified in a hierarchic manner into four main types (**1.2**). The two simplest are the **morphological** and **cascading systems**. In the former, the emphasis of investigation is on the physical properties and the statistical associations of the system's components (e.g. as in a study of drainage basin morphometry). The latter consist of a chain of subsystems linked by a cascading throughput, as for example the stage components of the hydrological cycle (see section 4.1). **Process–response systems** are formed at the intersection of cascading and morphological systems, where a change in the throughput of the former alters the equilibrium of the latter. In **control systems**, the intervention of people (decision-makers) is the prime focus. For example, in a flood management scheme where people attempt to regulate stream flow within a drainage basin, the control or intervention may be in harmony with nature (see section 4.7). In other instances, it may be mismatched, as in a programme of deforestation (see section 14.3). The degree of influence people have on the separate physical systems can vary from considerable (as in hydrology) to negligible (as in meteorology).

Depending on whether a system exchanges materials or energy with its

■ **1.2** Four different systems in physical geography

Morphological system

Morphological systems are the simplest. They involve relationships between measured properties.
For example:

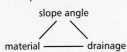

Process–response system

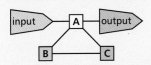

This type of system occurs where cascading and morphological systems meet. A change in the throughput of the former has an impact on the latter.
For example:

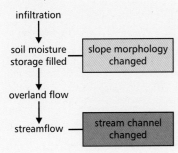

Cascading system

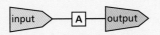

Cascading systems are formed from a series of subsystems which are linked by cascades of matter or energy. The input from one subsystem becomes the output for the next subsystem.
For example:

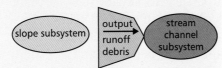

Control system

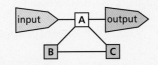

This system occurs where human decision-making and actions change the dynamic equilibrium.
For example:

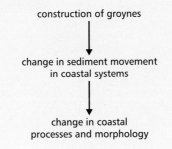

environment, it may be classified as either an open or a closed system.

- **Closed system** Here there is a transfer of energy (but not matter) between the system and its surroundings. The Earth as a planet may be regarded as a closed system; solar and terrestrial radiation exchanges occur, but not material exchanges (relatively rare meteorites excepted).

- **Open system** This is the more common situation, where systems receive inputs or transfer outputs of energy or matter across the boundaries between them. Sometimes the inputs are stored before being transferred to different parts within the system. The detailed study of inputs, outputs, storage and methods of transfer helps us to understand how systems work and may also give us a greater ability to manage them (or at least enlighten us on how they respond to our intervention).

When a change in one part of a system takes place, the transfer of energy and/or materials means that change is promoted in other parts. This is called **feedback** (**1.3**). If, as a result of a base-level fall, a river begins to erode vertically, the steeper slopes produced may feed so much material to the river that the channel is unable to cope and this results in deposition (see section 7.7). This may, in turn, lead to the lessening of downcutting, the prevention of slope steepening and, with decreased

removal of slope debris, the flattening of slopes by weathering. In other words, the ultimate outcome is the reversal of how the change began. Such **negative feedback** loops are very commonly found in operation in the systems of the natural environment, the effect of the initial change being compensated by subsequent changes in the system (**1.3a**). This kind of self-regulation situation is referred to as **dynamic equilibrium**. Failure to understand how natural systems operate in this way could well mean that people and their activities may seriously interfere with this self-repairing mechanism.

On the other hand, **positive feedback** occurs where an original change causes a snowball effect, continuing or accelerating the original change (**1.3b**). Systems where positive feedback is found are prone to instability, often in short bursts of destructive activity. An example might be intense heating over tropical seas causing convective uplift. This draws in moist air from surrounding areas to continually 'feed' the system through the release of latent heat from massive condensation and precipitation consequent upon the cooling of rapidly rising air. Thus a relatively small tropical disturbance may grow into a large and destructive hurricane (see section 11.6). Some understanding of this mechanism would clearly be useful in the context of forecasting.

■ **1.3** Negative and positive feedback

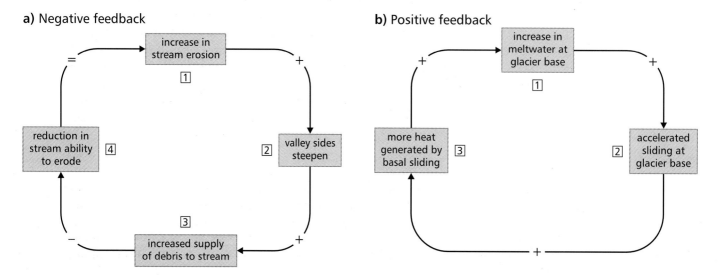

a) Negative feedback

increase in stream erosion
1
valley sides steepen
2
increased supply of debris to stream
3
reduction in stream ability to erode
4

b) Positive feedback

increase in meltwater at glacier base
1
accelerated sliding at glacier base
2
more heat generated by basal sliding
3

1.3 Natural events, disasters and hazards

IT2,5

Throughout the Earth's history there have been dramatic natural events such as floods, volcanic eruptions, avalanches, landslides and hurricanes. These may be studied in their own right as relatively small systems which demonstrate the linkages (in energy and material flows) between the biosphere, hydrosphere, atmosphere and lithosphere mentioned earlier (**1.1**). But such natural events also merit study when they occur in areas where people live, causing damage to property and loss of life – that is, when a **natural event** becomes a **natural disaster** or **hazard**. There is an important distinction to be made here. A volcanic eruption in densely populated Java would constitute a natural disaster, whereas a similar occurrence in the middle of Antarctica would constitute a natural event. The world is certainly a hazardous place in which to live. It has been estimated that within the last five centuries, over 200000 lives have been lost as a result of eruptions by the world's some 500 active volcanoes.

There are few areas of the world that are completely free from natural events with a hazard potential. Equally, some areas are more vulnerable than others; river flood plains, low-lying coasts and tectonic plate margins are examples of such areas. It would seem logical that people should avoid living in high-risk areas. However, the opposite appears often to be the case. For example, the metropolitan area of Tokyo, containing over 20 million people, is sited in an area that is particularly prone to earthquakes, whilst some 15 million inhabitants of Bangladesh live around the shores of the Bay of Bengal at a height of less than 3m above sea-level. This apparently perverse behaviour is to be explained in a number of ways. First, there is the human tendency to turn a blind eye to known risks and the unpredictability of some natural events. In this context, hazard perception is of considerable importance. Secondly, people may be forced to occupy hazardous locations either by economic necessity or by the lack of alternative, safer space.

IT2,5

1.4 Classifying hazards

IT2

Hazards may be classified according to a number of different criteria (**1.4**). One obvious basis is the scale of the damage and destruction caused. Another is the actual cause of the hazard. However, some might argue that the scheme shown in **1.4a** omits a third major category of hazards, namely those caused by human activities (such as atmospheric pollution and soil erosion). Strictly speaking, such hazards cannot be regarded as entirely the creation of people, but rather as cases where human activities are a 'trigger', setting off or augmenting the operation of physical processes. In this context, human influence on hazards may be direct, as with deforestation leading to landslides and soil erosion, or indirect, as through the production of greenhouse gases leading to long-term climatic and other changes.

IT2

One method of measuring the processes and consequences involved in hazards is to assess the impact the natural event has on human activity and the reaction of people to it. Some hazards, such as drought, may be long-term, affect wide areas and take years to reach a peak, whereas others, like a tornado, may last for a short time and affect only small areas. Some hazards occur regularly in the same location, others spasmodically and randomly. Perception of the characteristics of hazards can be represented on a hazard profile (**1.5**) which enables relevant aspects such as magnitude,

a) The most common natural hazards classified by cause

GEOPHYSICAL		BIOLOGICAL	
Climatic and meteorological	**Geological and geomorphic**	**Floral**	**Faunal**
Blizzards & snow	Avalanches	Fungal diseases, e.g. Dutch elm disease	Bacterial & viral diseases, e.g. malaria, bubonic plague and rabies
Droughts	Earthquakes		
Floods	Erosion		
Fog	Landslides	Infestations, e.g. weeds and water hyacinth	Infestations, e.g. rabbits and locusts; venomous animal bites
Frost	Shifting sand		
Hailstorms	Tsunamis		
Heat waves	Volcanic eruptions	Hay fever	
Hurricanes		Poisonous plants	
Lightning			
Tornadoes			

b) The most deadly natural hazards over a 25-year period

Type of disaster	Index of frequency	Percentage of deaths
Floods	100	39
Typhoons, hurricanes	73	36
Earthquakes	41	13
Tornadoes	32	1
Gales, thunderstorms	15	5
Snowstorms	13	1
Heat waves	8	1
Cold waves	6	1
Volcanic eruptions	6	2
Landslides	6	1

c) A selection of the major natural disasters in the last 100 years

Year	Location	Nature of hazard	Deaths
1883	Krakatau, Indonesia	Island volcano eruption, tsunami	36 000
1887	Huang river, China	Flood leading to famine, disease	900 000
1888	Moredabad, India	Hailstorm	246
1889	Johnstown, USA	Failure of dam after rainstorms	2200
1896	Honshu, Japan	Tsunami	26 000
1900	Galveston, USA	Hurricane, storm surge	6000
1902	Mount Pelée, Martinique	Eruption, hot ash, volcanic gas	30 000
1908	Messina, Italy	Earthquake	85 000
1916	Italian–Austrian Alps	Snow avalanches along military front	10 000
1920	Gansu, China	Landslides triggered by earthquakes	200 000
1927	Tien Shan, China	Earthquake	200 000
1931	Huang river, China	Flooding, famine	20 000
1932	Gansu, China	Earthquake	70 000
1951	London, UK	Smog (smoke fumes and fog)	2850
1953	Netherlands	Sea flooding in coastal areas	1835
1959	North China	Floods	2 000 000
1963	Italy	Landslide caused flood over dam wall	2500
1970	Huascarán, Peru	Mudslide started by eruption	21 000
1970	Bangladesh	Tropical cyclone, storm surge	300 000
1974	Honduras	Hurricane	7000
1975	USA	Lightning, deaths in an average year	150
1976	Tangshan, China	Earthquake	240 000
1985	Ruiz, Colombia	Mudslide after eruption	25 000
1986	Lake Nyos, Cameroon	Poisonous volcanic gas cloud	1600
1986	Bangladesh	Cyclone	2000
1988	Armenia	Earthquake	25 000

■ **1.4** Natural hazards

IT2 duration, speed of onset, area of extent and predictability, frequency of occurrence, etc. to be assessed on scales from high to low, severe to minimal, frequent to rare, rapid to slow, and so on.

Another way of investigating hazards, particularly their processes and consequences, is to consider not so much their immediate impact on human activity but rather the reaction of people to them.

1 Complete a profile for each of the other hazards covered in this unit: flooding, landslides, volcanic eruptions.

■ **1.5** Hazard profiles

		frequent					rare
	Frequency						
	Duration	long					short
TIMING							
	Speed of onset	slow					fast
	Temporal spacing	regular					random
	Areal extent	widespread					limited
SPACING							
	Spatial concentration	diffuse					concentrated

Key ○ blizzard   □ drought   ▲ earthquake

1.5 **Hazard perception and response**

IT2,5

The way people perceive and respond to the hazard potential of natural events is a crucial aspect of modern geography. Central here is the evaluation of risk, for it is this that largely determines the scale and type of human response. **1.6** tabulates different kinds of human reaction to hazards, whilst **1.7** illustrates how perception of the same specific hazard can vary even within a fairly homogenous and informed group of people. Perception ranges from complete ignorance through growing awareness to complete intolerance, and is conditioned by many factors. These include the frequency and magnitude of the hazardous event as well as socio-economic variables such as age, sex, occupation and educational attainment.

1.8 indicates that active response involves adjustment. Basically that adjustment can involve three different procedures:

- **Modifying the event** – for example, upstream water control in the case of flooding; cloud seeding in the case of drought.

- **Reducing vulnerability** – for example, constructing snow shields in the case of avalanches, and earthquake-resistant buildings.

- **Redistributing losses** – in other words, sharing the losses, as for example by emergency relief and insurance.

When it comes to choosing the actual type of adjustment to be made, **1.9** shows that the decision-making process is influenced by different factors. Some of these are to do with the quality of hazard information and the interpretation and evaluation of that information, whilst others relate to considerations of economic feasibility and practicality.

IT2,5

■ **1.6** Different human reactions to natural hazards

1	Deny its existence	'It can't happen here'
2	Deny its recurrence	'Lightning doesn't strike the same place twice'
3	Learn the frequency and accept it	'The hazard happens every five years'
4	Transfer responsibility to a higher power	'It's in the hands of God [or the Government]'
5	Find practical solutions to the hazard	'The hazard can be controlled'
6	Find practical solutions to its effects on people	'The hazard will happen but we can contain the damage'
7	Put the blame on others	'People have made the hazard worse'

Statement	Strongly disagree	Disagree	Neutral	Agree	Strongly agree
TOURIST INDUSTRY					
San Francisco will experience a tremendous loss of tourism because of the earthquake	12	44	20	22	3
Potential tourists will probably skip next season's trip to San Francisco	15	40	26	18	1
TOURIST DESTINATION					
Before the earthquake, San Francisco was believed to be an outstanding tourist destination	0	0	2	21	76
In spite of the earthquake, San Francisco remains an outstanding tourist destination	0	0	4	28	68
PERCEPTION ACCURACY					
Many of San Francisco's tourist attractions have been damaged by the earthquake	35	47	11	5	1
San Francisco's emergency services handled the earthquake very well	0	4	2	45	53
San Francisco's hotels were heavily damaged by the earthquake	26	44	18	3	0

■ **1.7** Travel writers' responses to attitude statements following the San Francisco earthquake of 1989 (percentages)

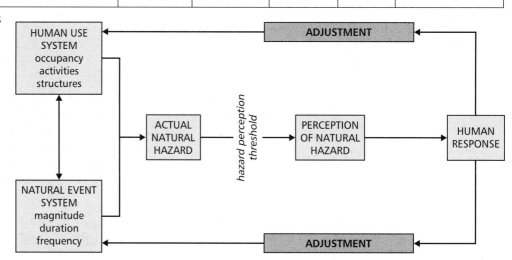

■ **1.8** Model of human perception of and response to a natural hazard

2 People who live in areas where there are natural hazards have many different attitudes to them. Choose one of the reactions from **1.6** to describe your reaction to earthquakes and flooding:
■ if you were living in a low-risk area such as the British Isles
■ if you were living in a high-risk area such as Bangladesh or Tokyo.
Compare your choice with those of others.

3 Make a list of the things that may influence people's perception of a natural hazard.

4 a Describe the feelings of the travel writers to the earthquake hazard in San Francisco.
b What may have affected the perception of the travel writers?
c What influence do you think the travel writers may have had on tourists?

5 a What types of adjustment are possible in seeking to cope with the hazard of frequent river flooding?
b Classify your suggestions under the headings of *technological* and *structural* adjustment.
c Assess the relative merits of each of your suggested adjustments.

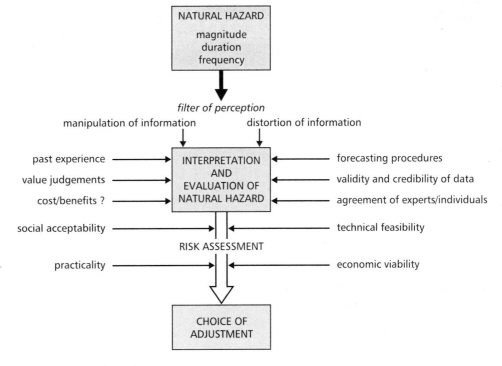

■ **1.9** The 'choice of adjustment' decision-making model

1.6 **Conclusion**

This opening chapter has outlined two of the important integrating themes of the book which figure prominently, but not exclusively, in the study of landforms and water. The first, the systems approach, provides a framework for studying the Earth's surface and the human occupation and utilisation of that surface. The emphasis is on processes, their interactions and resulting structures and patterns. The approach allows for investigation at a whole range of spatial scales from the local to the global. It is equally applicable to both physical and human geography. For this reason, it helps to link what for all too long have been regarded as two discrete components of the subject. The systems approach is also valuable in that it stresses the need to take into account human factors in physical geography, and physical factors in human geography. By so doing, it helps to weld modern geography into a cohesive and much more unified subject.

It is at this same interface between the abiotic and biotic worlds, or more specifically between natural systems and the human race, that the second integrating theme of the book is to be found – the vital issue of hazards. Whilst it is true to say that natural events only become hazards when they adversely affect people in some way or another (crudely put, there would be no hazards if there were no people), people do none the less contribute significantly to the hazardousness of such events. Indeed, as we have seen, there are some instances where people are the actual perpetrators. In the context of hazards, there are two developments giving rise to great concern. One is the continuing escalation of the world's population (see section 21.3). In order to satisfy human material needs, particularly for food, there is a strong and increasingly irresistible temptation to take risks with and abuse the environment. The second is the advance of human technology, which gives people the ability to disturb natural systems on an increasingly disastrous scale. The outcome of both developments is a significant rise in the frequency, scale and destructive potential of hazards. Clearly, it is vital that we learn more about the causes of hazards, particularly the human input, and in this context the adoption of a systems approach can provide a valuable insight.

2.1 **A jigsaw of continents and oceans**

■ **2.1** A reconstruction of the drifting continents

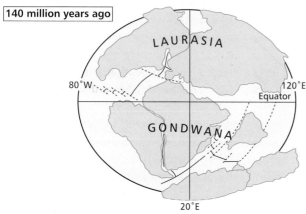

200 million years ago

140 million years ago

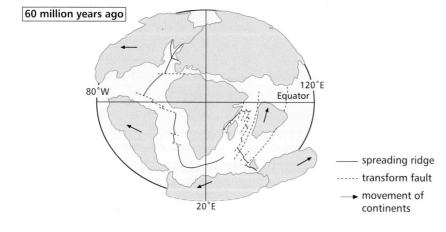

60 million years ago

—— spreading ridge

----- transform fault

→ movement of continents

It was in the early 17th century that the jigsaw-like fit between the west coast of Africa and the east coast of South America was first noted. Similar but less obvious fits were subsequently noted between other landmasses now separated by oceans. Nearly three centuries later, Alfred Wegener put forward the notion that the Earth's continents had once been joined together as one huge landmass, referred to as **Pangea**. Pangea had two main components – Laurasia (made up of North America, Europe and much of Asia) and Gondwanaland (made up of South America, Africa, India, Australia and Antarctica) separated by the Tethys Sea. Wegener's **theory of continental drift** recognised that large masses of the Earth's crust were capable of lateral movement over considerable distances and during long periods of geological time (**2.1**).

The evidence that Wegener used to support his theory was not just the jigsaw fit of today's continents. He was also able to show that rocks of the same age, type and structure were to be found in now separate landmasses, as well as similar fossils. Collectively, this geological evidence indicated a similarity in past climates and such a similarity, in its turn, could only be explained by the continents being located together in the same general latitude. More recently, carbon-dating has been able to confirm the existence of still more intercontinental similarities and correlations in minerals and rocks.

The most convincing evidence of moving landmasses has been derived from studies of rock magnetism in cores taken from deep-sea drillings. When volcanic rocks solidify or certain types of sediment are laid down, magnetic minerals (particularly iron particles) align themselves pointing to the magnetic pole and dipping at an angle that is dependent on latitude. Investigations of this magnetic evidence 'fossilised' in rocks (**palaeomagnetism**) have revealed three things:

- that the magnetic poles have experienced major shifts during geological time
- that the Earth's magnetic field has undergone many reversals (the north

and south poles have, as it were, changed places)

- that conflicts in the palaeomagnetic evidence of today's continents can only be reconciled by suggesting that they occupied different locations on the Earth in the past – for example, the evidence indicates that Europe and North America must have been 20° of longitude closer together 20 million years ago.

2.2 Sea-floor spreading and plate tectonics

Palaeomagnetic evidence has been invaluable in explaining the origin and form of one of the world's major morphological features – mid-oceanic ridges. Study of the the basaltic lavas lying either

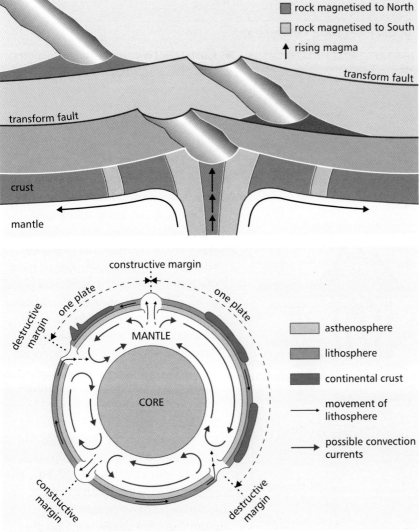

■ **2.2** Features of a mid-oceanic ridge

■ **2.3** The movement of tectonic plates

side of the Mid-Atlantic ridge have shown a pattern of **magnetic striping**. Although it records many reversals of the Earth's magnetic field, the pattern is symmetrical on either side of the main axis (**2.2**). The pattern can only be explained by assuming that over long periods of geological time, narrow bands of molten magma have continually welled up and solidified to fill a widening gap in the Earth's crust. Each band, imprinted with the magnetic field that existed at the time of solidification, has subsequently been split as the crustal gap has continued to widen. That splitting, in its turn, has allowed the extrusion of further bands of volcanic rock. The term used to describe this crustal divergence is **sea-floor spreading**. This process explains the origins not only of oceanic ridges, but also of major rift valleys. More importantly, proving the persistence of the process has provided the basis for the modern theory of plate tectonics.

Plate tectonic theory suggests that large sections of the Earth's crust behave like huge rigid plates (**2.3**). They are capable of substantial lateral movement relative to each other, moving over a plastic zone in the Earth known as the **asthenosphere**. Nine major and some ten minor plates can be recognised (**2.4**). The driving mechanism behind these moving plates is thought to be provided by large-scale convection currents in the Earth's asthenosphere beneath the crustal zone. As a result of these movements, three types of plate margin can be distinguished.

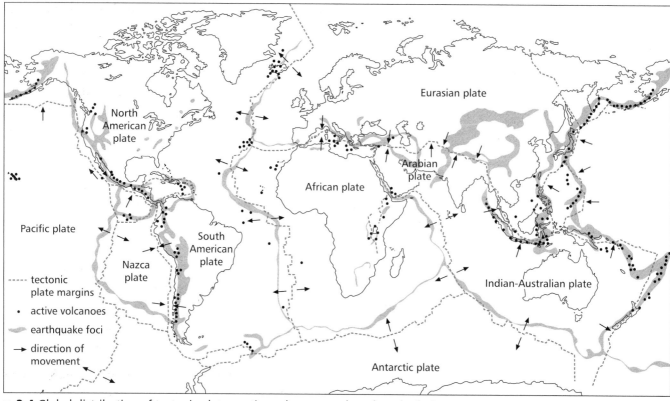

■ **2.4** Global distribution of tectonic plates, active volcanoes and earthquake foci

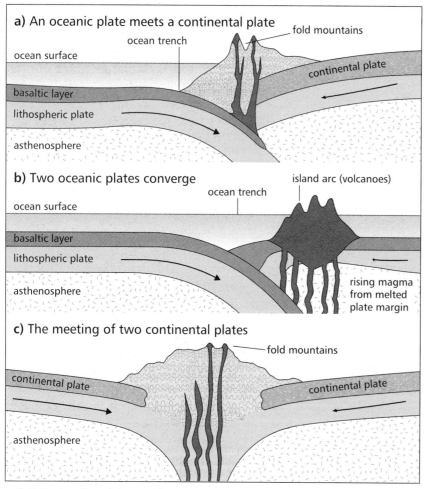

a) An oceanic plate meets a continental plate

ocean trench

fold mountains

ocean surface

continental plate

basaltic layer

lithospheric plate

asthenosphere

b) Two oceanic plates converge

island arc (volcanoes)

ocean trench

ocean surface

basaltic layer

lithospheric plate

asthenosphere

rising magma from melted plate margin

c) The meeting of two continental plates

fold mountains

continental plate

continental plate

asthenosphere

■ **2.5** Destructive plate margins

- **Constructive margins** occur where two plates are moving apart, as in the oceans, associated with large-scale rifting and the emergence of new materials from the mantle, producing volcanic landforms and creating the mid-oceanic ridges (**2.2**).

- **Destructive margins** occur where two plates move towards each other, resulting in one being submerged (**subducted**) beneath the other. Three types are recognised. The first occurs where a relatively 'light' oceanic plate encounters a 'heavy' continental plate, as off the west coast of South America where the Nazca oceanic plate is pushed beneath the denser South American plate. Here are to be found the classic features – the deep, elongated ocean trench, the parallel range of fold mountains formed by the crumpling of lighter sediments, and the volcanoes fed by the 'melting' of the oceanic plate as it descends closer to the Earth's molten core (**2.5a**). The second type of destructive margin occurs where two oceanic plates converge, as in the Western Pacific (**2.5b**), whilst the third involves the meeting of two continental plates, as in India (**2.5c**). The first two types are perhaps most characterised by a high frequency of earthquakes; the last is undoubtedly distinguished for throwing up the immense Himalayan mountain range.

- **Conservative margins** occur where plates slide laterally past each other, with varying degrees of friction. The typical example is the San Andreas fault area of California, between the Pacific and North American plates (**2.4**). Earthquakes are the key manifestation of this type of plate margin. The only impact on landforms are the 'offsets' or distortions (as for example of river valleys) caused by the plates moving in opposite directions.

The global pattern of the plates, their relative movements and margins provide the key to our understanding the origins and distribution of a number of global landforms – most notably fold mountains, but also rift valleys and mid-oceanic ridges. Whilst it is irrefutable that the first two of these features have had a profound impact on aspects of human geography, no less significant have been the two natural hazards created by plate movements – volcanoes and earthquakes.

---

1 Make a list of the ways fold mountains and rift valleys have influenced aspects of human geography.

2 Describe the relationships that exist between earthquakes, volcanoes and plate margins.

2.3 **Vulcanicity – landforms and hazards**

IT2

The distribution of the world's active volcanoes is shown in **2.4**. They are to be found in five different types of location:

- along the spreading mid-oceanic ridges of constructive plate margins where the upwelling of material is creating lithosphere (as in the North Atlantic)
- along continental rift valleys (as in East Africa)
- in island arcs created by the subduction of oceanic plates in destructive plate margins (as along the western margins of the Pacific plate)
- in fold mountain areas (as in the Andes)
- at isolated locations in plates, known as **hot spots**, and created by rising plumes of molten material (as within the Pacific plate).

Types of volcano

To the general public, the term 'volcano' conjures up the classic image of a cone-shaped mountain with its summit crater emitting a stream of lava. To the geographer, the term covers a much greater range of landforms which may be distinguished on the basis of four criteria.

IT2

The first is the nature of the opening or vent that allows materials from deep beneath the crust to emerge onto the Earth's surface. There are basically two kinds of vent:

- A single central vent which allows the build-up of material around its opening. The cone-shaped volcano falls into this category, but others may be more round-topped and may not display a crater, new material forming inside the volcano rather than being added externally (for example the *puy*, or domes, in central France).

- A fissure, vent or crack which may extend for many kilometres, allowing the emission of materials along its whole length. This tends to create sheets or plateaus rather than the single volcanic cone or dome structure.

The second criterion is the kind of material emitted from the vent. This may range from lava (molten magma),

■ **2.6** Two different types of volcanic cone

through a variety of pyroclastic (explosion) products, varying in size from ash to large boulders, from gases to steam. The solid materials have different angles of rest and different degrees of durability, and this has an important impact on the shape of the volcano. For example, some lavas are viscous (the **acid lavas** – those rich in silica), whilst **basic lavas** are more free-flowing; small-calibre materials tend to support more gentle slopes than large boulders; ash is easily eroded by rainfall, streams and wind (**2.6**). Thus the areal extent, height and slope angle of volcanic landforms will vary. Ash cones, in general, tend to be small and do not survive very long; acid lava cones are steep-sided and dome-shaped, whilst basic cones are gently-sloping and often very extensive, as for example the shield volcanoes of Hawaii (**2.7**). Some volcanoes, such as those of Italy, are composite, being made up of alternate layers of ash and lava which are reflected in slope profiles.

IT2

Thirdly, the type of eruptive activity, ranging as it does from gentle to extremely explosive, can affect the shape and appearance of volcanic landforms (**2.8**). For example, in a caldera-type eruption, vast depressions kilometres in diameter can be caused by subsidence of the surface as a previously existing cone has been literally blown away. The 'violence' aspect is very important when considering volcanoes as 'hazards', and can clearly colour human perception of the event.

Fourthly, the frequency of eruption can have a bearing on volcanic landforms. Regular eruptions will encourage a steady build-up of materials, whilst infrequent eruptions will allow the forces of denudation to constrain, if not reduce, the dimensions of resulting landforms.

a) Ash cone

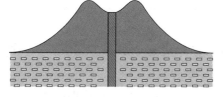

b) Silica lava dome

c) Basaltic lava shield

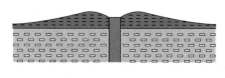

d) Composite cone

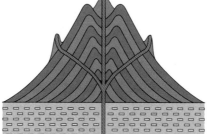

e) Caldera

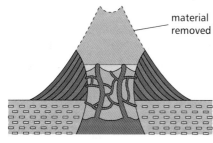

material removed

f) Volcanic plug or neck

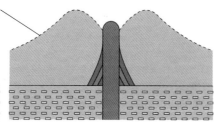

■ **2.7** Volcanic forms

Type of eruption	Characteristics
Icelandic	Lava issues gently from fissures.
Hawaiian	There is gentle and regular emission of fluid basalt from a central vent.
Strombolian	Basaltic lava is less fluid; spasmodic escape of gas causes small explosions.
Vesuvian	There are long periods of inactivity during which gas pressure builds up behind the lavas that clog the vent. The blockage is removed by a large explosion or a series of explosions.
Peléean	This violent type of eruption is marked by the nuée ardente (a glowing cloud of gas, ash and pumice).

■ **2.8** Types of volcanic eruption

a) Dykes

b) Sill

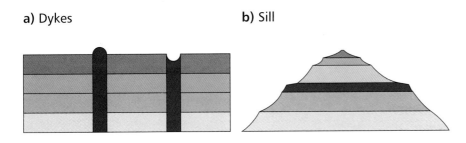

c) Laccoliths

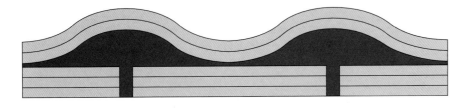

d) Phacoliths

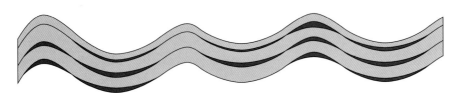

e) Batholith

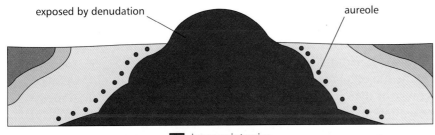

exposed by denudation   aureole

■ igneous intrusion

■ **2.9** Landforms produced by intrusive activity

Intrusive activity

The discussion so far has dealt only with those features created by the escape of lava and associated materials at the Earth's surface, referred to as **extrusive activity**. However, vulcanicity can also result in the penetration and solidification of magma within the Earth's crust. This is known as **intrusive activity** and can assume a variety of forms and scales. Large features known as **batholiths** are dome-shaped injections of granite associated with mountain-building; **laccoliths** are the result of magma being injected along bedding planes and causing overlying strata to arch up; **dykes** and **sills** are formed by the intrusion of sheets of lava either across or along bedding planes (**2.9**). It is when these various forms of intrusion are exposed at the surface by denudation that they assume a significance in terms of landforms. For example, the upland of Dartmoor in south-west England is a granite batholith.

Predicting volcanic eruptions

IT2

It has to be admitted that whilst plate tectonic theory has greatly advanced our understanding of vulcanicity, relatively little progress has been made in our ability to predict *when* volcanic eruptions will occur. At best, we know *where* they are most likely to occur and for any one active volcano we can, on the basis of past performance, arrive at some general 'feel' for the frequency and type of eruption (**2.8**). However, very close monitoring of the more active and hazardous volcanoes has in some instances revealed that there may be indicators which can give advance warning of an impending eruption on a scale of hours and perhaps days. These include changes in the composition of gaseous emissions and slight rises in the level of benign activity.

IT2,5

Two volcanic eruptions

Nevado del Ruiz – November 1985

This is the northernmost of the volcanoes in the Andes and reaches a height of 5400 m. Although there had for some time been signs of increased activity within the volcano, and there had been talk of evacuating people from surrounding towns and villages, during the evening of 13 November a large column of ash, steam and rocks was suddenly ejected. The hot ash falling on the summit melted part of the mountain's snowcap, and the combined ash and water rushed down into the valley of the Lagunillas river towards the town of Armero. The wave of mud (known as a **lahar**), travelling at a speed of 50 km/h, hit the town about midnight. Many people were in bed and within minutes the whole of the town was engulfed in mud up to 3.5 m deep; houses collapsed. To make matters worse, the lahar quickly set like cement. By the time rescuers reached the town next day, 23 000 of Armero's inhabitants lay encased within the mud.

Mount St Helens, Washington State, USA – May 1980

Prior to 18 May 1980, Mount St Helens was a much photographed, symmetrical snow-cone, just under 3000 m high. The last recorded volcanic activity was back in 1857. However, in March 1980 it began to show signs of increasing activity and as a consequence many sightseers and geologists came to have a look. By May a fracture nearly 5 km long had appeared and the northern side of the mountain had started to bulge. At 08.30 on 13 May, the volcano exploded. The bulging north side suddenly became a hugh rockfall and the molten lava which had been ponded up behind it burst out with terrific force. Large quantities of ash and dust were also ejected; a huge mudflow travelled some 45 km and the explosion triggered landslides. All in all, it is estimated that close to 2 km³ of matter were discharged. The eruption felled 52 000 ha of forest; over a million animals and birds were killed; 600 000 tonnes of ash were removed from the town of Yakima 160 km away; and 60 people died.

---

3 Explain the cause of each of the two eruptions.

4 Make a list of the possible reasons why the death toll following each of the two eruptions was so different.

5 What benefits might the volcanic activity have brought to:
 a Nevado del Ruiz
 b Mount St Helens?

2.4 Earthquakes

IT2

Causes and scale

The immediate cause of an earthquake is the elastic rebound of rock material to its original shape after it has been subjected to stress and deformation. Most earthquakes occur where downward convection currents are found, though some are linked to the upward currents at mid-oceanic ridges (**2.4**). As natural hazards, they have been the subject of much study, principally because of their location near to coastal concentrations of population. Energy is released as elastic waves which radiate outwards from the point of origin, known as the **focus**. Four types of wave are generated (**2.10**). **Compressional** and **shear waves** cause high-frequency vibrations which are more efficient than low-frequency waves in causing low buildings to vibrate. In contrast, **Love** and **Rayleigh waves** are low-frequency waves, which are more effective in causing high buildings to vibrate.

Earthquakes are often classified according to the Richter scale, a measure based on the total amount of energy released (**2.11**). The recorded strength of the earthquake is shown on a 10-point scale. For example, the

IT2

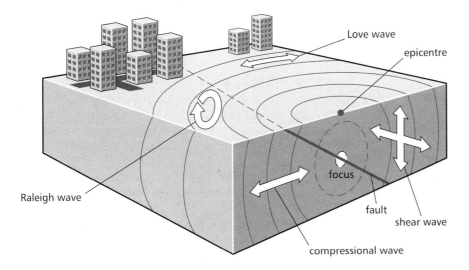

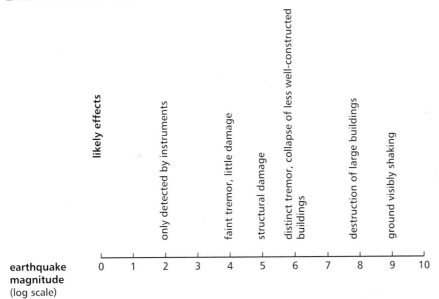

■ **2.10** The types of wave generated by an earthquake

■ **2.11** The Richter scale

San Francisco earthquake of 1989 measured 6.9 on the Richter scale. It is important to realise that a whole number increase on the scale represents a 10-fold increase in the size of the earthquake and a 31-fold increase in the energy released. Thus an earthquake on 5.0 of the Richter scale is very much more powerful and devastating than one classed as 4.0.

Distribution

2.4 shows that the distribution of earthquakes follows the same linear pattern as the distribution of volcanoes. The majority of earthquakes occur along the subduction and collision zones of destructive plate margins. However, a small but significant number do occur in two other types of location:

■ along the spreading mid-oceanic ridges of constructive plate margins, particularly along the vertical faults that bound the rift and along the transform faults that offset it

■ along conservative plate margins.

Minor earthquakes can also occur almost anywhere in the world, particularly as a result of movement along old fault lines, such as those triggered by isostatic change, for example.

Prediction

Seismologists have had some success in predicting the places where earthquakes are likely to happen, but have been unable to tell with any real degree of certainty when they will occur. For situations such as the San Andreas Fault in California, it is possible to use the 'seismic gap' approach. This involves looking at the magnitude, frequency and epicentres of previous earthquakes and on that basis predicting areas likely to be at risk in the future, with some suggestions as to the likely time-scale.

The San Andreas Fault is a strike-slip fault (**transform fault**) at a conservative plate margin. Two large plates, the North American and the Pacific plates, are moving north-westwards, but the former is moving more slowly (by about 5 cm a year). Thus the rocks immediately adjacent to the fault are subject to immense strain by this relative movement. At first, they can cope with the build-up of stress, but eventually they fracture as energy is released in the form of earthquake shock waves. Clearly, it is possible for scientists to measure the gradual distortion of rocks along the line of the fault and to use this as a basis for forecasting when another earthquake is likely. However, this technique can only give a rough approximation. The predictions can be supported by observations of other changes, for example background seismic activity, electrical conductivity and the physical character of rocks in the fault zone.

IT2, 5

The Mexican earthquake of 1985

On 19 September 1985, a major disaster was created by an earthquake which lasted for three minutes and reached 7.8 on the Richter scale, followed 36 hours later by a second earthquake measuring 6.5. The epicentre was located 50 km off the west coast of Mexico.

International agencies estimated that in Mexico City alone 100 000 people were killed, with another 20 000 injured, despite the fact that the epicentre was located over 250 km away (**2.12**). Dwellings destroyed or damaged meant that 150 000 people were made homeless. Most of the damage was concentrated in a small part of the city close to the central business district. Many important buildings were affected, with multistorey buildings, built during the previous 15 years, taking the brunt of the destruction. It is estimated that the earthquake cost as much as 2 per cent of the country's GDP.

Three factors helped to make this particular natural event into a major disaster. First, most of the structural damage to buildings occurred in a part of the built-up area which occupied an old lake bed. The soft, water-saturated clay deposits here increased the effects of the shock waves by an estimated factor of three. Secondly, the extraction of groundwater for industrial and domestic use had caused widespread subsidence and tilting of the buildings, thereby making them even more vulnerable to shock waves. Thirdly, the mass of many modern buildings was not distributed evenly across their foundations. Thus there was an inclination for them to twist, tilt and collapse during the earthquake.

A number of other factors helped to increase the death toll:

- In poorer countries like Mexico, measures for reducing earthquake risk are often not implemented.

- Programmes to improve earthquake protection do not necessarily benefit the majority of the population. Possibly as many as two-thirds of the people in Mexico City lived in buildings that offered little protection against earthquakes.

- Widespread corruption means that building regulations are often ignored.

- Even if prediction were possible, with a population of 18 million Mexico City was simply too big to evacuate.

- Economic interests command a higher priority than environmental and safety considerations. For example, a major oil refinery had been constructed within the built-up area; requests to relocate it were ignored.

■ **2.12** Damage caused by the Mexican earthquake, 1985

6 Referring to **2.4**, work out what type of tectonic feature caused the Mexico earthquake of 1985.

7 Identify the difficulties Mexico City will have in preventing damage from future earthquakes.

8 Critically examine the statement that 'an earthquake is as much a human as a natural disaster'.

IP1, IT2,4

Tokyo – living with earthquakes

After the Mexican earthquake, Japanese engineers boasted that damage caused by a similar earthquake in Tokyo would have been much less. The loss of 100 000 people this century through earthquakes has made the Japanese take preventive action. On average, Tokyo has three noticeable earthquakes every month.

Many people believe that the Japanese lead the world in earthquake protection. They have been actively increasing their public education programme by producing pamphlets, broadcasts and lectures about earthquakes. Households are encouraged to keep earthquake survival kits containing bottled water, rice, a radio, fire extinguishers and blankets. Many tower-block foundations are on rock, and deep piles anchor them to the ground. The shells of high-rise buildings are made of sturdy reinforced concrete with inner and outer walls. Each storey is built in box-like sections. Some buildings have 'shear walls' which act as shock absorbers. The very latest technology includes the use of computer-controlled tensioning systems in which cables running through a structure are adjusted by computer to withstand ground movements detected by sensors. As regards owner-occupied housing, the traditional anti-earthquake measures continue to be taken, namely using relatively light building materials and where possible keeping to single-storey structures. Since much of the city is located close to the shores of Tokyo Bay, protection against flooding (particularly due to tsunamis) is a high priority (**2.13**). **2.14** lists a series of measures that have been implemented by the Tokyo authorities to contain earthquake damage and to deal with an earthquake emergency.

In 1990, a resolution was passed in the Japanese parliament to transfer Tokyo's political and administrative roles to another part of Japan. One of the reasons given for this move was the fact that seismologists expect another large earthquake to occur, like the one in 1923 which caused 140 000 deaths. An earthquake of this scale is predicted to happen sometime within the next 40 to 50 years. The question is – will the modifying measures stand the test? The destruction caused by the 1995 Kobe earthquake suggests they may not.

9 Explain why Japan is so susceptible to earthquakes.

10 Pick out five of the actions listed in **2.14** which you think could be used in Mexico and set up at a relatively low cost.

■ **2.13** Protection against flooding

- ◆ Over US$ 5 million spent on making the urban fabric safer in the event of an earthquake
- ◆ Overcrowded districts redeveloped to reduce damage intensity
- ◆ 545 ha of housing improved by strengthening and fire-proofing
- ◆ Much public housing rebuilt using less flammable materials
- ◆ Major roads and bridges strengthened
- ◆ Fire-breaks created in residential areas
- ◆ Shelters and refuges provided in accessible areas throughout the city
- ◆ Parks preserved and maintained as refuge areas
- ◆ Old gas pipes replaced so as to reduce the risk of fracture, explosion and fire
- ◆ Slopes and cuttings protected so as to reduce the risk of landslides
- ◆ Flood protection schemes implemented to cope with the tsunamis which are likely to be generated by more severe earthquakes
- ◆ A disaster prevention centre set up, which will also double as a reception centre for disaster victims
- ◆ Emergency water tanks installed at sites throughout the metropolitan area to ensure 10 days' supply of drinking water
- ◆ Wharves and runways strengthened so that emergency supplies can be brought in from elsewhere

■ **2.14** A selection of earthquake-adjustment actions undertaken in Tokyo

It will be clear that earthquakes in themselves do not usually kill people: it is the collapse of buildings, bridges and other structures that causes death on a large scale. Much destruction and death are also caused by after-effects such as floods, fires, landslides and tidal waves (**tsunamis**). Earthquakes with the epicentre under the sea can generate particularly destructive tidal waves. Since 30 per cent of the world's largest and fastest-growing cities are located in earthquake-prone zones, the importance of developments in prediction techniques is self-evident. Earthquakes cannot be prevented nor, realistically, can populations be moved on a massive scale away from high-risk areas. Despite much research and considerable advances in seismic study, prediction of earthquakes is still unreliable, so the key to survival and coping with the consequences of the event is simply to be prepared.

11 Identify the types of control that people have over earthquakes.

12 How might the control that people feel they have affect their perception of earthquakes as a hazard?

2.5 **Volcanoes and earthquakes – the good and the bad**

It might seem strange to talk about the 'advantages' of earthquakes, and indeed the actual event itself can hardly be considered advantageous. However, the study of earthquake wave patterns has meant that we have discovered more about the inside of our planet, an advantage both in its own right, as 'knowledge', but also in the possibility of helping to trace mineral resources for future exploitation. The benefits of volcanic activity are more directly observable. They include soil enrichment from volcanic ash fall-out, the creation of new land (important in overcrowded islands), the generation of geothermal heat for energy (already extensively used in Italy and Iceland), mineral enrichment (as in the Johannesburg region of South Africa) and the generation of tourism borne out of the curiosity of people to visit the scenes of major disasters (the Mount St Helens area has been a notable beneficiary).

Though earthquakes and volcanoes can be studied as natural systems, this chapter has been primarily concerned with the human dimension, considering these natural events under the 'control system' category indicated in section 1.2.

Our understanding of plate tectonics enables us to identify the areas of the world that are most prone to earthquakes and volcanic eruptions. Earthquakes and volcanic eruptions are natural phenomena which have become 'natural disasters or hazards' owing to their juxtaposition with human settlement. Very often the damaging effects of such events are just as much a reflection of the type of settlement and country as the physical characteristics of the event. This is because settlements and countries vary in their ability to provide equipment to predict and set up preventive measures to reduce the severity of the disaster. Earthquakes tend to be more damaging than volcanoes, because they are more difficult to predict, they are inherently more violent, and often happen without any warning.

Earthquakes and volcanoes are often regarded as 'acts of God', as being beyond our control. However, it is largely up to people as to how disastrous their effects actually are. There is much that can be done to ameliorate their destructive potential:

- research into possible early warning and prediction systems
- investment in the design and technology of buildings and other structures to make them more earthquake and volcano-proof
- designing effective emergency procedures for operation after the event
- planning more carefully the location of settlement and economic activity.

Of course, the main questions are: How much do we want to spend and what sort of risk are we prepared to take? How necessary is it for us to take preventive measures to soften the blow of a natural event, the extent of which we do not know, nor indeed whether or when it will occur. It could happen within the next few minutes; on the other hand it might not occur for hundreds of years. Who knows? Who cares?

Weathering, Mass-movement and Slopes

3.1 Weathering

Most people become 'weather-beaten' when they are exposed to sun, wind and rain. When rocks are similarly exposed, they are chemically and physically changed by processes called **weathering**. Weathering is the first stage in the denudation or wearing down of any landform, since rock needs to be broken down before it is removed by erosion and transport. The breakdown and decay of rocks *in situ* gives rise to a mantle of waste or loose debris that can then be removed by other processes.

Types

Just as there are many different types of rock, so there is much variety in the way and the degree to which rocks respond to the processes of weathering. Three types of weathering are widely recognised. **Mechanical weathering** is the disintegration of rocks into fragments by entirely physical means, such as expansion and contraction, and without any change to their chemical make-up. **Chemical weathering** does involve chemical change. It is the decomposition of rock minerals by agents such as water, oxygen, carbon dioxide and organic acids. Among the most important processes of chemical weathering are carbonation, hydrolysis, oxidation and solution. **Biological weathering** is the breakdown of rocks by the actions of plants and animals. It can either be mechanical (as where tree roots prise rock apart) or chemical (as where humic acids are released by rotting organic matter). However, it should be stressed that it is not always easy to fit weathering neatly into these three categories. There is often much overlap between physical and chemical processes acting at the same time and often in concert with each other. Equally, one process follows another. Gaps and cracks made by mechanical weathering can be attacked chemically and biologically by air, water and the roots of trees.

Distribution

The processes of weathering are intricately related to climate and rock type. The former largely determines the types of weathering active at any particular location. **3.1** shows this critical link at the global level. Mechanical weathering is seen to be most active where there is a combination of very low temperatures and low precipitation, whereas chemical weathering flourishes in the opposite conditions. By superimposing the two distributions, it becomes possible to divide the world into a series of weathering regions. The global pattern is essentially one of transition from chemical to mechanical weathering as one moves from wet to dry and from warm to cold climates.

Rock type generally has more effect on the rate of weathering, because some rocks are more vulnerable to particular types of weathering than others. An obvious example is the susceptibility of limestone to chemical rather than mechanical weathering. In contrast, an intrusive rock such as granite is likely to be a victim of the mechanical processes of pressure release when it is exposed to the atmosphere.

Pollution

Although weathering is strictly a set of natural processes, it is important to

IT3

a) Mechanical weathering

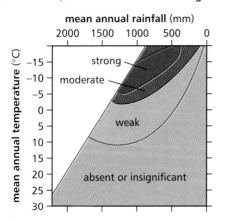

b) Chemical weathering

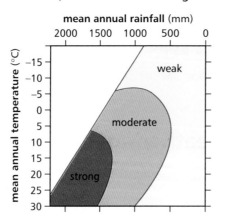

c) Weathering regions

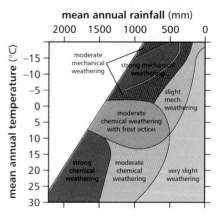

■ **3.1** Patterns of weathering and climate

recognise that people become involved in two different ways. On the one hand, inevitably the processes that cause rocks to weather also attack buildings and other human structures. In the Cotswolds, the weathering of stone houses seems to increase their aesthetic appeal but very often the effects have a more negative impact. Patches of white salts on buildings are evidence that the rock or building material has soluble salts within it which are evaporating as they move out of the rock. On the other hand, human pollution causes weathering rates to increase, principally through acidification. Nitrous oxides, sulphur and carbon dioxide released into the atmosphere by the burning of fossil fuels produce acidic solutions when absorbed by rain (**acid rain**). Acid rain reacts particularly on limestones, but it also attacks concrete and metal. As a result of atmospheric pollution, the speed at which rocks and building materials weather in an urban environment has increased with industrialisation. In 1925 an observer remarked that:

> Ever since the magnesian limestone, of which the New Palace at Westminster is built, was first exposed to the chemical constituents of the London atmosphere, it has been slowly and surely transformed into some sort of a heap of Epsom salts.

1 With reference to **3.1a**:
  a Define the climatic limits of strong mechanical weathering.
  b Explain the absence or insignificance of mechnical weathering over such large ranges of temperature and precipitation.

2 With reference to **3.1b**:
  a Define the climatic limits of moderate chemical weathering.

b Explain the incidence of strong chemical weathering.

3 With reference to **3.1c**:
  a In which weathering region does the British Isles fall?
  b Which region do you think experiences the greatest amount of collective weathering? Justify your choice.

IT3

Weathering and gravestones

Weathering takes place very slowly, so accurate measurements without sophisticated equipment are very difficult to achieve. One way, however, of determining the extent of weathering is by studying gravestones. They are eminently suitable for visual techniques because not only are they accessible at ground level, unlike weathering evidence on many public buildings, but since they are normally dated, the approximate time-scale resulting in particular states of decay can be calculated reasonably accurately. Moreover, they frequently involve different stone types in close proximity, so that

variables like height, aspect, degree of shelter, etc. can be controlled within the terms of the survey (**3.2**). Lichens on the gravestones give clues about the amount of pollution within the environment, since they obtain nutrients directly from rainwater and are sensitive to the absorption of pollutants. Thus, taking into account the age and composition of the gravestone, an assessment of the number of different lichens present and the degree to which they cover the surface, can give an inverse indication of pollution levels in the local area.

■ **3.2** Two different types of gravestone

4 a Describe the differences between the two gravestones in **3.2**.
  b Explain why one gravestone has been weathered more than the other.
  c If the same stones were in an arid environment, what would the difference between them be in terms of weathering?

5 Carry out your own local survey of gravestones. Note the following variables and analyse the degree of correlation:
- the date of the gravestone
- the type of stone
- the number of lichens or the percentage of the surface covered by lichens
- orientation (to prevailing wind direction).

3.2 Weathering, mass-movement and erosion

Weathering, already defined as the decomposition or disintegration of rock, takes place *in situ*, i.e. without removal of the weathered products. It can occur to varying depths, depending largely on the climate and properties of the rock concerned, together with the length of time that has elapsed. The term **regolith** is used to describe weathered rock extending from the surface downwards to the level where rock is as yet unaltered. Note that soil is not synonymous with regolith: soil is a much thinner layer and involves the operation of complex biochemical processes as well (see section 13.7).

Erosion is the removal of weathered products involving the action of transportation agents such as water (for example, in the form of rivers and waves), ice (as in glaciers and ice sheets) and wind. There is, however, a third

category of denudational process, which might be considered intermediary between weathering and erosion. This involves the gradual – often imperceptibly slow – movement of weathered material downslope in response to factors such as gravity and saturation by groundwater. This is **mass-movement** or **mass-wasting**. There are, however, problems with any attempt to produce watertight classifications such as the three-fold one proposed (see section 3.3). There is some 'blurring', as for example when a slope becomes so saturated with water that it begins to move rapidly as a mudflow. The question is, how mobile does a mudflow have to be before it is recognised as a river? It has been said of the Mississippi that it is 'too thick to navigate yet too thin to cultivate'. This being the case, is it strictly accurate to call it a river?

a) Flow

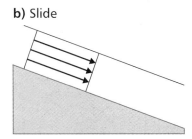

b) Slide

c) Heave

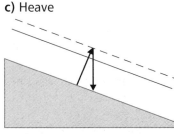

■ **3.3** The main types of mass-movement

■ **3.4** A classification of mass-movements

3.3 **Types of mass-movement**

It is important to remember that mass-movement is the downslope movement of material induced by gravity; it does not rely on transportation systems such as those provided by water, ice or wind. However, in many forms of mass-movement, water is usually present in the regolith and clearly helps the process largely by lubricating and therefore reducing the friction between particles of weathered material.

Mass-movement can take a variety of forms. Possibly the most significant differentiating factor is the speed of movement; with this, there is a continuum ranging from slow to fast. Another possible criterion is the type of movement; here geomorphologists usually distinguish between **flow**, **slide** and **heave** (**3.3**). This particular distinction also ties in closely with another possible classification variable – the amount of moisture present. Simply put, the higher the moisture content, the more likely it is that mass-movement will be of a flow type (**3.4**).

In the following descriptive account of the main types of mass-movement, the classification has been based first on type of movement and then on speed.

Flows

When regolith is relatively thick and is composed of particles capable of retaining moisture, a slow and more or less continuous downslope 'flow' will occur, even over relatively gentle gradients. Where gradients are steeper and there is effective lubrication by water, then faster flows will be experienced. In all cases, maximum velocities will be at the surface and the rate of flow will diminish with depth to the point where the regolith meets solid rock, where it will be zero (**3.3a**). This is due to the excessive friction that is generated towards the base of the weathered layer, where rock fragments tend to be larger, more angular and therefore less mobile.

Soil creep is probably the most widespread of all mass-movements and occurs over a wide range of climates. It may be defined as the slow downslope movement of soil and regolith as a result of the net effects of movement of its individual particles. The rate of movement is so slow as to be imperceptible. At the surface, the speed of movement may be in the order of 1 mm per year, but this decreases with depth within the regolith (see above). The effects of soil creep on slopes are to be seen in the bending of tree trunks and the formation of terracettes (**3.5**). As a process, it is strongly influenced by slope steepness, the amount of water contained in the regolith, and vegetation – the roots of trees and plants tend to bind and stabilise the soil and thereby inhibit movement.

Solifluction is a major process on slopes in periglacial regions (see section 7.6). Water released by the spring thaw so lubricates regolith that it flows downslope, but it is often helped by the fact that the top of the underlying permafrost acts as a sort of slide. As seen in **3.4**, solifluction is generally a faster flow movement than soil creep, particularly at the height of the summer thaw.

Of the fast movements, **earth flows** are common in humid regions where there is a deep mantle of regolith. Masses of earth on a hillside may slip quite suddenly, leaving a crescent-shaped scar above and a bulging 'toe' below. Common causes of earth flows

IT2

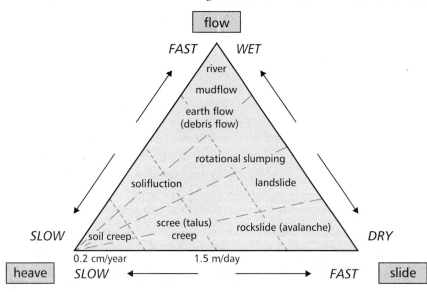

■ **3.5** Terracettes caused by soil creep

rejuvenation. They also occur where cliffs are undercut by the sea, or where a river has created a steep bank. Structural factors can also play a part, as where permeable beds overlie impermeable rocks, or where rocks dip in the downslope direction. **Debris avalanches** are a particularly hazardous form of mass-movement and occur when slopes suddenly lose their stability, for example if severely shaken by an earthquake. In May 1970 an earthquake at Huascaran in the Andes triggered a huge debris avalanche some 800m thick that fell about 1000m before thundering down a valley at a speed of a little under 500km/h and for a distance of 16km.

One type of mass-movement which involves a form of sliding, but which in most cases is also associated with some flow, is **rotational slipping** or **rotational slumping**. Weathered materials accumulate and eventually reach a critical weight that exceeds the regolith's resistance to shearing. The material then slumps downwards over a curvilinear shear plane. The slumping movement is rotational so that the top of the slump tilts backwards exposing a scar whilst the toe rises (**3.6**).

are the presence of spring-lines or seepage lines, spells of very heavy rainfall, and the basal undercutting of slopes by streams and rivers. An extreme type of earth flow is known as a **mudflow** (sometimes confusingly referred to as a **mudslide**), and occurs where the regolith is highly charged with water and comprises a high proportion of clay particles. This type of mass-movement occurs in mountainous areas after very heavy rain, in periglacial areas at the height of the summer thaw, and on the slopes of erupting volcanoes (see section 2.3).

Slides

These movements occur along a well-defined slide plane towards the base of the regolith (**3.3b**). Most noteworthy are **landslides** and **rockfalls**. These involve the very rapid sliding of masses of rock debris with little or no flow. Landslides occur on very steep slopes, usually in mountain areas where relief has been accentuated by glaciation or by deep

Heave

Heave involves the raising of regolith particles at right-angles to the slope and then falling downslope in response to gravity (**3.3c**). It most commonly occurs when regolith particles have absorbed water and are then subjected to freezing. The heave is provided by the expansion that accompanies the conversion of water into ice.

■ **3.6** Rotational slipping

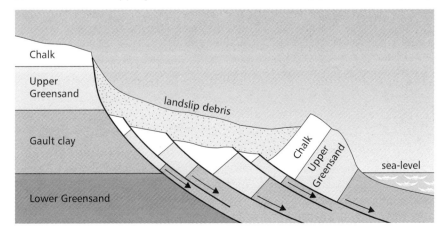

Chalk

Upper Greensand

landslip debris

Gault clay

Chalk

Upper Greensand

sea-level

Lower Greensand

6 Make a visit to a small area and collect field evidence about the processes of weathering and mass-movement that are currently at work.

7 Explain why mass-movements are not always easy to classify.

Landslides in Derbyshire

A national survey of recorded landslides has identified 709 within Derbyshire. These have caused damage to property and roads throughout the county. In 1979, following years of maintenance, the A625 disappeared where it crosses Mam Tor. Roads particularly need to be continually maintained wherever they cross active landslip areas. Snake Pass (A57) was affected by seven landslips between 1970 and 1985, and still suffers. **3.7a** shows the geology of the county, while **3.7b** maps the distribution of landslides. **3.8** shows the results of an analysis of the mechanisms of a sample of the landslides.

Recently, the Department of the Environment undertook a landslide review. It aimed to identify the distribution, causes and mechanisms of landslides plus an assessment of potential landslide areas, remedial measures and an assessment of the risk to communities.

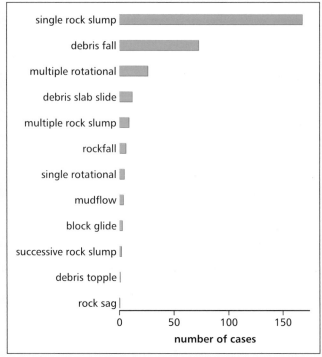

■ **3.8** Landslide mechanism for a sample of 319 incidents in Derbyshire

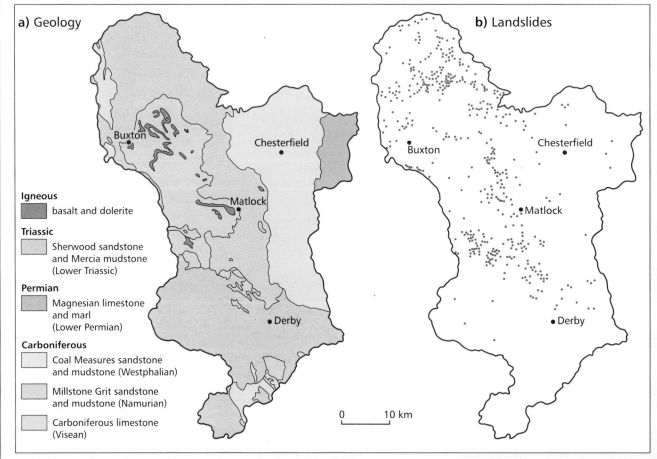

■ **3.7** The geology of Derbyshire and the distribution of landslides

8 a Referring to **3.7a** and **3.7b**, analyse the relationship between the distribution of landslides and geology. Explain how most landslides develop in Derbyshire.

  b Explain any possible causal link between geology and the incidence of landslides.

  c How does the information in **3.8** illuminate the answers you have given in **a** and **b**?

9 a Using **3.7** as a base, draw a sketch map of Derbyshire to show:
  - areas of high landslide risk
  - areas of potential instability
  - stable areas.

  b What additional information would you need in order to assess the degree of risk to communities?

  c Make a list of the advantages and disadvantages to people in Derbyshire of producing maps that analyse landslide risk.

3.4 **Slopes**

All students of geography are familiar with the contours used on OS topographic maps. They indicate changes in the altitude of land and the existence of slopes. Arguably, slopes are the most widespread and basic of all landforms; viewed in another way, slopes are the basic building blocks of all landforms.

The geographical study of slopes involves many aspects. These include angle and form, plan view, rock type, climatic regime and their development over time.

Profile

Clearly, the forms or profiles of slopes vary enormously around the globe, such variations being largely explained in terms of differences in rock type, climate and the impact of time. To add to the complexity of the situation, it is clear that most slopes are in effect amalgams of smaller units. This might be illustrated by the valley slope in Britain, many of which show a convex summit and a concave base separated by a rectilinear middle unit (**3.9a**). Indeed, geomorphologists have suggested that in temperate humid regions, it is possible to identify nine recurring slope units, each associated with a particular mix and balance of processes (**3.10**). The model integrates slope form and process. However, not all of these units are necessarily found on every slope. These nine units may in fact be grouped to divide the slope into three sections:

- **The waxing slope** (units 1, 2 and 3 on **3.10**). Here the main processes are surface wash and creep and removal by subsurface soil water. The gradient is so slight in unit 1 that nearly all movement is through the downward action of soil water. As the angle begins to steepen on the seepage slope there is a large component of downslope movement. In unit 3 the dominant process is creep; with increasing steepness, the slope becomes potentially unstable and terracettes are formed. The collective profile is convex in shape.

- **The constant or rectilinear slope** (units 4 and 5). This is characterised by steepness and therefore rapid movement in the forms of flow and slip. Both units show a consistency of slope angle; in other words, viewed in profile they are straight.

- **The waning slope** (units 6 and 7). This is generally an area of stability in which solution and the slow downslope processes are dominant. The steeper upper part of the foot-slope appears rectilinear, becoming concave lower down. The bottom unit is clearly an area of deposition, but is usually counterbalanced by the removal of material in units 8 and 9. If this were not to happen, then the concave slope created by deposition would steadily grow and eventually consume the back-slope.

Plan view

It is important to recognise that slopes have a plan dimension as well as a profile. Some slopes may focus or converge downhill, typically at valley heads. They are concave in plan and may be described as a form of waning slope (**3.9b**). The significance of this is that as material from higher up the slope is moved downhill, it is

a) Slope segments

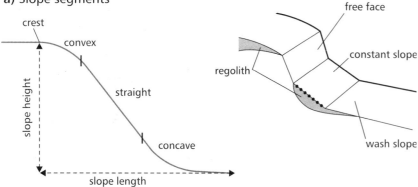

b) Slopes in plan view

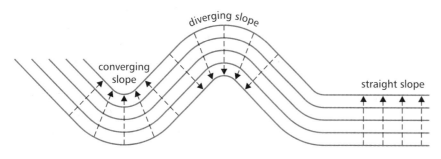

c) Theories of slope development

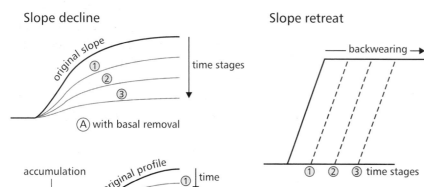

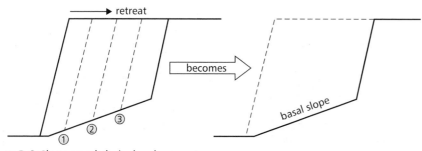

■ **3.9** Slopes and their development

concentrated in a smaller area, and will tend to accumulate unless there is an efficient method of removing the increased supply of material (such as a river at the base). Other slopes, for example at the ends of spurs, will spread out or diverge downhill and show a convex plan; these represent a form of waxing slope. Still others, as on valley sides, will retain the same areal extent as altitude decreases and therefore show a rectilinear form.

Thus if we look in plan view at the slopes of a valley from its head or source to its base, we notice that the relative importance of these three slope components typically changes downstream (**3.11**). The rectilinear component grows at the expense of the other two, and frequently shows two distinct facets.

Climatic regime

The significance of climate is that it largely determines the actual processes of weathering (**3.1**) and the types of mass-movement operational at any particularly location (**3.3**). Those processes, as indicated in **3.10**, have a direct bearing on slope angle and form. But climate has a significant indirect impact through the medium of vegetation. Vegetation, particularly its degree of cover and root systems, has a bearing on soil and regolith stability. Where stability is maintained, then there is the expectation that slope angle will be either maintained or reduced.

Rock type

The significant aspects of geology in the context of slope form are:

■ hardness and resistance to the processes of weathering – generally speaking, the greater these qualities, the steeper the slope

■ permeability and porosity – an impervious bedrock will encourage the overlying regolith and soil to become saturated and therefore more prone to mass-movements of a flow kind

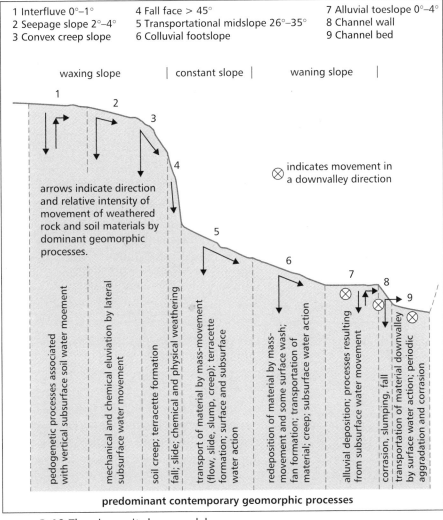

1 Interfluve 0°–1°
2 Seepage slope 2°–4°
3 Convex creep slope
4 Fall face > 45°
5 Transportational midslope 26°–35°
6 Colluvial footslope
7 Alluvial toeslope 0°–4°
8 Channel wall
9 Channel bed

waxing slope | constant slope | waning slope |

arrows indicate direction and relative intensity of movement of weathered rock and soil materials by dominant geomorphic processes.

⊗ indicates movement in a downvalley direction

pedogenetic processes associated with vertical subsurface soil water moement

mechanical and chemical eluviation by lateral subsurface water movement

soil creep; terracette formation

fall; slide; chemical and physical weathering

transport of material by mass-movement (flow, slide, slump, creep); terracette formation; surface and subsurface water action

redeposition of material by mass-movement and some surface wash; fan formation; transportation of material; creep; subsurface water action

alluvial deposition; processes resulting from subsurface water movement

corrasion, slumping, fall

transportation of material downvalley by surface water action; periodic aggradation and corrasion

predominant contemporary geomorphic processes

■ **3.10** The nine-unit slope model

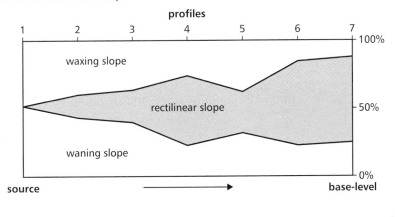

profiles

waxing slope

rectilinear slope

waning slope

source → base-level

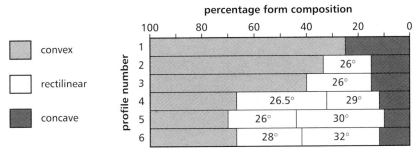

percentage form composition

convex
rectilinear
concave

■ **3.11** Slope elements of a valley side

joints and bedding planes – where these are present and well developed, they encourage water penetration and may eventually lead to sliding.

The impact of time

It is widely recognised that time, operating through the processes of weathering and mass-movement, has an effect on slopes, but the question is: Do slopes decrease in angle as time passes (i.e. decline), or do they maintain the same angle (i.e. retreat)? Studies have tried to correlate slope development with variables such as climate, vegetation cover and the role of agents of denudation. It might be argued that if there is no – or inefficient – removal of mass-wasting materials, then **aggradation** (or building up) occurs lower down as **degradation** (or lowering) continues higher up. But slope evolution is very complex, and it may be that because the time required to make significant changes in slopes is so great, definitive conclusions from studies may not yet be possible. As well as the theory of slope decline (pioneered by W. M. Davis in 1899) and parallel retreat (L. C. King in 1957), there is the theory of slope replacement proposed by W. Penck in 1924 (**3.9c**). In the last case, a steep slope undergoes parallel retreat and as a result is gradually replaced by a more gentle basal slope extending upwards from its original base.

10 Explain the changing slope composition shown by **3.11**.

11 Explain the links between vegetation, slope stability and slope angle.

12 Which of the three different views of slope development shown in **3.9c** do you favour? Justify your viewpoint.

3.5 **Slopes as systems**

It should by now be clear that a slope is the complex outcome of interacting processes and factors. Perhaps one of the best ways of understanding slopes is to consider them as working open systems. **3.12** suggests that the slope may be considered as a bedrock with a mantle of regolith and soil continually moving downwards as a result of past and present energy inputs. The stream acts as a base-level for the slope and provides a means for transporting water and soil brought down the slope across the system boundary. Such water and soil become outputs of the system. The important thing is not to regard the slope as an inert mass, but as a moving and dynamic mechanism involving complex interactions between gravity, precipitation, heat, vegetation and the rock of which it is made.

One characteristic of slopes directly related to the systems concept is their tendency to maintain the same profile and angles as they retreat over time. Where this is happening, it is claimed that the slope is in a state of **dynamic equilibrium** – that there is a condition of balance between the rate of produc-

tion of regolith by the processes of weathering and the rate of its removal by transportational processes such as soil creep and rainwash. Where the balance is unchanging, the slope form will not change. More commonly, however, the balance will need to adjust itself through time in response to external changes such as in climate and base-level. As a consequence, as the slope strives to achieve an equilibrium with the changing conditions, so the required adjustments will be reflected in changes in the slope form.

This chapter has focused on the processes and factors that affect slope form. These aspects are of concern to geographers for three reasons. First, weathered products will eventually be moved to the point where they can be eroded and transported by agents such as wind and water. In this way, weathering, mass-movement and slopes are factors relevant to the systems of landform development which are examined in the remaining chapters of this unit. Secondly, some forms of mass-movement present natural hazards to people, and understanding of the mechanisms involved is needed in terms of prevention or 'control' measures, and in terms of regulating potentially adverse human impacts on the environment. Thirdly, slopes directly affect many human activities and vice versa. For this reason, they constitute a key topic located at the interface between physical and human geography. What geographers learn here is potentially valuable to many different sections of society, from the farmer to the town planner, from the road engineer to the insurance company.

■ **3.12** The slope as an open system

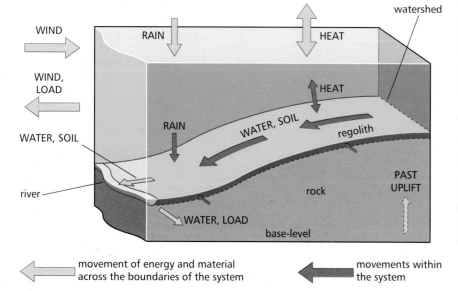

4.1 **The hydrological cycle**

IT1

The interface between people and the physical environment is no more critical than in the context of water management. Water is a two-faced resource; it is both life-giving and life-threatening. Of all the global systems, the circulation of water (referred to as the **hydrological cycle**) is one of the fastest in terms of operation and for this reason is one of the quickest to show the effects of people. But since it is a system which prevails throughout the hydrosphere, it makes a considerable impact on both people and landforms. So far as the latter are concerned, the action of running water has operated over a longer time-scale and over a larger proportion of the Earth's surface than any other agent of denudation. It is the pre-eminent creator and moulder of landforms.

The hydrological cycle is a simple circulation of water (**4.1**). Water is evaporated from oceans, lakes and other water surfaces; from there it is transported over land areas, largely in the form of clouds, where it falls as precipitation and then, in a variety of ways, particularly via streams and rivers, it eventually finds its way back to the sea. Effectively this is a closed system (see section 1.2), since the atmosphere and lithosphere combined have a finite amount of water, and there are no gains and losses in the overall cycle.

IT1

The key unit of the hydrological cycle so far as the Earth's land surface is concerned is the drainage basin (**4.2**). The drainage basin may be defined as the land area within a **watershed**, the watershed simply being the rim of higher ground, the boundary that separates one basin from its neighbours. The watershed also delimits what is referred to as the **stream** or **river catchment** – the area within which all surface and subsurface water will eventually find its way into the same river. Thus the terms 'drainage basin' and 'stream catchment' might seem to be referring to one and the same thing. That is true to an extent, but the former term is perhaps more appropriately used when referring to the land within a watershed, whilst the latter relates rather more to any water it contains.

As tributaries unite to form larger rivers, individual stream catchment areas combine into larger drainage basins, creating a nested hierarchy of drainage basins. As a discrete area of the Earth's surface, the drainage basin represents an open system of objects

■ **4.1** The hydrological cycle

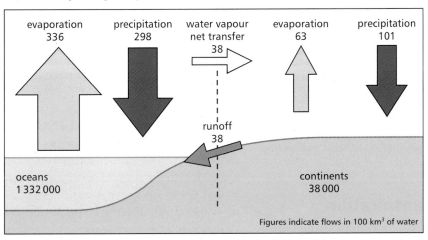

evaporation 336 precipitation 298 water vapour net transfer 38 evaporation 63 precipitation 101

runoff 38

oceans 1 332 000   continents 38 000

Figures indicate flows in 100 km³ of water

■ **4.2** Part of a drainage basin

■ **4.3** The drainage basin as a system

(stream channels, slopes, etc.) maintained by flows of energy and materials between them. Because the basin receives inputs, then stores and transfers them, and finally releases them as out-

puts, it can also be regarded as a cascading system of smaller subsystems, the output from one becoming the input for another. The main elements in the drainage basin system are shown in **4.3**.

Finally, by way of introduction, it should be pointed out that just as the drainage basin may be viewed as a subsystem of the hydrological cycle, so the perspective may be reversed. Drainage basins may equally be seen as having their own hydrological cycles. The circulation may be less watertight, but certainly a proportion of any catchment is being recycled as a result of localised evaporation and precipitation.

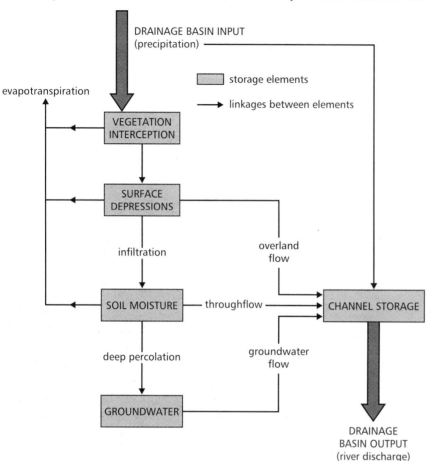

1 Write an explanatory account of the relative importance of the flows within the hydrological cycle (**4.1**).

2 Place a piece of tracing paper over part of the OS 1:50000 map for your local area. Attempt to draw the watershed for a sizeable drainage basin and for smaller basins nested within it.

4.2 **Drainage basin processes**

In showing the components of the drainage basin as a system, **4.3** draws our attention to its interlinked processes. From the point of view of circulation, the key processes are precipitation, evapotranspiration, interception, infiltration, runoff, throughflow and groundwater flow.

Precipitation

This is the process which delivers the key input to the system. There are several dimensions to consider, namely type, intensity, duration and variability (see section 10.7).

Evapotranspiration

This is the loss of moisture at the Earth's

surface by direct evaporation from water bodies and the soil, plus transpiration from growing plants. Since the hydrological cycle is about pathways and the relationships between them, it is clear that the precipitational characteristics outlined above need to be taken into consideration when examining the routeing of water through the catchment. However, any consideration of precipitation as an input needs also to take into account certain outputs, most notably that of evapotranspiration. This input–output relationship can be expressed as the **water balance**. This refers to the proportion of the precipitation (P) at a place which is disposed of by evapotranspiration (E), runoff (R) and changes in groundwater storage (S). It is stated by the water balance equation:

$$P = E + R \pm S$$

The water balance is affected by many of the same factors, but it is not to be regarded as the same thing as the hydrological cycle. When the balance is 'positive', i.e. there is an excess of water over and above that lost to runoff and evapotranspiration, increased infiltration and percolation allow groundwater volumes to rise. When it is 'negative', the water table falls through discharge from springs (plus also through human use) to maintain river flows. The seasonal fluctuations in the water balance thus influence springs (whether they are permanent or intermittent), river discharge (via base-flow) and the occurrence of ephemeral streams in wet seasons. A graph showing monthly precipitation and evapotranspiration values allows periods of surplus, deficit and groundwater recharge to be distinguished.

Interception

This is the process by which raindrops are intercepted by plant surfaces, particularly the leaves of large trees, and thus prevented from falling directly onto the soil surface. During periods of prolonged rainfall, the capacity of the foliage will be exceeded and water will begin to drip from the canopy to the ground (**throughfall**). Some water will also run along branches and down the trunk (**stemflow**). Water droplets retained by the leaves will eventually be evaporated or absorbed (**interception loss**), thus reducing the effectiveness of the rainfall as a whole. Interception is particularly important in tropical rainforests in that it helps to reduce the effects of rainsplash erosion on fragile soils.

Infiltration

The relative permeability and porosity of the ground on which precipitation falls will determine how quickly and what proportion of the water moves into the soil. The greater the permeability and porosity, the faster the rate of infiltration and the greater its capacity. The rate of infiltration of water changes with time. Shortly after rain begins to fall, the rate will be relatively high since there will be more available air spaces between the soil particles. As they become filled, the infiltration rate will be reduced, but it will fall to a constant level as eventually a balance is reached between water infiltrating into and draining from the soil.

Runoff

This is the surface movement of water derived directly from rainfall and from melting snow and ice. It usually takes the form of sheetwash, but the water may also run downslope in very small rivulets. Runoff is generated when rainfall intensity exceeds the infiltration capacity of the soil, leading to the build-up of a surface layer of water. The amount of runoff is affected by the vegetation cover, surface roughness and the gradient and length of the slope. The term **overland flow** is used to refer to the proportion of total rainfall which is not intercepted by vegetation and does not infiltrate the soil.

Throughflow

This is the subsurface movement of water in a downslope direction, in contrast to the vertical movement of water towards the water table (**percolation**). Throughflow tends to be concentrated in the subsoil, particularly if this rests on a relatively impermeable bedrock. It is thought to be a far more important process than overland flow in the disposal of rainwater on the hillsopes of humid temperate regions.

Groundwater

This is water contained within the soil, the regolith and underlying rocks. It is derived mainly from the **percolation** of rainwater and meltwater. Groundwater is contained within the pores, joints and bedding planes of rocks, and where these 'storage' areas are linked together, lateral movement of groundwater is possible. This movement is known as **baseflow** and takes place below the water table. Where the water table reaches the surface, groundwater issues forth as **seepages** or **springs**. The amount of groundwater and the level of the water table

3 Explain how the relative importance of runoff and throughflow are affected by the following precipitation characteristics:
■ type
■ intensity
■ duration.

4 Explain why the percentage of rainfall becoming runoff is inversely proportional to the degree of ground cover.

5 Rural areas around Moscow experience mean annual evapotranspiration amounting to 600 mm, whereas for the city the figure is 190 mm. Explain this difference.

6 Explain why, if more water is lost through evapotranspiration in the summer months, groundwater is at its lowest level during the autumn.

vary seasonally. For example, in temperate environments of the Northern Hemisphere, groundwater levels are likely to be lowest in September, October and November following the relatively dry summer when not only are rainfall receipts less, but also rates of evapotranspiration. Levels are also relatively low beneath urban areas which tap the groundwater resources by wells and bores to provide a significant amount of their water supply.

4.3 **River channel processes**

Transportation, erosion and deposition

Within a river or stream, turbulence causes particles to move. Any energy surplus to that required to overcome friction will be used to transport materials known as **load**. Load is carried in four ways:

- in **solution** – dissolved minerals such as salt and limestone
- in **suspension** – particles are carried along in the body of a stream and are supported by the water itself
- by **traction** – material is dragged or rolled along the river bed
- by **saltation** – the jumping of relatively small particles along the bed caused largely by turbulence.

Most rivers have three-quarters of their load made up of suspended sediments, but the exact proportions of each type of load carried by a particular river will depend on rock type, climate and velocity; the proportions may well vary seasonally. For example, so far as rock type is concerned, limestones will tend to be carried in solution. Velocity has considerable influence. In general, the faster a river is flowing, the greater its load-carrying capacity and particularly the greater its ability to move large particles.

Erosion is a collection of processes which deliver a significant amount of load for transportation.

- **Corrasion** is the process by which load particles wear away the river channel, in much the same manner as sandpaper. According to its principal direction, it is possible to distinguish between downward corrasion (sometimes known as **abrasion**), lateral corrasion and headward erosion.
- **Attrition** refers to the wearing and breaking down of load particles as a result of rubbing and knocking against each other.
- **Corrosion** is the purely chemical erosion of rock surfaces by flowing water, as in limestone which is attacked by carbon dioxide dissolved in streams. By weakening rock structure, corrosion also assists the other erosive processes.

A river's ability to erode and transport, particularly the latter, is referred to as its **competence**. As indicated with reference to capacity, competence is directly proportional to velocity – the so-called Sixth Power Law states that a doubling of velocity will increase competence by 2^6 (that is, by a factor of 64). However, that rule must be treated with caution, particularly when large fragments are involved. If these are angular in shape, there is a tendency for them to become wedged together and transport will be difficult, whereas if they are rounded they will be more readily moved. So perhaps we should refine the earlier statement and say that competence is influenced principally by velocity, but also by the nature of the load (its size, shape and composition).

As for erosion, the nature of the rock into which the channel has been cut is significant. Unconsolidated rock may be eroded and transported in one go, but resistant rock may require weakening before erosion and transportation takes place. A process which facilitates erosion is the one by which potholes are formed. The force of the water on the rock causes a scouring action which can be accentuated by the grinding of carried load. **Cavitation** occurs where water pressure is reduced below vapour pressure, causing bubbles to form. When the pressure is increased, the bubbles implode sending out damaging shock waves. This is particularly common in plunge pools below waterfalls and in rapids.

Rivers that are flowing rapidly but without a load, as for example when sediment has been removed downstream from a dam, are potentially very erosive. Having been deprived of load and now flowing in a channel used to transport much more load than is currently available, the river actively scours the channel to replenish its load. This is known as **clear-water erosion**, a somewhat confusing term since what ultimately happens is a reduction in channel gradient. Gradually, stream energy is lowered to the point that its capacity is just sufficient to carry the reduced load. This adjustment is referred to as **degradation**.

When rivers and streams slow down (as they enter the sea, for example) or when their volume is reduced (as during a period of drought), they usually deposit part of their load. Assuming that the reductions in velocity and volume are reasonably gradual, it will be the heaviest particles that are deposited first, grading over time and space to the finest. However, the load in solution is retained long after the river has run into the sea; indeed, the minerals help to keep the sea salt.

4.4 shows the relationships between these three processes of erosion, transportation and deposition and the key variables of stream velocity and load size. There

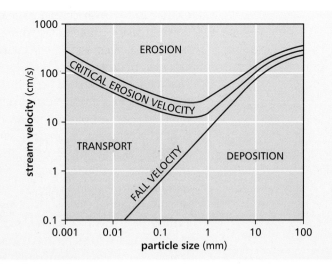

4.4 The relationships between process, stream velocity and load size

are clearly two vital thresholds. For example, a minimum velocity is needed for the **entrainment** (picking up) of particles of a given size resting loosely on the bottom and sides of the stream channel. This is the **critical erosion velocity**. The curve indicates that relatively high velocities are needed to entrain the

extremes of very fine and coarse loads. In contrast, the threshold between transportation and deposition (the **fall velocity**) shows a simpler relationship of fall velocities decreasing logarithmically with particle size.

7 For a river channel made of each of the following rock types, suggest and justify what you think will be the main process of transportation:
   a clay
   b glacial gravel
   c sandstone
   d limestone.

8 With reference to **4.4**, explain why the critical erosion velocity of silt and clay is higher than that of sand.

4.4 **Channel profiles**

The long profile

A popular perception of streams and rivers is that in their upper reaches they are fast-flowing and efficient, whilst in their lowest reaches they are slow and sluggish. This could not be further from the truth. Research has proved that the characteristics of river development hinge, in particular, on the relationship between velocity and efficiency. The power and efficiency of headwaters are negligible in comparison with the lower reaches of the river. From **4.5** it will be

seen that whilst velocity and discharge increase downstream, turbulence, friction, channel roughness and the ratio of load to discharge decrease. These last four variables are closely related in that a rough channel creates friction with the passing water; the dragging effect encourages turbulence which, in its turn, increases the ability of the river to entrain and transport load.

What **4.6a** also shows is that the long profile of a river is typically concave in form – it shows a smooth decrease in gradient towards its mouth. This is sometimes referred to as the **graded profile** and represents the model to which all streams and rivers aspire as they tune their course to base-level. **Base-level** is the theoretical limit, usually regarded as sea-level, below which rivers cannot erode their courses. In other words, it represents the lowest level to which a land surface can be reduced by river processes. If, however, base-level is changed in any way, then rivers will be encouraged to adjust their long profile

4.5 Trends in the long profile of a river

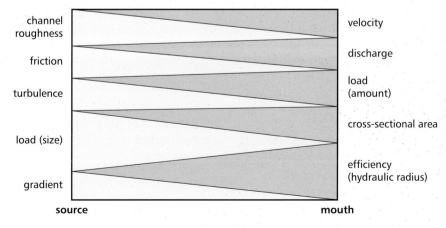

a) The graded profile

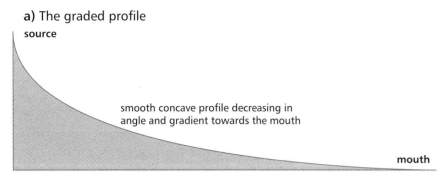

source

smooth concave profile decreasing in angle and gradient towards the mouth

mouth

b) Irregularities in the long profile

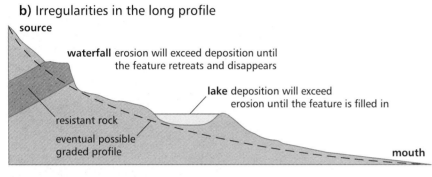

source

waterfall erosion will exceed deposition until the feature retreats and disappears

lake deposition will exceed erosion until the feature is filled in

resistant rock

eventual possible graded profile

mouth

c) Rejuvenation

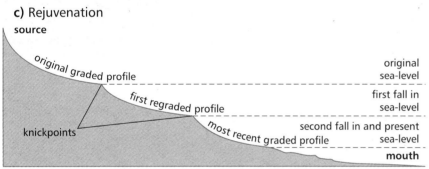

source

original graded profile

original sea-level

first regraded profile

first fall in sea-level

most recent graded profile

second fall in and present sea-level

knickpoints

mouth

■ **4.6** The long profile of a river

accordingly. If base-level falls, as during tectonic uplift of the land, then this sets in train what is called **rejuvenation** (see section 7.7). The most obvious impact of the fall is an increase in the overall gradient; as a consequence, stream velocity increases as also does the erosive potential of the river. Adjustment to the new base-level starts at the sea and gradually works its way up the river course, the point of change being marked by the **knickpoint** (**4.6c**). In contrast, if base-level rises, as during an interglacial period, then adjustment is required in the form of deposition rather than erosion.

Channel cross-section

Another dimension of change as one moves down the long profile of a river is the river channel itself (**4.5**). To appreciate this point we can look at the river channel in cross-section. The most obvious change

is that the cross-sectional area increases downstream – that is, the river channel becomes bigger. It also becomes more efficient. In order to explain this particular characteristic, reference needs to be made to two vital measures. **Wetted perimeter** refers to that part of the channel that is in contact with water at any particular time (**4.7b**). The fuller the channel, the greater the wetted perimeter and therefore the more water exposed to the frictional drag of the channel sides. The **hydraulic radius** of a stream channel is calculated by dividing its cross-sectional area by the length of its wetted perimeter. It is a measure, therefore, of how much water there is in relation to the amount of the channel currently occupied by the stream. The higher the value of the hydraulic radius, the greater the efficiency of the occupying stream or river. High values are typically associated with streams that have a large discharge and those that have a cross-section that is approximately semi-circular. Indeed, just as streams and rivers seek to achieve the efficient graded profile, so in their channels they try to achieve the most efficient cross-sectional shape. In contrast, streams with low values are typically wide and shallow.

One final point to be made here concerns the final downstream trend shown on **4.5** – the general increase in hydraulic radius values. It is this increasing channel efficiency that helps to explain the first trend we identified, namely the downstream increase in stream velocity. Also playing a part in the explanation is the fact that as one moves downstream, load particles tend to become smaller, more rounded and more effective in helping to smooth the bed and banks of the channel. Such particles are also more mobile and therefore impede stream velocity to a lesser degree than angular load.

9 Explain each of the trends shown by **4.5**.

10 Suggest reasons for the upstream movement of knickpoints.

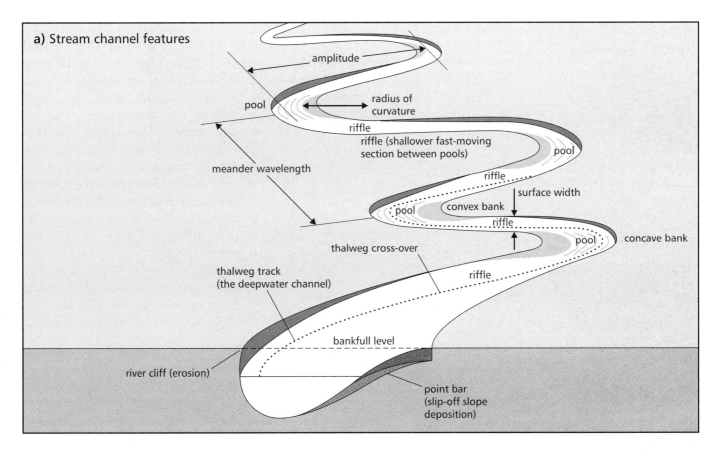

a) Stream channel features

amplitude

pool

radius of curvature

riffle

riffle (shallower fast-moving section between pools)

pool

meander wavelength

riffle

surface width

pool

convex bank

riffle

concave bank

thalweg cross-over

pool

thalweg track (the deepwater channel)

riffle

bankfull level

river cliff (erosion)

point bar (slip-off slope deposition)

b) Wetted perimeter and hydraulic radius

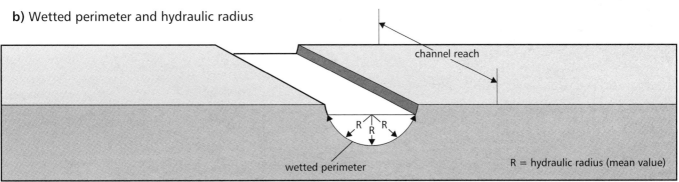

channel reach

R R R

wetted perimeter

R = hydraulic radius (mean value)

■ **4.7** Stream channel terminology

4.5 Fluvial landforms

Potholes, waterfalls and rapids

The processes at work in the river channel produce a suite of distinctive morphological features. To begin with, the upper reaches of the river channel are usually rocky and littered with boulders. Potholes can form as the water swirls on the uneven bed. Pebbles scour circular depressions and these gradually develop into **potholes**. **Waterfalls** and **rapids** occur where the bed of the river is suddenly steepened (**4.6b**). They are caused by differences in the hardness of rocks; soft rocks are eroded more quickly leaving the hard rock to form the starting point of a rapid or the lip of a waterfall. Rejuvenation and its associated knickpoints (**4.6c**) or obstacles such as landslides, lava or lakes can also create waterfalls and rapids.

Interlocking spurs

Bends in the river channel become emphasised because the current is stronger on the outside of the bend. Here banks are eroded and undercut to form river cliffs, whilst on the other side there is deposition rather than erosion and a gentle slip-off slope is formed. These two actions help to form interlocking spurs which are then gradually worn away by the downstream migration of the meanders. Gradually, the river cuts for itself an ever-widening swathe of fairly level land.

Riffles and pools

Deposition takes place along the length of the river channel, and not only at the insides of meanders where point bar deposits collect. Depending on the discharge of the river and related to the general tendency for attrition to lead to comminution of the load (i.e. by wearing against each other particles get smaller), even where the channel bed is composed of alluvial material, inequalities occur with zones of larger-calibre, gravelly material (**riffles**) separated by areas of finer deposits (**pools**)(**4.7a**). Riffles and pools provide alternating shallows and deeper stretches in the channel and seem to be characteristic of alluvial streams, both straight and meandering. Turbulence occurs over the riffles, resulting in high energy losses, whilst smoother flow across the pools allows energy to be conserved. Research has shown that the distance between riffles appears to be related to the width of a stream along a given stretch. One theory for the occurrence of riffles and pools is that they represent a natural mechanism for equalising the distribution of energy within a section of stream, producing equilibrium within the system. This matter is dealt with in more detail below.

Meanders

Meanders, the curving bends in a river channel, are one of the most widespread of fluvial landforms (**4.8**). They are

■ **4.8** Meander features and development

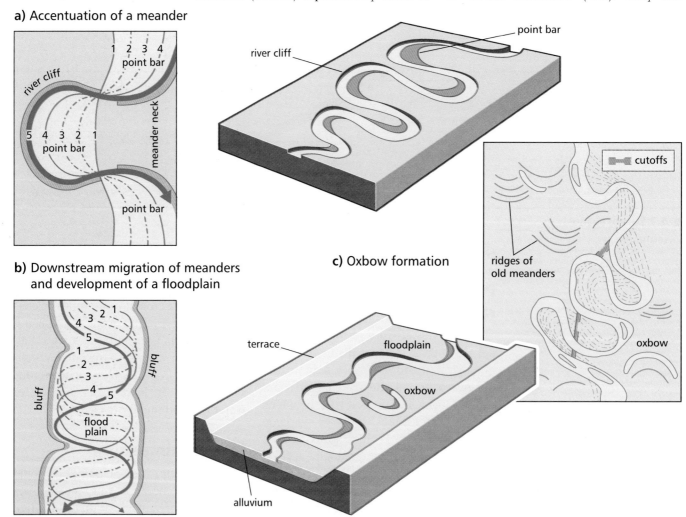

a) Accentuation of a meander

b) Downstream migration of meanders and development of a floodplain

c) Oxbow formation

found in streams of all sizes and at all elevations (not just restricted to lower courses), and appear to reflect both the mechanics of fluid flow and the processes of erosion, transportation and deposition within the channel. Bank erosion, shifts in channel position and changes in plan shape are normal river behaviour.

In the laboratory situation, straight and uniform channels have consistently been shown to develop pools and riffles and then to migrate sideways to produce meanders. Another line of research has been to link meanders to helicoidal flow, that is to the spiral or corkscrew-like movement of water molecules in the river in a downstream direction. It is thought that materials eroded from the outside of a meander are deposited on the inside of the next and subsequent meanders, but whether this kind of movement is a result of established meanders or a cause of meanders in the first place is not decided.

Engineers invariably create semi-circular, obstacle-free straight channels to improve the efficiency of urban drainage networks. In nature, straight channels are rare, only occurring where a glacier has scoured a trough or where streams flow down precipitous hillsides. The natural form of a river channel undoubtedly appears to be a winding one. Many misconceptions about meander evolution have been quoted in the past. Bank falls and uprooted trees do not start their formation, nor does the presence of an obstruction.

Meanders develop in stages (**4.8**). First, small dips and shallows appear in the stream bed and these affect the pattern of currents. Soon the water beings to swing from side to side and once it starts to meander, a stream does not stop unless there is an obstacle that prevents it. Within the meandering stream, riffles and pools become regular features along the bed. Once initiated, meanders are constantly evolving, principally in a manner that ultimately reduces the stream's directional change. Loops are enlarged by erosion on the outside bend of the curve, while deposition occurs on the inside bank. When the loop grows too large, it is cut off from the rest of the meander to form an **oxbow lake** or **cutoff**.

One intriguing feature of meanders is the relationship between channel width and meander wavelength (**4.9a**). Meander wavelength is usually between 8 and 12 times the width of the channel (on average, it is 11 times). If a wavelength is 10 times the width, then pools at meander bends will be spaced 5 times the width apart. Also noteworthy is the fact that stream flow within a meander is fastest when the radius of curvature is between 2 and 3 times that of the channel width. The line of fastest stream flow is called the **thalweg** (**4.7a**). Where obstacles cause a distortion in the regularity of the meanders, the increased resistance will be compensated by increased bank erosion – this will reshape the bend and adjust it towards its ideal form. **4.9b** shows another relationship, namely a positive one between meander wavelength and stream discharge.

Floodplains and levees

Most rivers are for most of the time in an 'underbankful' state; bankfull discharge is much less frequent. None the less, there are times when water not just fills but overtops the bank. Repeated flooding

■ **4.9** Relationships associated with meandering

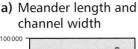

a) Meander length and channel width

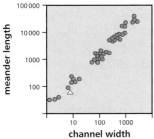

b) Meander wavelength and stream discharge

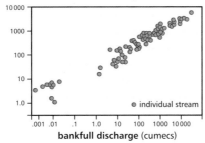

c) Discharge, slope and channel habit

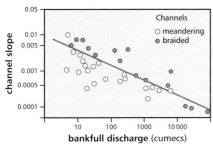

d) Channel patterns and bed material

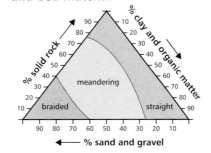

over long periods leads to the build-up of sediments on the valley floor and so to the creation of a **floodplain** (**4.8b**). Because sediment accumulates nearest to the banks, rivers may eventually come to flow between natural embankments or **levees**. Other features typical of floodplains are **meander cutoffs** (the final product of meander development), **meander scars** (produced by stream channel shifts) and **river cliffs** (at the contact point between the river channel and the valley-side beyond the floodplain).

Deltas

As rivers approach base-level, at the coast or in a lake, velocity decreases and load is deposited, gradually building up a low-lying, swampy plain known as a **delta**. The principal methods of deposition are dumping of bedload, settling of suspended sediment, and **flocculation** – a process by which clay particles in suspension coagulate on contact with sea-water and settle rapidly. If the delta is to grow, then it needs to be fed by upstream erosion, and the rate of deposition needs to exceed that of coastal erosion. If sediment continues to accumulate, the river itself becomes choked and forced to divide into a number of separate channels called **distributaries**. Four main types of delta are recognised (**4.10**).

■ **4.10** Types of delta

a) Cuspate

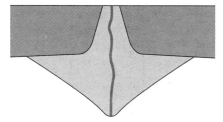

b) Arcuate

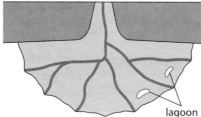

lagoon

c) Bird's foot, or lobate

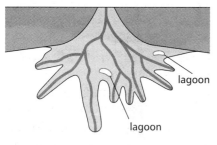

lagoon

lagoon

d) Estuarine

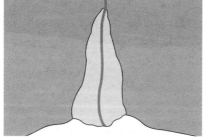

Valleys

The valley is irrefutably the prime landform of drainage basins; no stream or river is ever without one. Valleys would have near vertical sides if rivers alone were responsible for excavating them. However, whilst the river is largely cutting downwards, weathering and mass-movement attack the sides of the valley and they assume a V-shaped cross-section. If the rocks are hard, resistant or porous, there will be relatively little weathering and the valley may be very steep-sided. If the rocks are soft and easily worn away, the valley becomes much more open-sided. Generally speaking, valleys become broader downstream and valley sides more gently inclined.

Terraces

River terraces are near-level surfaces in a valley, usually covered by gravel and alluvium. Many of them are the result of erosion and deposition from a time when the river was graded to a higher base-level (see section 7.7). As a result of rejuvenation, increased river energy has been expended, cutting into the former valley floor or floodplain and leaving it upstanding on either side (**4.11**). Thus such terraces appear to be paired and converge upstream of the knickpoint that marks the impact of the same rejuvenation on the long profile (**4.6c**). A series of terraces can often be seen etched in the valley cross-section, reflecting a sequence of intermittent land uplift or sea-level fall.

Limestone landforms

It may seem perverse to conclude this section with some comments about fluvial landforms in areas that are widely recognised as being essentially dry. Everyone knows that if there is any water about in limestone areas, then it is below ground. The fact of the matter is, however, that many of the features that characterise such areas do owe their origins to the actions of water. These include steep-sided gorges (**dolines**), possibly formed by the collapse of a line of caves carved by

■ **4.11** Paired terraces resulting from rejuvenation

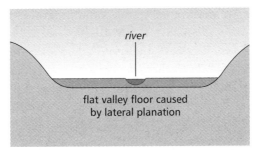

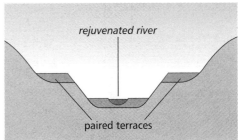

■ **4.12** Some limestone landforms

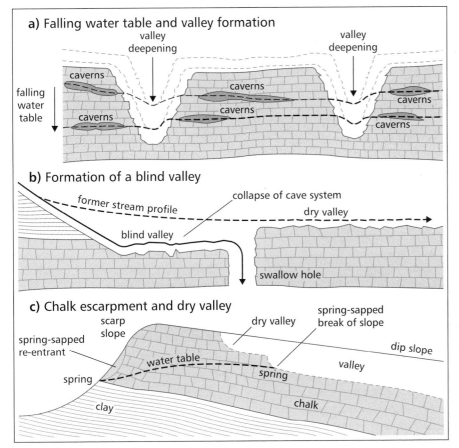

a) Falling water table and valley formation

b) Formation of a blind valley

c) Chalk escarpment and dry valley

an underground stream, and the **dry valleys** of chalk areas, possibly cut during periglacial conditions (**4.12**). Chalk is a particularly pure form of limestone and because of its softness gives rise to a gently rolling landscape, except where strata have been tilted and escarpments have developed. Then there are the **swallow holes** or **sinks** down which surface streams disappear as they encounter limestone outcrops, and the **limestone pavements** etched by corrosive effects of acid rainwater.

11 What effect would rejuvenation have on meanders?

12 How might the following actions affect delta development:
  a deforestation upstream
  b dam-building upstream
  c building of groynes on the coast?

4.6 **Drainage patterns and networks**

Patterns

If we look at river channels in plan view, three types of drainage course can be distinguished:

■ **Straight** These are rare in a natural form and are mainly the outcome of human interference.

■ **Braided** These occur where a change in the river's flow starts the build-up or release of extra material, particularly gravel. Material may fill part of the channel leading to reduced efficiency, the formation of a riffle or colonisation by vegetation, and therefore cause a

splitting of the river into a series of inter-connecting channels.

■ **Meandering** By far the most common characteristic.

4.9c indicates that meandering tends to occur in channels that have a relatively gentle slope and that the tendency to meander decreases with stream discharge. **4.9d** shows that the three types of drainage channel reflect differences in the type of bed material.

However, rather than identify single components, it is perhaps more useful to take a wider view and summarise the essential characteristics of a catchment's

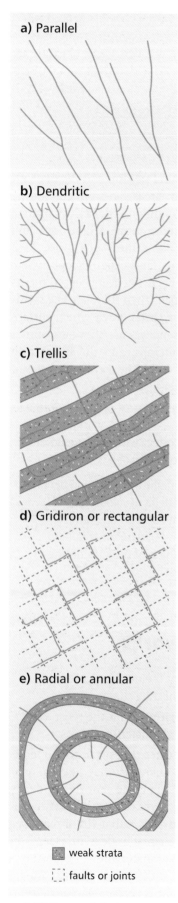

a) Parallel

b) Dendritic

c) Trellis

d) Gridiron or rectangular

e) Radial or annular

▨ weak strata

⬚ faults or joints

■ **4.13** Types of drainage pattern

drainage network. Five recurring basic patterns are commonly identified (**4.13**):

- **Parallel** – perhaps likely to develop on the dip slopes of escarpments
- **Dendritic** – like the vein pattern in a leaf and thought to occur in areas of uniform and gently dipping rock
- **Trellis** – where rocks of different resistance occur in parallel zones
- **Gridiron** or **rectangular** – similar to trellis, but with a more 'open' pattern, following structural weaknesses such as fault lines
- **Radial** or **annular** – streams draining outwards from a central dome structure or volcanic cone.

These patterns imply that rivers adjust themselves to geological structure. For example, earth movements causing the tilting of sedimentary rocks encourage the development of a trellis pattern, whilst the intrusion of a large mass of magma into the Earth's crust and subsequently cooling to create a hill mass such as Dartmoor, would encourage the development of radial drainage. But some streams and rivers are able to respond to counter the effects of tectonic movements. The Brahmaputra, for example, has kept pace with the uplift of the Himalayas by cutting gorges hundreds of metres deep. This is called **antecedent drainage** and is **discordant** to the structure of the area. A similar discordance is achieved when a drainage network, initiated on a young geological outcrop, eventually cuts down into an underlying and older geological formation. Since the structure of the latter will, in most instances, be different from that of the younger rock, the drainage network becomes **superimposed** – the initial drainage pattern is imprinted on the older rocks.

River patterns can also reflect the geomorphological history of an area. Where there has been a period of glaciation, pre-existing river courses can be 'disturbed' or 'deranged'. It has also been shown that streams compete with each other, resulting in **river capture** or

piracy. Where two stream systems are involved, each with a separate outlet to the same base-level, the river with the steeper gradient, the more rainfall input or flowing over less resistant rocks, may be expected to extend itself by headward erosion until it absorbs or captures part of the other stream. A simple river capture is shown in **4.14**, where geological conditions have favoured developments. Tributary X of river A has been able to extend its course by headward erosion to the point that it eventually captures the upper reaches of river B. This point is known as the **elbow of capture**; a col marks the former course of the captured river and as a result of its 'beheading' the downstream section of river B becomes a **misfit stream** (that is, it occupies a valley that is much larger than the river could have cut in its now reduced size).

---

13 a Explain the relationships shown by **4.9c**.
   b From **4.9d**, identify the conditions that appear to favour **i** straight and **ii** braided channels.

14 Describe the geological conditions you would expect to be associated with each of the drainage patterns shown in **4.13**.

Networks

The capacity to see patterns and piratic events of this sort, however, may be rather subjective, and doubtless depends on the scale of observation. Such patterns are more readily seen when the focus is rather distant and on the main drainage lines. By bringing into the frame more and more 'lesser' stream courses, closer scrutiny tends to blur the pattern. In order to avoid these perceptual problems associated with the application of descriptive labels to drainage patterns, more quantitative, objective assessments may be made using two different measures.

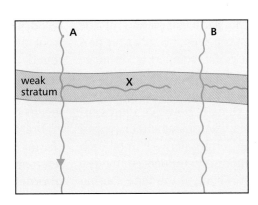

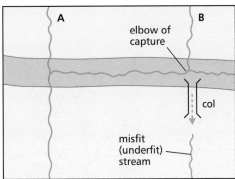

■ **Drainage density** This is the ratio of total channel length to drainage basin area. By giving an indication of the frequency of streams, it can be used to show the influence of rock type, slope, precipitation, vegetation, and so on. Other variables being equal, high densities are associated with impermeable rock, steeper slopes, well-vegetated and high-rainfall areas.

15 Explain how you would expect each of the following factors to affect drainage density:
   a rock type   **c** vegetation cover
   b rainfall   **d** time.

■ **4.15** Stream ordering

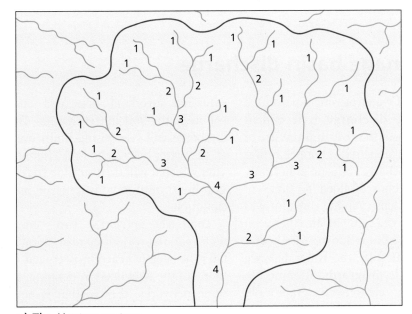

a) The Horton system

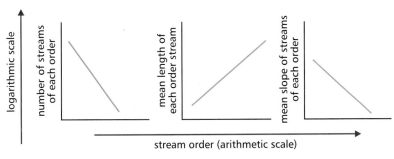

b) Some stream order relationships

■ **Stream ordering** In order to identify differences between drainage basin morphology, Horton developed a system of measuring branches within the hierarchy of a stream (**4.15a**). Streams without tributaries at the head of a river system are called first-order streams. When two first-order streams join, they form a second-order one, and so on. It has been calculated that the number of streams within each order decreases with regularity. This is known as the **law of stream numbers**. Similarly, if stream order is plotted against the length of each order, or stream order is plotted against the area drained by each order, a straight-line relationship is always shown (**4.15b**). The **bifurcation ratio** indicates the number of streams in a given order in relation to the number of streams in the next order. For example, if in one drainage basin there are 240 first-order and 80 second-order streams, and in another basin there are 200 first-order streams and 50 second-order streams, the bifurcation ratios will be 3.0 and 4.0 respectively. The higher ratio in the second drainage basin is a measure of its greater complexity as a network.

One of the particular values of the measures just considered is that they provide yardsticks for comparing drainage basins. Such comparisons help to throw light on the significance of factors such as geology and climate. However, some caution is needed when using either type of measure: the results derived from each will be significantly influenced by the conditions prevailing at the time. During times of flood, for example, much more surface drainage will be in evidence, whilst during spells of drought streams will dry up completely and so 'disappear' from the map (**4.16**). The sensible way round this is to measure the drainage network during 'normal' conditions, but the problem here is in defining the parameters of normality.

Drainage density assessment and stream ordering are a part of what is referred to as **drainage basin morphometry** (measurement). The next section looks at other quantifiable aspects of the same system.

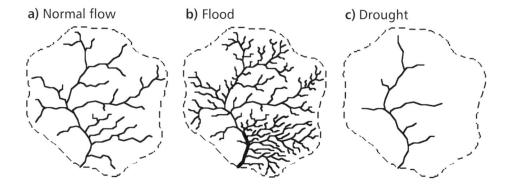

a) Normal flow **b) Flood** **c) Drought**

■ **4.16** The impact of flood and drought conditions on the drainage network

4.7 **Drainage basin discharge**

IT2

The volume of water passing a point in a given time, the **discharge**, is dependent on the velocity of the river and the size or cross-sectional area of its channel at that point. The discharge, of course, not only varies from times of flood to times of drought, but is also varying constantly as a result of the changing balance between precipitation, evapotranspiration and storage indicated by the water balance equation. A **hydrograph** attempts to display this relationship graphically (**4.17**). It shows how a stream responds following an input of precipitation. Obviously, when rain falls, only a small percentage will fall into the channel directly. There will be a **lag-time** between the time that rain hits the ground and its arrival in the channel. It will arrive by various pathways at different times. Direct overland flow will arrive first. Baseflow will be an ongoing process since water is generally already in the system. Throughflow will depend on the infiltration rate. When the soil is

saturated, overland flow will contribute to the flow in the channel. The discharge will rise (rising limb) until all the water has reached the channel, after which it will then subside (recession limb) until there is renewed precipitation.

IT2

Drainage networks vary enormously in the ways they react to rainfall. The type of reaction is crucial in terms of the likelihood of flooding. In some networks, the reaction is both quick and concentrated; in others it is slow and prolonged. Clearly, the risk of flooding is much higher in the former circumstances. The critical lagtime is conditioned by many factors. **4.18** indicates some of the most significant of these.

Three of the variables in **4.18** require some qualification. For example, so far as precipitation form is concerned, if it falls and persists in the form of snow, it will be held in store (thereby extending lag-time). But

■ **4.17** Measuring stream discharge

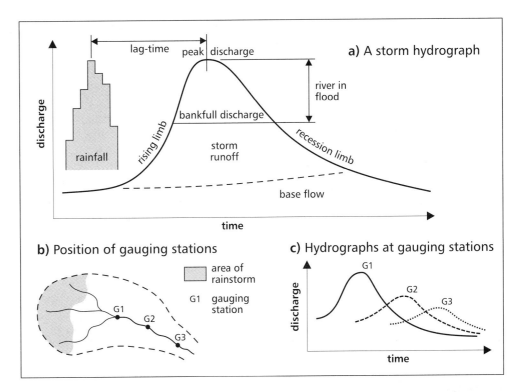

a) A storm hydrograph

b) Position of gauging stations

c) Hydrographs at gauging stations

should a marked thaw set in, then much water will be suddenly released, thereby increasing the risk of flooding. As for land use, clearly there are many variants here. In general, we might say that the less the vegetation cover and the more compact the surface associated with the use, the shorter will be the lag-time with a consequent rise in flood risk. In this context, land use changes can be particularly significant, as with deforestation and urbanisation, for example.

16 For each of the variables in **4.18**, explain its impact on lag-time and the risk of flooding.

17 The table **4.19** provides data for two drainage basins in south-east England.
  a Construct an annual hydrograph for each basin.
  b Compare the two hydrographs and explain the differences you have identified.

■ **4.18** Factors affecting lag-time and the risk of flooding

	Variable	Variable trend	Impact on lag-time	Flood risk
Precipitation	intensity	increasing	reduced	increased
	duration	increasing	reduced	increased
	form	depends	see text	see text
Drainage basin	size	increasing	increased	reduced
	shape/roundness	increasing	reduced	increased
	slopes	increasing	reduced	increased
	drainage density	increasing	reduced	increased
Rock and soil type	porosity	increasing	increased	reduced
	impermeability	increasing	reduced	increased
Vegetation	degree of cover	increasing	increased	reduced
Land use	type	depends	see text	see text
Urbanisation	built-up area	increasing	reduced	increased

■ **4.19** Data for two drainage basins

	J	F	M	A	M	J	J	A	S	O	N	D
BASIN A												
Discharge cumecs	0.39	0.84	0.21	0.39	0.15	0.10	0.06	0.13	0.05	0.13	0.25	0.95
Rainfall mm	60	148	23	105	47	85	85	88	26	18	88	185
Evapotranspiration mm	4	14	35	44	85	101	87	78	45	16	2	0
BASIN B												
Discharge cumecs	0.73	0.91	1.32	0.92	0.91	0.56	0.32	0.22	0.17	0.12	0.18	0.47
Rainfall mm	52	143	161	24	65	60	63	86	55	261	103	123
Evapotranspiration mm	5	15	36	47	89	88	90	78	51	22	6	0

CASE STUDY

IP2, IT2, 8

Bangladesh flooding – causes and cures

Scarcely a year goes by without hearing of some form of flooding in Bangladesh. However, in 1987 and 1988 the scale of the flooding was disastrous: 1657 lives were lost in 1987 and 2379 in 1988. In 1988, 82 000 km^2 of the country was covered by water. Some people regard such disasters as 'acts of God'. Certainly, misfortunes seem to be an occupational hazard of living in a country like Bangladesh with its unpredictable monsoons and low-lying terrain. Some scientists maintain that people are the cause of the severity of the floods, not nature. In particular, they blame the deforestation of the Himalayas. However, there are others who argue that the link between deforestation, sediment build-up and increased flooding is a myth. They say that there is no published evidence for a recent increase in the severity of flooding in the Ganges and Brahmaputra floodplains. They believe that high runoff and erosion rates are linked to natural processes. Deforestation has been taking place for centuries on the Himalayan slopes, so linking the severity of recent flooding to this cause is misleading. Neither is there any evidence of changes in the frequency and severity of flooding being linked to the greenhouse effect and its impact on base-levels.

Links between the Himalayas and Bangladesh are very strong. **4.20** shows that the mountains are the source of the major river systems in the region. Most of Bangladesh is a low-lying floodplain. During a normal year parts of Bangladesh are regularly flooded (**4.21**).

There are three main types of flooding:

■ **Flash floods** These are the result of extremely heavy rainfall on surrounding upland areas. They cause limited damage to crops or property but can breach embankments when water is flowing fast. This means that crops on the other side of the broken defence are submerged. The flooding can lead to tremendous sediment deposition on the land and on river beds. Ultimately, this can lead to levee formation and river beds being raised above the level of the surrounding land.

■ **River floods** These are largely caused by a combination of melting snow in the high Himalayas and heavy monsoon rains over the Himalayas, Assam and Tripura hills, nearby floodplains and the Central Indian Plateau. Floods can be extremely serious when high water levels in the Brahmaputra and Ganges coincide. Their effect is usually strongly felt along the floodplains. Embankments can be breached and the water covers extensive areas. Damage is most pronounced when the flooding occurs early in June along the Brahmaputra and Meghna and after mid-August along all the rivers. Alluvium can bury the fields, and crops can be uprooted by the swift flow of the water. This type of flooding can also damage settlements.

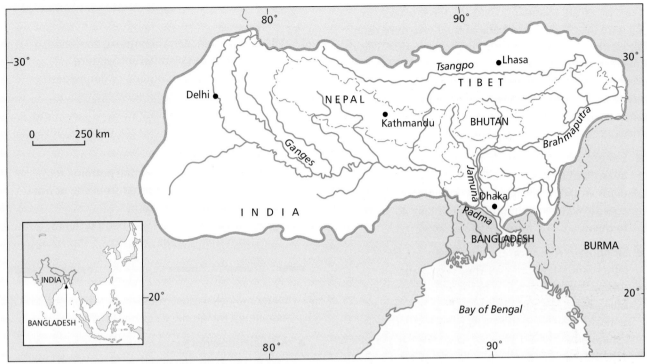

■ **4.20** Catchment area of the Ganges, and Brahmaputra rivers

Occasionally where high tides and high river levels coincide, dramatic flooding occurs along the coast.

■ **Rainwater floods** These are largely due to heavy rainfall in Bangladesh itself. This frequently happens in the monsoon season and affects all floodplain areas.

4.22 analyses the loss of rice production caused by the 1987 and 1988 floods. The evidence suggests that there was a significant difference in the type of flooding involved. However, this destructive hazard does have a silver lining: in those years following really bad floods there is often a noticeable rise in rice production.

■ **4.21** Flooding in Bangladesh

Traditionally, many people believe that covering an area with alluvium can rapidly improve its fertility. In Bangladesh this myth prevails. Farmers do not realise that much of the land receives clear rainwater. Moreover, newly-deposited alluvium takes several years to ripen and is initially infertile. To account for the increased rice production, it is necessary to attribute increased fertility to nitrogen fixing by blue-green algae which live in the water feeding on decomposing waterlogged plants. Moreover, phosphorous and other nutrients become more available to plants in the chemically reduced submerged topsoils.

Flood defence

In July 1987, major aid donors agreed at the G7 Summit Meeting in Paris that the World Bank should coordinate the efforts of the international community to achieve a real alleviation of the effects of flooding in Bangladesh. The World Bank prepared an Action Plan for Flood Control (**4.23**). The plan involves the completion of embankment schemes. It is planned to create compartments behind these by building internal embankments. Controlled flooding would be allowed to aid agriculture. It has been argued, however, that an embankment strategy would not be the best one to follow. Objectors cite the case of the Mississippi, and the three major Chinese rivers where the beds of the rivers have risen above the level of the surrounding countryside. This means that dredging is necessary, as well as high maintenance costs to ensure that the embankments are never breached. If they were, the effects would be catastrophic. Three alternative flood control measures have been suggested:

- **Stream storage** – to hold back 10 per cent of the peak flood flow entering Bangladesh. Seven huge dams would be needed at an estimated cost of US$ 30–40 billion, and they would take 40 years to build.

- **Floodplain retention basins** – these can be either natural or artificial. They would absorb excess flows by diverting much water from the main rivers. The stored water would be released only after the flood peak had passed. It has been estimated that 12–15 basins would be needed in order to bring about a significant reduction in the extent of flooding. The problem is that natural basins already absorb lots of flood water and that both types could already be full of rainwater before the onset of a flood. Diversion of river

18 With reference to the information about areas affected by different types of flooding, trace an outline of Bangladesh. Using suitable cartographic techniques, highlight those areas that experience flash floods, river floods and rainwater floods.

19 Referring to **4.22**:
   a describe how the rainfall patterns for 1987 and 1988 differed from the normal annual rainfall patterns
   b suggest how the 1987 flood differed from that in 1988.

water may also cause siltation of the basins, and associated maintenance costs could be high.

- **Artificial downdraw** of groundwater to absorb excess monsoon rain and river flow. Water would be drawn from the Himalayan water table to reduce it by several tens of metres during the dry season (8 months). This would create underground storage capacity to absorb monsoon

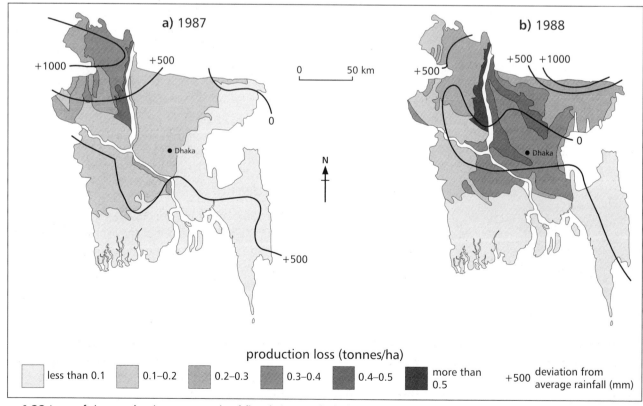

■ **4.22** Loss of rice production as a result of floods in Bangladesh

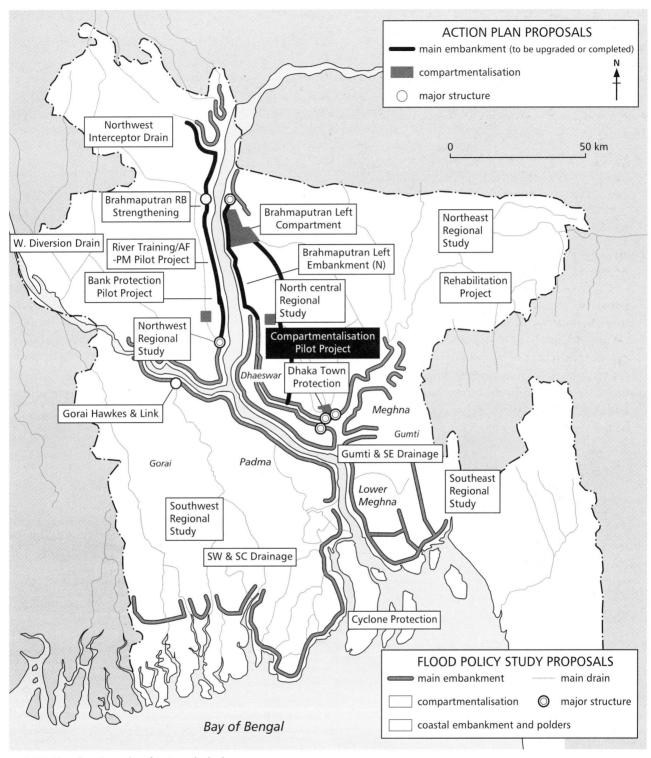

ACTION PLAN PROPOSALS

— main embankment (to be upgraded or completed)

▨ compartmentalisation

◯ major structure

N

0 — 50 km

Northwest Interceptor Drain

Brahmaputran RB Strengthening

Brahmaputran Left Compartment

Northeast Regional Study

W. Diversion Drain

River Training/AF -PM Pilot Project

Brahmaputran Left Embankment (N)

Rehabilitation Project

Bank Protection Pilot Project

North central Regional Study

Northwest Regional Study

Compartmentalisation Pilot Project

Dhaeswar

Dhaka Town Protection

Gorai Hawkes & Link

Meghna

Gumti

Gorai

Padma

Gumti & SE Drainage

Southwest Regional Study

Lower Meghna

Southeast Regional Study

SW & SC Drainage

Cyclone Protection

Bay of Bengal

FLOOD POLICY STUDY PROPOSALS

━━ main embankment   ── main drain

☐ compartmentalisation   ◎ major structure

☐ coastal embankment and polders

■ **4.23** Flood action plan for Bangladesh

rainfall and river flow – 500 wells flowing at a rate 1500 m³ per hour for 240 days a year would withdraw 21 billion m³ of water from groundwater for irrigation and could absorb 10 per cent of the Ganges flow to stop that river's contribution to flooding. Brahmaputran floods would still not be stopped because less irrigation is practised along its length. See also the case study on pages 194–195.

IT1

The coast is the interface where both subaerial and marine erosion and deposition shape the landscape. It is also the zone where most of the world's population live. The coast, like the drainage basin, is a geomorphological system. There are inputs of energy in the form of waves, winds and tides, together with sediment derived from coastal erosion as well as that brought to the coastal zone by rivers. The outputs of the system are the energy expended by waves, and sediment deposited on beaches and the seafloor (**5.1**). As with all systems, the coast is constantly seeking to achieve a state of dynamic equilibrium. If it is achieved, then coastal features such as beaches will undergo little change over time. In reality, the coastal system has to absorb and adjust to much change, as for example to seasonal and longer-term changes in climate. Then there is the response needed to cope with human intervention on an increasing scale. For a long time, people have tried to tame the coast and to exploit its resources, unaware that it is a balanced system. Obstacles such as groynes and piers, which alter tidal currents and sediment flow patterns, can have far-reaching effects on the coastal system. In order to manage the coastline, there is much that we need to know and understand about its physical processes and characteristics.

5.1 **Waves**

Motion

Waves are the vital energy input of the coastal system. These mobile undulations of the sea mainly result from the frictional drag of wind passing over its surface. Within each wave, water particles are involved in a series of circular motions, the size of which diminishes downwards until at a depth equal to half the wavelength they cease. **5.2a** illustrates some of the vital dimensions of waves.

Since waves are largely caused by wind, it follows that their size and strength are directly conditioned by certain characteristics, namely:

- **wind speed**
- **wind persistence** – the length of time wind of a particular strength and direction has prevailed
- the **fetch** (the distance of open water over which the wind has blown) – the longer the fetch, the greater the wave size and strength.

Types of wave

There are two types of wave. **Free waves** start somewhere in the middle of the ocean and move forward under their own momentum; as they do so, their wavelength increases and their amplitude decreases. They are often referred to as **swell**. **Forced waves** are driven onshore by the wind. They have shorter

■ **5.1** The coastal system

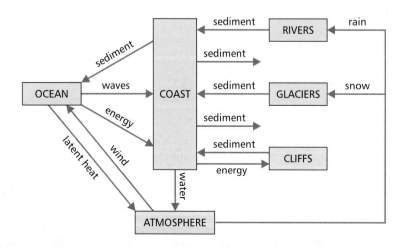

a) Features of waves

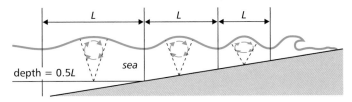

b) Wave action on approaching the shore

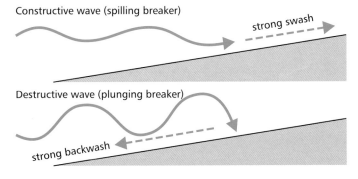

c) Constructive and destructive waves

Constructive wave (spilling breaker)

strong swash

Destructive wave (plunging breaker)

strong backwash

■ **5.2** Wave characteristics

wavelengths, a large amplitude, and break with greater frequency.

Waves approaching the shore undergo significant change (**5.2b**). As the water depth decreases, so the orbiting particles at the base of the wave are slowed down by friction with the sea-floor. Wavelength and period are reduced, the wave steepens and the orbital motion becomes elliptical. Eventually, the forward motion of the crest of the wave exceeds the wave's velocity and the wave front collapses or breaks. The water from the broken wave rushes up the beach. This is known as the **swash**, whereas the return flow running back down the beach under the influence of gravity is called **backwash**.

Geomorphologists distinguish between two types of forced wave (**5.2c**):

■ **Constructive waves** – these have longer periodicity, 10 or more seconds

between wave arrival at a beach; they tend to be 'flatter' in wave form and emphasise the swash action. For this reason, they tend to lead to a net transport of sediment up the beach.

■ **Destructive waves** – frequently of 'steeper' form, they arrive at much closer intervals (a period of three to six seconds) and disturb the backwash action of the previous wave. This results in a turbulent 'combing-down' of beach material – that is, an overall erosive effect.

Refraction

The relationship between the direction in which waves are travelling and the orientation of the coast is important in the development of coastal landforms. **Wave refraction** is the process by which waves undergo a change of direction as they approach headlands and beaches or pass the far ends of spits and bars. In these situations, refraction results from the shallowing of the sea-floor and the effect of this in reducing wave velocity. Thus waves which approach the shore obliquely are 'turned' by friction with the sea-floor so that their crests become nearly parallel to the shore by the time breaking occurs (**5.3a**). **Orthogonals** are lines drawn at right-angles to the wave crests. Not only do they show the pattern of wave refraction, they also give an indication of potential wave energy. A convergence of orthogonals indicates a concentration of wave energy. **5.3b** shows the impact of offshore shingle banks on the pattern of orthogonals which, in turn, clearly signals a regular alternation of energy concentration and dispersion as one moves along the shoreline.

In many cases, refraction does not achieve a completely parallel wave approach. In such instances, the swash of the breaking wave runs diagonally up the beach, but the backwash is at right-angles to the water line. The net outcome is a gradual zigzagging of water and beach material along the beach in the direction of wind and waves (**5.3a**). This

a) Longshore drift

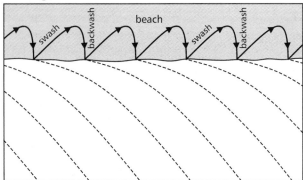

b) Effect of offshore shingle banks on wave refraction

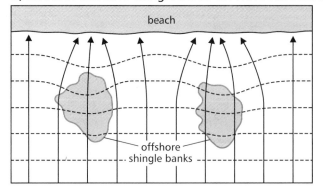

c) Refraction of waves around a headland

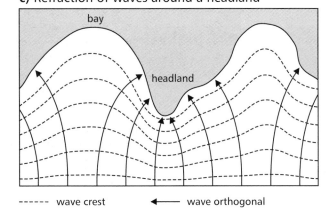

d) Longshore drift and formation of a spit

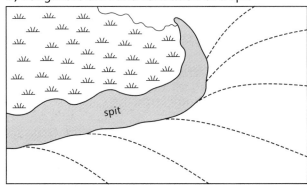

- - - - - - wave crest   ◀—— wave orthogonal

■ **5.3** Longshore drift and wave refraction

is known as **longshore drift**, and it is the main medium for the transfer of sediment along the coast. As indicated by the pattern of orthogonals, the effects of refraction around headlands is to concentrate wave energy and thus the erosive potential of waves, producing such features as caves, arches and stacks, whereas in intervening bays wave energy is somewhat dissipated and deposition is encouraged (**5.3c**). In the case of spits, refraction may be largely responsible for the development of recurves at their distal ends (**5.3d**).

---

1 Identify a type of wave not generated by wind and explain how it is set in motion.

2 **a** Using an atlas, work out the direction of maximum fetch for the following locations:
   - Aberdeen
   - Dover
   - Penzance
   - Llandudno.

b Which location has the longest maximum fetch?
c What are the implications of this in terms of
   i potential coastal change and **ii** hazards?

3 Make a tracing of **5.3d** and draw on it the wave orthogonals.

5.2 **Tides**

The tides are regular oscillations of the sea's surface occurring within a 24-hour period. They are caused by the gravitational attraction exerted on the Earth's water surface by the Moon and the Sun. Most sea coasts experience two high tides a day, but the height of such tides at any one location varies during the lunar month. **Spring tides** are relatively high or low tides that occur shortly after each new and full moon and so are roughly 14 days apart. **Neap tides** occur roughly midway between spring tides and represent the smallest **tidal range** – that is, the difference between high and low tides. However, the tidal range varies not only during the course of a month and with the seasons, but also from place to place.

Tidal range is a significant factor in the context of coastal processes. For example, a large range means that a substantial area of the foreshore is exposed to weathering and erosion, and also that sediment does not have much time in which to settle. Conversely, a small tidal range means that wave action is narrowly concentrated, and weathering related to sea-water restricted.

5.3 **Coastal erosion**

Processes

When waves break against the foot of a cliff, air in joints, bedding planes, cracks and crevasses is suddenly compressed and then released, often with an explosive force that is capable of gradually breaking up the apparently solid cliff. This is **wave quarrying** or **hydraulic erosion**. Any loosened debris is subsequently washed away. But breaking waves can also use this debris, together with weathered material that has fallen from the cliff face, as an abrasive that helps to grind away at the base of the cliff. This is known as **wave corrasion**, and is an important process in the excavation of caves and **geos** (narrow, steep-sided inlets) along lines of structural weakness. One other outcome of corrasion is **attrition**, the rounding and grinding down of the debris involved.

Two chemical processes should be noted – the **solution** of certain rocks, most notably limestone and chalk, and **salt crystallisation**. The latter involves the growth of chloride crystals derived from salt in seawater. This attacks a wide variety of rocks, and its main effect is to loosen rock fragments for other erosional processes to work on. Reference should also be made to **biological activity**. Not only does this assist solution (as for example through secretions by blue-green algae), but molluscs in their search for food actually wear down rock surfaces. Added to this, the growth of seaweed on rock fragments increases their surface area and makes them more easily transportable. Finally, it should be noted that all those areas of the coast lying above the low-tide line may well be exposed to the same processes of weathering and mass-movement as are experienced further inland.

Sea cliffs and platforms

The two principal features produced by wave erosion are cliffs and wave-cut platforms (**5.4**). Together these represent a wedge-shaped mass that has been cut away from the land. As a result of undercutting and subaerial weathering, the cliff retreats (**5.4b**). As it does so, it leaves behind a platform of increasing extent. This, in turn, is subject to a gradual lowering by the process of corrasion.

■ **5.4** Coastal zones

a) Main elements of beaches

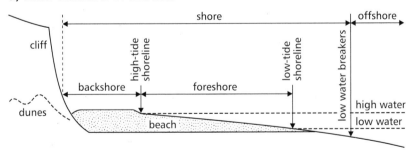

b) The process of cliff retreat

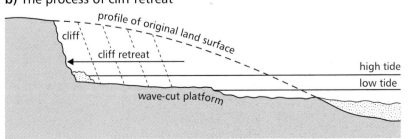

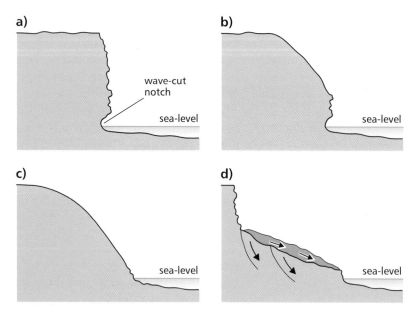

a)

b)

wave-cut notch

sea-level

sea-level

c)

d)

sea-level

sea-level

■ **5.5** Recurrent cliff profiles

■ **5.6** Cliffs in (a) east Norfolk and (b) at Flamborough Head

It is thought that as the platform extends further seawards, it absorbs more wave energy and thereby reduces the rate of cliff erosion.

Cliffs vary enormously in height and profile. **5.5** shows some recurrent profile types. Of the many factors affecting cliff form, three are particularly important:

■ **The balance between the rate of erosion at the base of the cliff and the rate of recession of the cliff face as a result of weathering, mass-movement and gullying.** Where the former exceeds the latter, as on an exposed headland, then very steep, and in places vertical, active cliffs are produced. However, where wave erosion is limited, as in a sheltered bay, a cliff-foot beach

gradually accumulates, progressively absorbing wave energy and offering the cliff increasing protection from the ravages of the sea. In these circumstances, the angle of the dead cliff is slowly reduced by the process of subaerial denudation.

■ **The lithology of the rock exposed in the cliff.** Clearly, rocks vary in terms of their resistance to the processes of marine erosion. A cliff formed largely of clay will be readily undercut at its base and become susceptible to slumping (**5.5d** and **5.6a**), whereas granite, chalk or limestone may be expected to yield steep cliffs (**5.5a** and **5.6b**).

■ **Angle and direction of rock dip relative to the sea, and also jointing**. For example, where strata are horizontal or joints vertical, steep cliffs may be expected. Conversely, where rocks or their joints incline gently towards the sea, so the cliff profile will follow accordingly.

Capes and bays

Just as rock resistance is important in terms of the cliff profile, so too it is significant in plan view. Where rock outcrops of varying strength run transversely to the coastline, the expectation is that the weaker rocks will be eroded more readily to form embayments, whilst adjacent harder rock outcrops will protrude in the form of headlands or promontories. But the coastal system

a)

b)

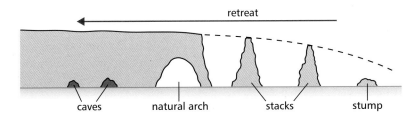

■ **5.7** The retreat of a headland

seeks to counteract this differential erosion of capes and bays by concentrating destructive wave energy on the headlands (**5.3c**) and allowing the accumulation of beach material in the low-energy conditions of the bays. In the former case, the sequence from cave through arch to stack and stump represents the staged destruction of the headland (**5.7**). In the latter case, deposition affords the bay-head increasing protection against further erosion and retreat. Thus by these twin processes the irregu-

lar coastline originally created by the outcrop pattern of contrasting rocks is progressively smoothed out.

The alignment of the coastline relative to the general structural grain of the land is a noteworthy influence on coastal configuration, particularly if there has been a rise in sea-level and widespread submergence (see section 7.7). Where the coast is **discordant** (it runs across the structural grain), then the coastline is characterised by deep inlets (**rias**, or drowned estuaries) separated by long, crenellated headlands, as for example along the south-west coast of Ireland (**5.8a**). Where the coast runs parallel, the resulting **concordant** coastline is relatively smooth, with long channels or **sounds** separating lines of elongated islands, as along the Dalmatian coast of Croatia (**5.8b**).

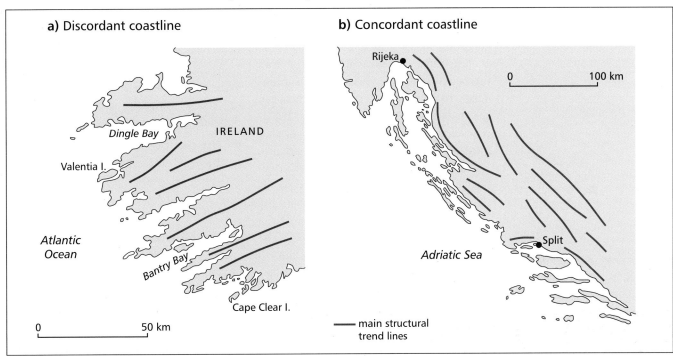

■ **5.8** Concordant and discordant coastlines

4 Compare rivers and the sea as agents of erosion.

5 Suggest an explanation for:
  a the two different cliff profile components shown in **5.5b**
  b the hogsback cliff shown in **5.5c**.

6 With reference to a stretch of coastal cliffs known to you in the field:
  a draw what you think is a typical cliff profile
  b make assessments of **i** cliff height, **ii** mean cliff angle and **iii** wave-cut platform width
  c write an explanatory account of the form and development of the cliffs.

5.4 Coastal deposition

As with rivers, coastal deposition occurs where the load-carrying capacity of the sea is reduced. In most instances, this results from a reduction in wave velocity and energy and can give rise to a diversity of depositional landforms (**5.9**).

Beach forms

The **beach** is the area between the lowest spring tide level and that reached by the highest spring tide and storm waves. It is made up of deposited material which usually builds up on a wave-cut platform where the sea is shallow (**5.4**). Friction with the sea-floor causes the water movement to slow down, with a consequent deposition of material. The type of wave arriving onshore also has a bearing on whether a beach will be formed or not. **Constructive waves** generally mean that a beach will accumulate, since the swash is greater than the backwash and the net result is a tendency to deposit material. Most beaches are in bays and inlets where the coastwise flow of water is retarded, having moved quickly around a headland, sweeping away eroded material. Bayhead beaches are usually crescent-shaped. The profile that typifies many beaches takes a concave form with a backing of sand dunes or cliffs. The beach grades seawards from shingle to sand, and may be interrupted by protru-

sions of rock marking the existence of a wave-cut platform below.

Whilst most beaches show two major elements – the upper beach or **backshore** and the lower beach or **foreshore** (**5.4a**) – no two beaches are the same. On some beaches, coarser material is piled up into a series of ridges (**berms**) near high-tide level (**5.10**). Often the lowest berm has cut into it small, regular embayments knows as **beach cusps**. Other beaches show **ridges** and **runnels** lying at right-angles to the direction of the approaching waves. Frequently, some of the runnels are occupied by pools of sea-water. Sometimes these will be breached by **rip channels** cut by surf moving seawards at high velocity. Running down sections of the beach will be networks of minute **anastomosing channels** which carry in fresh water from the upper beach and salt water from sand exposed as the tide falls. Whether or not these microscale features are to be found on a particular beach depends on several factors:

- **The composition of the beach** – if the beach material is exclusively sand, the gradient of the upper beach is reduced and features such as berms and cusps are not much in evidence.

- **The type of wave action** – for example, during periods of constructive wave action, berms are

■ **5.9** Depositional features of the coast

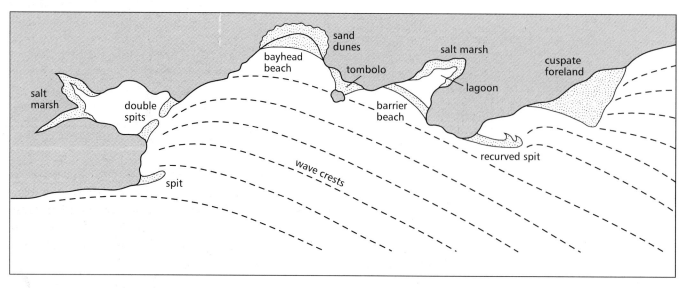

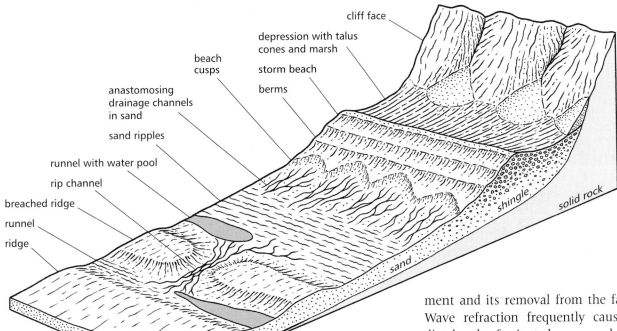

Labels on figure:
cliff face
depression with talus cones and marsh
beach cusps
storm beach
berms
anastomosing drainage channels in sand
sand ripples
runnel with water pool
rip channel
breached ridge
runnel
ridge
shingle
solid rock
sand

■ **5.10** Beach features

likely to be conspicuous as well as ridges and runnels, whereas periods of destructive activity may be expected to produce beach cusps and a breaching of ridges.

■ **The strength of longshore drift** – this has the power to encourage the development of features parallel to the shoreline, such as ridges and runnels.

Above all, the transitory nature of most beach features needs to be emphasised. Constantly changing tidal, wind and weather conditions virtually mean a continuous remoulding of beach morphology.

Spits and bars

Longshore drift plays a vital part in the formation of spits and bars (**5.9**). Spits usually develop at points where the shoreline undergoes a sharp change in direction or at estuary mouths, particularly on their windward side. In these locations, sand and shingle being moved by longshore drift is deposited (presumably because of a reduction in drift velocity) in the form of a projecting beach ridge (**5.3d**). Once initiated, the spit continues to grow until an equilibrium is reached between the deposition of sedi-

ment and its removal from the far end. Wave refraction frequently causes the distal ends of spits to be recurved inland.

At the mouths of some estuaries, two spits are to be found seemingly growing towards each other from opposite banks (**5.9**). The existence of such double spits suggests that the longshore drift on either side of the estuary can be in opposite directions. This is certainly the case with the double spit at the entrance to Poole Harbour in southern England. In other instances, it may be the narrowness of the mouth that is the vital factor, allowing sediment to cross from the spit on the windward side to sustain the growth of a spit on the leeward side.

Bars are accumulations of beach material parallel to the shoreline (**5.9**). In many instances they lie offshore, sometimes forming a line of **barrier islands** (for example, the Friesian Islands off the coasts of the Netherlands and Germany), while similar **barrier beaches** are to be found sealing off the mouths of estuaries, as at Loe Bar near Helston in Cornwall. Where a bar joins an island to the mainland, the term **tombolo** is used. Many of these bars and barriers are thought to have been built of material – possibly of a glacial or fluvioglacial origin – that has been rolled landwards from offshore locations. They are most characteristic of stretches of shallow coastline with a small tidal range.

Forelands

These are large areas of sand and shingle accumulation which result mainly from the modification of spits or bars (**5.9**). The great shingle mass of Dungeness on the south coast of England is thought to be derived from the reworking of a major spit into two parts, each adjusted to the direction of the dominant waves (that is, the maximum fetch). Forelands can also result from the formation of successive beaches on an open coast, as at Winterton Ness in Norfolk, for example.

Sand dunes

Sand dunes are a common feature of those coasts where extensive sandy beaches are exposed at low tide (**5.9**). If the sand is dried by the sun and wind, then it is possible for it to be blown inland by onshore winds. Such driven sand accumulates where some obstacle blocks its landward progress. In this context, vegetation is important as a 'fixer' of dunes, most notably marram grass and sea couch. The root systems of these plants bind the sand, whilst their stalks trap new supplies of sand. Where the supply is abundant, successive lines of dunes may form, each separated by a **slack** (depression). These dune ridges may also be distinguished by their seral development – the older and further inland the ridge, the more advanced is the plant succession (see section 19.7). Sand dunes are very fragile systems,

and any removal of or damage to the vegetation cover can easily trigger **blowouts**, hollows of unprotected sand which can be enlarged by wind erosion at such a speed that the dune is threatened with destruction.

Salt marshes

Salt marshes are the result of the accumulation of silt in sheltered locations such as in estuaries and on the landward side of spits and bars. Fine sediment carried in suspension is transported into these locations by tidal currents. Around high tide, the water becomes relatively motionless and the suspended material settles out as a thin layer. Slowly, the layers accumulate to a considerable thickness, in some instances to a level that is only inundated during the highest of spring tides. As with dunes, vegetation has an important part to play in the formation of salt marshes. Gradually, the accumulating mud becomes colonised by salt-loving plants, such as *Salicornia*, which help to trap the mud and thus facilitate development of the marsh and eventually help to raise its level above the sea. Even at this late stage, the salt marsh displays an intricate network of creeks which allow tidal waters to enter the marsh each day (see section 17.4).

Finally, it is important to note that beaches and larger-scale features such as forelands, spits and bars do not depend only on the erosion of head-

IT1

■ **5.11** Inputs and outputs of the sediment budget

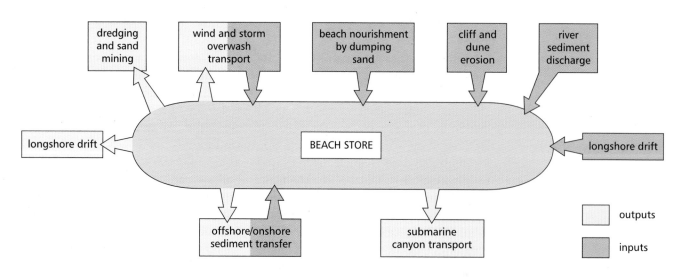

lands for their supply of building material. There are least four other sources contributing to the system (**5.11**):

- Material moved landward from the offshore zone – rising sea-levels in the past have undoubtedly swept up vast quantities of material from the continental shelf areas around the British Isles. Here extensive spreads of glacial and fluvioglacial materials were deposited during a period of lower sea-level. Such beach materials are now being reworked and sorted by wave processes, longshore drift and tidal currents.

- Rivers bring considerable quantities of sediment into the coastal zone, although sand and gravel are probably only delivered by the most turbulent discharges.

- Material is also supplied to beaches by the erosion of other beaches, or the reworking of raised beaches. The material is delivered by longshore drift.

- Beach nourishment by people, used

in specific instances to prevent or slow down land loss or to maintain the beach as an economic asset, may be regarded as a fourth source.

---

7 Explain in some detail the factors that make beach features so ephemeral.

8 a Choose a spit in Britain and compare its shape and extent as depicted on successive editions of OS maps of the area.
b Write a brief explanatory account of what your researches in **a** have shown.

9 Do you regard formation of sand dunes and salt marshes as a good or a bad thing? Present arguments to support your view.

10 Explain how coastal erosion and deposition are interrelated.

5.5 **Coastal change and the costs of protection**

Coastal erosion is a vital part of the natural coastal system. The system seeks constantly to maintain its dynamic equilibrium by adusting to the change triggered by that process. Crudely put, coastal systems move sediment around to fill in the holes and to counteract dramatic changes. Today, however, throughout much of the world, the erosion of cliffs and dunes is on the increase. The following may be cited as being among the major contributors:

- sea-level rise

- earth movements and subsidence

- climatic change which, in particular, has increased the number of storms

- human causes such as dredging, gravel extraction, infilling or reducing sediment supplies from freshwater sources (**5.12**).

In other locations, changes in the rate of coastal deposition are taking place

and in a generally upward direction. Contributory factors include:

- isostatic uplift of land

- increased sediment discharge from rivers, largely the outcome of increased soil erosion in their catchments

- human activities such as mining, land reclamation, spoil tipping and the control of longshore drift (**5.12**).

In this changing scenario, it is the relationships between erosion and deposition on the one hand, and submergence and uplift on the other, that are critical (**5.13**). A coast that is being submerged and eroded rapidly is in serious retreat, whereas one that is being uplifted and subjected to deposition is an advancing coastline. Uplift and erosion work in opposition, just as submergence and deposition do. It is

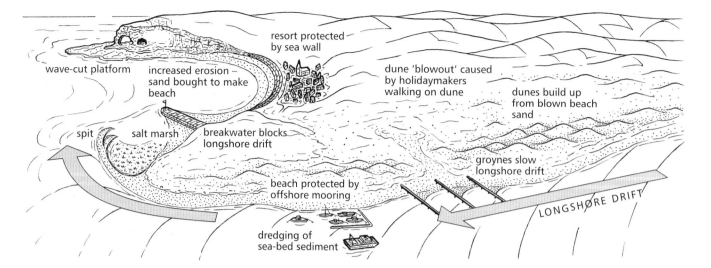

- **5.12** Main forms of human intervention on the coast

clear that retreating coasts pose the more serious threats to people and are more in need of management and protection.

In theory, deliberate intervention in the workings of the coastal system to achieve greater protection for a stretch of coastline will only be undertaken if the benefits outweigh the costs. The problem is that some costs and benefits are extremely difficult to measure. Assessing aesthetic and scenic appeal is one example; determining the value of a coast as a wildlife habitat or as a recreational asset is another. Often in the past, such evaluation was simply omitted from the overall assessment, or undertaken so crudely that it was meaningless. In some instances, the difficulties of measurement have been used as an excuse for doing nothing at all. After all, the cheapest option on a coast threatened by erosion is to do nothing and to let nature take its course. If this is not acceptable, then some form of management action will be necessary.

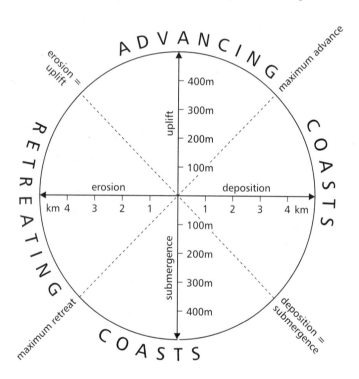

- **5.13** A classification of coasts

CASE STUDY

Cliff retreat – an environmental hazard?

Landslips may be regarded as a normal part of cliff erosion and retreat (**5.14a**). They only become hazards when they threaten to pitch human settlements into the sea. In the past, the construction of a settlement too close to a retreating coast, as at Dunwich in Suffolk, might be excused on the basis of ignorance of the processes and pace of coastal change. It is much less excusable in the 20th century when cliff-top developments have been permitted in reasonably full knowledge of the likely consequences. Such was the case at Barton on the

Hampshire coast. During the 1950s and 1960s, the cliff retreated by an average of 1 m per year, but the rate was probably increasing owing to offshore working of sand and gravel and the construction of groynes in the updrift direction. In the late 1960s, as a result of pressure from local residents who were anxious to prevent their homes from sliding into the sea, the local authority completed an elaborate and expensive cliff protection scheme (**5.14b**).

But now came the supreme folly. Thinking that the cliff-top was secure, the local authority once again allowed new building in the vicinity. In 1974 two natural events – a severe storm and a prolonged period of heavy rain – brought about the virtual destruction of the new cliff defences. Since then, efforts to protect cliff-top property have continued: rock strong-points have replaced groynes, a sloping stone wall has replaced the timber piles, and beach feeding has become a regular ritual. Clearly, the crucial question here is: Are the costs of defending Barton's cliffs really justified? Would it not be better to admit that cliff retreat is inevitable, and to plan accordingly? Why create hazards by building in vulnerable locations?

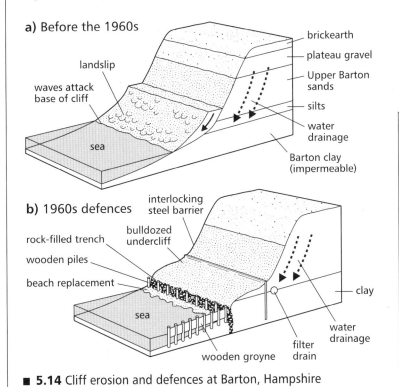

■ 5.14 Cliff erosion and defences at Barton, Hampshire

11 Explain the link between:
   a submergence and coastal erosion
   b uplift and coastal deposition.

12 What problems, if any, are posed by advancing coasts?

13 **a** With reference to a map of the south coast of England, explain why Barton is so vulnerable to coastal erosion.
   b In what ways might the orientation of the coast at Barton contribute to that erosion?

5.6 **Coastal zone management**

`IT1,7,8`

Understanding the causes of coastal erosion, monitoring the rate at which it occurs and grasping its effects on local communities and their economies, require knowledge of entire coastal systems and even of those drainage basins that feed into them. Sediment budgets are the most important thing to monitor, for beaches are the most effective form of wave defence (**5.11**). However, the use of beaches for recreation and as sources of sand and gravel make them an economic commodity. It is therefore understandable that some local people

make determined efforts to protect and promote their particular commercial interests. Clearly there is a deep-rooted conflict just between these two uses of the beach resource. But this is only one of a number, and that is one of the basic problems. There are simply too many interested parties along many stretches of coastline for good strategic planning to take place.

In the UK, it has too often been the case that coastal schemes have been implemented by one local authority without consulting its neighbours.

`IT1,7,8`

Thus, as one authority strengthens its defences against coastal erosion, so the problem is shifted downdrift. A national policy for coastal protection is necessary if cooperation and effective planning are to take place. In preparing such a policy or strategy, and before any more coastal defences are constructed, it is crucial that much information about the coastal zone (its processes and features as well as the human demands upon it) needs to be collected, collated and analysed at a national level.

Coastal zone management is essentially about establishing priorities in a situation of intense competition between demands. It requires formulating policies based on:

- a thorough understanding of the coastal environment and its processes

- insights into the perceptions and values of key players (coastal users)

- achieving a balance between conservation and development.

One of the most dramatic changes likely to affect coastal systems in the near future is a rising sea-level (**5.13**). This has happened in the past as a result of natural climatic change, and it is likely to be exacerbated by the greenhouse effect (see section 12.6). On the eastern coast of Britain, this looming threat is already affecting the planning of sea defences. The problem is acute here because the coast has been slowly sinking for many centuries. People here therefore have the choice of either making sea defences even bigger, or accepting that some areas of land will be lost to erosion (**5.15**). There comes a point when the costs of defence become significantly greater than the value of the land being protected. This is exactly the same issue as was raised in the case study on pages 60–61. Already there are a few schemes where controlled retreat is being seen as a positive way of tackling the problem. In such cases, defences are not renewed, and landowners are compensated for the eventual flooding of their farmland. Much of this land will change initially to salt marsh and provide a good habitat for wildlife. Another consolation is that somewhere along the coastline, the products of this accelerated erosion will accumulate to form new land. This is the beauty of the coastal system: someone's loss is another's gain.

As with all systems where nature and people meet, it is not only the human pressures that are complex. The coastal environment is a classic illustration of the complicated interaction of natural processes involving different degrees of energy, acting on different time scales. Some of these processes, such as wave action, act at a virtually constant rate; some, such as tides, undergo frequent and regular fluctuations. Then there are the relatively low-frequency, high-energy events or processses, such as storm surges and landslides – irregular, unheralded, and generating hazards of differing dimensions and severity. Finally, there is the long-term process of changing sea-level – slow, yes, but of immense consequence, if only because such a large proportion of the world's population lives and works in the coastal zone. It is this last geographic fact that must put the management of coastal systems high on the agenda of human affairs.

■ **5.15** Coastal defences at Sheringham, Norfolk

6

Processes and Landforms in Hot Environments

■ **6.1** Global distribution of three tropical environments

The environments to be examined in this chapter fall mainly within the tropics. Whilst they are all characterised by high temperatures, there is considerable variation in terms of precipitation. On the basis of this latter climatic variable, three different types of environment might be distinguished (**6.1**):

■ humid (rainforest)
■ seasonally humid (savanna)
■ arid and semi-arid (desert).

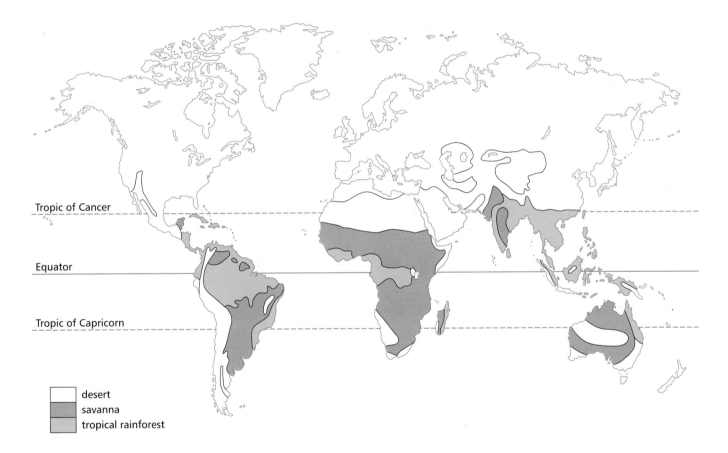

Tropic of Cancer

Equator

Tropic of Capricorn

☐ desert
▨ savanna
▨ tropical rainforest

6.1 **Landform processes in the humid tropics**

Chemical weathering

You may have wondered why pictures of settlements in tropical rainforests rarely feature buildings built from large blocks of stone. Large, unweathered rocks are scarce in tropical rainforests, unless you care to dig down to considerable depths. Bare rock outcrops seldom occur apart from some crystalline rocks or in areas of tropical karst. Explosives are never needed when digging roads through tropical rainforest areas. This is because the rock is so weathered and rotten it can be removed by machinery alone. However, the natural removal of weathered material by mass-movement, erosion and transport is slower than its rate of production. Thus regolith accumulates to considerable depths, particularly in areas undisturbed by tectonic or human activity. Chemical weathering is the dominant landform process in tropical humid regions. Deep weathering is promoted by the following factors:

- high temperatures throughout the year (chemical processes such as hydrolysis are speeded up about three times for every 10°C rise in temperature)

- high rainfall amounts, since water is the principal reagent needed for chemical weathering

- release of large quantities of organic acids from the vegetation cover, especially in forested areas

- long periods of geological stability and as a consequence the absence of rejuvenation

- a vegetation cover which holds regolith *in situ*, and retains water particularly in its root systems, and thus promotes chemical weathering at depth.

The depth of weathering generally decreases as rainfall totals decline, and that trend continues across the savanna zone towards the deserts.

Regolith

Because of the efficacy of chemical weathering as compared with the processes of mass-movement and fluvial transport, regolith or weathered rock is abundant everywhere in the humid tropics. In many places, it reaches depths in the order of 30 to 60 m below the surface; in particularly favoured locations, it may be as much as 100 m thick.

Mass-movement

IT2

Mass-movement is widespread on slopes. On steeper slopes, it takes the form of landslides, slips and slumps, whilst soil creep is characteristic of gentler slopes. Although many slopes are bound at the surface by the roots of the vegetation cover, the regolith is often so deep that movement takes place well below the surface. The lack of coherence, together with the heavy rainfall that tends to saturate the regolith, are factors that encourage slope failure and the incidence of landslides.

Water action

IT1

In spite of the high rainfall totals, rainwash and fluvial action may be less effective in the humid tropics than for example in the temperate regions of the world. So far as rainwash is concerned, the nature of the vegetation cover is an inhibiting factor. In rivers and streams, suspended load quantities are not as great as might be expected. This appears to be related to the dominance of chemical weathering and once again the protective role of vegetation, especially forests. Furthermore, much that is produced by weathering is taken up by the vegetation biomass. Some have argued that, despite the high inputs of energy (solar heat) and precipitation (and unless there is human interference), rainforest areas represent 'closed' systems of great stability. However, what is very evident in the landscape is the existence of well-developed drainage networks, often deeply incised and with smoothly graded valley sides (**6.2**).

■ **6.2** Smooth graded valley sides and incised drainage of tropical humid areas

Limestone areas

A notable exception to the prevalence of a deep regolith is provided by those areas of the humid tropics where there is limestone. When weathered, limestone yields very little by way of regolith. Instead, heavy rainfall combined with humic acids from decaying vegetation mean that the limestone experiences consider-able vertical solution. This gives rise to distinctive surface landforms ranging from the hollows and dolines of **cockpit** or **cone karst** through the sequence of landscape development to the **mogotes** (vertical-sided, isolated relics) of **tower karst** (**6.3**). Beneath the surface there are extensive caves and passages through which the drainage network operates.

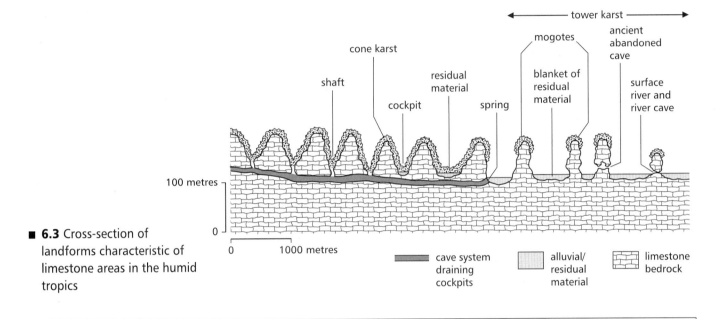

■ **6.3** Cross-section of landforms characteristic of limestone areas in the humid tropics

1 Explain the significance of each of the following in terms of its influence on the rate and degree of chemical weathering:
   a temperature
   b rainfall
   c vegetation
   d tectonic stability.

2 **a** Outline the likely sequence of events on a slope that might be triggered by removal of its forest cover.
   b Do you think that landslides represent a serious hazard in tropical humid areas? Justify your viewpoint.

3 Describe the sequence of tropical karst development illustrated by **6.3**.

6.2 **Savanna areas and their landforms**

Duricrust and its dissection

Regolith is also an important landscape feature of those humid areas with seasonal rainfall (**6.1**), but its depth is less, ranging from about 25 m deep in wetter areas to about 5 m on the desert margins. A second distinguishing feature of regolith in savanna areas is the widespread pres-ence of duricrusts. **Duricrusts** are the surfaces of regolith that have been cemented by iron, silica or calcium miner-als into very tough layers, often several metres thick. One of the best known duri-crusts is **laterite**, which is due essentially to the leaching of iron and alumina by water percolating downwards. These

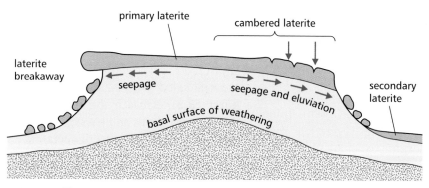

■ **6.4** Landforms associated with dissected duricrust

minerals become concentrated below ground and are hardened into concrete-like layers by alternating wetting and drying. Although such duricrusts are the outcome of the savanna's climatic regime of wet and dry seasons, it should be noted that duricrusts also develop in tropical humid areas where the forest cover is removed and the underlying soil is exposed.

The significance of laterites is that they form resistant caps which prevent removal of weaker regoliths underneath. Table-like plateaus edged by free faces

emerge (**6.4**). If the laterite is broken by joints or is porous in sections, then rainwater will penetrate and emerge as springs at the base of the lateritic cap. Such seepage accentuates lateral back-wearing, and may also result in settling down or cambering of the cap at its edges, so that the plateau may appear slightly dome-shaped. The laterite cap therefore maintains a slope profile sequence of a free face, a constant slope and basal slope of fine sediment. Slope retreat eventually leads to the destruction of the isolated, capped hills and the creation of an extensive but slightly lower plain covered by secondary laterite. This plain is derived in part from denudation of the original (or primary) laterite and from *in situ* weathering.

Theories of landform development

The basal surface of weathering in the savanna, as in the tropical rainforest, is not a level one. There are rises and falls depending on the joint pattern. A relative absence of joints creates a domical rise at the base of the regolith. The theory is that as a result of climatic change or rejuvenation, erosion increases and causes a stripping off of the regolith and the exposure of domical rises as **inselbergs**.

This theory of deep weathering and stripping (also known as the **exhumation theory**) offers an integrated explanation of two landforms – inselbergs and pediments – that seem often to be spatially related. The basal surface is at first only slightly exposed and the domical rises produce low whaleback hills called **ruwares**, but with further stripping they may grow into steeper-sided, more conspicuous and island-like features generally referred to as **inselbergs (6.5)**.

An alternative possible explanation for the landforms shown in **6.6** is provided by the **pediplanation** (or back-wearing) **theory**. In this theory, the inselberg is regarded as a late-stage residual hill resulting from scarp retreat and the creation of pediments by back-wearing (see section 6.5).

■ **6.5** The formation of inselbergs by exhumation

a)

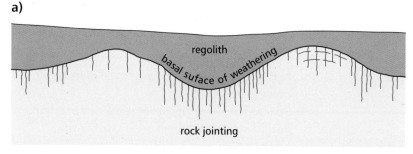

b)

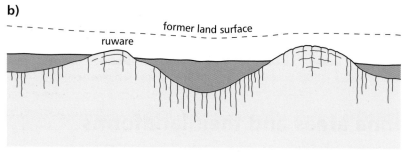

c)

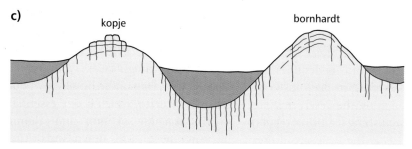

4 Compare savanna and tropical rainfall areas in terms of the processes of weathering, mass-movement and erosion.

5 What type of slope retreat is assumed to take place in the evolution of landforms associated with dissected duricrust?

6 Identify the essential differences between the theories of exhumation and pediplanation as explanations for the origins of inselbergs.

7 Explain how investigation of regolith helps our understanding of the origins and form of hot environment landforms.

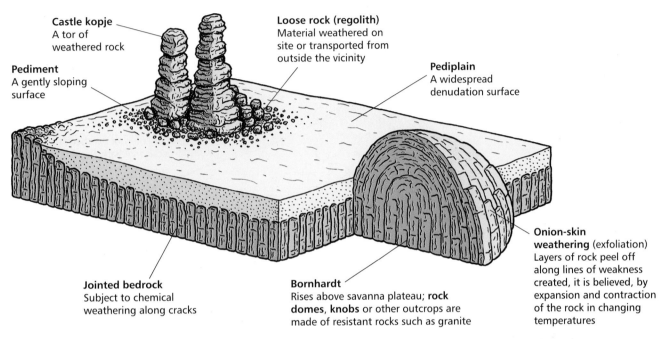

Castle kopje A tor of weathered rock

Loose rock (regolith) Material weathered on site or transported from outside the vicinity

Pediment A gently sloping surface

Pediplain A widespread denudation surface

Jointed bedrock Subject to chemical weathering along cracks

Bornhardt Rises above savanna plateau; **rock domes**, **knobs** or other outcrops are made of resistant rocks such as granite

Onion-skin weathering (exfoliation) Layers of rock peel off along lines of weakness created, it is believed, by expansion and contraction of the rock in changing temperatures

■ **6.6** Landforms of the savanna

6.3 **Deserts defined**

If you ask people to conjure up an image of a desert, it is likely that they will describe sand dunes. In reality, hot deserts show considerable variations in landscape, and several different types may be recognised (**6.7**):

■ extensive, bare, rocky plains (**pediments**) as in Africa and Australia

■ areas of inland drainage (i.e. not connected by an outlet to the ocean) containing temporary salt lakes (**playas**) and marshes surrounded by plains leading up to steep, dissected uplands

■ deeply-dissected uplands with steep valley systems (**wadis**), often with boulder-strewn steep slopes at their border

■ extensive areas of sand and **sand dunes** (such as the ergs of the Sahara).

The world's arid landscapes (**6.1**) can, therefore, be said, to reflect:

■ **Tectonic conditions** – for example, the extensive **pediments** of Africa owe their existence to the long stability of much of that continent, permitting uninterrupted operation of the same processes. In contrast, in the south-west USA recent faulting is responsible for the complex system of basins and uplands characteristic of that region.

■ **Precipitation** – this is not only low but highly variable. Annual values of 300 mm may be used broadly to delimit arid areas, but evapotranspiration in relation to temperatures allows for a much better definition than yearly rainfall totals. Rainfall tends to be episodic, unpredictable, often with long periods (maybe years) of total drought in between. Conversely, when it occurs, rainfall is characteristically of high intensity and is capable of much erosive activity, as evidenced by the wadi and the bajada (**6.7**).

■ **Temperature** – a wide diurnal range of temperature is typical of deserts. Absence of cloud and high insolation lead to rapid heating of surfaces by day but equally rapid heat loss through unimpeded terrestrial radiation at night.

■ **Vegetation** – or rather the lack of it (the true meaning of the word 'desert') – results in exposure to unrestricted wind and an absence of a binding or 'retaining' factor for debris and sediments on slopes. This possibly explains the sharp breaks of slope or **knicks** often characteristic of hot desert landscapes.

■ **6.7** Landforms of the hot desert

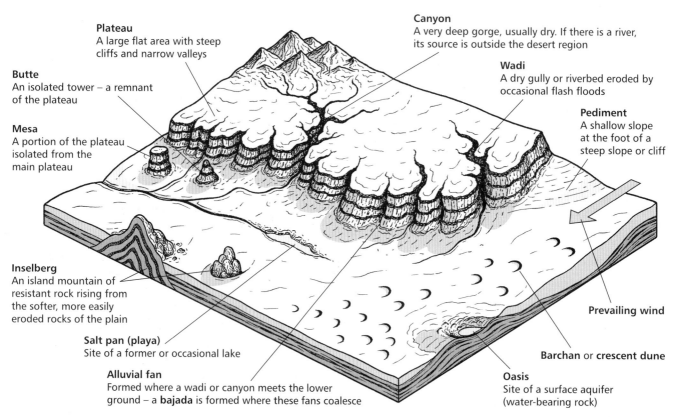

Plateau
A large flat area with steep cliffs and narrow valleys

Butte
An isolated tower – a remnant of the plateau

Mesa
A portion of the plateau isolated from the main plateau

Inselberg
An island mountain of resistant rock rising from the softer, more easily eroded rocks of the plain

Salt pan (playa)
Site of a former or occasional lake

Alluvial fan
Formed where a wadi or canyon meets the lower ground – a **bajada** is formed where these fans coalesce

Canyon
A very deep gorge, usually dry. If there is a river, its source is outside the desert region

Wadi
A dry gully or riverbed eroded by occasional flash floods

Pediment
A shallow slope at the foot of a steep slope or cliff

Prevailing wind

Barchan or **crescent dune**

Oasis
Site of a surface aquifer (water-bearing rock)

6.4 **Desert processes**

The processes of landform development in hot deserts can be considered under three headings: weathering, running water and wind action.

Weathering

The processes of **physical weathering** are largely associated with the diurnal regime of heating and cooling, and the resulting expansion and contraction of rocks in a shallow surface zone. There are at least three different outcomes:

■ **exfoliation** – the peeling away of layers or sheets of rock from exposed surfaces

■ **block weathering** – where the alternate heating and cooling causes rocks to fragment along joint systems

■ **granular disintegration** – breakdown of rock into its constituent mineral or groups of minerals because of differences in colour and coefficients of expansion.

At one time it was thought that weathering in hot deserts was exclusively of a physical kind. However, chemical processes are now believed to be deeply involved in desert weathering. Since such processes require water, one might think that the climate would not promote the reactions that are at the heart of chemical weathering. But it is now known that small quantities of water, from infrequent rain showers, from dew (produced by the large diurnal range in temperatures) and from capillary moisture drawn up from the ground, mean that such processes are operative quite regularly, particularly at the base of slopes and in depressions.

Running water

During episodic, high-intensity rainfall events, normally dry courses become stream floods that carve steep-sided valleys and transport huge quantities of load. Because they are short-lived and because evaporation rates are high, this load is soon deposited on valley floors and as fans at mountain fronts where streams debouch onto bordering plains. During rainstorms, however, level undissected plains and slopes experience **sheet floods**. These involve not so much uniform layers of water running over the whole surface but rather interlinked networks of minor threads of water or **rills**, which are none the less capable of sweeping fine material away. Remember, of course, that whilst freak rainfall events may generate much geomorphological work, they are highly unpredictable and irregular in occurrence in both time and space, and many desert areas may be dry for long periods.

Wind action

Sand is carried in three ways within desert areas:

- as fine grains in suspension
- as coarse grains creeping across the surface
- as blown sand moved by **saltation** (a hopping movement).

Saltation is the most important process in the building of sand dunes, but the type of saltation varies according to the size and weight of grains, the speed of the wind, and the angle of take-off, which is related to the nature of the land surface.

6.5 Desert landforms

Pediments

Of all the hot desert landforms, the one that attracts most attention is the pediment (**6.7**). This is partly because of its widespread occurrence, but rather more because there is considerable controversy as to its origins. Pediment formation has been variously ascribed to the following factors:

- **Spring sapping** at upland edges – but this is unlikely to be sufficiently widespread all around.

- **Lateral planation** by streams issuing from wadis – currently they do not last long enough, but perhaps they were more effective in the past, during wetter periods.

- **Sheet-flood erosion**, though it seems more probable that these sheet floods are the result of the pediment rather than the cause.

- **Parallel slope retreat** at the weathered upland front, with the pediment as a basal slope of replacement. Active weathering could certainly be linked with the second and third processes outlined above, whilst the existence of the buried rock band suggests the growth of weathered material upslope. The gently concave profile of the pediment suggests that it is a slope of transportation involving the removal of fine-calibre material in suspension.

- **Survival** from the past when climatic conditions were different. There is much evidence to support the notion that the hot deserts of today were much wetter at the time of the Pleistocene Ice Age. They would have been more like the humid tropical areas of today, where chemical weathering is known to take place to great depths. Following the end of the glacial period up to the present, increasing aridity may have meant the stripping-off of the regolith to expose the unweathered basal surface, the 'rises' of which may be the inselbergs, and the pediments the relics of former deeper weathering fronts. Parallel slope retreat and fluvial processes finally modified the pediments into the features they are today. This exhumation theory of inselberg and pediment formation (see section 6.2) is considered by many to be the likely explanation for features in tropical Africa, but not for the faulted areas of south-west USA.

IT8

Wadis and gullies

IT2,8

Deserts are characterised by their aridity and so water does not feature very regularly. Occasionally, desert areas experience very heavy convectional rainstorms. On these occasions, runoff is great and evaporation in the storm area is limited owing to the saturation of the air. For these reasons, the water either percolates into the underlying sand and gravels or runs quickly into the normally dry watercourses known widely as **wadis** (**6.7**). These are linear, steep-sided, flat-floored landforms which display features of normal river valleys in that they are arranged in dendritic patterns and have smoothly concave long profiles. There seems little doubt that the wadis of the Sahara and Arabian deserts were mainly eroded during times when the climate was more humid. There are notable historical accounts of events in these wadis, such as that of the Great Fish river in south-west Africa where a river bed was dry one day and then next day filled by a water channel several hundred metres wide and nine metres deep. Such floods are easily able to transport the huge quantities of weathered material that accumulate on the valley floor. Once out of the upland areas, the debris is disgorged onto the plains in the form of allu-

vial fans. Alternatively, there may be enough water for it to wash across the plain as a sheet of running water (**sheetflow**). Where the alluvial fans of neighbouring wadis coalesce, a continuous belt of sands and gravels, known as a **bajada**, is formed at the foot of the uplands.

Wind erosional features

Wind armed with sand grains can create erosional features such as those illustrated in **6.8**:

- faceted stones and boulders, representing wind-blast polishing
- ridge and furrow features, usually in line with the prevailing wind direction, creating **yardangs** and **zeugens**
- **pedestal** or **mushroom rocks**, as boulders or rock masses are undercut by sand-blast action at levels close to the ground surface
- grotesque, fantastic shapes, due to differential sand-blast effects
- steepened and emphasised joint lines, fault zones or valley sides where wind is channelled and its erosive power concentrated.

But all of these are relatively small-scale, minor features: wind is not now considered to be the cause of the larger-scale plains and plateaus encountered in the desert. One exception to this are the **deflation hollows** such as the Qattara Depression of western Egypt. This is 130 m below sea-level and some several hundred kilometres in extent, but even here the probability is that chemical weathering first rotted the rock before it was removed by deflation, and that basal undercutting at the edges was the cause of its lateral extension. Such deflation hollows suggest that wind may be more important as a transporting agent.

Dunes

There is no doubt that large areas of desert are nothing more than great accumulations of wind-blown sand. **Dunes** is the collective term used to describe

■ **6.8** Wind erosional landforms

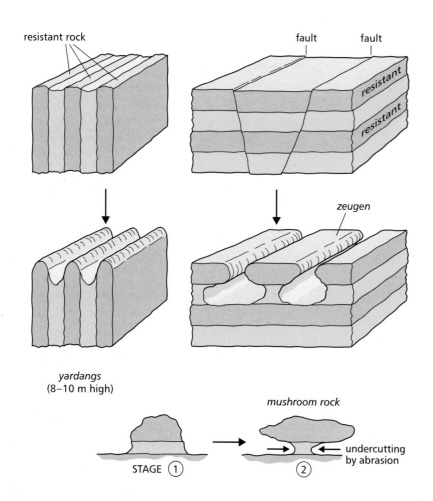

resistant rock

fault   fault

resistant

resistant

zeugen

yardangs
(8–10 m high)

mushroom rock

STAGE ①   ②   ← undercutting by abrasion →

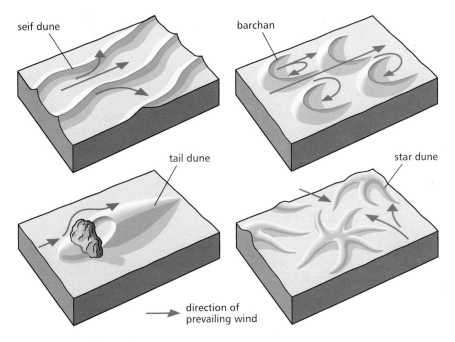

■ **6.9** Dune formations

such accumulations, but their scale and form can vary immensely from narrow ridges reaching heights of over 150 m and many kilometres in length to lower and broader mounds known as **whalebacks**. Two smaller but recurrent depositional forms are the **seif dune** and the **barchan** (**6.9**). With these, wind direction is critical. The former run parallel to the prevailing wind direction, but their development would seem to be helped by secondary cross-winds. In some instances they may even have originated as barchans, that is as crescentic accumulations that move in the direction of the prevailing wind. Sand is transported up the gentle windward slope, over the crest and down the lee slope where it accumulates. The outcome is that the dune gradually shifts downwind.

CASE STUDY

IT2,8

Sand control in Saudi Arabia

Dunes and other sand movements present problems within Saudi Arabia because they bury, abrade and clog settlements, pipelines, public utilities, agricultural land and industrial plant. In the Eastern Province of Saudi Arabia, oil has been exploited during the past 30 years and there have been major problems associated with the most intensively worked area around Jafurah. Here strong unidirectional winds and less than 80 mm rainfall mean that sand dunes are moving at an average of 14.6 m per year (**6.10**).

Certain guidelines are followed when designing and

constructing buildings and infrastructural installations in this area. These include the following:

■ Pipelines are laid parallel to the direction of the dominant wind.

Transposing	The removal of accumulated sand. Rarely successful and economic; never-ending.
Trenching	Cutting trenches across dunes alters their symmetry and can lead to their destruction.
Planting	Vegetation can reduce sand movement, as well as bind and protect the surface. Planting is reasonably permanent and attractive but it is very expensive to install and maintain.
Paving	This is designed to increase saltation, thereby increasing erosion and reducing deposition.
Panelling	Solid barriers are built in front of the area to be protected. In general, not a very satisfactory solution, but it is used in emergencies.
Fencing	Porous barriers are used to stop or divert sand movement. It is relatively cheap and reasonably portable.
Oiling	This involves covering the sand with oil. It may seal the surface of the sand, but it will destroy any vegetation. It is a cheap and quick method for oil-rich states.

■ **6.10** Using trees to anchor a dune

■ **6.11** Methods of aeolian sand control

- Construction is encouraged in those areas where the dominant sand-moving winds blow over gently rising ground, as conditions here encourage transport rather than deposition.

- The disruption of airflow caused by new structures is minimised by airstreaming.

A number of sand control methods have also been devised (**6.11**).

8 Which of the methods given in **6.11** do you think would be most suitable for stabilising a belt of coastal dunes in the UK?

9 Identify the landform evidence which supports the idea that today's hot desert areas have experienced a more humid type of climate.

10 With reference to **6.9**, write a brief account explaining the formation of:
a a tail dune
b a star dune.

11 In what ways is moisture important to landform processes in hot deserts?

6.6 **The hot environments – a comparison**

The tropical areas of the world present strongly contrasting physical environments ranging from the humid, lushly vegetated and essentially rounded landscapes of the rainforest to the barren and rather angular landforms of the hot deserts. The transition between these environmental extremes is marked by a shift from chemical to physical weathering, and from water to wind action. It is within the savanna zone that these transitions are effected.

One characteristic common to all three hot environments is that their present landforms bear the marks of past climatic regimes that were significantly different to those that now prevail. For example, the evidence suggests that at the end of the last Ice Age, the tropical rainforest was significantly less extensive than it is today. The discovery of fossil dune fields in West Africa, for example, indicates that the Sahara extended some 600 km further south than it does today. Similar evidence has been found in the rainforests of South America. Equally, it is clear that sizeable areas of today's hot deserts have at some time experienced wetter conditions. Again, given its transitional position, the savanna embraces landform evidence of climatic change in the twin directions of increased aridity and increased pluviality.

The rainforest and savanna regions have both suffered from human interference, principally through the clearance of vegetation. The climatic impacts of these actions are examined elsewhere in this book, but the processes so triggered – desertification (section 15.1) and global warming (section 12.6) – have important implications for landform processes. The very act of deforestation, whether it is in rainforest or savanna regions, also immediately increases the exposure of landforms to the forces of denudation. In this way, people have become a significant factor in landform development, and this ironically in parts of the world where population numbers are relatively low by global standards. In both environments, the incidence of soil erosion and landslide hazards has increased. What the impact of human interference has been on the hot deserts' most notorious natural events – the flash flood and inundation by sand – is much less certain.

12 Compare the three hot environments in terms of:
a weathering
b mass-movement
c erosion.

13 What impact do you think human actions have had on the incidence of flash floods in desert areas? Give your reasoning.

Processes and Landforms in Cold Environments

CHAPTER 7

7.1 Glacial and periglacial regimes

In its history, the Earth has experienced a number of periods of extreme cold. During these, there has been a much wider incidence of ice and snow on the surface of the planet than is the case today. The last major Ice Age was in the Pleistocene period, starting some 2 million years back and lasting to as recently as about 10 000 years ago. At its peak, 30 per cent of the land surface was covered by ice-sheets and glaciers, compared with a figure of 10 per cent today (**7.1**). From these values, the important point is drawn that significant land areas of the Earth, although now experiencing what we might describe as non-glacial conditions, do in fact still bear the scars of their time under snow and ice. These areas formerly occupied by glaciers and ice-sheets are described as **glaciated**, as distinct from **glacial** areas where glaciers and ice remain. Geographers are able to study glacial areas and to use that knowledge and understanding in their investigation of landforms surviving today, which were either created or substantially modified by ice-sheets and glaciers that have since disappeared (**7.2**).

Within the global zone formerly covered by ice, and accounting for the greater part of it, it is possible to recognise a significant cold environment to which the term **periglacial** is applied. Literally, the term means 'around the ice', but in geographical studies it is used to describe those areas that have a very cold climate of severe winter freezing and a brief summer thaw. Although there are heavy snowfalls, they all melt during the summer and so there is no accumulation of ice over the years. However, at varying depths below the surface, the ground remains permanently frozen (the **permafrost**). For many, the occurrence of permafrost in a continuous, discontinuous or sporadic form is the hallmark of a periglacial area, together with the dominance of frost processes. Just as ice-sheets and glaciers formerly extended their limits further equatorwards than they do now, so too did periglacial conditions, thereby giving rise to **periglacial areas** (**7.1**).

Much of this chapter is devoted to a separate examination of these two sets of cold climate processes – glaciation and periglaciation. The focus of attention then widens to consider in more general terms the impact of environmental change on landforms and their development.

■ **7.1** Past and present limits of glaciation in the Northern Hemisphere

■ principal areas presently covered by glacial ice

principal areas covered at the last glacial maximum

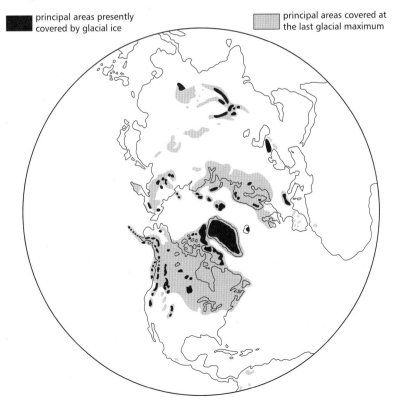

1 a Referring to **7.1**, describe the distribution of areas still experiencing glacial conditions.

b To what extent is it possible to recognise two different types of glacial area?

■ **7.2** Glacial and glaciated landscape

7.2 **Formation of ice and glaciers**

The snow that eventually makes up ice-sheets and glaciers appears to undergo a sequence of conversion stages:

- **settling of snow** – loose, granular consistency

- **nivation** – annual and diurnal temperature changes lead to thaw–freeze alternation, and the conversion of snow into ice crystals

- **firn** or **nevé** – increased pressure between individual grains causes pressure melting to eventually change the loose snow into a dull, white, structureless mass, with far less pore space which is therefore more impermeable

- **sintering** – continued 'fusion' and squeezing out of air as a result of further compression by the continuing accumulation of snow and ice

- **glacier ice** – bluish in colour and containing little air.

The conversion of snow into glacier ice might be expected to take longer in a polar area than in an alpine one, because the severity of the former's climate limits the necessary rapid alternation of thaw and freeze conditions for long periods. The time scales involved may range from 200 years in the former to 20 years in the latter. Accumulation of such ice is facilitated in sheltered hollows, particularly those that are oriented away from the direction of the midday sun.

Once formed, ice moves in three basic ways:

- Dramatically as an **avalanche** – the breaking away and rapid descent of a large mass of ice, rock and powdery snow down a steep mountainside.

- By **basal sliding** – this is the movement of ice over the valley floor; meltwater and geothermal heat lubricate the surface so that the ice moves. This is important in temperate glaciers (**7.3**).

- By **internal plastic flow** – plastic deformation of ice occurs under pressure (individual particles of ice melt around their edges allowing air to escape; one by one the particles slip forward on the thin film of water and immediately refreeze) and the influence of gravity; layers of granules in the ice slide across each other (**7.3**). This creates tension in the ice. The ice deforms under its own weight and so the glacier or ice-sheet begins to move downslope aided by the pull of gravity. The creep rate is influenced by the amount of debris in the ice, its thickness and temperature, and by the angle of slope.

7.3 draws attention to the fact that glacier movement is retarded by friction with the valley floor and sides. Movement is greatest at the glacier surface and in the middle of the valley. This is why glacier snouts are usually lobe-shaped.

Glaciers, in their turn, may be differentiated on the basis of size:

- **Niche glaciers** – occupying small north-facing gullies and hollows in the Northern Hemisphere.

- **Cirque glaciers** – larger than niche glaciers and occupying semi-circular mountain hollows characterised by steep head and side-walls and frequently by a lip where the glacier overspills into a valley.

- **Valley glaciers** – long, tongue-like glaciers occupying a clearly defined mountain valley, often fed by cirque glaciers.

- **Piedmont glaciers** – broad glaciers formed where constricted valley glaciers flow onto an open lowland and are thus able to spread laterally and fuse.

- **Ice-sheet and ice-cap** – very extensive and

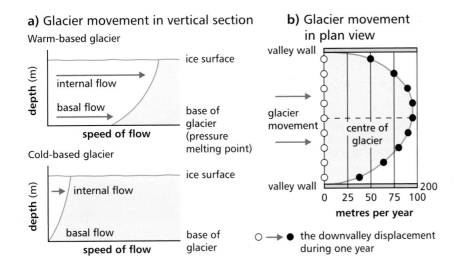

a) Glacier movement in vertical section

Warm-based glacier

depth (m) / speed of flow
- ice surface
- internal flow
- basal flow
- base of glacier (pressure melting point)

Cold-based glacier

depth (m) / speed of flow
- ice surface
- internal flow
- basal flow
- base of glacier

■ **7.3** Glacier movement

b) Glacier movement in plan view

valley wall

glacier movement — centre of glacier

valley wall

0 25 50 75 100 200
metres per year

○ → ● the downvalley displacement during one year

continuous areas of ice; ice-sheets are of continental dimensions (Antarctica and Greenland); ice-caps are of a

lesser scale (for example, the mountain ice-caps of Iceland or the lowland ice-caps of northern Canada).

2 Discuss how the following factors may influence the thickness of glacier ice:
a latitude
b altitude
c aspect.

3 Which types of glacier do think persisted in those parts of the British Isles covered by glacier ice during the peak of the last Ice Age?

7.3 **Glaciers as systems**

IT1

Glaciers are systems in that they involve recognisable inputs, stores and through-puts (**7.4**).

The nourishing of glaciers takes place at their heads in the so-called **accumulation zone** which may comprise a number of coalescent corries or a high-level snowfield. It is here that the glacier's vital life-blood, **firn** (the winter snow that survives the summer melt and becomes compressed by the next winter's snowfall), forms.

The output side of the glacier is largely concentrated at its end in the **ablation zone**, where lower altitude and a warmer climate encourage melting of the glacier ice (**7.5**). In fact, ablation (the combined loss of ice due to evaporation and melting) increases downglacier from the firn line, where it is nil, to the glacier snout, where it reaches a maximum. The nature of the balance between annual ablation and the glacier's forward motion is critical. If ablation is the greater, then the glacier front will 'retreat', and vice versa. In the ablation zone, the ratio of ice to rock debris in the glacier is greatly reduced.

The stores of the glacier are the ice, and the considerable amount of rock debris that either has been picked up by the ice from the surfaces over which it is moving or has fallen onto the glacier from adjacent higher ground.

As in any system, the glacier is in a state of dynamic equilibrium determined by the ever-changing relationship between inputs and outputs. If they balance exactly, then the glacier will be in a **steady state** – it will be neither advancing nor retreating. In

IT1

■ **7.4** The glacier system

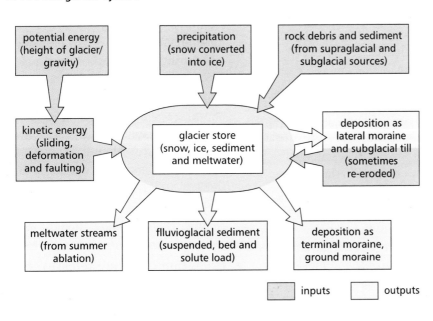

potential energy (height of glacier/gravity)

precipitation (snow converted into ice)

rock debris and sediment (from supraglacial and subglacial sources)

kinetic energy (sliding, deformation and faulting)

glacier store (snow, ice, sediment and meltwater)

deposition as lateral moraine and subglacial till (sometimes re-eroded)

meltwater streams (from summer ablation)

flluvioglacial sediment (suspended, bed and solute load)

deposition as terminal moraine, ground moraine

inputs   outputs

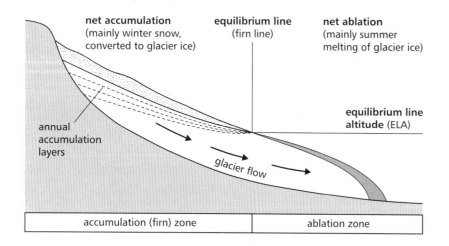

■ 7.5 Accumulation and ablation on a glacier

IT1

net accumulation
(mainly winter snow,
converted to glacier ice)

equilibrium line
(firn line)

net ablation
(mainly summer
melting of glacier ice)

equilibrium line
altitude (ELA)

annual
accumulation
layers

glacier flow

accumulation (firn) zone

ablation zone

IT1 the case of the glacier, however, it is the nature of the balance between accumulation and ablation that is particularly critical (**7.5**). The difference between the two is referred to as the **mass balance** or **glacier budget**. Where the former exceeds the latter, then it is positive and there is the expectation of glacier advance, and vice versa. The **equilibrium line** occurs where both are equal and is marked by the snow-line or firn line. **IT1**

> **4** In its response to climatic warming and cooling, does the glacier system display negative or positive feedback? Justify your answer.
>
> **5** Explain why glacier advance leads to increased summer ablation, and vice versa.

7.4 **Glacial erosion**

There is a temptation to think that, apart from differences in size, all glaciers are similar – after all, they all consist of snow converted into ice. But there are some significant differences, particularly so far as temperatures are concerned. On the basis of this criterion, two types are recognised (**7.3**):

■ **Warm glaciers** Temperatures throughout their depth are close to 0°C; they are close to melting and during the summer discharge large quantities of meltwater. Because there is always a layer of meltwater between the mass of the glacier and its bedrock created by the friction and pressure between them, there is considerable basal sliding and the glacier is relatively mobile. As a result, it has an enhanced ability to erode and transport. The glaciers of temperate mountain areas fall into this category.

■ **Cold glaciers** Temperatures at the base of the glacier may be well below 0°C and therefore the glacier is frozen to its bedrock. As a result, basal sliding is not possible and movement is only by internal flow. The erosive powers of such glaciers are extremely limited. The glaciers of polar and subpolar areas are largely of this type.

Glaciers undertake their erosive work by a number of different actions or processes (**7.6**). The two most important are:

■ **Plucking** Ice in contact with rock surfaces may thaw slightly then refreeze around rocks protruding from the bedrock and so 'pluck' or tear them away with continued movement forward. Plucking would seem to require considerable loosening of the bedrock by previous weathering or some other process; it is most effective in well-jointed rocks.

■ **Abrasion** Ice containing load may polish, scratch and gouge the rock over and past which it is moving. But it does not always do this, since it depends on the relative resistance of the load and the nature of the underlying surface.

Another process is now thought to be a major contributor:

■ **Dilatation (pressure release)** As ice erodes rock it occupies the space thus created, but since ice is less dense, this means that the weight on the underlying rock is lessened. It therefore tends to expand upwards, creating sheeting joints (roughly parallel to the surface) which promote weathering processes and assist plucking and abrasion. The dilatation factor is thought to be highly influential in respect of the semi-circular form of corrie hollow and the U-shaped cross-profile of glaciated troughs (**7.6**).

Further processes to consider include:

■ **Rotational movement** As snow accumulates on the upper parts of corrie glaciers, the increased weight may result in periodic adjustment of the whole ice mass in order to achieve a state of equilibrium. The resulting rotational slumping is probably responsible for accentuating the 'hollow' form of the corrie (**7.6**).

■ **Frost shattering** The jagged appearance of arêtes and land surfaces generally protruding above ice-sheets and glaciers bears witness to the efficacy of physical weathering. But freeze–thaw weathering is also considered to be important beneath ice masses where temperatures are close to 0 °C. In corries, the

bergschrund crevasse may be important, formed as ice moves away downhill from the back wall and allowing the ingress of meltwater (**7.6**). However, some have questioned whether the crevasse actually reaches the corrie floor and whether temperature fluctuations there are sufficient to promote significant freeze–thaw activity.

■ **Meltwater erosion** Glaciers can produce huge quantities of meltwater which create streams that are sufficiently powerful to erode the valley floor beneath the glacier itself by normal fluvial processes.

Some of the results of these processes in terms of landform development are shown in **7.7**.

---

6 Suggest ways in which rock type might influence:
  a the rate of glacial erosion
  b the character of glacially-eroded landforms.

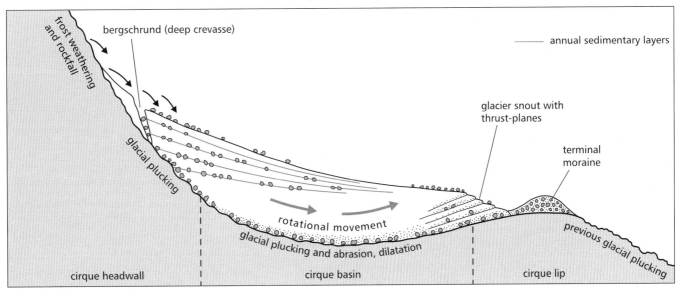

■ **7.6** A glacial cirque – processes and features

7.5 **Glacial transportation and deposition**

Glaciers carry large loads ranging from fine sediments to large boulders. That material is carried at three different levels, thereby defining three types of load (**7.8**):

■ **Supraglacial** – material carried on the glacier's surface and made up of debris that has fallen onto it from the valley sides.

■ **Englacial** – material carried within the body of the ice-sheet or glacier; some of this material is probably

supraglacial load that has fallen into crevasses.

■ **Subglacial** – material moving along at the base of the glacier, much being derived by the process of plucking.

Load is mainly deposited in the ablation zone, particularly at or close to the glacier snout. **Drift** is the name given to all the materials deposited under glacial conditions. Drift may be of two kinds:

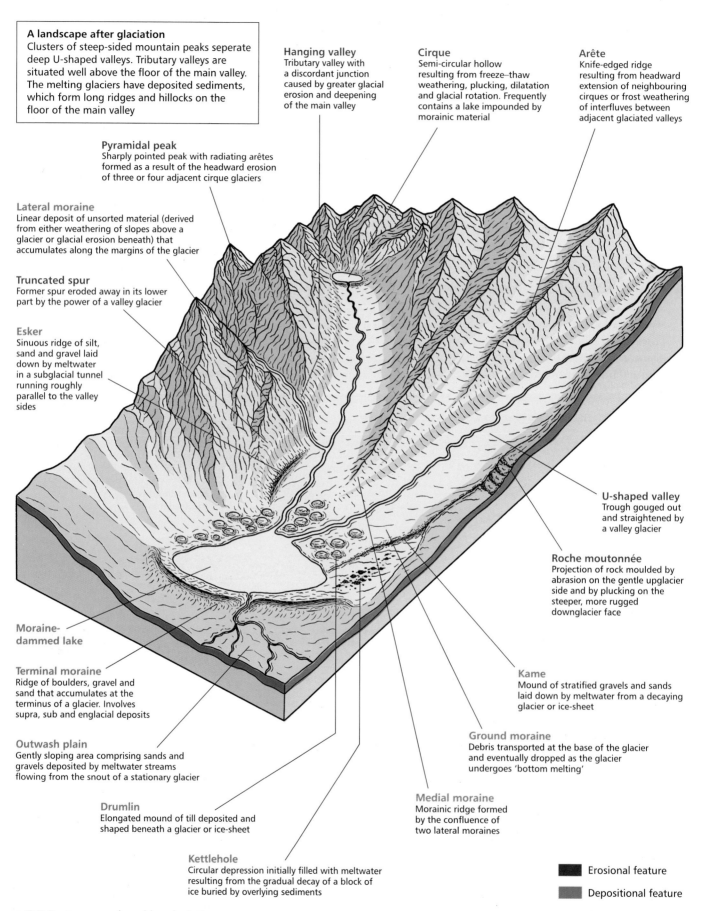

A landscape after glaciation
Clusters of steep-sided mountain peaks seperate deep U-shaped valleys. Tributary valleys are situated well above the floor of the main valley. The melting glaciers have deposited sediments, which form long ridges and hillocks on the floor of the main valley

Hanging valley
Tributary valley with a discordant junction caused by greater glacial erosion and deepening of the main valley

Cirque
Semi-circular hollow resulting from freeze–thaw weathering, plucking, dilatation and glacial rotation. Frequently contains a lake impounded by morainic material

Arête
Knife-edged ridge resulting from headward extension of neighbouring cirques or frost weathering of interfluves between adjacent glaciated valleys

Pyramidal peak
Sharply pointed peak with radiating arêtes formed as a result of the headward erosion of three or four adjacent cirque glaciers

Lateral moraine
Linear deposit of unsorted material (derived from either weathering of slopes above a glacier or glacial erosion beneath) that accumulates along the margins of the glacier

Truncated spur
Former spur eroded away in its lower part by the power of a valley glacier

Esker
Sinuous ridge of silt, sand and gravel laid down by meltwater in a subglacial tunnel running roughly parallel to the valley sides

U-shaped valley
Trough gouged out and straightened by a valley glacier

Roche moutonnée
Projection of rock moulded by abrasion on the gentle upglacier side and by plucking on the steeper, more rugged downglacier face

Moraine-dammed lake

Terminal moraine
Ridge of boulders, gravel and sand that accumulates at the terminus of a glacier. Involves supra, sub and englacial deposits

Outwash plain
Gently sloping area comprising sands and gravels deposited by meltwater streams flowing from the snout of a stationary glacier

Kame
Mound of stratified gravels and sands laid down by meltwater from a decaying glacier or ice-sheet

Ground moraine
Debris transported at the base of the glacier and eventually dropped as the glacier undergoes 'bottom melting'

Drumlin
Elongated mound of till deposited and shaped beneath a glacier or ice-sheet

Medial moraine
Morainic ridge formed by the confluence of two lateral moraines

Kettlehole
Circular depression initially filled with meltwater resulting from the gradual decay of a block of ice buried by overlying sediments

■ Erosional feature
■ Depositional feature

■ **7.7** Features produced by glaciation

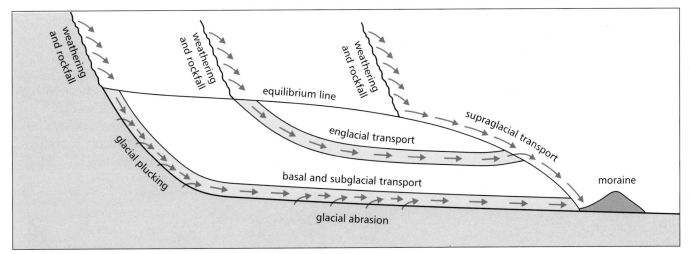

■ **7.8** Processes of glacial transportation

■ **Till** – material carried and directly deposited in an unsorted form by the ice. There are two types of till: **lodgement till** is laid down beneath the ice by a sort of plastering process, and **ablation till** is dropped *in situ* by a stationary glacier as it begins to melt. **Moraine** is the term given to the surface form assumed by till.

■ **Fluvioglacial deposits** – the sorted materials laid down by meltwater both within and beyond the ice-sheet or glacier.

The spatial pattern of glacial and fluvioglacial depositional landforms is shown in **7.7**. However, areas of deposition are often extremely complex. Ice-front advance means that truly glacial depositional features are superimposed on fluvioglacial deposits formed beyond the ice-front at an earlier time. An ice-front 'retreat' would have the reverse effect. As well as ice accumulation and ablation variables during glacial times, the effects of interglacials also influence the present distribution of drift materials.

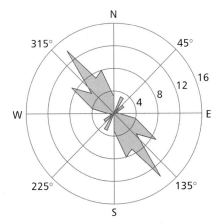

■ **7.9** Rose diagram showing the orientation of stones in a sample of till

7 The rose diagram in **7.9** shows the orientation of stones in a sample of till. The data below show the orientation of a sample of corries in Snowdonia.

a Plot this data on a rose diagram.
b Explain the pattern that is shown by your completed diagram.
c What conclusions do you draw from **7.9** and your diagram?

0–45°	45–90°	90–135°	135–180°	180–225°	225–270°	270–315°	315–360°
19	15	6	4	1	1	2	9

CASE STUDY

IT2

Hazards in the highlands

Although cold environments are by global standards sparsely populated areas, there are enough people living and working there to raise at least two natural events to the status of natural hazard. **Avalanches** are large masses of snow, ice and rock that suddenly and rapidly move down steep mountainsides. They occur most commonly in winter and in spring. In winter, avalanches are made up mainly of large masses of recent, uncompacted snow which can become unstable or dislodged; in spring they involve the breaking away of partially thawed layers of older snow. Many avalanches develop along well-used avalanche tracks. These can be mapped and precautions taken to minimise potential damage by careful control over the siting of new buildings, or by constructing avalanche sheds over roads and railways. But sometimes avalanches follow previously unused paths; it is these that constitute a most serious hazard to life and property. What is very evident is that in some cases it is people who actually trigger avalanches by skiing down unstable snow slopes or by generating vibrations (through shouting, the rumbling of traffic, jet aircraft flying overhead, etc.).

Outbursts or **glacier floods** are high-energy events unrelated to the normal melt process and regime. Although short-lived, an outburst can take the form of a sudden and catastrophic flood caused by the sudden release of meltwater that has accumulated within or on the surface of a glacier. In most cases, the water is retained by some form of ice barrier and it is the melting, breaching, overflowing or lifting of this barrier that causes the outburst. For those

outbursts emanating from surface accumulations of water, it is possible to alleviate the hazard by constructing relief drainage channels which 'bleed' water from the lake or reservoir before it reaches critical levels (**7.10**). But the hazard threat persists in the case of those that originate from water pockets inside glaciers. Not only are they extremely difficult to monitor, but as yet there are no means of draining them in a controlled way.

■ **7.10** A relief channel in the Swiss Alps, near Zermatt

---

8 Examine the arguments for and against the construction of barrages to contain outbursts.

9 Do you think that global warming will reduce or increase the hazard risk in glacial areas? Justify your viewpoint.

CASE STUDY

IT6,7

The costs and benefits of tourism in cold environments

Given rising personal affluence and increasing leisure time, the glacial and glaciated areas of Europe, North America and Japan have been enjoying a prolonged boom in tourism based on their twin resources of snow and fine mountain scenery. The snow sustains a lucrative winter sports industry (the season often extending to half the year or more) and the mountains support a mixture of summer recreational opportunities such as walking, climbing and birdwatching. The problem is that if tourism is to take off, much construction work has to be undertaken – access roads, hotels and restaurants are needed for

both types of tourism. Winter sports have additional requirements in the form of chairlifts and properly managed ski-slopes. Not only does the construction work intrude into and scar landscape of high scenic value, it also upsets delicate environmental balances. Runoff is increased, soil stability decreased and natural buffers and barriers removed. Unfortunately, experience has shown that such building all too often results in the intensification of the avalanche, landslip and flood hazards that have always been part of living in these areas.

Whilst the environmental costs are considerable, it has to be acknowledged that tourism has its benefits, bringing much-needed employment and income to areas where other resources are in short supply. Tourism is helping to maintain the demographic and economic viability of many mountain areas today.

Thus we come face to face with the key issue – how to reconcile the competing and often conflicting demands of tourism and conservation.

10 Identify those features of glacial and glaciated areas that might be seen as resources in the context of tourism.

11 Assess the relative merits of the following strategies for coping with the growth of tourism in an alpine region:

■ place an immediate ban on any further tourist developments

■ encourage only summer-season tourism
■ concentrate future developments in small areas
■ disperse future developments throughout the region.

7.6 **Periglacial processes and features**

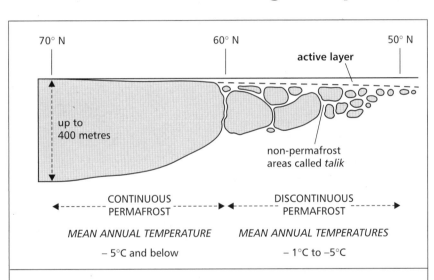

ACTIVE LAYER – KEY POINTS

1. Long hours of sunshine at high latitudes counteract the low sun angle: surface ground temperatures are sufficient to melt the permafrost.

2. Because the ground beneath remains impermeable, surface layers become very waterlogged.

3. Flows/sludging become major processes in this highly mobile zone, leading to solifluction terraces and lobes, and a general process of crest flattening and valley in-filling.

4. With the onset of winter, re-freezing re-commences from the surface downwards. Trapped, mobile active layer materials are therefore under increasing pressure, resulting in contortions and disturbed arrangements (e.g. involutions).

5. Because groundwater drainage is prevented, melting of ice and snow fields accentuates stream discharges (though streams rarely last for long, since they are melt-fed rather than rain-fed).

■ **7.11** Permafrost and the active layer

At the beginning of this chapter it was stated that one of the widely recognised hallmarks of a periglacial area is the persistence of some permanently frozen ground (**permafrost**). Permafrost gets thicker towards the Arctic, whilst on its surface a much thinner melt layer (the **active layer**) becomes thicker to the south, although even in the most favourable conditions this is only up to about 5 m thick, whereas permafrost can be hundreds of metres deep (**7.11**). Whilst there is no denying the significance of permafrost and the active layer in the periglacial regime, periglacial processes are also experienced in regions where there is no such ground, as for example on mountain tops where altitude causes reductions in temperature.

The landform processes of periglacial areas are essentially fivefold:

■ **Frost shattering** This is one of the most widespread processes involving alternate freezing and thawing of moisture in the cracks and joints of rock. Freezing causes the moisture to expand and creates enough pressure for the rock to be forced apart.

■ **Frost heave** This involves basically the same process as above except that the pressure comes from ice in the ground and the result is an upward movement of rock.

- **Solifluction** This is the most characteristic transportational process. It is the slow flow of material saturated or well lubricated by meltwater over slopes of quite gentle gradient.

- **Fluvial action** During the short summer, meltwater is available and when channelled is capable of undertaking the three tasks of erosion, transport and deposition. There is the view that stream action is generally weak, and this is supported by the braided characteristic of many periglacial streams.

- **Wind action** This plays a significant part in the transport and deposition of fine sediments of glacial and fluvioglacial origin. The process can be quite effective in fairly level areas that have little or no vegetative cover.

7.12 illustrates the main landforms and landscape features produced under periglacial conditions. Section 16.3 draws attention to some of the problems associated with settlement and development in permafrost areas.

■ **7.12** Features produced by periglacial processes

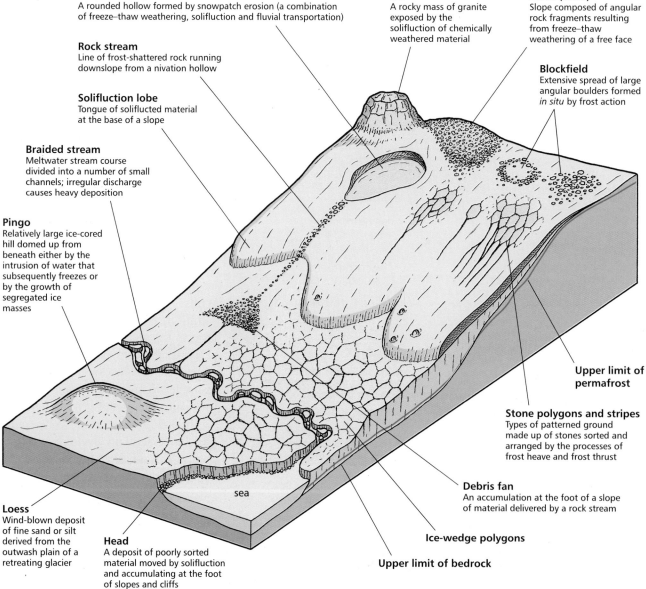

Nivation hollow
A rounded hollow formed by snowpatch erosion (a combination of freeze–thaw weathering, solifluction and fluvial transportation)

Rock stream
Line of frost-shattered rock running downslope from a nivation hollow

Solifluction lobe
Tongue of soliflucted material at the base of a slope

Braided stream
Meltwater stream course divided into a number of small channels; irregular discharge causes heavy deposition

Pingo
Relatively large ice-cored hill domed up from beneath either by the intrusion of water that subsequently freezes or by the growth of segregated ice masses

Loess
Wind-blown deposit of fine sand or silt derived from the outwash plain of a retreating glacier

Head
A deposit of poorly sorted material moved by solifluction and accumulating at the foot of slopes and cliffs

sea

Tor
A rocky mass of granite exposed by the solifluction of chemically weathered material

Scree (talus)
Slope composed of angular rock fragments resulting from freeze–thaw weathering of a free face

Blockfield
Extensive spread of large angular boulders formed *in situ* by frost action

Upper limit of permafrost

Stone polygons and stripes
Types of patterned ground made up of stones sorted and arranged by the processes of frost heave and frost thrust

Debris fan
An accumulation at the foot of a slope of material delivered by a rock stream

Ice-wedge polygons

Upper limit of bedrock

12 a Classify the features shown in **7.12** according to what you think is the dominant periglacial process in its formation.
   b Which features were difficult to classify, and why?

13 Given a valley trending east–west in a periglacial area of the Northern Hemisphere, suggest how and why the valley sides might show different slope characteristics.

14 Compare glaciated and periglaciated areas in terms of:
   a landform processes
   b landform characteristics.

7.7 Environmental change and landforms

IT1, 8

In Britain, relict features of past glacial and periglacial periods are a constant reminder of the dynamic nature of landforms. That evidence ranges from the great cirques of Snowdonia and the Scottish Highlands to the dry valleys of England's chalklands, and from the drowned estuaries to the raised beaches of the west coast.

Changes in the physical environment take place over different time scales. Long-term change is exemplified by the movement of the Earth's main structures, namely its drifting tectonic plates. Constructive and destructive plate margins with their associated landforms, such as rift valleys, deep-sea trenches, fold mountains and island arcs, are clear evidence of this dynamism operating over time scales that have to be measured in terms of millions of years.

During the last Ice Age, much of the land raised by the Alpine orogeny became depressed by the great weight of snow and ice that accumulated on it. When the snow and ice began to melt, the land started to rise again. This state of balance in the Earth's crust is known as **isostasy**, and the changes consequent upon

■ 7.13 Evidence of rejuvenation: the river has cut a deep meander into its former floodplain

glaciation are referred to as **isostatic adjustments**. The Ice Age also caused water formerly in the oceans to become locked into glaciers and ice-sheets. This led to **eustatic change**, or a fall in sea-level. Base-levels of erosion and deposition are determined by sea-level and therefore any change in that level is bound to have a profound effect on the rates of those two processes as well as on subaerial denudation. When sea-level rises, features tend to be covered by deposits or submerged. When sea-level falls, the process of **rejuvenation** becomes active, leaving old landforms above the new base-level and encouraging the formation of new landforms at a lower level (**7.13**). Thus isostatic and eustatic change working through the medium of base-level represent a second major aspect of environmental change which is significant in terms of landform evolution. Such change has repercussions that reach well inland from the coast (**7.14**).

IT1, 8

Climatic change perhaps even rivals tectonic movements as a dimension of environmental change that has an impact on landforms; indeed, most landforms bear its marks. The significance of climatic change is that it alters the character and balance of denudational processes and therefore resulting landforms. Climates can and do change far faster than landforms, and it is for this reason that relics of past climatic conditions persist in the present landscape. Often the landforms that we see today, particularly in upland and mountainous areas, are more heavily marked by past rather than present processes.

Whilst it is true that most landform development proceeds at a pace that is scarcely perceptible on a human time scale, there are some changes that take place over quite short periods of time. These are usually the result of high-energy, catastrophic events, such as storm surges and landslides, or of human interference in natural systems, as for example through coastal protection, reservoir construction and land reclamation. It is in our efforts to manage and modify

IT1, 2, 8

RISING BASE-LEVEL (isostatic fall, eustatic rise)	
Ria	Coastal inlet, usually irregular in outline, resulting from the drowning of a former river valley
Fiord	Deeply glaciated valley in a coastal region which has been partially occupied by the sea in post-glacial times
Island arc	Line of elongated islands representing the breached seaward side of a former valley running parallel to the former coastline
Buried channel	Former river channel gradually submerged beneath an accumulation of sediment when deposition and aggradation keep pace with the rise in base-level

FALLING BASE-LEVEL (isostatic rise, eustatic fall)	
Raised beach	Deposit of sand, shingle and broken shells resting on a platform cut by wave erosion during a period of higher sea-level. Usually between 1 and 50 m above present sea-level
Erosion surface	Extensive near-level surface formed by denudational processes working over a long period of time to a stable base-level, but subsequently raised by a base-level fall
River terrace	A near-level surface in a river valley, usually covered by a thin layer of gravel or alluvium. Represents a former floodplain into which the rejuvenated stream has become incised, dividing it and leaving it as two separate portions on either side of the valley
Knickpoint	Transitory point along the long profile of stream indicating the upstream movement of a rejuvenation; often marked by rapids or a waterfall
Incised meander	A deeply cut meandering valley caused by the stream cutting down into its former floodplain

■ **7.14** Features resulting from base-level changes

IT1, 2, 8 landform and hydrological systems that we particularly need to understand how those systems work. This is crucial if we wish to minimise the chances that intervention might have unwanted backlashes in the form of irrevocable environmental damage or the triggering of hazards.

15 For a small area that you are able to visit, make a list of the field evidence which supports the view that its landform processes have varied over time.

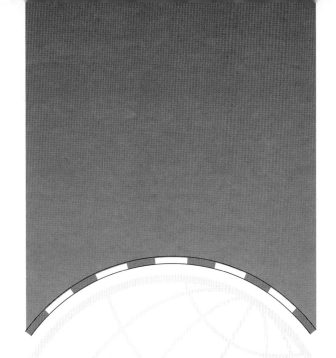

Weather & Climate

Weather and Climate: the human–physical interface

On 30 November 1991, 18 people were killed in a multiple crash on Highway 5 linking Los Angeles and San Francisco. This serial accident was caused by dust storms, formed by strong winds removing topsoil from nearby fields parched after several years of drought. Not only is this an example of the ultimate effect that weather and climate may have on human well-being, it also highlights the linkages that exist between weather and climate and other aspects of both physical and human geography.

8.1 Pollution

IT3

A United Nations report (1992) predicted an alarming increase in the rate of ozone depletion in the atmosphere of the Northern Hemisphere and the development of a 'hole' over Britain and Western Europe similar to that already present over the Antarctic. Ozone depletion is the latest and potentially most damaging form of atmospheric pollution.

Pollution is one of the integrating themes running through this book. You will find references to it in other sections (see Matrix 1 on page vii). **Pollution** is the invasion of a natural system or environment, such as the ocean or the atmosphere, by a substance or substances in such quantities as to result in a deterioration in, or damage to, the natural functioning of that system. Pollution may be classified in a number of ways (**8.1**) and is most commonly associated with rapid economic development and the creation of waste products. For many centuries, the exploitation of the environment and its resources was based on a belief that nature would be able to cope with any of these waste products; that the atmosphere and oceans would be in some way self-cleansing. Unfortunately, this has not been proved to be the case. Environmental damage has occurred, adversely affecting human well-being and posing problems for future economic development. **8.2** illustrates such unsustainable development.

IT3

■ **8.1** A simple classification of pollution

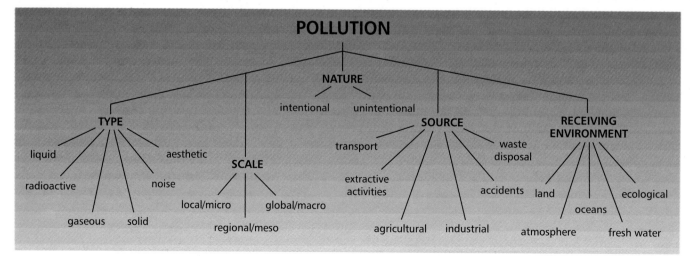

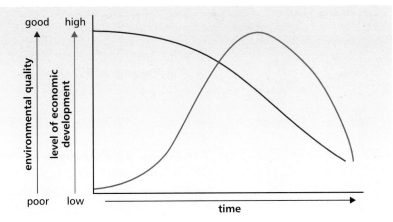

■ **8.2** Unsustainable development

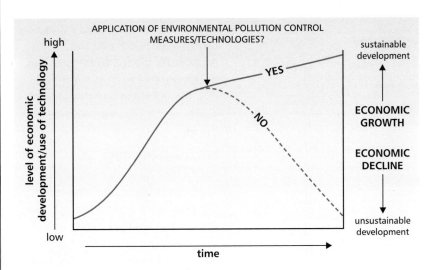

APPLICATION OF ENVIRONMENTAL POLLUTION CONTROL MEASURES/TECHNOLOGIES?

■ **8.3** To sustain or not to sustain?

The realisation of this interrelationship between development and the environment has gradually gained support. In the UK, the Public Health Act (1848) was the first attempt to control pollution. It is now generally accepted that the environment is no longer a threatening enemy to be conquered, but rather an ally to be befriended and nurtured. Viewed in this way, the environment has the potential to support and enrich human existence. **8.3** illustrates the basic dilemma facing the world as it reaches the end of the 20th century. If the interface between economic development and the environment can be managed successfully, then the prospects are fairly bright.

1 Volcanic eruptions can eject huge quantities of solid and gaseous material into the atmosphere which may cause environmental problems (see sections 2.3 and 12.4).
  a What materials are ejected by volcanic eruptions?
  b Does this mean that nature itself is a polluter?

CASE STUDY

'Up to the Smoke'

This phrase, 'Up to the Smoke', was widely used earlier in the 20th century to describe a journey to London and thus it acknowledged the increased problem of air pollution in the capital city. Urban areas have always had the ability to pollute the air and Charles Dickens noted this in his novel *Bleak House*, written in 1852:

> LONDON . . . . . . Smoke lowering down from chimney-pots, making a soft black drizzle, with flakes of soot in it as big as full-grown snowflakes gone into mourning, one might imagine, for the death of the sun.

London became famous for its 'pea-souper' fogs: foul-smelling yellow fogs produced by the high concentrations of smoke particles in winter radiation fogs. However, it took the dramatic consequences of the London **smogs** of the 1950s to really bring home the dangers of highly polluted fog. In fact, these smogs proved to be a milestone in environmental thinking in the UK.

London, situated in the basin of the river Thames which opens to the east, is relatively sheltered from Atlantic gales and is naturally prone to fairly frequent radiation fogs during winter. Under settled anticyclonic conditions, with an associated inversion of temperature, these fogs can persist for several days, as they did in January 1918, November 1921,

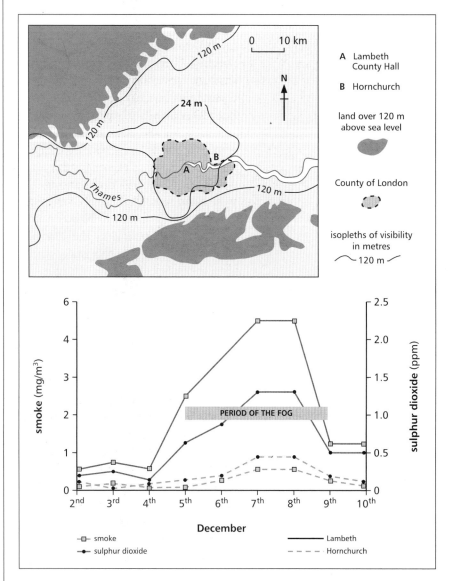

■ **8.4** Spatial and temporal extent of the December 1952 smog

December 1924 and November 1934, to mention but a few occasions. With the 'lid' effect of the inversion and the absence of wind, pollutants accumulate and concentrate within the fog. The minute particles of smoke and sulphur derived from the burning of coal and other fossil fuels act as hygroscopic nuclei and this encourages the fog to thicken. This thickening makes it even less likely that the following day's weak winter sunshine will evaporate and clear the fog.

On 5 December 1952, an anticyclone became centred over southern England and remained fairly static for a period of five days. With these conditions, and after a very damp autumn, a thick and persistent fog developed. Gradually, the smog extended over much of the Thames basin for distances up to 45 km (**8.4**) and achieved a depth of nearly 120 m.

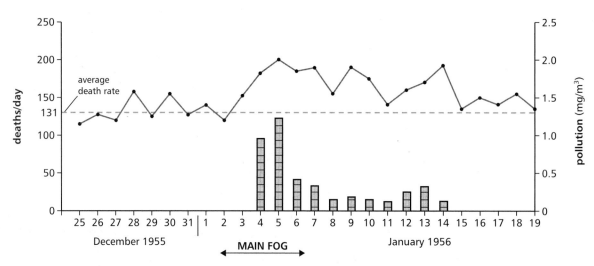

■ **8.5** Daily death rate in Central London, 25 December 1955 – 19 January 1956

The hazard and the cost

It has been calculated that approximately 4000 extra deaths occurred as a result of the London smog of 1952. Most of these deaths were confined to sufferers of bronchial and asthmatic disorders. **8.5** illustrates the close relationship between increasing pollution in the thickening fog and the daily death rate during the London smog of January 1956. The cost to society can be measured in other ways too. The slowing down of economic activity due to reduced mobility and the increased payments of sickness benefit are two such examples. The 1952 smog even managed to penetrate buildings in central London, and a performance at Covent Garden had to be abandoned after the first act!

Responses

The costs of recurrent smogs eventually persuaded the UK to take decisive action. This was in the form of the Clean Air Act of 1956. This Act required that over 300 local authorities should establish 'clean air zones'. As a result, 90 per cent of London's population now lives in smoke-controlled areas. Changes in energy usage and the requirements of the Act resulted in 1980 smoke emissions being reduced to one-tenth of their 1956 levels; this was accompanied by a rise in recorded hours of sunshine.

CASE STUDY

IP1, IT3,5

Atmospheric pollution in Tokyo

Japan's remarkable post-war economic growth has become focused on areas of fragmented lowland, particularly along the Pacific coast of Honshu. Here, the huge metropolitan area of Tokyo, with a population approaching 25 million, is the leading centre of both that growth and its attendant pollution. The coastal location means that land and sea breezes play an important role in the distribution of pollution. The breezes can sometimes push polluted air more than 40 km inland.

The Tokyo area illustrates how atmospheric pollution can pass through a series of distinct stages (**8.6**). Each stage poses a pollution challenge which, in turn, leads to an appropriate response in the form of controlling legislation. Thus the Soot/dust stage saw the introduction of controls, whilst the next stage, the SO_2 stage, led to further laws concerned with the introduction of desulphurisation techniques and the promotion of low-sulphur fuels. The final stage, Photochemical smog, is particularly challenging. The sheer pace of economic growth and rising personal affluence (for example, car numbers trebled between 1964 and 1984) has meant that despite strict controls, pollution levels have fallen only slowly.

■ **8.6** A pollution stage model for Tokyo

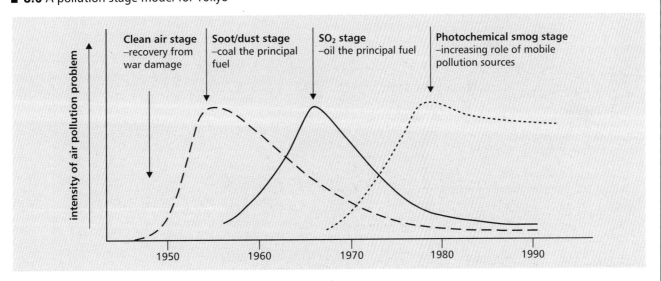

Despite legislation, Tokyo and other large cities around the globe still experience smogs, but today's are **petrochemical smogs** rather than the **chimney-pot smogs** of 30 or 40 years ago. The villain of the piece is the motor vehicle. A typical vehicle exhaust system emits a remarkable cocktail of gases, of which nitrous oxides are the most serious in this context. Ironically, it is bright sunshine which plays a critical part in the formation of this relatively new form of smog. In bright sunshine, some nitrous oxides are subject to chemical change and converted into nitrogen dioxide. Under certain atmospheric and topographic conditions, this lethal substance accumulates to form smog which not only impairs visibility, but also presents a serious health hazard to people, animals and plants. At present, photochemical smog seems to be accepted as the inevitable cost of our love affair with the motor vehicle. But the time has come to take effective action against this form of atmospheric pollution.

8.2 Links with physical geography

In the lithosphere, landforms and the processes responsible for them are to a large extent the result of an interaction with atmospheric variables over time. The changes in climate that initiated and ended the Ice Age have left a legacy in many parts of the world. The same processes are still active in polar and some mountainous areas (see Chapter 7). **8.7** shows the extent of the periglacial environment. Here a variety of landforms is related to the depth and persistence of a permafrost layer beneath the ground which is, in turn, a reflection of past climatic extremes and present temperature regimes (see section 7.6).

2 Glaciers persist in both the west Norwegian mountains and in the northern Urals at approximately 50°–60° N (see **7.1**).
  a Find out the main differences in the climates of these two areas.
  b What factors have favoured the survival of glaciers in these two areas?

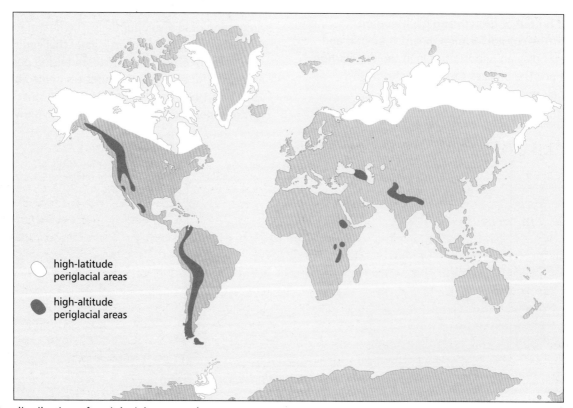

high-latitude periglacial areas

high-altitude periglacial areas

■ **8.7** The distribution of periglacial areas today

In fact all the processes of denudation – glacial, fluvial, marine and aeolian – are controlled by climatic conditions; so too are the type and rate of weathering. Freeze–thaw activity or frost shattering is an obvious case in point, while even chemical weathering is related to temperature and humidity (see section 3.1). The hot humid conditions prevailing in parts of the tropics encourage rapid chemical weathering that penetrates well below the surface (see section 6.1), whereas its significance wanes in colder and drier areas.

---

3 a Describe a form of mechanical weathering other than frost shattering and investigate how it is controlled by atmospheric conditions.
  b Suggest one way in which human activity is accelerating chemical weathering.

In the biosphere, climatic factors play a crucial role in soil formation, particularly in those processes associated with the movement of groundwater and the consequent transfers of mineral salts. Thus leaching, podsolisation and salinisation are all related, to a significant degree, with atmospheric conditions prevailing above ground level. Some of these processes may be modified by human activity, for example salinisation by irrigation, while the product of thousands of years of soil-forming processes can be destroyed by a lethal combination of climatic conditions and inappropriate agricultural practices.

The vegetation of an area and much of its fauna are strongly influenced by climatic conditions. Trees require

---

4 Irrigation represents a human modification of climate intended to benefit agriculture.
  a Find out why this may lead to the problem of salinisation, and describe an example of where this has happened.
  b Can the problem be solved?

---

a temperature of 10 °C in the warmest month and an annual minimum of 200 mm of moisture to grow successfully, while major climatic controls such as the length of the growing season and the rainfall regime have a direct impact on the global pattern of biomes. At a local level, microclimatic variations produced, for example, by aspect, slope and exposure to salt-laden winds can influence the type and density of vegetation cover. Indeed, all ecosystems function within specific climatic controls; their energy is derived from solar radiation, while most nutrients are either received through atmospheric processes or released via weathering and the decay of organic matter (see Chapter 13). Both weathering and decay are directly related to climate.

---

5 a What precisely is meant by the term **biome**?
  b What biome is associated with the areas depicted in **8.7**?
  c Construct a map to show the distribution of the world's major biomes and analyse how two of these are affected by climate.

8.3 Links with human geography

IT1 An agricultural system is perhaps the most obvious example of this relationship. Nearly all agricultural activities, with the exception of certain types of horticulture (where a modified microclimate is created under plastic or glass), depend on the patterns and variations of a complex range of atmospheric variables. Most plants possess very critical limits of cultivation imposed by variables such as average summer temperatures, the length of the frost-free season or the amount and character of the rainfall regime. Climatic influences have produced distinct spatial patterns of crops and agricultural systems. These patterns reflect a comparative climatic advantage that one area possesses over another area and form the basis for the interchange of

agricultural commodities. When a New Zealand apple or a Leeward Islands banana is consumed in the UK, we are in reality importing the particular climatic advantages of those islands. These spatial patterns exist on an altitudinal as well as a latitudinal scale. **IT1**

Although it is now quite justifiable to think of agricultural systems as being influenced more by human inputs, the overall control of physical factors including climate remains strong. Climate definitely imposes broad limits within which a particular agricultural activity can flourish, and occasional extremes may have a damaging or even disastrous effect. Thus the UK drought of 1975–76 added greatly to the cost of a bag of chips as potato yields slumped, while late spring frosts in 1991 had a spectacular effect on the price of several French wines, including champagne.

The influence of climate on other forms of economic activity is less obvious, but is never totally absent. Opencast mining, the nature of forestry plantings, energy production, the construction and fishing industries are all examples in this respect. Whilst most manufacturing takes place inside buildings and therefore is in a sense weatherproof, the influence of climate may be felt indirectly because the transport systems on which manufacturing firms depend are affected by the weather. However, there are some manufacturing activities, such as the clothing industry, that are more obviously geared to the weather. Changes can increase or depress demand for a variety of manufactured goods, as is clearly illustrated by the advertisement in **8.8**.

The post-war period has witnessed a significant shift in the structure of economic activity in developed countries. Modern manufacturing activities, together with some tertiary and quaternary activities such as research and development, are far more footloose in their locational requirements. The environmental quality of the workplace is now an important factor to be considered and some of this significance is recognised in the southward shift of economic activities within the USA to what have become known as the 'sunbelt' states (see section 28.5). Indeed, as informa-

tion technology based economic activities grow, the locational decisions will increasingly be influenced by environmental quality and comfort factors. With a computer link, it is quite conceivable to think of a workbase on the Florida coast rather than in cold, windy New York!

> **6 a** Make a list of the ways in which the fishing industry is affected by climatic conditions. (The fishing weather forecast might assist you here.)
> **b** How may energy production be influenced by climate?
> **c** Make a list of other types of manufacturing activity that are influenced by climatic conditions.

In the developed world, and increasingly in many developing countries, the tourist and leisure industry has expanded dramatically over the past 50 years. Here the links with climate are so obvious that we need not dwell on them too long. The guaranteed sunshine of the Mediterranean coasts and, until some recent years, the guaranteed snow of the European Alps, are two very obvious examples. Virtually all recreational and related outdoor activities are weather-dependent, with holidays representing a year's savings being made or marred by the prevailing weather conditions (see section 29.7).

■ **8.8** Advertisement placed by a major retailing group during a recent damp summer

Every CLOUDBURST has a SILVER LINING!

HUGE *Rainfall causes* HUGE *PRICEFALL*

As the rain kept pouring our stocks kept rising! Now we are forced to slash our prices for immediate clearance. If you've put off buying garden furniture, or barbecues, or anything for the garden . . .

HELP US CLEAR OUR STOCKS & HELP YOURSELF TO AN UNREPEATABLE SAVING!

BARBECUES REDUCED!

> **7 a** Can you think of some ways in which climate has a detrimental effect on leisure or sport, i.e. it becomes a cost rather than a benefit ?
> **b** What about your own experiences in this respect?
> **c** How have some leisure and sporting activities sought to modify the effects of atmospheric processes?

Weather conditions affect transport in numerous ways and it is important to remember that this not only results in an inconvenience factor, but may also constitute a cost to society in delayed goods and services, lost work output, cancellation of a transport facility and occasionally the ultimate cost: a loss of human lives. Even aircraft which fly above most 'weather' have to take off and land through a series of rapidly changing weather conditions. Despite improved aircraft and airport technologies, delays can still occur and some air disasters have been directly attributed to adverse weather.

---

8 Keep a log of the interruptions to transport in your area that have been caused by the weather. In what ways is transport implicated in the problem of climatic change?

Movements of population or migrations are often affected by climatic factors (see Chapter 22). Climatic considerations certainly play an important role in the decision-making process of elderly people when they retire. Sometimes climatic factors become the prime determinant or **push factor** in migration, as for example the frequent Sahelian droughts of the 1980s and early 1990s. Even the developed world has not been immune in this respect, for during the 1930s part of the American Midwest experienced a negative migratory balance as tens of thousands of 'Okies' (poverty-stricken farmers from Oklahoma and adjacent states) fled the 'Dust Bowl'.

---

9 a Find out what is meant by the 'Dust Bowl'.
   b How did the 'Dust Bowl' relate to economic conditions prevailing in the USA during the early 1930s?

Whether people are at war or at peace, painting or composing music, the weather invariably has a part to play. The persistence of a large anticyclone in early June 1940, when the Dunkirk evacuation took place, provided very favourable conditions for this epic event. The weather was not so kind when Napoleon retreated from Moscow in 1812 or during Hitler's Russian Campaign during the Second World War. No less so, it has had a part to play in the strategy of more recent military episodes such as the 'Desert Storm' war in Iraq (see section 15.3).

These events remind us of the ultimate impact that atmospheric conditions may have on human well-being. Despite the technological advances that have enabled people to walk in space or on weatherless lunar surfaces, within our own atmosphere we still remain vulnerable to the vagaries of the weather and potentially to long-term predicted changes. This hazard aspect and climatic change are themes that will be explored in greater depth later in this unit.

CASE STUDY

IT2,4,7

Climate and economic development in southern California

Early Spanish settlers penetrating northwards from Mexico found nothing exceptional about the climate of California. In fact, sailors regarded the coast as treacherous on account of persistent fogs, and on land early Spanish missionaries found it necessary to irrigate their gardens to overcome the problem of drought. However, as settlers from the east of the USA arrived, the emphasis changed and by the 1890s the South California Information Bureau claimed that they sold the climate at so much an acre and then threw in the land free! Amazing claims were made as to the beneficial effects of the climate, some suggesting that longevity of migrants increased by 10 years! This climatic sales campaign was to set the scene for the phenomenal growth of this Pacific state, for the Californian success story is in no small measure a consequence of the opportunities that the climate provided for a wide range of economic and social activities.

8.9 goes some of the way to explaining why no other state in the USA tops the league in the production of such a wide variety of crops as California. Some parts of the south of the state have the potential to cultivate temperate crops such as lettuce, carrots, beans and peas in winter and then plant crops like cantaloup in the summer. Above all, the high annual totals of sunshine have rendered the state particularly suited to the cultivation of many fruit crops, and in earlier times some fruit was even dried out of doors to produce raisins, prunes and

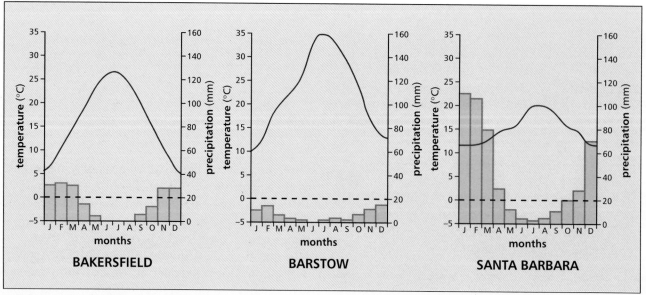

■ **8.9** Aspects of California's climate

sultanas. Little wonder that trade names such as 'Sunkist', 'Sunmaid' and 'Sunsweet' evolved. Finally, localised variations in climate produced by altitude, latitude, aspect and distance from the cooling waters of the Californian current result in spatial specialisations in certain crop types. Thus the dry, sunny conditions of the Napa valley favour grapes whereas the penetration of sea mists into the Salinas valley benefits the lettuce crop, as does the cooler coastal climate for artichokes near Moss Landing.

It is important to remember, however, that the dry sunny conditions initially favoured only ranching and winter wheat. Human ingenuity and technology were able to exploit the effects of variations in relief on climate within the state and made it possible to

transfer vast quantities of water southwards and westwards across the state to irrigate what now amounts to approximately 4 million ha of farmland. This water supplemented by local well water has not only allowed farming to expand, but has also sustained rapid industrial and urban growth. Development in south California is in no small measure a result of the management of water resources in this part of the USA.

10 Water shortages could restrain future economic growth in the state.
  a What are the principal uses of water in California?
  b Evaluate the options for sustaining economic growth in view of this potential shortage.

The management of water resources brings other advantages too since most of the dams serve as dual-purpose schemes in that they also produce HEP. The heavy snows of the Sierra Nevada troubled early migrants moving west through mountain passes, and continues to create problems for modern transport systems (**8.10**). But they do provide the basis for irrigation and act as one of the varied tourist attractions of the state.

■ **8.10** Snow in the Sierra Nevada

The earliest industries in California, following the gold rush in 1849, were related to the processing of primary products, particularly those of agriculture. However, two other 20th-century industries owe much of their initial impetus to climatic advantages. When Cecil B. de Mille rented a barn in the Los Angeles area in 1913, it precipitated a film rush which resulted in all the major US producers locating in this area by 1920. The variety of natural and human landscapes available, the proximity to the Mexican border for escape for illicit film producers, and the fact that the finished product – a can of film – was easy to transport, were all factors that encouraged the growth of Hollywood; but it was the climatic advantages that really provided the most important **comparative advantage**. The relatively warm temperatures throughout the year, the virtual absence of strong winds and, most important of all, the dry sunny weather with bright light, provided the dependable shooting weather for film companies which in the infancy of the industry relied to a large extent on outdoor filming in the local area to minimise costs.

These climatic advantages were also exploited by the aircraft assembly industry. The excellent visibility, warm temperatures and light winds were perfect for the test-flying of small early aircraft models by enthusiasts such as Lockheed and Douglas. It even became possible to assemble aircraft in the open air, thus avoiding the cost of large heated hangars. Little wonder that by the late 1930s California was the leading area in the USA for aircraft assembly. Both these industries have exerted a multiplier effect, spawning associated industries which in the case of the aircraft industry include electronics, missiles, aerospace and the defence industry.

The subsequent rapid economic and demographic growth (the Los Angeles district experienced a 123 per cent increase in population during the 1920s) has encouraged the setting up of a wide range of tertiary and quaternary activities. All of these, together with an increasing array of high-tech industries, have been partly attracted here by the favourable climate which underpins the Californian lifestyle. These activities recruit large numbers of highly skilled personnel. Since the skills of these educated and mobile personnel are in great demand, they have been able carefully to select their workplace. As a consequence, environmental quality becomes an important element in their personal decision-making process.

California boasts an ideal climate for a wide range of tourist and leisure activities, and it has undoubtedly been the non-hostile, and in some ways therapeutic, climate, and the prospect of all-year recreational activities that have attracted many retired people to the state. The presence of this age group, often with considerable disposable income, has also been of significant economic benefit to the state. It goes without saying that the 'pool and patio' culture of California owes much to the climate, as do early architectural style, dress, particularly leisurewear, and indeed youth culture. The Beach Boys in the 1960s and Bay Watch in the 1990s epitomise the leisure lifestyle of this sunshine state.

---

11 The early Spanish architectural style consists of overhanging eaves, thick walls, small windows and low-pitched roofs. In what ways is this style adapted to the climate?

Probably no climate in the world is without its problems, and in California there are several aspects of it with which society has to come to terms. The February 1992 storms and associated floods represent a classic example of flash floods, the inevitable consequence of a combination of an unreliable rainfall, an intermittent drainage system and the spread of settlement onto the steep hillslopes fringing the Los Angeles basin. The not infrequent brush fires in autumn, which are encouraged by the dry, hot summers and sometimes spread by the Santa Ana wind (as in November 1993), also play a part. This wind can be a hazard in its own right; for example, in 1961 a Santa Ana wind recorded gusts of 100 mph (160 km/h). Droughts, such as the five-year drought which preceded the February storms, also present a problem. For 40 years prior to 1913, San Diego had never recorded a temperature below 0°C, but in January of that year −4°C was recorded. This cold spell resulted in agricultural damage of $40 million. Adaptation to this hazard includes the setting up of early-warning systems and the use of protective measures such as heaters, wind machines and paper cones.

12 What associated problems can drought and unreliable rainfall cause?

13 In what ways do brush fires increase the threat of flash floods?

Over the past several decades the sunshine on which California built its reputation has been increasingly limited by the emergence of the new hazard of smog, in this case photochemical smog.

The climate of California has without doubt played a vital role in the economic development of the state. In fact it has consistently been used as a promotional selling point. It does impose some limits as to what can be done and yet Californian growth has occurred in spite of a severe water deficiency. At the same time, it provides many opportunities for economic and social advancement. This valuable resource is presently threatened by pollution and in the long term by a water shortage, both created by the sheer volume of people and economic activity attracted to this golden state.

8.4 **Effects on human health**

IT5

The health risks associated with increasing ozone depletion (see section 12.7) are now fully realised, but the UN report which predicted its increase attempted to shatter complacency towards this issue by estimating 300 000 additional cases of skin cancer within eight years directly as a result of existing ozone depletion (see case study on pages 162–63). It also noted the disturbing link with damage to the human immune system which may speed up the spread of the AIDS virus, not to mention the probable rapid increase of eye cataracts. This graphically illustrates the effect that climate may have on human health. It should also reinforce our concern regarding the potential that human activities have for dangerously degrading the atmosphere, one of our most valuable life support systems.

Climatic effects on human health range from a minor irritation when a change in the weather spoils our planned leisure activity through to serious injury or even death associated with certain major climatic hazards. The human species evolved in tropical regions where temperatures averaged somewhere between 20 °C and 25 °C. Over a long period of time, the human species migrated and adapted to a whole range of different climatic conditions. However, we still find temperatures above 25 °C increasingly uncomfortable and such conditions cause us to sweat to

induce a cooling of our skin surface. At certain combined values for temperature and humidity, our bodies overheat and heat stroke can occur. With a relative humidity of 100%, this will occur at 27 °C, whereas in very dry air (relative humidity 20%) temperatures as high as 40–45 °C are tolerable.

IT5

14 a How does sweating aid the cooling process?
  b What effect does the relative humidity of the air have on this process?

15 Why do you think the death rate from heat waves has declined this century (**8.11**)?

16 Study **8.12**.
  a In what way does the pattern for Canada and the north of the USA differ from that of the south of the USA?
  b Why do Black people have a higher death rate than White people?
  c Why is this difference particularly noticeable in summer?
  d How would you explain the peaks at A and B?

Year	No. of deaths
1901	9508
1936	4768
1980	1265

■ **8.11** Deaths caused by US heat waves

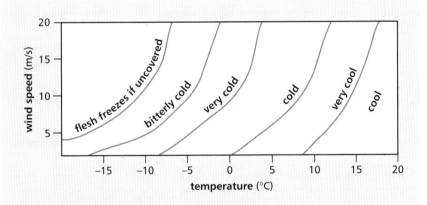

■ **8.12** Generalised death rates from cardiovascular disease for population groups in the USA and Canada

IT5

It is not only extreme heat that can be a danger to health. As temperatures fall below 20 °C we also experience increasing discomfort and we begin to shiver – our body's way of stimulating heat through muscular activity. A combination of falling temperatures and increasing air flow or wind intensifies this feeling of coldness. This is termed the **wind-chill effect**, which is experienced as our bodily heat loss via radiation and convection, i.e. the metabolic heat loss, rises with increasing air movement.

As you can see from **8.13**, when a wind of 5 m/s accompanies a temperature of 10 °C, it feels somewhat cooler since the WET (the wind-chill equivalent temperature) – the temperature we feel or sense – is approximately 3 °C lower. Remember that these calculations assume cloudy conditions. **8.13** also translates these WET temperatures into the sensations or feelings of coolness experienced. These sensations have been plotted as **isopleths** (lines joining points of equal value – see section 8.6).

There are many other instances of correlations between specific weather conditions and the incidence of certain physical ailments. For example, studies in the USA have indicated such a relationship between the aggravation of duodenal ulcers and the temperature curve over a five-year period. A sudden fall in temperature seems to increase the likelihood of such problems, whereas the influenza virus develops and travels best during dry, calm weather. We will now consider these relationships in a little more detail in relation to the 'summer scourge' which regularly affects one in ten of the UK population.

IT5

■ **8.13** Wind chill

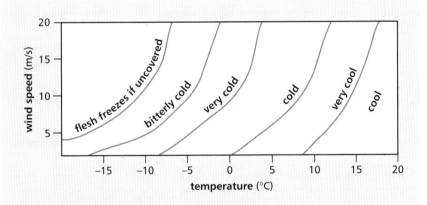

a) Wind-chill 'sensation' isopleths

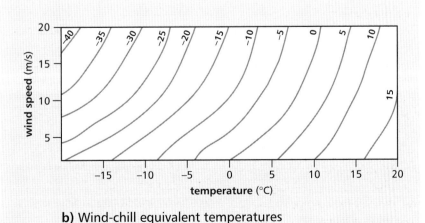

b) Wind-chill equivalent temperatures

IT5

Hay fever and climate

Sneezing is one of the symptoms of hay fever, the summer scourge for approximately 6 million people in the UK. **8.14** illustrates how the daily pattern of pollen concentration mirrors the average daily temperature regime. However, this only provides a partial indication of the great variety of different airborne particles which can cause an allergic reaction producing the characteristic hay-fever symptoms of rhinitis and conjunctivitis, not to mention aggravating conditions for asthma sufferers. Little wonder that for these 6 million people the weather forecast with pollen-count estimates is an eagerly awaited daily event in midsummer.

For some allergic people, one grain of pollen is sufficient to initiate a hay-fever attack, and people react in different ways to different types of spore. The principal pollen spores are derived from grasses

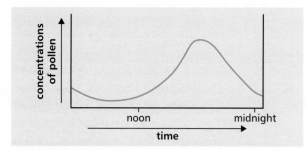

■ **8.14** Variations in pollen concentrations during a midsummer day

(*Gramineae*) and other flowering plants and weeds such as nettles (*Uticaceae*), though in some areas tree pollens are important. For example, in Japan cedar pollen is the main allergen, while in Finland birch pollen is significant. Fungus and mould spores are another group of allergens and the incidence of all of these is influenced by weather patterns.

Once the air temperature exceeds 5.5°C, then most plant growth commences; in the Northern Hemisphere the grass pollen season begins in late April and usually reaches a peak in June or July.

Within an urban area there can be significant spatial variations in pollen concentrations (**8.15**). On a temporal basis the declining agricultural practice of cutting hay and the increase in grass-cutting for silage, i.e. before it flowers, has led to a steady decline in *Gramineae* pollen counts in southern Britain, but at the same time the increasing incidence of hay fever suggests that other allergens are becoming involved. This has raised the question as to whether particulates connected with air pollution are guilty.

17 With daily pollen counts and forecasts available, a study of the relationship between these and a variety of weather variables might prove to be an interesting topic for a personal investigative study.

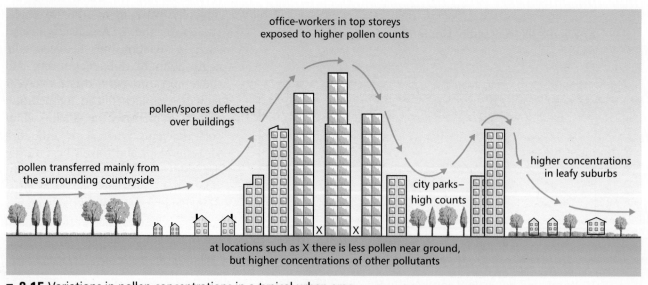

■ **8.15** Variations in pollen concentrations in a typical urban area

So far we have considered only the health problems associated with a particular group of people interacting with their local environment. However, increased mobility means that there is more contact with health problems associated with different climates, and occasionally these problems can be carried on the return journey home.

18 Most tropical areas are afflicted by three main groups of disease: endemic, epidemic and diet deficiency diseases.
  a Find out three examples of each of these disease groups.
  b Suggest how each group is related to climate conditions.

Sometimes people will deliberately move to a different climate environment for health reasons. Many of the Alpine winter sports resorts began as climate spas,

while in tropical countries European settlers traditionally moved to 'hill stations' during the heat of summer both for increased comfort and to avoid the increased incidence of the diseases associated with that hot humid season. The Cameron Highlands was an example of such a hill area in Malaysia.

19 Give an example of a contemporary population movement encouraged by the linkage between climate and human health.

Remember that variations in human health are the results of the interplay of a variety of factors, but climatic conditions do often play a significant part. Furthermore, there is increasing concern regarding the manner in which human interference with atmospheric processes may be causing climatic change, with further potentially serious consequences for human health.

8.5 **Climatic hazards**

The most dramatic and the most disastrous way in which human well-being may be affected is by the occurrence of a hazardous climatic event. A climatic hazard occurs when some extreme atmospheric condition poses a threat to the biological, economic and social existence of a group of people.

Natural hazards, such as extreme cold or heat, flood, drought, strong wind, hail, heavy snow or blizzard, lightning or fog, have historically been unpredictable in terms of their magnitude, frequency and duration. Although early identification and warning systems have improved immeasurably, even with satellite technology mistakes can still occur. Thus in contrast to the other ways in which climate affects human well-being and activities, hazards represent an occasional but dangerous reminder of the extent to which the natural forces of the atmosphere are seemingly unpredictable and uncontrollable. The awe in which these events are held means that they eventually pass into the weather memory bank or folklore of successive generations. Such was the case with the winter of 1886–87 on the Great Plains of the USA. During this winter, intense cold with temperatures as low as –40°C and prolonged blizzards lasted from 13 November 1886 until 2 March 1887, with one brief respite in mid-December. When a chinook (see section

10.2) heralded a more permanent thaw during the first week in March, the economic cost of this winter became evident. Apart from the loss of human life, the great range herds of cattle had been virtually wiped out. Only one group of people benefited from the 'winter of the blue snows' and these were the bone-pickers who collected cattle skeletons for the fertiliser companies. In all probability the severe flooding in southern California in February 1992 will similarly take its place in the weather folklore of the USA.

20 Find out about the 'hurricane' of October 1987 in southern Britain.
  a What weather records were broken?
  b What damage was caused?
  c Why was this hazardous event not identified and forecast much earlier (see section 1.3 and the case study on page 148)?

21 Can you explain why the November 1972 tropical cyclone caused so much damage in Bangladesh, despite early warning by the TIROS satellite?

The hazards discussed so far can be termed 'natural' and are caused by a variety of factors totally unrelated to human existence. However, there is now clear evidence that human activities may be creating new and potentially more dangerous climatic hazards. In fact, the history and success of the human species on planet Earth to a large extent reflects the degree to which we have innovated and used new technologies to subdue and manipulate the natural environment. As people gained increasing dominance over their environment, population was able to increase rapidly and economic well-being was advanced. This, in turn, accelerated the exploitation of the environment and its resources which has invariably led to environmental degradation and a series of environmental problems.

Some of these new hazards are local in scale, as for example smog in the London or Los Angeles basins,

while others, such as the greenhouse effect, have taken on a global significance. Whatever the scale, the knowledge that these new hazards are a consequence of human interference with the atmospheric system means that they have become matters of intense public and political debate; environmental problems have become environmental issues. This theme of climatic modification and change is discussed in greater depth in Chapter 12.

Finally, the scenarios advanced for the effects of global warming seem to suggest an increased variability in future weather patterns with a probable increase in the incidence of extreme episodes of weather. Thus people-induced hazards seem destined to increase the likelihood of more natural hazards; for this reason, they are to be seen as an example of a feedback mechanism.

CASE STUDY

Acid rain – a transnational problem

Acid rain became a meteorological problem during the mid-1970s, yet it is quite clear that it existed long before this, in fact ever since people began burning fossil fuels. **8.16** reminds us that acid rain is in fact a natural phenomenon, since all precipitation is slightly acid owing to the absorption of carbon dioxide by water in the atmosphere to form a weak solution of carbonic acid. Therefore although 7 is the neutral value on the pH scale, a value of 5.5 is regarded as quite normal. What has happened is that, as a consequence of human activities, this value has steadily fallen and, in some spells of acid rain, values of below 4 have been recorded, with even lower values occurring during acid mists. The result

has been visible ecological damage to forests and fauna, transforming the problem into an issue.

The two major pollutants involved in the formation of acid rain are sulphur dioxide (SO_2) and nitrous oxides. Sulphur dioxide is produced during the burning of fossil fuels in power stations, industrial plants and in vehicle engines, though in the UK almost two-thirds is emitted by power stations. The amount of sulphur produced depends both on the sulphur content and the calorific value of the fuel being burnt. For example, some US coals have a low sulphur content, whereas the dramatic expansion of power production in recent years in the former East Germany and in Poland is based on high-sulphur, low calorific-value lignite or brown coal. Nitrous oxides are also released during energy production based on fossil fuels, but

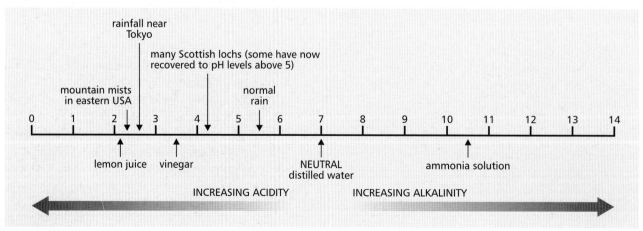

■ **8.16** Key points on the pH scale

their most dramatic increase has been associated with motor vehicle use, with up to 50 per cent of the total in Western Europe and the USA being now attributable to this source. Both SO_2 and nitrous oxides are transformed in the atmosphere into acids, i.e. sulphuric acid and nitric acid.

These pollutants return to earth as dry or wet deposition; in fact some authorities prefer the term **acid deposition** to acid rain. **Dry deposition** occurs as the larger particles fall to earth relatively close to the emission source. This normally accounts for 50 per cent of the emissions. Most of the remaining pollutants are absorbed by water droplets in the atmosphere, some in fact acting as hygroscopic nuclei. These form the **wet deposition** which will again frequently fall fairly close to the emission source. However, since SO_2 can last in the atmosphere for up to four days there is considerable potential for this to travel. (You might like to consider how far SO_2 carried by a 60 km/h wind would travel in 36 hours.) In this way, acid rain becomes an international problem since it is now a form of transnational pollution.

---

22 a What are hygroscopic nuclei?
   b With a low calorific value, a high ash and water content and invariably high sulphur content, explain why lignite is still used for energy generation in so many countries.

Acid rain leads to ecological, aesthetic, medical and economic problems.

Ecological problems

Plants and animals possess varying degrees of tolerance to acidity in the soil, water and air. When this critical level of tolerance is exceeded, damage and possibly death occurs. Trees receive acid via precipitation and thus damage to the upper foliage or crowns is often a visible sign of acid attack. But trees are also affected by the increasing acidity in the soil which leads to trace mineral shortages. The combined effects of these are varied, but symptoms include the rapid growth of shoots, early shedding of leaves and, most important of all, a reduced

resistance to climatic damage, pests and diseases. Dieback or defoliation and eventually death occurs, which has important knock-on effects for slope stability, the forest microclimate and faunal habitats. The direct fall of acid rain on lake and river surfaces and the throughflow and overland flow of increasingly acidic water leads to the acidification of freshwater areas. This change may be exacerbated by naturally infertile soil and the acidifying effect of conifer plantations with their acid-rich litter and humus. It is not surprising that in an increasingly acidic environment many types of fauna should suffer too. Fish fail to breed well, develop deformities and die prematurely. Birds such as ducks, grebes and ospreys are affected because of their reliance upon food from acidified watercourses and lakes. The effect of acid rain thus passes along the food chain.

Aesthetic problems

It was the sight of forest dieback more than anything else which convinced the public of the reality of the acid rain problem. Nowhere is this felt more keenly than in Canada where the maple, the national symbol, is under serious threat in eastern provinces, particularly Quebec.

Medical problems

The acid rain problem has a medical cost because the atmospheric pollutants concerned are also dangerous to human health. For example, in the USA SO_2 is recognised as the major cause of lung disease after active and passive smoking. The famous London smogs of the 1950s were, in reality, acid, and the inhalation of this polluted fog produced severe health problems for many people (see case study on pages 87–89).

Economic problems

This is a comparatively underestimated cost to society, since most attention has inevitably been focused on the ecological aspect of acid rain. In Quebec (Canada), reduced maple sugar production has amounted to a loss of $5.8 million, while timber growth has also declined markedly. Forest dieback in the Swiss Alps is causing increasing concern as it will increase potential damage by avalanches. In Poland the costs of acid-rain damage are equivalent to 10 per cent of the country's GNP.

23 a In what other ways does acid rain represent a cost to society?
   b Why does Norway produce very low SO$_2$ emissions?

The response to this problem has occurred both at a national and an international level with the latter becoming increasingly significant. Remedial action at a local level includes liming and restocking waters with fish, and while this can be successful, it is not a permanent solution to the problem. The main response is concentrated on reducing emissions of pollutants. In the case of energy production, this involves switching to low-sulphur fuels, developing renewable energy resources and expanding nuclear power (see Chapter 27). Technological innovation now makes it possible to reduce emissions by using desulphurisation processes at power plants, while fluidised bed combustion will, it is claimed, make it possible to burn low-grade sulphur-rich coal efficiently and cleanly in or near urban areas. This will both increase the efficiency of the power plant and reduce transmission costs. Unfortunately, the new lignite-burning plants in Poland have included 300 m-high chimney stacks to push the problem higher into the atmosphere, thus providing a perfect launch for the pollutants on what will probably be an international journey.

The technology to tackle these problems is thus present, but the political will is not always there. The best hope lies in increasing international cooperation and significant in this respect is the '30% Club for Reduced Sulphur Emissions' whose members agreed to reduce their 1980 emissions by this amount by 1993. More recently, a similar organisation has developed to reduce nitrous oxide emissions. What is important for the future is not only the progress that can be made in the developed world, but also what is likely to happen in the developing world. It is ominous that while the World Health Organisation reported a 10 per cent reduction in SO$_2$ emissions in Europe and North America in 1987, at the same time it recorded a 5 per cent increase in Asia.

24 The 1980 and 1987 emissions of SO$_2$ for the countries in Europe are given in **8.17**.
   a Calculate the percentage difference in emissions for the period 1980–87 for each country.
   b Using a choropleth technique, plot this data on a base map of Europe.
   c Analyse the spatial pattern revealed by your map.
   d Do the trends indicated by the data suggest that the 30% Club will achieve its stated objective?

8.6 **Techniques: Isopleths**

Isopleths are lines which join points of equal value. Thus contour lines on an OS map join up places of equal height. Isopleths are used quite frequently in climate studies. On synoptic charts **isobars** are used to join places with the same atmospheric pressure, while **isotherms** join locations with the same mean temperatures (see **10.2**). **Isohyets**, joining places with equal rainfall totals, and **isohiels**, joining equal sunshine values, are two other examples of isopleths.

The technique of drawing isopleths on a map is called **interpolation**. **8.18** should be traced and used to practise this skill. If you look at the synoptic charts produced by the Meteorological Office, you will note that isobars in common

with all other isopleths form smooth curved lines which never touch or cross. On **8.18** the isobar for 1008mb has already been interpolated. Copy the map, and carefully estimating by eye, attempt to interpolate the other isobars at 4mb intervals.

25 Trace **8.13a** and superimpose it on **8.13b**. You can now calculate and record the approximate numerical values for each of the sensation zones demarcated by the isopleths on **8.13a**.

■ **8.17** Sulphur dioxide emissions in Europe, 1980 and 1987

Country	1980	1987	Difference	Promised
	'000 tonnes sulphur		%	reductions
Former Soviet Union (European section only)*	6400	5100	−20	30% by 1993
East Germany	2500	(2500)	0	30% by 1993
United Kingdom	2335	1840	−21	30% by 1999
Poland	2050	(2270)	+10	—
Italy	1900	(1252)	−34	30% by 1993
France*	1779	(923)	−48	50% by 1990
Spain	1625	(1581)	−3	—
West Germany*	1600	(1022)	−36	65% by 1993
Czechoslovakia*	1550	1450	−6	30% by 1993
Hungary*	817	(710)	−13	30% by 1993
Yugoslavia	588	(588)	0	—
Bulgaria*	517	(570)	+9	30% by 1993
Belgium*	400	(244)	−39	50% by 1995
Finland*	292	162	−44	50% by 1993
Netherlands*	244	141	−42	50% by 1995
Sweden*	232	(116)	−50	68% by 1995
Denmark*	219	(155)	−29	50% by 1995
Greece	200	(180)	−10	—
Austria*	177	(75)	−58	70% by 1995
Turkey	(138)	(177)	+22	—
Portugal	133	(116)	−13	—
Ireland	110	(84)	−24	—
Romania	100	(100)	0	—
Norway*	70	(50)	−29	50% by 1994
Switzerland	63	(31)	−51	57% by 1995
Albania	(25)	(25)	0	—
Luxembourg	11	(6)	−45	58% by 1990
Iceland	3	(3)	0	—
TOTAL	26 078	21 471	−18	

* members of 30% Club 1987
Figures in parentheses are estimates.

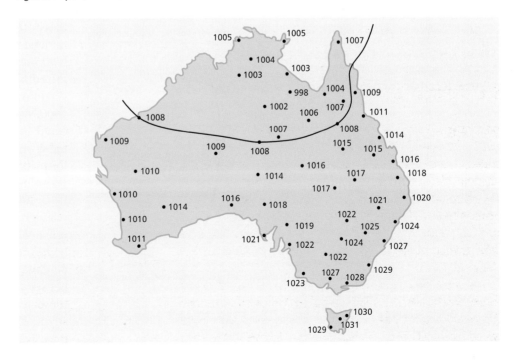

■ **8.18** Pressure reading for Australia, 1200 hrs 27 February 1992

9.1 Weather and climate

You may already be aware of the basic distinction between weather and climate and that climate has traditionally been defined as 'average weather'. When we plan tomorrow's activities we consult the weather forecast, whereas when we decide between several locations for a future holiday it is the climate data that we use as a guide to the most likely weather conditions to expect.

The weather is thus a short-term view of several atmospheric variables. It refers to existing or immediately pending conditions. It is also possible to refer back to the conditions that existed in the near past; thus we can compare the weather we are experiencing this summer or winter with the main weather memories we retain of last year's season. **Weather**, therefore, describes the conditions which persist over a relatively short period of time. The science which studies and seeks to explain these atmospheric conditions is called **meteorology**.

Once we begin to generalise about weather conditions, we enter the realm of climate. **Climate** is defined as the average of weather conditions that have been recorded over a continuous period of 30 consecutive years. Thus the weather data recorded on a day-to-day basis eventually become the climate statistics for an area. The study of these average conditions and their spatial variations is called **climatology**.

9.2 Measuring weather

Remote sensing

Since the 1960s, our knowledge and understanding of the atmosphere and its workings have been advanced by the introduction of weather satellites. Early versions, such as TIROS launched in 1960, simply used television cameras and could not take pictures at night, but today more advanced technology in the form of radiometers enables infrared scanning of the Earth and its atmosphere from heights of up to 35 000 km. Little wonder that this is referred to as 'remote sensing'. This enables cloud patterns to be recorded both at night and during the day, and it is also possible to discriminate between warm and cold clouds. When these temperature images are relatively slight, computer enhancement can introduce even more precise detail.

■ **9.1** The two main types of weather satellite

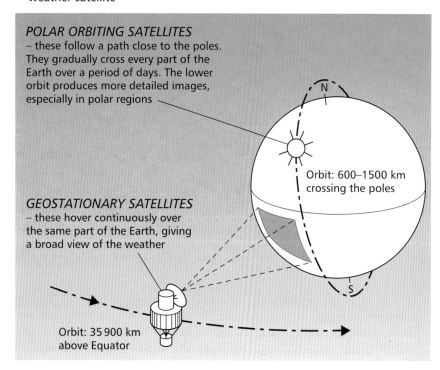

POLAR ORBITING SATELLITES
– these follow a path close to the poles. They gradually cross every part of the Earth over a period of days. The lower orbit produces more detailed images, especially in polar regions

GEOSTATIONARY SATELLITES
– these hover continuously over the same part of the Earth, giving a broad view of the weather

Orbit: 600–1500 km crossing the poles

N

S

Orbit: 35 900 km above Equator

9.1 illustrates some of the essential differences between the two basic types of weather satellite in use. Geostationary satellites are positioned at a height of 35 900 km directly above the Equator. The speed of these satellites is exactly the same as the Earth's rotation and hence they appear to remain stationary. From this great height they can scan a large area, but towards the polar regions the lower angle of their view means that pictures of these areas lack precision. However, they do transmit photographs as they are taken and this makes it possible to develop a time-lapse sequence of the movement of clouds and weather systems.

Polar orbiting satellites take a much lower orbit at between 600 and 1500 km and their north–south orbit over a revolving Earth means that they cross every part of the Earth's surface over a period of days. In contrast to geostationary satellites, they produce much more detailed views of polar regions and they also possess the ability to pick up smaller cloud and storm systems, even those measuring no more than 1 km in diameter.

The geostationary satellite called METEOSAT was launched in 1977. Its location inevitably focuses on Europe together with the Mediterranean, Africa and the eastern Atlantic (**9.3**). Remote-sensing images from METEOSAT are now being introduced into schools in the UK and these provide a rich vein of material both for consolidating your understanding of atmospheric processes and for research for your individual study.

In addition to clouds, satellites also provide detailed vertical profiles of temperature and moisture, record the extent of snow and ice cover, and will also monitor any injection into the atmosphere of ash and dust from volcanic eruptions. Satellites also provide other invaluable environmental information, including the spatial extent of desertification and drought. Together with information from seismic and tsunami-measuring stations on the Earth's surface, they provide a valuable service by relaying this information back to a major collecting centre. Other satellites such as LANDSAT concentrate on resource monitoring. More recent satellites now collect information from the upper levels of the Earth's atmosphere, while it is planned to expand their utility still further by the introduction, for example, of a lightning mapping sensor which will record this activity over a wide area of the Earth's surface.

---

1 What use might be made of geostationary time-lapse photography by:
   a weather forecasters in the UK
   b fruit farmers in Florida?

2 Suggest some ways in which satellite technology might assist the campaign to limit environmental degradation.

3 What economic benefit might the proposed new lightning sensor provide?

Weather stations

Despite the advent of space satellites, the vast proportion of weather data is still collected at traditional surface stations. If this is to be of any use in forecasting, it has to be gathered from as large and as dense a network of stations as possible and then processed immediately. Technology in the form of teleprinters and computers now assists greatly in this, though several basic problems remain. First, these forecasts are based on a patchy network of recording stations. **9.2** illustrates the global pattern of variations in the density of climate stations. Secondly, this weather information has to be understood worldwide and this is why a numerical code is used to ensure that this data is diffused rapidly and intelligibly.

Another important feature is that this spatial coverage is almost entirely land-based, while about 70 per cent of the Earth's surface consists of ocean. Data from the oceans is derived from a very small number of weather ships and from ships on their way from one continent to

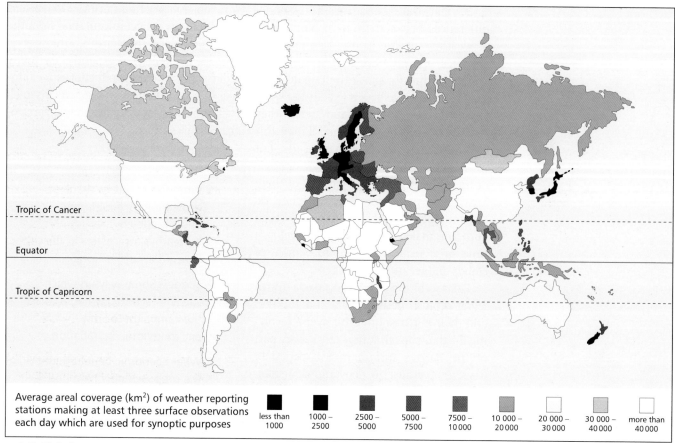

Average areal coverage (km²) of weather reporting stations making at least three surface observations each day which are used for synoptic purposes

| less than 1000 | 1000 – 2500 | 2500 – 5000 | 5000 – 7500 | 7500 – 10 000 | 10 000 – 20 000 | 20 000 – 30 000 | 30 000 – 40 000 | more than 40 000 |

■ **9.2** Global patterns in the density of weather stations

■ **9.3** Satellite image of Africa showing clouds near the Equator

4 a Comment on the pattern revealed by **9.2**.
b How might this pattern affect development in parts of tropical Africa?

5 Why is it mutually beneficial for countries to share their weather information?

another. This represents a serious deficiency since all weather systems are mobile and will sooner or later affect adjacent land areas. It is probably still true to say that with the rapid expansion in satellite technology and with the economic impetus provided by oil companies, we know more about upper-air conditions over the sea and seabed geology, than we do about weather conditions in the lower atmosphere over what is nearly three-quarters of the Earth's surface.

Nevertheless, it is all this information gathered from a variety of locations and over a range of time scales that makes it possible to build up a picture of the generalised conditions termed **climate**. With this, it becomes feasible to map the normal or average conditions which in turn reveals a spatial pattern of climatic types recurring over the Earth's surface. These are climate regions which several climatologists have attempted to classify or arrange into groups.

9.3 Techniques: Statistics

There are three statistical techniques which can be used to establish the norms that constitute climate; these are referred to as **measures of central tendency**.

On climatic graphs, the **mean** or average temperature is calculated by dividing 30 consecutive years of temperature records by 30. A second approach is to focus on the middle or **median** value in a set of data. This is useful when the majority of values are clustered, for example near to the highest value. A final calculation involves concentrating on the most frequently occurring value by establishing the **mode**. This exercise clarifies these procedures.

Taking the data in **9.4a,** the mean of 375 mm is easily calculated but it is significant to note how the low values of 200 mm and 250 mm have depressed this despite the fact that five of the values exceed 400 mm.

To obtain the other measures, the data must first be ranked (**9.4b**). Finally, for this set of data the mode is 480 mm. This appears irrelevant, but if we recognise that a trend in the data is developing, it becomes much more accurate, for example for the past four years. It has now become common practice to calculate mean values using periods of years, such as every five or ten years, as this has the effect of highlighting trends rather than masking them in a mean calculated over a longer time span. This is called a **running mean**.

None of the above is particularly accurate and does tend to conceal differences in how the values are dispersed about the measure of central tendency. This is where measures of dispersion become useful. Of these, the temperature range will be referred to in relation to different climatic types. However, greater accuracy can be obtained by calculating the **inter-quartile range** and through the statistical measure termed **standard deviation**.

The inter-quartile range for the above data is calculated thus:

1 Rank the data.

2 Calculate the median point – in this case the mean of the two central values, i.e. 380 mm.

3 The upper quartile is now obtained by calculating the median of the values above 380 mm. This is 480 mm.

4 The lower quartile is now obtained by calculating the median of the values below 380 mm. This is 270 mm.

5 The inter-quartile range is the difference between the upper and lower quartile, i.e. 210 mm.

The standard deviation is a very frequently used statistical measure of the degree of dispersion of data about the mean $(\bar{x})$. This is best understood by working through an example using the same data.

To calculate standard deviation, a table must first be prepared (**9.4c**). Symbols now replace the headings so that the formula can be applied.

■ **9.4** Calculating measures of central tendency for rainfall at station X

Year	Total rainfall mm
1	250
2	400
3	350
4	200
5	270
6	360
7	480
8	490
9	470
10	480

a) Ten years' rainfall data

Total rainfall mm
490
480
480
470
400
360
350
270
250
200

b) Ranking the data

Year	Total rainfall x mm	Deviation x − x̄	(x − x̄)²
1	250	−125	15 625
2	400	25	625
3	350	−25	625
4	200	−175	30 625
5	270	−105	11 025
6	360	−15	225
7	480	105	11 025
8	490	115	13 225
9	470	95	9 025
10	480	105	11 025

c) Calculating the standard deviation

Agra mm	Darjeeling mm
815	3083
764	2686
683	2893
520	2463
284	3136
818	2363
657	2191
605	2328
951	3260
511	2841
606	2851
927	3327
413	2858
453	3355
1016	2802
468	2444
376	2512
1072	2736
820	2495
547	2778
776	2811
598	3173
1051	2467
822	2616
995	3257

■ **9.5** Annual rainfall for Agra and Darjeeling over a 25-year period

The formula to calculate standard deviation is:

$$\sigma = \sqrt{\frac{\Sigma \left(x - \overline{x}\right)^2}{n}}$$

σ is the standard deviation

Σ is the sum of all the $(x - \overline{x})^2$

$\sqrt{}$ is the square root of

x and $\overline{x}$ are defined above

n is the number of values in the data set (i.e. 10 in this example).

The first task is therefore to add up all the values in the column headed $(x - \overline{x})^2$; the result is 103050.

Next divide this by n; the result is 10305.

Finally, the square root of this is calculated: 101.51.

This large value for the standard deviation indicates that the values are widely spaced about the mean.

Another technique which can be used to illustrate the spread of data is a **dispersion diagram**. By plotting each value, using a symbol such as a dot, this provides a clear visual pattern of the distribution. Where two sets of data are plotted side by side, then a comparison can easily be made. The labelling of the median point and the quartiles will make any analysis much easier. You should practise this skill using the rainfall data for station X before proceeding to the much more difficult task below.

---

6 a Calculate the mean, median and mode for the rainfall data in **9.5**.

b Plot a dispersion diagram, and calculate the inter-quartile range and standard deviation, for the rainfall data for Agra and Darjeeling.

c Comment on your results and suggest how these patterns might affect agricultural activities in these two parts of India.

9.4 Climatic regions

In your study of geography for GCSE, you will already have encountered some aspects of identifying climate regions and classifying climates. **9.6a** is an attempt to classify the climatic conditions of the British Isles using merely average temperatures, whilst in **9.6b** precipitation characteristics have been used to provide an equally simple classification.

Geographers are constantly seeking explanations for the variety of physical, economic and social conditions prevailing on the Earth's surface. Classification attempts to reduce this complexity and bring some order into these patterns by grouping together areas where, for example, similar climatic conditions are repeated. It is in this way that classification produces a spatial pattern of climatic regions.

Spatial variations in climatic conditions or climatic regions can occur on a variety of scales but three are introduced here.

Microscale climates

Sitting in the shade of a small grove of sycamore trees in the grounds of a hotel in eastern France on a hot August day, the author was reminded how atmospheric conditions can vary within a small area. Over the concrete slabs of the poolside patio the heat was intense, while under the shade provided by the trees on a grass-covered surface it was much cooler. Nearby the clockwise hiss of a sprinkler system was creating yet another microclimate.

A **microclimate** refers to the specific atmospheric conditions within a small area. At one time, it was defined simply as those conditions prevailing in the lower

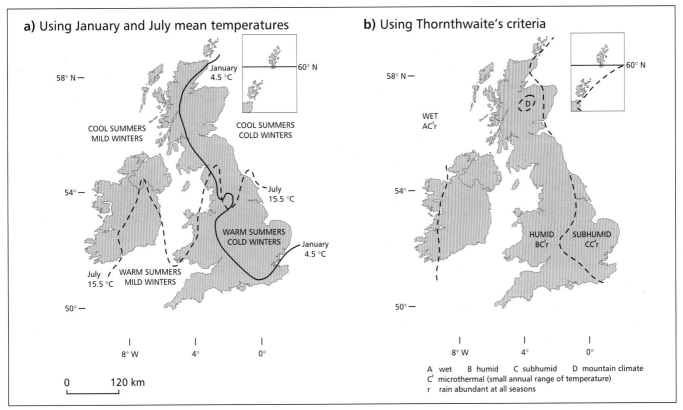

a) Using January and July mean temperatures

58° N —

January 4.5 °C

60° N

COOL SUMMERS MILD WINTERS

COOL SUMMERS COLD WINTERS

54° —

July 15.5 °C

WARM SUMMERS COLD WINTERS

January 4.5 °C

July 15.5 °C

WARM SUMMERS MILD WINTERS

50° —

8° W   4°   0°

0   120 km

b) Using Thornthwaite's criteria

58° N —

60° N

D

WET AC'r

54° —

HUMID BC'r   SUBHUMID CC'r

50° —

8° W   4°   0°

A wet   B humid   C subhumid   D mountain climate
C' microthermal (small annual range of temperature)
r rain abundant at all seasons

■ **9.6** Climatic classifications of the British Isles

metre of the atmosphere. However, the term is used synonymously with **local climate**. It is very important to remember that a microclimate refers to a climate which is strongly influenced by local site conditions and is therefore that occurring in the lower atmosphere. Local site condi-

tions can modify the atmosphere in a variety of ways. Natural factors associated with site conditions include altitude, slope, aspect, soil type, vegetation cover and water surfaces. Two of these modifying factors are considered in the following case study (see also section 12.5).

CASE STUDY

IT8

The effects of soils and vegetation on climate

Santon Downham on the East Anglian Breckland is the only lowland station in the British Isles which has recorded an absolute minimum air temperature below 0 °C in every month over the period 1931–60; ground frost can be expected in every month. These extremely low temperatures are basically a reflection of the highly porous and consequently very dry nature of the sands of this area. Sandy soils are poor conductors of heat because of the large air spaces between particles of sand. This means that heat energy received from the sun is absorbed rapidly in the upper layer of the soil, but does not conduct very far down within the soil. Therefore this heat is also rapidly radiated away at night. On light, dry, sandy soils extremes of temperature are thus the norm.

Everyone will have noted the pronounced cooling sensation experienced on entering a forest on a hot summer's day. This cooling, which can represent an 8 °C drop in temperature compared with the surrounding countryside, is primarily a consequence of the way that incoming solar radiation is partly used in evaporating leaf/canopy moisture and is reflected or absorbed by foliage surfaces. Consequently, less than 10 per cent may penetrate down to the forest floor. Within a forested area, the major heat exchanges are at the boundary between the canopy and the atmosphere, the so-called **outer effective surface**, while the forest floor experiences a much smaller temperature range. In this way forests tend to develop their own surface inversion during the day (**9.7**).

With all this evaporation, humidity levels increase within and above the forest. Evaporation and

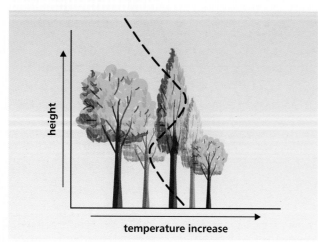

■ **9.7** Daytime vertical temperature profile in a forested area

transpiration, which in combination are termed **evapotranspiration**, thus supply the atmosphere with large amounts of moisture. In addition, interception, which can account for two-thirds of light rainfall in a pine forest, has the effect of holding water for a longer period in the foliage, thus encouraging evaporation and permitting a more gradual addition to groundwater stores. Finally, woodlands inevitably reduce wind speeds and this can amount to a dramatic 80 to 90 per cent reduction in some cases.

These modifications are significant not only at a microclimatic level, but also because there are implications for human activity here. Any change in land use will of necessity modify the atmospheric processes in that area. Thus deforestation will significantly reduce humidity levels and result in increased surface exposure to winds. Conversely, reafforestation or afforestation has been used as a measure to stabilise soils on slopes, while shelter-belts are used to protect soils in drier farmlands.

The significance of microclimatic influences on farming activities has been recognised in France, where the Agrostat programme provides vital information on local weather conditions using data collected from a series of weather recording stations linked to the Minetel computer system. This helps farmers with decisions such as when to spray against mildew, or provides them with harvest date yield predictions.

7 Construct a vertical temperature profile, similar to **9.7**, for a forest area on a clear, calm night.

8 What links have been established between firewood collecting and desertification?

All these physical and human factors create a complex pattern of microclimates. Human activities are frequently able to exploit these to advantage, while in other instances they have been ignored at considerable cost. Microclimatic conditions are important since these are the actual conditions that we experience. It is these that not infrequently render the national weather forecast annoyingly inaccurate as far as we are concerned!

Mesoscale climates

On a larger (meso) scale, **9.8** illustrates some of the major variations in climatic conditions experienced in the South Island of New Zealand. Despite its limited area (155 000 km²), there is a considerable variety in climatic conditions, a reflection of variations in the controlling factors of altitude, latitude, aspect and distance from the sea. Some of these variations are small in scale, but nevertheless it is possible to classify these conditions and suggest a regionalisation of the climate of this part of New Zealand. Remember that these are broad generalised regions and that there is also a great number of microclimate regions, some of them representing modifications relating to land use changes such as afforestation, reservoir construction and urbanisation.

9 a Use the data provided in **9.8** to draw a map showing the climatic regions of the South Island.

b Suggest some other data which might prove useful in confirming this pattern of climatic regions.

10 All Advanced and Advanced Supplementary syllabuses contain a requirement to present a piece of personal investigative work. The study of some aspect of the weather of a manageable area could certainly constitute an interesting topic for research. There is a wide range of topics to choose from, not least the effect that human activities have on climatic conditions, as in urban microclimates. If the data is collected accurately, in sufficient quantity and in the appropriate locations, then this bank of valid statistics can form the basis for a precise analysis of the interaction between atmospheric processes and human activities in a small area. Above all, this data will readily lend itself to statistical testing, graphical and cartographical analysis, which should make the process of interpretation more meaningful. It is the experience of many examiners that field investigations in this particular sphere of geography can prove to be most rewarding for candidates in terms of grades achieved. It will certainly consolidate your understanding of weather-making processes and this may well encourage you to select with confidence a question from this part of the syllabus in examinations.

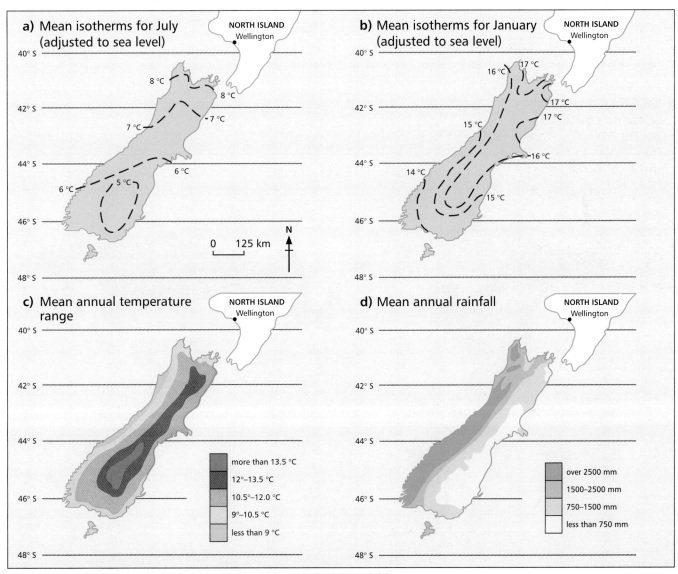

■ **9.8** South Island, New Zealand: isopleths for selected climatic variables

Macroscale climatic regions

It was the Greeks who first identified areas of different climatic conditions, and using the familiar controls of temperature and sunshine they recognised three latitudinal zones of torrid, temperate and frigid climates. However, it was not until the 20th century that detailed attempts at global classification were developed.

The German scientist W. Köppen's classification of 1918 was based on the criterion of seasonal temperature variations. This resulted in a relatively simple pattern with a latitudinal form to the regions. He later included some reference to precipitation in his classification. The American climatologist C. W. Thornthwaite placed much more emphasis on precipitation than Köppen; temperature was relegated to a secondary importance (**9.6b**). He used mathematical ratios to explore the relationships between temperature, precipitation and evaporation.

These early classifications were based on observable elements of climate or on the observed effects of climate such as the distribution of vegetation types. This approach to classification is referred to as the **empirical** approach. A more recent approach has been to emphasise the underlying causes of the spatial pattern of climatic types; this is the **genetic** approach. Thus Strahler's work in 1969 proposed three major global divisions and related these to the predominance of various airmass types.

What one notices from these various attempts at climate classification is that there are many common elements, and undoubtedly it is the Köppen classification which remains the starting point for most of the more recent approaches. It is Trewartha's modification of the Köppen classification that is most widely referred to today (**9.9**). It has to be said, however, that whilst it is important to be informed about weather and climate at different locations around the globe, the whole topic of climatic classification and the detailed study of climatic types and regions are not high on the agenda of modern geography, particularly at A and AS levels.

■ **9.9** A modern modification of Köppen's classification of climate

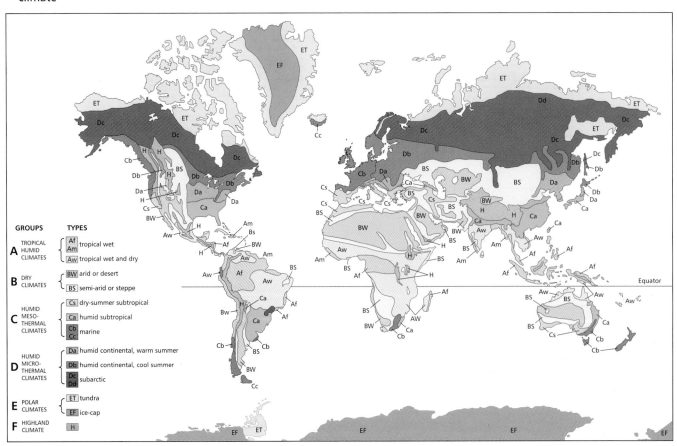

GROUPS	TYPES	
A TROPICAL HUMID CLIMATES	Af Am	tropical wet
	Aw	tropical wet and dry
B DRY CLIMATES	BW	arid or desert
	BS	semi-arid or steppe
C HUMID MESO-THERMAL CLIMATES	Cs	dry-summer subtropical
	Ca	humid subtropical
	Cb Cc	marine
D HUMID MICRO-THERMAL CLIMATES	Da	humid continental, warm summer
	Db	humid continental, cool summer
	Dc Dd	subarctic
E POLAR CLIMATES	ET	tundra
	EF	ice-cap
F HIGHLAND CLIMATE	H	

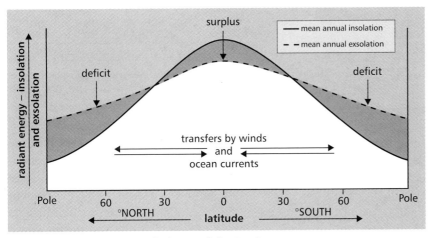

■ **10.1** Generalised energy balance of the Earth

a) January

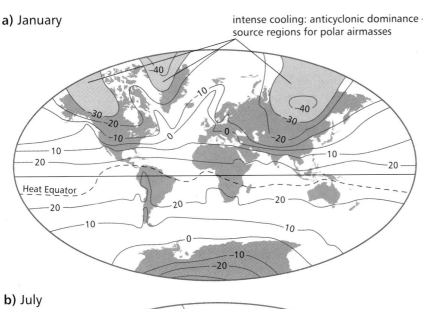

intense cooling: anticyclonic dominance – source regions for polar airmasses

b) July

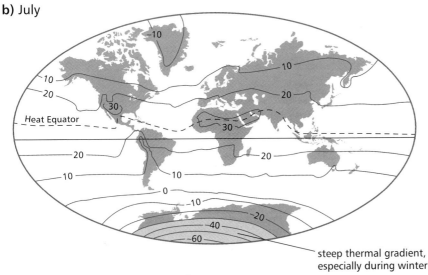

steep thermal gradient, especially during winter

Heat and humidity are two fundamentally important properties of the atmosphere. They have a very considerable bearing on our weather and climate; they are absolutely vital to our existence on this planet.

10.1 **Temperature**

The temperature of the Earth's surface is basically the outcome of two processes working in opposite directions through the atmosphere: the inward receipt of **insolation** (solar energy) and the outward loss of heat by radiation (**exsolation**). The volume or level of each process decreases from the Equator to the poles, and so too does the resulting energy budget (**10.1**). But since the trend in insolation receipts is more steeply inclined than that of exsolation, the energy balance changes at around latitude 35° from surplus to deficit. This spatial variation in the global energy budget is the principal factor determining the spatial pattern of temperatures over the Earth's surface. For this reason it is not surprising, therefore, that the simple pattern of global climatic zones runs from tropical (energy surplus) in low latitudes to polar (energy deficit) in high latitudes. Such a pattern implies that latitude has a significant influence.

Variations of temperature at the Earth's surface can be considered in two ways. **10.2** depicts the basic spatial variations, but because these are seasonal maps they also hint at the temporal dimension. This second dimension may be considered at five different scales.

■ **10.2** World mean surface temperatures. Figures are °C

10.2 Temporal variations in temperature

At the first scale, temperatures can vary quite markedly in certain areas in association with the small-scale **advection** (horizontal movement) of relatively cold or warm air. This variation can occur at any time and can be a sudden and dramatic change, as for example at the onset of **föhn**-type winds, such as the **chinook** of the western high plains of the USA and Canada.

A second scale is the diurnal or daily scale, with this range of temperatures being a distinguishing feature of many climate types. **10.3** demonstrates that the daily range of temperatures is very modest in equatorial climates, whilst in drier climates and in continental locations it can be extreme.

A third scale is associated with spells of a particular weather type. Under cer-

tain conditions abnormally cold or hot air can be advected on a large scale to produce heat waves or cold spells. The interior of the USA is particularly prone to dramatic spells of this type of weather, with advections of air from distant origins producing remarkable temperature changes. Thus Browning in Montana experienced a fall of temperature of 55 °C in 24 hours one January.

A fourth scale is the seasonal variation in temperature which is quantified as the annual range of temperature. Generally, this range is greatest in continental locations and much more moderate near to the coast, although other factors such as the humidity of the air and the incidence of cloud cover are important too.

The final scale is represented by long-term changes or trends, which are discussed in Chapter 12.

These temporal changes can be classified simply into two groups:

- **Periodic changes**: these are linked to changes in the receipt of insolation, such as those occurring on a daily or seasonal scale.

- **Non-periodic changes**: these are not related to variations in solar input, but are associated with occasional air movements advecting colder or warmer air into an area.

In the case of periodic changes there is a constant, predetermined time factor, whereas in non-periodic changes there is an absence of time consistency, and such changes can occur at irregular and unpredictable intervals.

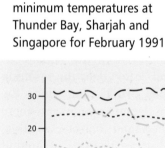

■ **10.3** Daily maximum and minimum temperatures at Thunder Bay, Sharjah and Singapore for February 1991

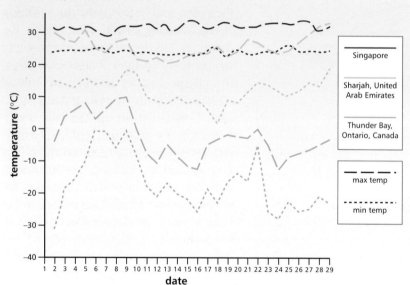

10.3 Factors controlling spatial variations in temperature

From a geographical viewpoint, the most significant variations in temperature are those that occur from place to place. Such spatial variations are the outcome of a number of interacting factors.

Latitude

The reasons why latitude is important have already been mentioned. Its effect is present virtually everywhere, although it reaches its maximum in the climates

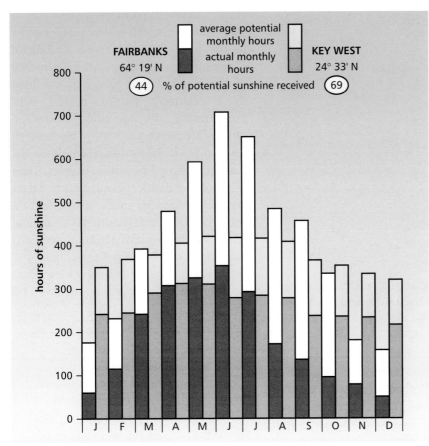

10.4 Potential and actual sunshine hours at Fairbanks and Key West

1 a Why is potential sunshine higher at Fairbanks during the summer months, and yet it is located 40° north of Key West?
b Why does Key West record a higher percentage of potential sunshine hours?

Land and water bodies

In general, water bodies, ranging from ocean basins to even small lakes, respond in a much more sluggish manner to incoming solar radiation than areas of land and they also lose any heat gained at a much slower rate. This results in a much reduced daily and annual range of temperature over and near to water bodies. This is the moderating or modifying effect which may also manifest itself in a seasonal lag of temperatures with perhaps February being the coldest and August the warmest months.

Water is a good conductor and thus the heat received penetrates deeply, whereas on land this heat is absorbed by only a comparatively thin surface layer. This is particularly the case where the rock or soil contains large quantities of air. Water bodies are constantly affected by tides, currents and waves and this produces greater mixing and heat is dissipated to greater depths. Oceanic areas tend to be cloudier than the land areas and thus insolation receipts are further reduced.

This differential heating experienced by land and water has an impact on the climatic conditions of many areas of the world. The Great Lakes region of the USA and Canada is certainly modified in this way (**10.5**). On a larger scale, **10.6** illus-

of high latitudes. Here the very short days during winter and an increasing period of continuous darkness polewards of the Arctic and Antarctic Circles result in very low inputs of insolation.

10.4 illustrates the potential and actual receipts of sunshine at Fairbanks in Alaska and at Key West in Florida. The low totals received at Fairbanks are the primary reason for the very low temperatures, but the very low angle of the sun in the sky results in an extremely meagre capability for heating the Earth's surface. The low temperatures in turn result in a continuous snow cover for more than six months and consequently much of the meagre low-angle sunlight is lost owing to **albedo** (reflection back into space).

10.5 Modification of seasonal temperatures by the Great Lakes

Location		Mean January temperature °C	Lowest extreme temperature °C	Mean July temperature °C	Highest extreme temperature °C
Manistee	lake shore	−4.2	−30.6	20.6	37.8
Mason City	250 km from lake shore	−8.7	−34.4	22.8	41.7

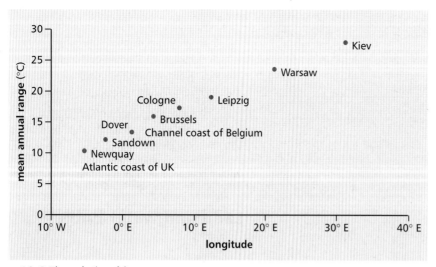

■ **10.6** The relationship between distance from the sea and the mean annual range of temperature

trates the impact that increasing distance from the sea has on the annual temperature range in western Europe. When considering these temperatures, it is important to remember that we are considering a landmass where the moderating effect of the prevailing westerly winds can be advected inland with relative ease, because of the absence of any north–south aligned relief barriers. By contrast, the

■ **10.7** Temperature data for Narvik and Riksgränsen

	Average daily maximum °C		Average daily minimum °C	
Narvik, Norway 68° 25'N, 17° 23'E	J	−1.9	J	−7.0
	F	−1.6	F	−7.0
	M	1.3	M	−5.4
	A	5.2	A	−1.7
	M	9.4	M	2.5
	J	13.5	J	7.1
	J	18.1	J	10.7
	A	16.4	A	9.6
	S	11.5	S	6.0
	O	5.9	O	1.7
	N	2.6	N	−2.0
	D	−0.7	D	−4.6
Riksgränsen, Sweden 68° 26'N, 18° 08'E	J	−7.5	J	−14.8
	F	−8.1	F	−15.0
	M	−4.2	M	−10.6
	A	−0.5	A	−7.8
	M	4.8	M	−1.4
	J	9.4	J	3.1
	J	15.4	J	8.3
	A	12.9	A	7.0
	S	7.4	S	2.6
	O	1.1	O	−3.2
	N	−2.8	N	−8.1
	D	−6.9	D	−13.3

North American continent possesses a very effective north–south relief barrier in the form of the Western Cordillera. Consequently, the moderating influence of the North Pacific Ocean is confined to a relatively narrow coastal belt. Furthermore, the prevailing westerlies, which are onshore winds in western Europe, are in fact offshore winds on the eastern seaboard of North America. Thus the North Atlantic Ocean, which exerts such a pronounced moderating effect on the eastern side of its basin, has a minimal effect on the western (North American) side. On a much smaller scale, land and sea breezes advect this moderating effect inland on a daily basis (see sections 11.7 and 12.5).

> **2 a** Calculate the annual temperature range for Narvik (Norway) and Riksgränsen (Sweden) – see **10.7**.
>
> **b** Compare the two stations in terms of temperature characteristics.
>
> **c** Suggest explanations for the differences you have noted in **b**.

Ocean currents and drifts

The role that the movement of ocean waters plays in redistributing the inequalities of heating produced by insolation has already been introduced. **10.8** illustrates the principal features of this circulation. It is important to remember that the terms 'warm' and 'cold' do not denote any specific temperature value; they simply indicate that the water in any particular current is warmer or colder than expected for that latitude. Thus the 15 °C sea water in the North Atlantic Drift off the coast of north-west Europe is warm for that latitude, particularly so in winter, whereas the similar temperature of the Canaries current off the coast of north-west Africa is most definitely cool for that latitude. These currents generally accentuate the moderating effect of the

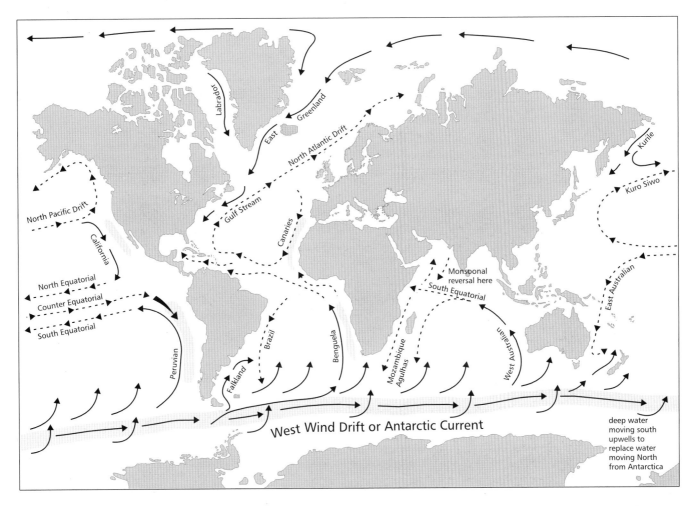

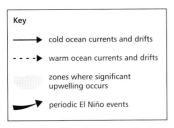

Key

→ cold ocean currents and drifts

- - -► warm ocean currents and drifts

▨ zones where significant upwelling occurs

➤ periodic El Niño events

■ **10.8** Major components of oceanic circulation

oceans, and this is especially the case where the prevailing winds are onshore. The North Atlantic Drift, for example, exerts a much more powerful effect on the climate of the adjacent land areas than the Kuro Siwo does. Warm ocean currents in tropical areas have rather different effects, particularly with respect to the humidity of the air.

The cool waters of the Labrador and Kurile currents severely moderate the summer temperatures of nearby coasts, but perhaps the most pronounced effect is experienced in the desert climates where cool ocean currents occur along western coasts (see Santa Barbara in **8.9**).

Altitude

The temperature of the air invariably decreases with height because of the progressive inability of gradually less dense air to absorb heat. The general windiness of higher altitudes also limits heat gains, and any air rising from lower elevation is

cooled as it rises in response to decreasing pressure, a process called **adiabatic cooling** (see section 10.6). The rate at which the atmosphere cools with height, i.e. the **lapse rate**, does vary and can change at different heights at any one time. If we were able to climb rapidly up a steep mountain slope or ascend in a balloon recording the temperature at different heights, we could construct a vertical temperature profile or 'sounding'. This lapse rate is called the **environmental lapse rate**. The average global lapse rate is 0.65 °C per 100 m, which means that temperature generally decreases one hundred times faster with altitude than it does with latitude.

Extensive plateau regions, such as the Tibetan Plateau, nevertheless do heat up more effectively and it is therefore important to remember that the relationship between altitude and temperature is not always simple. Intermontane basins can distort this relationship, just as differential insolation receipts on north- and south-facing slopes do. Finally, mountain areas not only generate their own climate, but they can also have a dramatic effect on the conditions of adjacent lowland areas.

Other influences

Another natural factor influencing the temperature of any particular location in the lower atmosphere is the movement into that area of air possessing contrasting temperature characteristics. Winds can therefore advect warmer or colder air into an area. This is further discussed in section 11.5 on airmasses.

Reference has already been made to the effect that different surfaces can have on temperature, and the effect of urban areas is a case in point here. Urban areas can modify local temperature patterns through the generation of an urban heat island. This example of climatic change is discussed in section 12.5.

Finally, it is important to remember that temperature is closely related to other basic properties of the air, such as moisture content or humidity, pressure and motion.

3 a Construct a simple graph with the following scales on the two axes:

vertical axis – altitude in metres 0–5000
horizontal axis – temperature in °C ranging from –30°C on the left to 30°C on the right

On the grid, plot the data (right) to construct the environmental lapse rate.

b Describe the essential features of the environmental lapse rate, noting in particular the changes that occur in the lower 1000m of the atmosphere and those occurring above 4km.

Altitude	Temperature
m	°C
0	7
300	12
1000	10
1700	7
2000	6
3000	0
4000	–8
4300	–12
4800	–8
5000	–9

10.4 **Water in the air – humidity**

■ **10.9** Changes in the state of water

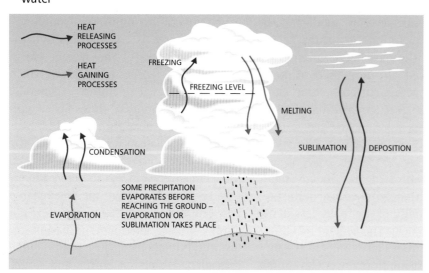

All air has the capacity to hold moisture and the degree to which this occurs is called the **humidity** of the air. Water is a vital constituent of many atmospheric processes and its abundance or deficiency can, to a large extent, be a determinant of the quality of human life. Water vapour is one of the major, naturally-occurring, greenhouse gases and recent events in many parts of world have emphasised the ever more urgent need to manage this resource carefully. In combination with temperature, it has already been identified as a significant factor in certain aspects of human health (see section 8.4).

Within the atmosphere, water is perhaps the most important of the variable gases and its volume may vary from close to nil in polar areas to approximately 6 per cent in certain tropical regions. Water is unique in that it can exist in three different states: gaseous as water vapour, liquid as water, and solid as ice. **10.9** illustrates these different states of water, the transformations or changes between them that can take place in the lower atmosphere, and how these either release or absorb energy.

The atmosphere gains moisture mainly through evaporation. Added to this is moisture derived through transpiration from plants. Additional water comes from volcanic eruptions, and at any given location large amounts may be carried in by winds. While it is usual to think of this in terms of onshore movements of air, it should be remembered that seemingly dry, continental airmasses can carry large amounts of moisture. It has been calculated that at times, 'dry' continental air sweeping south over the USA can arrive at the Gulf coast carrying huge quantities of water vapour estimated to be the equivalent of nine times the discharge of the Mississippi river! Human activities also add considerable amounts of water to the atmospheric store, particularly but not exclusively in urban areas.

4 Make a list of those human activities which you think contribute moisture to the atmosphere.

Losses from the atmosphere occur every time condensation on the ground or precipitation takes place. Plants absorb some moisture through leaf surfaces, and direct use by human activities represents another potential loss. However, it is very difficult to separate gains and losses because of all the transfers and transformations that are taking place within the hydrological cycle (see section 4.1). There are no definite indications that the total of water in the global system is changing, although the atmosphere contains only a meagre 0.036 per cent of the total amount of water in the global system. However, there are indications that spatial patterns do change over time and there is concern that an enhanced **greenhouse effect** may initiate even more dramatic changes (see section 12.6).

■ **10.10** Mean annual oceanic evaporation rates

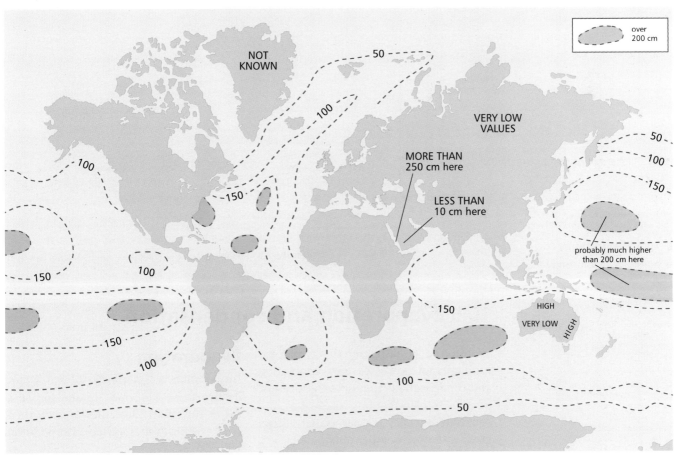

5 Study **10.10** and answer the following questions:

a What is the general spatial pattern of evaporation over the world's oceans? Explain this pattern.

b How do you account for the shape of the 100 cm isoline in the North Atlantic?

c Why is there such a sharp gradient of evaporation in the area over and adjacent to the Red Sea?

d Why are evaporation rates higher over the Aral Sea than over the Black Sea?

e In what ways is human activity affecting the Aral Sea as a future potential source of water vapour for the lower atmosphere?

Measurements of humidity

The humidity of the air is calculated using readings from wet- and dry-bulb thermometers and hygrometers. Humidity can be represented by three different measures:

■ **Absolute humidity** – the mass of water vapour in a given volume of air.

■ **Vapour pressure** – the pressure exerted by water vapour molecules in a given volume of air.

■ **Relative humidity** – this is the most important measure of them all. Basically it tells us how close a body of air is to becoming saturated. It represents the water vapour content compared with the amount the air could hold at a particular temperature and pressure. Relative humidity is measured as a percentage. **10.11** illustrates the relationship between humidity and temperature. Warm air has a greater capacity to absorb moisture. Air at a temperature of 35 °C can hold approximately four times the amount of water vapour of air at 10 °C.

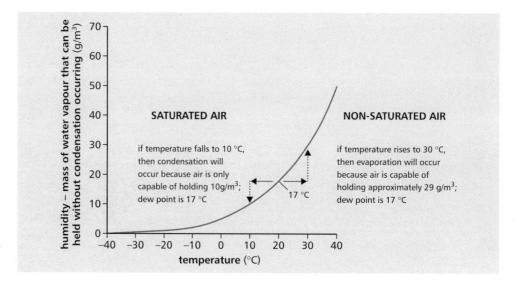

■ **10.11** Temperature–humidity relationships

10.5 **Evaporation and condensation**

Within the atmosphere, the two most fundamental processes are evaporation and condensation. They account for most of the transformations of water and consequently they are associated with a great variety of weather phenomena.

Evaporation

Evaporation is the transfer of water molecules from a surface to the air at a faster rate than molecules are returned from the air to that surface. Evaporation will take place if:

- there is abundant moisture available – it is not surprising therefore that an estimated 85 per cent of the global total of evaporation occurs over the oceans
- the vapour content of the air is such that the air is not saturated
- the temperature of the air is high and certainly above that level at which condensation occurs
- the air is in motion so saturated air is quickly removed from contact with the surface and additional non-saturated air can replace it
- there is an energy source to sustain this transformation – this may come in the form of direct sunlight or from advected air containing sufficient heat energy.

Condensation

Condensation can occur on the surface or in the air itself, but in the air it requires solid particles on which the condensation can take place. These particles may consist of salt, smoke from forest fires, sulphur from volcanic eruptions, or phytoplankton and dust. Water-attracting particles of this nature are called **hygroscopic nuclei**. Salt, which is naturally abundant in the lower atmosphere, is the most efficient in this respect.

Condensation occurs when air is cooled. As the air cools, its relative humidity increases and when this reaches 100% the air becomes saturated. The temperature at which saturation is achieved and condensation commences is called the **dew point**. As long as the temperature remains above dew point then the air will remain unsaturated.

Cooling is therefore a prerequisite of condensation and this can be caused by:

- the advection of warm air over a colder surface which results in the cooling of the air through conduction
- the mixing of warm and cold air
- the advection of very cold air over a much warmer surface
- the rapid loss of heat by radiation which chills the surface by conduction
- the upward movement of air which initiates adiabatic cooling.

Condensation on the ground – dew and frost

When cooling occurs on clear, calm nights, the temperature of the air close to the ground may fall below dew point. When this occurs, water particles condense on surfaces such as grass to produce **dew**. Dew can account for up to 50 mm of rain equivalent in some midlatitude areas. If the dew point of the air is below or very

■ **10.12** Formation of a temperature inversion in a valley

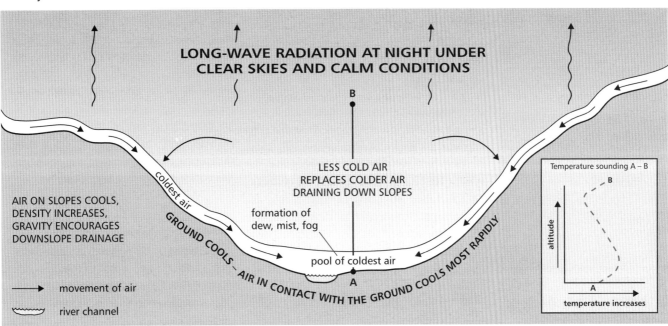

LONG-WAVE RADIATION AT NIGHT UNDER CLEAR SKIES AND CALM CONDITIONS

B

LESS COLD AIR REPLACES COLDER AIR DRAINING DOWN SLOPES

formation of dew, mist, fog

pool of coldest air

A

AIR ON SLOPES COOLS, DENSITY INCREASES, GRAVITY ENCOURAGES DOWNSLOPE DRAINAGE

coldest air

GROUND COOLS – AIR IN CONTACT WITH THE GROUND COOLS MOST RAPIDLY

Temperature sounding A – B

B

altitude

A

temperature increases

→ movement of air

〰 river channel

a) Altocumulus

b) Cirrus

c) Cumulus

d) Cumulonimbus

e) Stratocumulus

■ **10.13** Some different cloud types

close to 0°C then **white frost** or **hoar frost** rather than dew will form. Meteorologists distinguish between **ground frost** and **air frost**. The former is recorded on grass thermometers, while the latter is recorded in the Stevenson screen at a height of approximately 1 m. Ground frosts are more common than air frosts.

Condensation near the ground – fog

Fog occurs when visibility is reduced to less than 1 km by the presence of water droplets in the air. The two main types of fog are radiation fog and advection fog. **Radiation fog** is normally a nocturnal fog which develops when:

- clear skies allow unrestricted long-wave radiation and temperatures to fall to near or below dew point

- there are calm conditions, since this permits the air near to the ground to cool, partly through conduction – strong winds will interrupt this contact and hinder this cooling process.

These conditions are commonly associated with areas of high pressure such as anticyclones or ridges of high pressure. (See case study on pages 87–89.) A **temperature inversion** frequently develops when these synoptic conditions prevail. Air descending in the centre of the anticyclone, which is the cause of the higher pressure at ground level, warms adiabatically by compression as it descends. Beneath this, closer to the ground, there is air which is cooling rapidly as the ground chills under the clear skies and calm conditions. This cold air is now effectively trapped under the warmer air above. An inversion can also develop where there are variations in relief (**10.12**). As this cooling air collects on the valley floor, fog or mist forms as the temperature reaches dew point. If the temperature falls low enough, frost may also occur; such low-lying areas which are prone to frost are called **frost hollows** or **pockets**.

In contrast, **advection fog** most commonly develops over water surfaces.

More specifically, it develops when warm air moves over a cold ocean current. The air is cooled to dew point and fog forms. Sea breezes can cause this fog to drift inland over coastal areas. The California coast is one area where advection fogs are common. Coastal areas of the UK and northern Europe also experience this sea fog or 'haar' and it is most frequent in spring and early summer when sea temperatures are still low. Advection fog may also form where warmer air moves over a colder land surface, e.g. over snow-covered surfaces as a thaw commences.

There are other types of fog, for example **hill fog** which is basically low cloud produced by the cooling to dew point of air rising against a relief feature. **Arctic fog** or **sea smoke** develops when very cold air passes over warmer water. The Great Lakes of North America experience this type of fog early in the winter. Then, of course, there are the **smogs** which were discussed in section 8.1. Fogs and smogs have a general hazard potential and can result in considerable costs to society. Fog can interrupt sporting occasions but more importantly, it can seriously affect transport. There are accidents and even loss of life when people do not appreciate or perceive the hazard of this reduction in visibility. 'Motorway madness' is a newspaper headline frequently used to describe the incidence of motorway multiple accidents occurring in such conditions. Surprisingly, though, there are instances when fog can be regarded as an asset. For example, in some tropical coastal desert areas it is an important source of moisture for plants, and in parts of California overnight fog droplets can amount to the equivalent of 1 mm of rain.

6 Keep a weather diary of the types of human activity affected by fog in your home region. What hazards and costs were involved on such occasions?

Luke Howard's classification 1803

CIRRUS – 'HAIR' CLOUDS

STRATUS – LAYER CLOUDS

NIMBUS – RAIN CLOUDS

CUMULUS – HEAPED CLOUDS

A modern classification of clouds

Cloud group (subdivisions based on shape)	Average height of cloud base (m)		
	Tropics	Temperate latitudes	Polar regions
HIGH cirrus cirrostratus cirrocumulus	6000–18 000	5000–13 000	3000–8000
MIDDLE altostratus altocumulus	2000–8000	2000–7000	2000–4000
LOW stratus stratocumulus nimbostratus	0–2000	0–2000	0–2000

A fourth group must be added – clouds of great vertical extent:

cumulonimbus

tops may extend into the tropopause 12–18 km high

ice crystals

ice crystals, snow and supercooled water

water

base may be as low as 1000 m

■ **10.14** Classification of clouds

Condensation in the upper air – clouds

Over the centuries, the state of the sky has been used as an indicator of future weather conditions. A whole series of folklore sayings, such as 'Red sky at night, sailors' (or shepherds') delight', survive to this day. Since they are based on generations of experience, they contain a large element of truth. Luke Howard produced the first classification of clouds in 1803 and this was based on their visual appearance. He proposed a fourfold division of cirrus, stratus, cumulus and nimbus clouds. The original criterion of appearance has been retained in the modern classification, but here cloud height is the starting point, with shape being used to subdivide the main groups, and there are numerous variants on these cloud forms (**10.13** and **10.14**). The all too frequent appearance of contrails which are usually produced by the condensation of water from jet exhausts reminds us that even at heights of more than 10 000 m, human activity has an impact on atmospheric processes.

Apart from providing clues to probable future weather developments, clouds are important in several other ways. Since they are the results of the process of condensation, they release huge quantities of latent heat into the atmosphere. This heat can have a very significant effect, as in the formation of tropical revolving storms (see section 11.5). Secondly, clouds play a critical role in maintaining the energy balance within the atmosphere by reflecting and scattering insolation and also by absorbing out-going infrared energy. Finally, precipitation is associated with clouds, particularly with the low-level group and those of great vertical development. To a large extent, we see clouds from beneath or from a side view. Aircraft provide the opportunity to view clouds from above. Satellites of course perform this important task continuously over the entire globe.

7 Describe and explain:
  a what happens to the evaporation rate in any area of tropical rainforest which is clear felled
  b why ground frost is more frequent than air frost in any one area
  c in what other ways human activity may affect the development of clouds.

10.6 **Rising air, descending air**

When we think of movements of air, we immediately think in terms of the horizontal dimension, i.e. winds. We are conscious of, and sometimes threatened by these movements, but vertical movements can be extremely important and the consequences can certainly be seen and felt at ground level. The **environmental lapse rate (ELR)** has already been defined (page 117); it is important to remember that it exists at all times, although it will vary both in a spatial and in a temporal context. However, when air itself begins to rise then it cools adiabatically and similarly warms up adiabatically when it descends. Cooling occurs because air expands as it rises through an increasingly less dense atmosphere and thus it occupies a greater volume. The cooling is not due to any effect or exchanges from the surrounding air.

10.15a illustrates, on a **tephigram** or temperature height graph, the two rates of adiabatic cooling and the average environmental lapse rate. There are two features of the **saturated adiabatic lapse rate (SALR)** which need to be noted. First of all, its reduced rate compared with the **dry adiabatic lapse rate (DALR)** is, of course, a consequence of the release of latent heat which accompanies the onset of condensation once air becomes saturated. Very approximately, therefore, this release amounts to 4 °C/1000 m. Secondly, the SALR is not constant, since it will vary with the temperature of the air. It has already been established that warm air can absorb and hold more water vapour than cold air. As a result, there will be greater releases of latent heat and, therefore, a reduced SALR for air

■ **10.15** Different atmospheric conditions

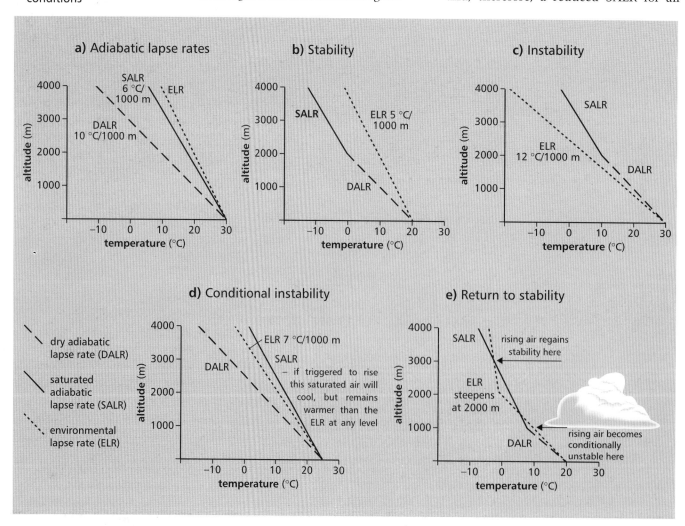

with higher temperatures and higher absolute humidities. At temperatures approaching −20°C, the SALR is almost 9°C/1000 m whereas at 20°C it is only just above 4°C/1000 m. This often means that the SALR increases with altitude.

Therefore when air rises, and only when it rises, it takes on its own new internal rates of cooling. This adiabatic cooling will probably result in it acquiring temperatures at certain levels which leave it either cooler or warmer than the surrounding air through which it is rising. If a rising mass of air is cooler, it will tend to stop rising and spread out, or even sink back. This condition is referred to as **stability** and it can be identified by rather flat-topped or subdued cloud forms such as altostratus or stratus clouds. **10.15b** shows that wherever the ELR is less than the SALR, stable conditions will prevail. Stability results from the cooling of the lower layers of the atmosphere which, in turn, leads to a steepening of the ELR. Cooling at these low levels produces a temperature inversion. An inversion frequently develops at night in clear, calm conditions simply because radiation is so rapid. As we have seen, dew or frost may well form under these conditions. Similarly, the advection of very cold air into a region or the movement of air over a much colder surface can also result in the development of an inversion. Finally, the gradual sinking or subsiding of a layer of air (as associated with anticyclones or valleys) can produce an inversion and consequently stability (**10.12**).

In contrast, if a rising mass of air becomes warmer than the surrounding air it will continue to to rise; this condition is known as **instability**, and can be identified by well-developed cumuliform clouds which may grow vertically to become cumulonimbus clouds. **10.15c** illustrates that where the ELR is greater than the DALR, air will rise spontaneously at all levels. The most common cause of atmospheric instability is the heating of a land or water surface which then initiates vertical or convectional air movements. Instability may also result from much warmer air being advected into an area or from colder air advected over a warmer surface and subsequently being warmed in its lower layers. Colder polar air reaching north-west Europe becomes unstable in this manner and is associated with the 'showers and bright intervals' type of weather which is so common over the British Isles.

10.15d demonstrates another type of instability. Here instability depends upon whether the air is saturated or not. With the ELR and SALR so close together, then some 'trigger' or push, such as a relief barrier, is needed to lift the air which, because it is cooling at the SALR, will become warmer than the surrounding air. This type of instability is called **conditional instability** and occurs when the ELR is between the DALR and SALR. Conversely, any rising unstable or conditionally unstable air may regain stability at a higher altitude, as shown by **10.15e**.

---

8 a Which of the three lapse rates ELR, DALR and SALR remains constant with height?
b Explain why this is the case.

9 Explain why a relief barrier, such as a hill range, encourages shower activity.

10 a Construct a tephigram using identical axes to those in **10.15a** to illustrate the following data:
   i Bottom of air layer which is saturated has a temperature of 10°C at an altitude of 500 m.
   ii Top of this air layer at a height of 1000 m has a temperature of 12°C and is unsaturated.
   iii Air layer rises for 2000 m. The top of this layer cools at the DALR while the lower part cools at a constant SALR of 6°C/1000 m.
b Describe what happens to the stability of this layer of air.

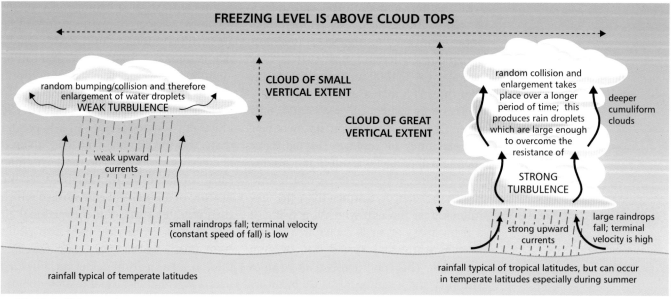

FREEZING LEVEL IS ABOVE CLOUD TOPS

random bumping/collision and therefore enlargement of water droplets
WEAK TURBULENCE

CLOUD OF SMALL VERTICAL EXTENT

CLOUD OF GREAT VERTICAL EXTENT

random collision and enlargement takes place over a longer period of time; this produces rain drops which are large enough to overcome the resistance of
STRONG TURBULENCE

deeper cumuliform clouds

weak upward currents

small raindrops fall; terminal velocity (constant speed of fall) is low

strong upward currents

large raindrops fall; terminal velocity is high

rainfall typical of temperate latitudes

rainfall typical of tropical latitudes, but can occur in temperate latitudes especially during summer

■ **10.16** Collision and coalescence theory

10.7 **Precipitation**

■ **10.17** Ice-crystal theory

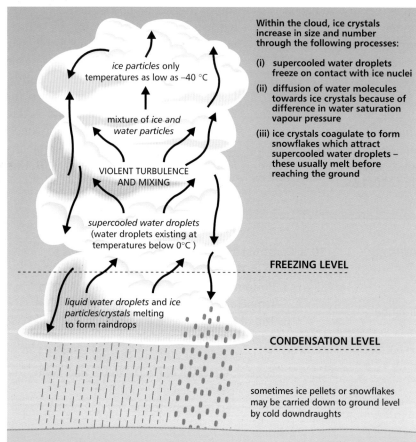

ice particles only temperatures as low as –40 °C

mixture of *ice and water particles*

VIOLENT TURBULENCE AND MIXING

supercooled water droplets (water droplets existing at temperatures below 0°C)

FREEZING LEVEL

liquid water droplets and *ice particles/crystals* melting to form raindrops

CONDENSATION LEVEL

Within the cloud, ice crystals increase in size and number through the following processes:

(i) supercooled water droplets freeze on contact with ice nuclei

(ii) diffusion of water molecules towards ice crystals because of difference in water saturation vapour pressure

(iii) ice crystals coagulate to form snowflakes which attract supercooled water droplets – these usually melt before reaching the ground

sometimes ice pellets or snowflakes may be carried down to ground level by cold downdraughts

When condensed water vapour, either in a liquid or solid state, falls to the ground it is called **precipitation**. Some authorities also include forms of condensation which develop at ground level, such as dew and frost, in this category. It has been established that condensation occurs on hygroscopic nuclei when the temperature falls close to or below the dew point (see page 121). The water vapour that condenses and gathers on these minute nuclei forms cloud droplets that are extremely small, frequently only 0.002 cm in diameter. Even allowing for gravity, these cloud droplets are still far too small and light to fall, particularly when we remember that most cloud droplets are formed where there are upward movements of air. In order for precipitation to occur, it is obvious that some increase in size is necessary to augment gravitational attraction and counteract any upward thrust of air. There are two main theories which attempt to explain how this enlargement of cloud droplets occurs.

The collision and coalescence theory

This theory holds that raindrops form from cloud droplets as a result of the two processes of collision and coalescence, causing droplets to merge into each other (**10.16**). This presupposes that water is in its liquid state, and means that the theory is associated with clouds

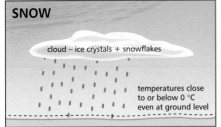

SNOW

cloud – ice crystals + snowflakes

temperatures close to or below 0 °C even at ground level

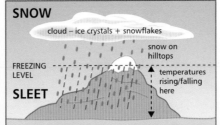

SNOW

cloud – ice crystals + snowflakes

snow on hilltops

FREEZING LEVEL

SLEET

temperatures rising/falling here

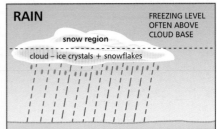

RAIN

FREEZING LEVEL OFTEN ABOVE CLOUD BASE

snow region

cloud – ice crystals + snowflakes

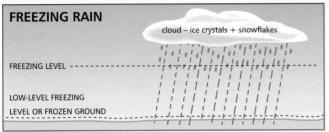

FREEZING RAIN

cloud – ice crystals + snowflakes

FREEZING LEVEL

LOW-LEVEL FREEZING LEVEL OR FROZEN GROUND

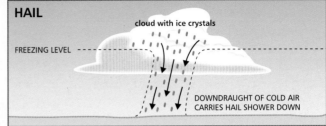

HAIL

cloud with ice crystals

FREEZING LEVEL

DOWNDRAUGHT OF COLD AIR CARRIES HAIL SHOWER DOWN

■ **10.18** Types of precipitation and related temperature conditions

where the temperatures are still high enough for no ice to be present. It is therefore associated with warm clouds.

The ice-crystal theory

As the name suggests, this process is associated with clouds where at least some of the water present exists in its solid state. Consequently, it occurs in clouds whose tops rise above the freezing level; these are called **cold clouds**. Most cold clouds are in fact mixed in their composition, with water droplets in the lower layers and supercooled water and ice above. **10.17** illustrates how raindrops may form in such a cloud which has acquired sufficient vertical

development to breach the freezing level. In clouds like this the rainfall can be intense and the raindrops may reach their potential maximum size of 6 mm diameter. Updraughts and downdraughts within the cloud can produce sudden showers and associated sharp boundaries or edges to the extent of the precipitation reaching the ground. Occasionally this can produce such a sharp division that one part of a village might receive rain while another part remains dry. Under certain conditions, the ice pellets or snowflakes may not melt before reaching the ground and thus fall as **snow**, **sleet** or **hail**. The lower the freezing level, the more likely are these alternative forms of precipitation (**10.18**).

10.8 Precipitation and hazards

Any form of precipitation may constitute a hazard if it occurs with abnormal intensity or duration, but in view of their very nature, freezing rain and hail always contain something of a hazard element. The aggregation of ice crystals which make up **snowflakes** are a delight to some people when they fall, but references to blizzards remind us of the hazard element too. **Sleet** has a different connotation in the USA compared with other areas such as the UK. In the USA, sleet refers to small ice pellets which result from snowflakes that have melted on descent, but then quickly refreeze nearer ground level. In most other areas, sleet is classified as a mixture of rain and snowflakes which occurs in a transitional period as the temperature is falling or rising close to freezing level. On account of its very temporary nature, it hardly constitutes a hazard. **Freezing rain** is rain which freezes on contact with cold objects such as the ground or overhead wires; an alternative name for this

phenomenon is **glazed ice**. Although relatively rare, it can cause chaos to transport systems.

Serious flooding caused by heavy rainfall is occurring almost continually somewhere on the Earth's surface. When associated with other hazards, such as strong winds or tidal surges, damage can be severe. The southern California floods of February 1990 and in northern Italy in November 1994 are fairly recent examples, although the effects of flooding in developing countries such as Bangladesh are frequently even more disastrous. On a smaller scale, flooding is quite common during winter on the flat glaciated valley floors of upland areas, such as Snowdonia, where heavy rainfall produces rapid runoff from only partially forested, impermeable hill slopes. Soil erosion, as in the Tennessee river basin earlier this century, and hazardous driving conditions are two other implications of heavy rainfall.

■ **10.19** Rainfall totals for stations in Singapore, 1989

Station number	Rainfall cm
1	254.9
2	260.6
3	268.8
4	280.8
5	241.2
6	226.2
7	263.0
8	246.3
9	285.1
10	252.2
11	258.5
12	238.7
13	213.9
14	256.0
15	275.9
16	248.5
17	235.4
18	273.7
19	264.8
20	269.8
21	204.7
22	256.5
23	282.3
24	263.0
25	229.5
26	262.2
27	278.2
28	261.4
29	199.5
30	231.3
31	209.3
32	218.2
33	208.0
34	241.5
35	defective
36	240.5
37	243.9
38	248.7
39	defective
40	215.1
41	242.8
42	225.0
43	239.0
44	237.0
45	244.2
46	237.0
47	252.4
48	274.2
49	278.1
50	208.0

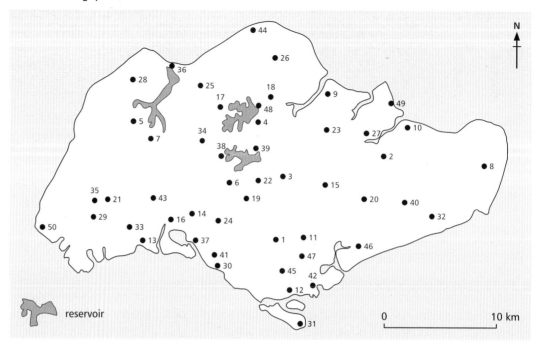

reservoir

0   10 km

11 It is important to remember that human activities may play an important part in rainfall-initiated flooding.
  a Investigate the causes of the following flooding incidents:
    i the Aberfan disaster of October 1966
    ii the Lynmouth floods of August 1952
    iii the Bangladesh floods of 1988.
  b Evaluate the extent to which human activities may have been involved as a causal factor in these incidents.

12 Keep a log of any rainfall-initiated flooding which may affect your local area while you are studying your geography course. Analyse the causes and consequences of any such flooding incidents.

13 a Use the map and data in **10.19** to draw an isohyet map for Singapore.
  b What factors might account for the spatial variations in rainfall in such a small area?

14 a Use proportional symbols to plot the data in **10.20** on an outline map of the USA.
  b What are the salient features shown by your map?

15 Examine the costs and benefits of heavy snowfall to human activity in various parts of the world.

Buffalo	2668.5
Rochester	2595.0
Minneapolis–St Paul	1580.0
Salt Lake City	1597.5
Albany	1577.5
Cleveland	1567.5
Denver	1460.0
Milwaukee	1377.5
Detroit	1157.5
Chicago	1097.5
Pittsburg	1052.5
Hartford	1045.0
Boston	1042.5
Providence	860.0
Dayton	837.5
Indianapolis	810.0
Columbus	792.5
St Louis	690.0
Cincinnati	675.0
Philadelphia	667.5

■ **10.20** Snowfall totals (cm) for the 20 snowiest major cities in the USA, 1975–85

Pressure, Winds, Airmasses and Weather Systems

So far two important properties of the atmosphere – temperature and humidity – have been analysed. Certain concepts relating to atmospheric motion, such as advection and convection, have also been introduced. It is now time to consider atmospheric motion in greater detail and at several levels within the atmosphere.

11.1 **Pressure**

11.1 serves as a reminder of the basic definition of pressure and that there is a decrease in pressure with altitude. Pressure is recorded by a barometer with the average reading at sea-level being 1000 mb. In fact, all pressure readings are corrected for altitude and are shown as for sea-level. If this correction was not carried out then a pressure chart would basically reflect any variations in relief. It is also important to note that the temperature of the air has an important influence on pressure, with cold temperatures resulting in an increase in surface pressure, while a warming of the air leads to a fall of pressure in the lower levels of the atmosphere.

When atmospheric pressure is recorded at a variety of locations then it becomes possible to construct isopleths for various pressure levels (see section 8.6). These lines are called **isobars** and are usually drawn at 4 mb intervals. Isobaric charts reveal two basic features:

- There are usually significant spatial variations in pressure with distinct areas or centres of high pressure and low pressure.
- There are variations in the pressure gradient between areas of high pressure and low pressure.

As with a topographical map, closely-packed isobars indicate a rapid change in pressure or a steep pressure gradient, while more widely-spaced isobars reveal a gentler gradient. Wind is the atmospheric response to these variations in pressure levels and gradient.

Pressure variations at the surface are the result of vertical movements of air – subsiding air increases pressure while rising air leads to a reduction in surface pressure. These movements may in turn be linked to changes in air temperature: heating will lead to buoyant or rising air, while cooling – perhaps as a result of intense radiation – will cause the cold, dense air to settle near the surface and thus force pressure values higher. There are also important links between the surface variation in pressure and the movements of air in the upper layer of the atmosphere.

■ **11.1** Atmospheric pressure and altitude

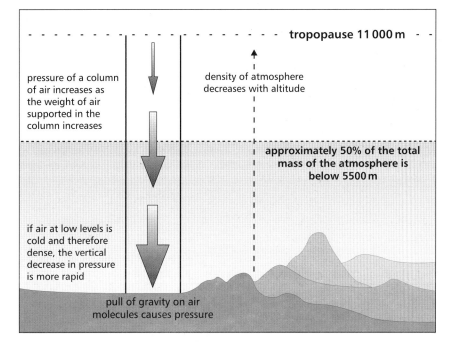

tropopause 11 000 m

pressure of a column of air increases as the weight of air supported in the column increases

density of atmosphere decreases with altitude

approximately 50% of the total mass of the atmosphere is below 5500 m

if air at low levels is cold and therefore dense, the vertical decrease in pressure is more rapid

pull of gravity on air molecules causes pressure

11.2 **Factors affecting wind speed and direction**

There are three forces that have an influence on surface wind direction and speed.

Pressure gradient force

Whenever a can of drink is opened or a balloon or tyre is punctured, the immediate outward rush of air represents a response to a considerable pressure difference. Air always moves towards areas of lower pressure and the speed of this movement depends upon the pressure gradient. The situation in **11.2a** illustrates a relatively gentle pressure gradient, while in **11.2b** the gradient is much steeper. The force exerted on the air by this difference is called the **pressure gradient force**. On synoptic charts, the generally larger areas of high pressure or anticyclones normally have gentler pressure gradients than the smaller areas of low pressure or depressions.

Coriolis force

If the pressure gradient force was the only influential factor, then winds would blow directly from areas of high to low pressure. However, once air begins to flow it is affected by the apparent force exerted by having to flow over the rotating surface of the Earth. With the Earth rotating from west to east, this has the effect of deflecting winds and ocean currents to the right of their initial compass direction of movement in the Northern Hemisphere, while in the Southern Hemisphere there is a leftward deflection. This statement regarding the deflection of winds is termed **Ferrel's Law**. Because the Earth rotates more slowly at the Equator than at the Poles, Coriolis force is much more powerful in higher latitudes than within the tropics. Coriolis force also increases in proportion to any increases in wind speed.

Friction

Both of the forces referred to above influence winds blowing at any height in the lower atmosphere. However, friction is almost totally confined to the lower 1000 m of the atmosphere. Friction varies from area to area, being greatest in thickly forested areas and hilly regions and least over calm ocean surfaces. Friction slows down the wind speed and it also has an effect on its direction, as will become clear when a comparison is made of the relative effects of these factors on upper-level and surface winds.

■ **11.2** Winds and pressure gradient force

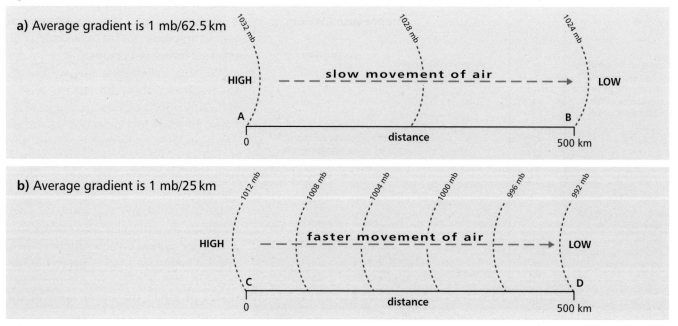

11.3 Upper air waves and jet streams

Any upper-level chart for either hemisphere reveals that the isobars do not form a uniformly parallel and concentric pattern, but in reality consist of a series of huge loops or meanders. These are the **Rossby waves** which are named after the famous meteorologist who first detected this phenomenon. These waves can be very large indeed with wavelengths (i.e. from crest to crest or from trough to trough) of up to 8000 km. At any given time, there is an average of between four and six of these long waves circulating the Earth in the upper-level westerly flow. It is thought that these waves may be caused by the presence of substantial relief barriers such as the Andes, the Rockies and the Tibetan Plateau, although sharp contrasts in surface temperatures related to ocean currents and large continental landmasses are also thought to play a part.

Another dramatic feature of these Rossby waves is the wind speed associated with them. Winds in the upper atmosphere above the friction level are inevitably much stronger. However, during the Second World War aircraft detected unusually strong winds at certain locations and thus the presence of what became known as **jet streams** was confirmed. Jet streams consist of long but relatively narrow and shallow currents of very fast-moving air. Although

their length can frequently be of the order of several thousand kilometres, their width can be measured in hundreds of kilometres while their thickness or depth is rarely more than a few kilometres. Wind strengths are usually in the order of 200 km/h, but in the core of a jet stream winds in excess of 450 km/h are known to exist. **11.3** shows the average location of the two most important jets in the Northern Hemisphere – the polar front jet and the subtropical jet. However, it should be noted that their precise locations do vary a great deal, particularly on a seasonal basis.

It has been established that wind speed is a direct response to the pressure gradient. It is not surprising, therefore, to find that the major jet streams are located close to steep pressure gradients. The principal factor involved here is the pronounced temperature contrast between cold polar and warmer tropical air. This boundary is marked by the position of the polar front which extends down from the tropopause to the Earth's surface. It is this temperature contrast which produces the steep pressure gradient which, in turn, is responsible for the much stronger winds of the jet stream. This temperature contrast intensifies and moves equatorwards during winter. The jet stream tends to migrate south in the Northern Hemisphere during winter and

■ **11.3** Average locations of the polar front and subtropical jets

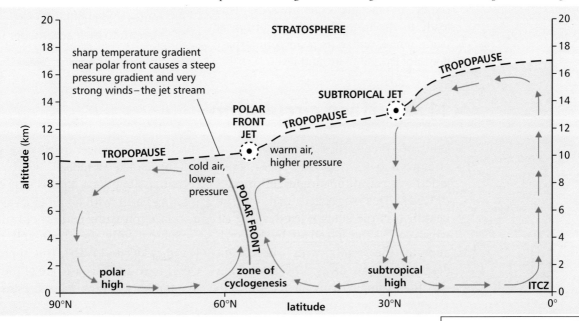

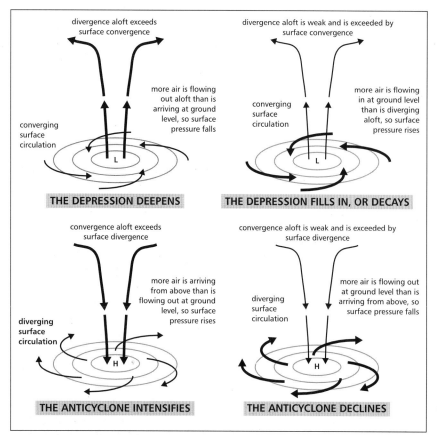

divergence aloft exceeds
surface convergence

more air is flowing
out aloft than is
arriving at ground
level, so surface
pressure falls

converging
surface
circulation

THE DEPRESSION DEEPENS

divergence aloft is weak and is exceeded by
surface convergence

converging
surface circulation

more air is flowing
in at ground level
than is diverging
aloft, so surface
pressure rises

THE DEPRESSION FILLS IN, OR DECAYS

convergence aloft exceeds
surface divergence

more air is arriving
from above than is
flowing out at ground
level, so surface
pressure rises

diverging
surface
circulation

THE ANTICYCLONE INTENSIFIES

convergence aloft is weak and is exceeded by
surface divergence

diverging
surface
circulation

more air is flowing out
at ground level than is
arriving from above, so
surface pressure falls

THE ANTICYCLONE DECLINES

■ **11.4** Depressions and anticyclones

The significance of jet streams and Rossby waves in the transfers of warm and cold air has already been noted, but it is the interrelationship with surface weather systems that must now be investigated.

A large proportion of day-to-day weather conditions are the result of the movement of centres of low pressure (**depressions** or **cyclones**) and centres of high pressure (**anticyclones**); these systems are particularly influential in temperate latitudes. With the inward and anticlockwise circulation around a depression and the outward and clock-wise circulation around an anticyclone (in the Northern Hemisphere) there is always a compensatory movement of air aloft. Thus in either hemisphere above a centre of low pressure there is upper-air divergence, while above a centre of high pressure there is convergence (**11.4**). Convergence and divergence, in a sense, provide the vital link between upper-air movements and surface weather systems.

it is also a much more pronounced fea-ture at this time of year. During the northern summer, however, a weakening of the temperature contrast and pressure gradient results in a weakening and northward retreat of the jet stream.

The subtropical jet stream, which is at a higher altitude than the polar jet, is located close to where a marked temper-ature contrast develops between very warm poleward-moving tropical air and cooler air moving equatorwards. This leads to the formation of a subtropical front, which unlike its polar counterpart does not extend to ground level.

---

1 a Find out what Buys Ballot's Law is.

b Use this law to determine the spatial pattern of surface pressure systems if you were standing with your back to the wind and to the sea at Durban, South Africa.

2 Select three international air routes that might utilise jet streams to their advantage.

11.4 **Surface circulation**

One of the earliest models which attempted to describe atmospheric circu-lation was called the **single-cell model** (**11.5a**). This suggested that intense heating over the Equator led to rising air which cooled and spread out to the north and to the south with subsequent descent in polar areas. The circulation was then completed by air returning to the Equator at lower levels. The single-cell model, like all models, was based on certain assumptions, in this case a non-rotating Earth, with no tilt to its axis and a surface consisting entirely of water.

Subsequently the **three-cell model** was developed (**11.5b**). This approaches closer to reality because one of the above assumptions is now relaxed. This time,

a) The single-cell model

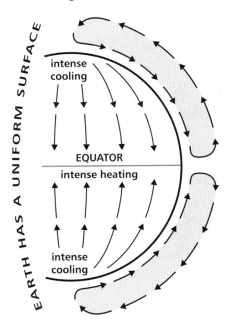

b) The three-cell model

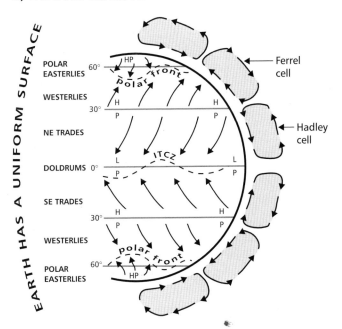

■ **11.5** Models of atmospheric circulation

on a rotating Earth's surface the driving force of the global circulation is once again seen to be the intense heating received in equatorial areas. This produces deep convection with the rising air carried up to the tropopause by the release of vast quantities of latent heat. The tropopause and its associated inversion force the rising air to spread out horizontally towards the poles. The Coriolis force results in this air being deflected to become part of the global flow of upper-air westerlies.

At approximately 30°N and 30°S, there is some convergence of this poleward moving air resulting from the decreasing circumference of the globe over which this air is flowing (**11.5b**). This upper-air convergence leads to a rise in surface pressure in the form of the **subtropical high**. The descending air associated with this high is warmed by compression and near the surface it diverges. Some of the air returns equatorwards and is deflected to the right by the Coriolis force to form the trade winds. At the Equator, there is surface convergence. This, combined with intense heating, leads to rising air which, in turn, is facilitated by divergence aloft. This zone is called the **intertropical convergence zone** (**ITCZ**–see **9.3**). This almost totally tropical circulation is known as the **Hadley cell**. At the same time, some air moves poleward from the subtropical highs and, deflected by the Coriolis force, produces the prevailing westerlies. These converge with air moving equatorwards from the poles along the polar front. Another circulation or cell is thus completed, the **Ferrel cell**.

The remaining cell is primarily a consequence of intensely cold air settling over polar regions (**11.5b**). This cold, dense air produces a surface zone of high pressure from which air diverges in the form of the polar easterlies. This diverging air meets tropical air along the polar front and after rising, some returns at higher levels to subside over the poles.

In reality the general circulation (**11.6**) is rather more complex, reflecting the controls exerted by latitudinal variations in heating, the seasonal displacement of the zone of maximum heat (the **heat equator**), the variable pattern of the distribution of land and sea over the Earth's surface, the interactions between the atmosphere and the oceans, and finally the effect of rotational spin. Thus while the actual pattern displays many similarities to the three-cell model, it is

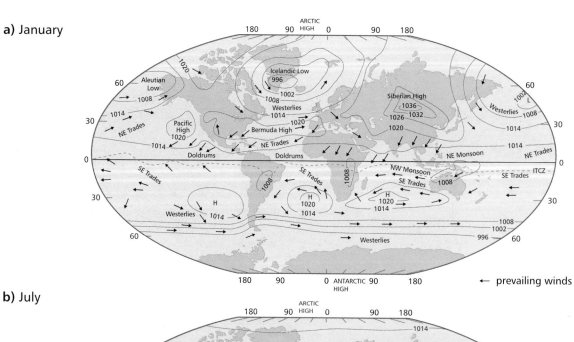

a) January

b) July

← prevailing winds

■ **11.6** Mean sea-level pressure and major wind flow patterns for January and July

modified and complicated by these controls. Nevertheless, certain permanent or semi-permanent features in this global circulation do emerge, namely the ITCZ, the subtropical highs, the subpolar lows and the polar highs.

It is readily apparent from **11.6** that there is a latitudinal shift in pressure systems between January and July. This is generated by the seasonal alternations of summer and winter between the two hemispheres. Another complicating macroscale factor is the effect that the differential heating of continental and oceanic areas has on seasonal pressure and wind patterns. This is the so-called **monsoonal effect**. This exerts a considerable influence on the climate of large areas of the Earth's surface, particularly

in East and South-east Asia. Land areas become intensely heated during the summer, creating low pressure which draws in humid air from the tropics. A reverse flow is generated in the winter, when intense cold over the continental interior results in high pressure and the outward movement of cold air.

3 a Find out what is meant by 'the tropical easterly jet stream'. Describe its location and the reasons for its formation.
   b What effect does this jet stream have on surface weather systems?

11.5 **Airmasses**

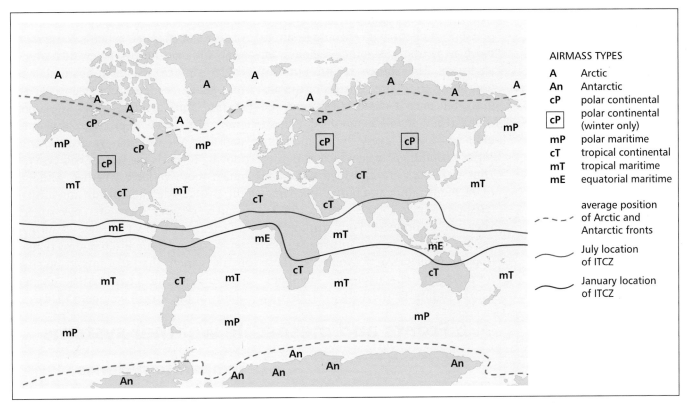

■ **11.7** Major airmass source regions

When a high-pressure system stagnates or moves only very slowly, there is an opportunity for the air within it to acquire the specific characteristics of that particular area. It is in this way that **airmasses** are formed. The longer air is able to stagnate in one of these relatively 'quiet weather' areas associated with high-pressure cells, then the more likely it is to acquire the characteristics peculiar to that area. If these regions are areas of fairly uniform surface conditions then the airmasses display common characteristics in all directions at any given altitude. An airmass thus exhibits a uniformity of temperature, humidity and vertical structure within the lower atmosphere. Such high-pressure areas are called **source regions**. The major source regions are shown in **11.7**.

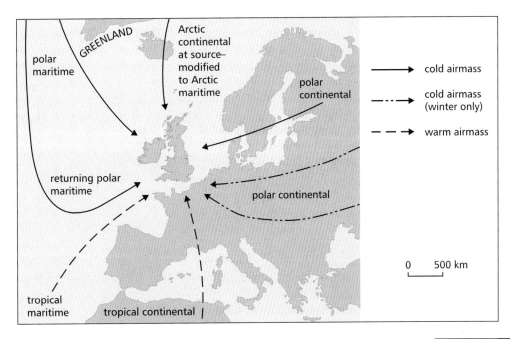

■ **11.8** Airmasses affecting the British Isles

Occasionally an entire high-pressure system will move and carry its airmass with it, or more commonly a steepening pressure gradient will encourage air to move away from the source region as an airstream. The source region puts an imprint on the characteristics of the airmass, but once it moves away from the source region it will be modified, at least in its very lowest layers, by the changing surface conditions over which it moves. Thus airmasses are classified according to the temperature and humidity characteristics of their source regions (**11.7**). They can be continental or maritime, but are further subdivided into equatorial, tropical, polar or Arctic/Antarctic. These source region characteristics are modified according to the path or trajectory followed by the airmass which will depend upon whether it follows a direct or an indirect route, and upon the season of year. For example, when a warm maritime airmass moves polewards over a colder surface, its environmental lapse rate (ELR) becomes less steep near the surface and therefore it becomes more stable. This tends to produce fairly quiet, non-dramatic weather, whereas polar air moving towards the tropics will generate much more variable weather. Although the British Isles lie outside any airmass source region, they are nevertheless affected by a great variety of airmass types coming from different directions. It is this variety that accounts in no small measure for the characteristic changeability of the British weather (**11.8**).

11.6 **Fronts and mesoscale weather systems**

Temperate cyclones

Dominance by a particular airmass type results in spells of rather persistent weather conditions. However, the variability which prevails in large areas outside the tropics is in no small measure due to the advance and retreat of different airmass types and their meeting and interaction along zones of convergence known as **fronts**. A front is the contact zone between two airmasses of different temperatures, humidity, density, speed and direction of movement. The contact creates friction which, in turn, causes waves to develop in a similar manner to the way in which waves develop between moving air and water. A poleward push by warm air in one of these waves is the initial stage in the growth and development of a temperate cyclone or depression (**11.9a**). The activity which takes place along a front and results in the growth of these waves into fully-fledged depressions is called **frontogenesis**. As a wave begins to develop, convergence and uplift commence at the apex of the wave, which in time allows surface pressure to fall. However, the anticlockwise spiral of onward-moving and rising air that now develops could not grow without the significant role that divergence in

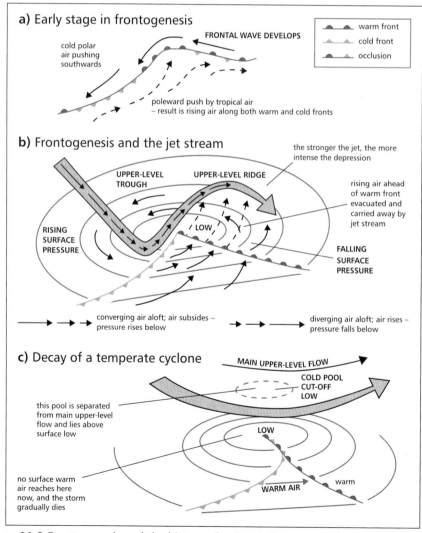

a) Early stage in frontogenesis

FRONTAL WAVE DEVELOPS

cold polar air pushing southwards

poleward push by tropical air – result is rising air along both warm and cold fronts

warm front
cold front
occlusion

b) Frontogenesis and the jet stream

the stronger the jet, the more intense the depression

UPPER-LEVEL TROUGH   UPPER-LEVEL RIDGE

rising air ahead of warm front evacuated and carried away by jet stream

RISING SURFACE PRESSURE

LOW

FALLING SURFACE PRESSURE

converging air aloft; air subsides – pressure rises below

diverging air aloft; air rises – pressure falls below

c) Decay of a temperate cyclone

MAIN UPPER-LEVEL FLOW

COLD POOL CUT-OFF LOW

this pool is separated from main upper-level flow and lies above surface low

LOW

no surface warm air reaches here now, and the storm gradually dies

WARM AIR

warm

■ **11.9** Frontogenesis and the history of a depression

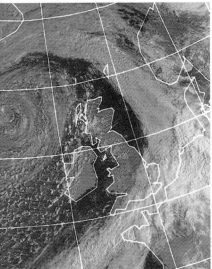

the upper air plays. This divergence allows the rising air in the surface wave to be evacuated and carried away at higher levels by the jet stream. It is only when this occurs that a depression will deepen and mature. This relationship is fundamental to frontogenesis and is illustrated in **11.9b**.

The jet stream affects surface depressions in other ways too. **11.9b** shows how the strength of the jet can influence the nature of frontal activity and the intensity of the system. The latitudinal position of the jet can be crucial to surface weather conditions. Thus if depressions are steered to the south by the jet stream, this track will leave the British Isles in the cold sector of the system with polar airmasses dominating, and precipitation is more likely to be in the form of snow in winter. However, when the jet is displaced well to the north, then the British Isles will experience at least periods of milder weather as tropical air extends northwards in association with the warm sector of these systems.

The decaying stages of a depression are illustrated in **11.9c**. The principal feature to note here is the way in which the cold front catches and merges with the warm front, squeezing and in fact lifting away from ground level the wedge of warm air which was formed during frontogenesis (**11.10**). This process gives rise to an **occlusion** and is a direct consequence of the more rapid movement of the cold front compared with the warm front (**11.11**). Cold fronts may travel at speeds of between 15 and 25 knots with a slope or gradient of between 1:50 and 1:100, whereas warm fronts travel up to 10 knots slower and have a gradient of between 1:150 and 1:300. This more rapid movement of the cold front is primarily due to the sinking of air from the jet stream associated with upper-level convergence on the upstream side of a trough where air is de-accelerating. This causes surface air to undercut the warm air, pushing it forward at a steep angle and at a relatively rapid speed. This squeezing, lifting and cutting-off of the warm sector begins first at the head of the wave and proceeds outwards. Eventually, when all the surface air has been eliminated, the depression has virtually decayed and consists of a weakening occluded front with the swirl of air remaining only in the upper troposphere. This is referred to as a **cut-off low**. **11.11** demonstrates the main differences between warm and cold occlusions.

No two depressions are identical in their depth, rate of development, track or speed. Nevertheless it is possible to consider the structure and weather sequence of an idealised depression. **11.12** illustrates this for a mature depression.

Temperate cyclones play a vital role in the temperature equalising process between the hot tropical and cold polar areas. Their development and the interplay of contrasting airmass types ensures the continued transfer of polar and tropical air.

Finally, it needs to be pointed out that frontal cyclones are a phenomenon

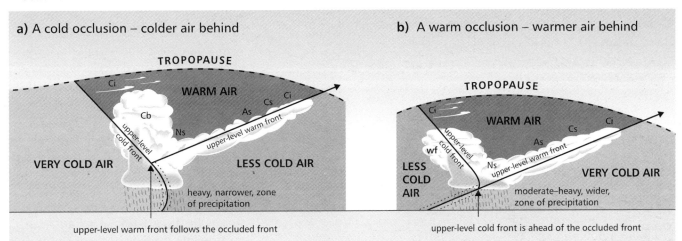

a) A cold occlusion – colder air behind

TROPOPAUSE

Ci   WARM AIR   Cs Ci
Cb   As
Ns   upper-level warm front
upper-level cold front

VERY COLD AIR   LESS COLD AIR

heavy, narrower, zone of precipitation

upper-level warm front follows the occluded front

b) A warm occlusion – warmer air behind

TROPOPAUSE

Ci   WARM AIR   Cs Ci
                 As
wf   upper-level warm front
upper-level cold front   Ns

LESS COLD AIR   VERY COLD AIR

moderate–heavy, wider, zone of precipitation

upper-level cold front is ahead of the occluded front

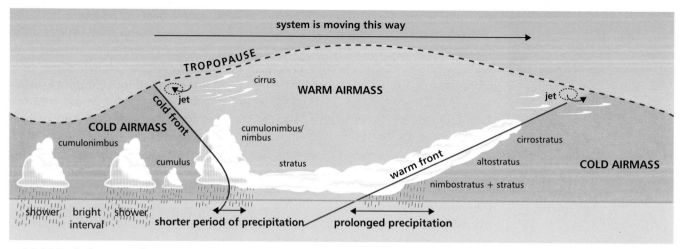

system is moving this way

TROPOPAUSE

cirrus

jet

WARM AIRMASS

jet

cold front

COLD AIRMASS

cumulonimbus

cumulus

cumulonimbus/
nimbus

stratus

warm front

cirrostratus

altostratus

COLD AIRMASS

nimbostratus + stratus

shower | bright interval | shower

shorter period of precipitation

prolonged precipitation

■ **11.12** Basic features of a mature depression

essentially of the temperate world; their influence within the tropics is of little significance. The principal reason for this is that the airmasses involved in the ITCZ do not exhibit sufficiently contrasting characteristics. However, frontless cyclones do develop.

Anticyclones

In many temperate areas, frontal systems frequently appear in a seemingly endless procession, particularly during the winter season when temperature contrasts are at their greatest. However, this frontal activity is occasionally disrupted by the appearance of anticyclones and even more transient ridges of high pressure. Occasionally, anticyclones may build or extend within temperate latitudes to produce a **blocking** situation (**11.13**).

■ **11.13** Typical blocking situation for the British Isles

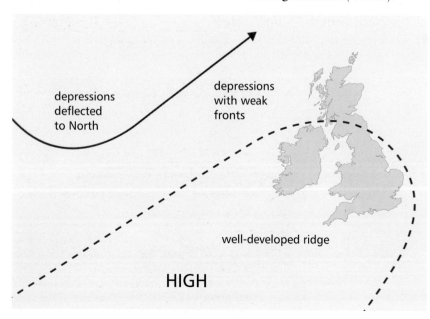

depressions deflected to North

depressions with weak fronts

well-developed ridge

HIGH

Over the British Isles persistent summer anticyclones can generate a series of fine, sunny and occasionally hot days. At night, dew and shallow mist patches develop, but in midsummer at least these are quickly evaporated the following morning. A larger than normal diurnal range of temperature is another characteristic of this type of weather. During the autumn and winter the longer nights mean an increased risk of dew, frost and thicker and more extensive fog patches which may be slow to clear or even persist the next day. Under certain conditions both frost and fog may persist for several days. Despite the descent of gradually warming air in their centres, anticyclones may also occasionally be associated with persistent overcast conditions, known as **anticyclonic gloom**.

Hurricanes

IT2

The summer of 1992 was certainly a season of above-average hurricane activity and news. In August, hurricane Andrew struck The Bahamas, Florida and the Gulf coast of the USA, while less than three weeks later hurricane Iniki devastated the Hawaiian islands. Hurricanes are mesoscale disturbances which affect many tropical areas (**11.14**); their socio-economic costs far outweigh their size and for this reason alone they deserve special treatment. **Hurricane** is the name given to these tropical revolving storms in the Atlantic and Caribbean areas, while the same type of storm is

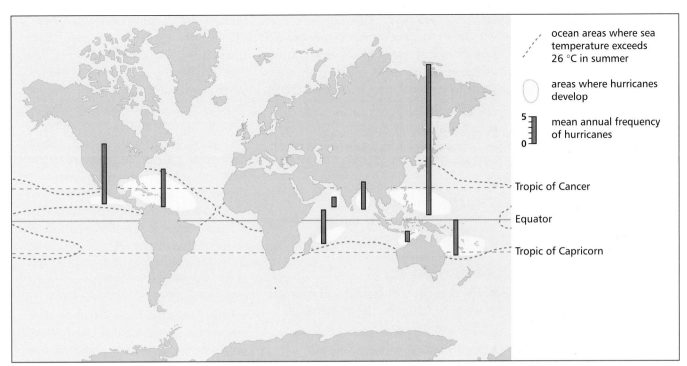

Legend:
- ocean areas where sea temperature exceeds 26 °C in summer
- areas where hurricanes develop
- mean annual frequency of hurricanes

Tropic of Cancer
Equator
Tropic of Capricorn

■ **11.14** Global distribution of tropical revolving storms

■ **11.15** The Saffir–Simpson hurricane damage-potential scale

IT2 called a **typhoon** in the Pacific and a **cyclone** in the Indian Ocean. It has become common practice since the late 1970s to 'christen' hurricanes in the North Atlantic and the Eastern Pacific with alternating boys' and girls' names. The Saffir–Simpson scale is used primarily as an indicator of potential damage, but it also serves as a useful measure by which to classify tropical revolving storms in terms of the intensity of the weather processes involved (**11.15**).

11.14 shows that the formation of hurricanes is confined to tropical oceanic areas between approximately 5° and 20° either side of the Equator. In such areas the sea is uniformly hot and maintains a temperature of at least 26°C during the period from midsummer to early autumn. The origins of many tropical revolving storms have been traced back to **easterly waves** along the ITCZ. In certain conditions at this time of year the thunderstorm **IT2**

Category	Central pressure mb	Winds km/h	Storm surge m	Damage
1	≥ 980	118 – 152	1.5 – 2.0	■ Trees and unanchored mobile homes
2	965 – 979	153 – 176	2.0 – 2.5	■ Trees blown down ■ Some roof damage ■ Exposed mobile homes
3	945 – 964	177 – 208	2.5 – 4.0	■ Large trees blown down ■ Mobile homes destroyed ■ Structural damage to small buildings
4	920 – 944	209 – 248	4.0 – 5.5	■ All signs blown down ■ Extensive structural damage – roofs, windows, doors ■ Major damage to structures on the coast ■ Flooding extends 10 km inland
5	< 920	> 248	> 5.5	■ Severe damage to all buildings ■ Small buildings blown away ■ Major damage to coastal buildings up to 4.5 m tall within 500 m of shore

activity and convectional rain associated with these relatively minor tropical disturbances may grow into a major storm centre or hurricane. A number of factors seem to encourage such ominous development. These include:

- the heat energy and abundant supply of humidity provided by warm ocean currents

- the release of vast additional quantities of latent heat by condensation within the convection cells and thunderstorms, thereby providing fuel for further convectional activity

- the deep layer of humid and unstable air to be found on the western sides of ocean basins

- a circulatory motion of the air, encouraged by the Coriolis force, which is anticlockwise in the Northern Hemisphere.

These and other factors result in the formation of a definite area of low pressure around which thunderstorms become more organised as a swirling mass. However, whether or not this tropical low or depression develops still further into a tropical storm or hurricane hinges on the conditions in the upper air. A cold upper-level trough extending equatorwards from middle latitudes provides the perfect con-

ditions for atmospheric instability. Finally, the existence of a feedback mechanism, involving the wind, sea and evaporation, should be noted. As surface pressure falls, wind speeds increase and the sea becomes choppy. This, in turn, facilitates evaporation by the converging winds which means that even greater amounts of latent heat are released, thereby deepening the centre of low pressure.

11.16 represents a cross-section of a typical tropical revolving storm and it highlights many of the processes referred to above, as well as the principal features of its anatomy. Some fully-grown storms may persist over warm oceanic surfaces for more than two weeks, but most will die or dissipate within a week. Three factors hasten this decay:

- If the track of the storm takes it over cooler water, then its main energy source – the evaporation of water from a warm ocean surface – is reduced.

- When the storm begins to track over land, it soon begins to weaken because evaporation is reduced sharply and greater surface friction causes the winds to blow more directly into the centre, allowing pressure to rise.

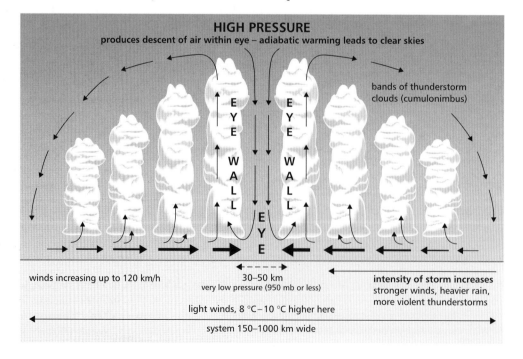

HIGH PRESSURE
produces descent of air within eye – adiabatic warming leads to clear skies

bands of thunderstorm clouds (cumulonimbus)

E Y E   W A L L

E Y E   W A L L

E Y E

winds increasing up to 120 km/h

30–50 km
very low pressure (950 mb or less)

light winds, 8 °C–10 °C higher here

intensity of storm increases
stronger winds, heavier rain, more violent thunderstorms

system 150–1000 km wide

■ **11.16** Processes and patterns within a typical hurricane. Hurricanes sometimes 'spawn' tornadoes

- If divergence in the upper air slows down, this causes excess convergence at the surface, which will result in pressure rising at the centre of the storm.

As the storm dies and moves polewards, the drawing-in of contrasting airmass types and the development of fronts may transform it into a temperate cyclone. These surface processes will be enhanced by the presence of an upper-level trough. At certain times of year, tropical revolving storms play a significant role in the poleward transfer of warm oceanic water and warm air.

Hurricanes are invariably associated with disasters and in the past the loss of life and the damage was often colossal. A hurricane claimed the lives of 6000 people in Galveston, Texas in 1900, while more recently in November 1970 approximately 300 000 lives were lost when a tropical cyclone struck the coast of Bangladesh. In more recent years, death tolls, though perhaps not physical damage, have been reduced and the annual loss of life in the USA now averages 50 people only. The hazard is related to five main features of these storms:

- Strong wind speeds – hurricane Hugo (1989) generated maximum wind speeds of 222 km/h.

- Heavy rainfall and associated flooding – hurricane Agnes in June 1972 produced rainfall totals exceeding 40 cm in 24 hours.

- High seas with waves of up to 10–15 m – if these conditions coincide with a high tide then coastal flooding is inevitable.

- Sometimes a sudden and abnormal rise in sea-level produces a **storm surge**. This is usually produced by a combination of the effects of strong winds, an exceptionally high tide and the rise in sea-level of up to 50 cm (a response to the very low air pressure in the centre of a storm). For example, hurricane Camille in 1969 generated a 7 m storm surge along the coast of Mississippi with most of the 200-plus fatalities being directly

attributable to the effects of flooding.

- There is a tendency for tropical revolving storms to spawn tornadoes and even microbursts, both of which can cause severe local damage.

In addition to the loss of life, the cost of damage can be staggering. Thus hurricane Hugo may only have resulted in 21 deaths in the USA, but the total bill for damage amounted to approximately $7 billion. In some of the smaller Caribbean nations, the loss of life, the damage and the economic hardship can be even greater, particularly where the economy is dependent on a narrow range of agricultural activities or tourism.

As with most hazards, the perception of, and the reaction to, the threat varies from country to country. The level of technology and the previous knowledge of such a hazard play a role here, while the adjustment and recovery times are clearly linked to the technological development and the economic capability of the country. For example, following the hurricane of 1906 a sea wall was built at Galveston and this was responsible for a reduced death toll of 275 when an equally severe storm hit the city in 1915.

As our understanding of the mechanisms involved in hurricanes has increased and as weather-forecasting accuracy improves, particularly with the use of reconnaissance aircraft, satellites and hurricane prediction models, so the hazard risk has been reduced. Reaction in terms of early warning and evacuation procedures has also resulted in a reduced risk, for authorities invariably play safe and ensure that a much larger area than is really necessary is warned and evacuated. Despite all this improvement in technology, however, hurricanes are still to a degree unpredictable, as the case study on hurricane Andrew illustrates.

4 a Why do tropical revolving storms in the North Atlantic initially move north-westwards, then north-eastwards and finally decay as they move into temperate latitudes?

 b Why are these storms relatively rare in the South Atlantic and the eastern South Pacific?

 c Why do so few of these storms affect southern California?

 d Why is it possible for these storms to travel far to the north off the east coasts of North America and Asia ?

5 Use the data in **11.17** to construct a world map displaying a series of frequency graphs. Analyse the pattern that emerges.

6 Make a list of the differences between temperate and tropical cyclones. Organise your list so as to classify the differences in the following way:
 a causes, b anatomy and c associated weather.

7 a The 1876 cyclone which devastated the Chittagong area of Bangladesh caused the deaths of 100 000 people due to drowning and of a further 100 000 from disease after the storm. Why does disease still claim the lives of many in cyclone- and typhoon-devastated areas?

 b Why is Bangladesh particularly prone to cyclone damage ?

 c What effect does this damage have on the economy of Bangladesh ?

8 Suggest why damage from tropical revolving storms might increase in the future.

Area	J	F	M	A	M	J	J	A	S	O	N	D
North Pacific (east)	4	3	3	0	3	4	4	20	41	12	3	3
North Pacific (west)	1	0	1	1	4	7	19	20	21	14	9	3
Bay of Bengal	1	0	2	4	7	11	15	11	12	17	16	4
Caribbean & North Atlantic (west)	0	0	0	0	0	5	5	15	31	31	13	0
South Pacific (west)	11	14	35	8	8	6	6	1	4	1	2	4

■ **11.17** Average monthly frequencies of tropical revolving storms in selected locations

CASE STUDY

IT2

Hurricane Andrew

This was the first hurricane to hit the Miami area since Betsy in 1965. It turned out to be the third most severe storm of this century and certainly the most expensive, with an estimated $30 billion worth of damage (**11.18**).

First detected as an easterly wave over West Africa on 14 August 1992, it moved into the Atlantic Ocean where it developed into a tropical depression and into a storm on 17 August. By 22 August, it had been upgraded to a hurricane. Initially threatening Florida, it suddenly faltered offshore owing to the effect of a depression to the north which weakened the pressure gradient. When this storm moved away north into the Atlantic, Andrew ran up against a ridge of high pressure over the east of the USA (**11.19**). The steep pressure gradient encouraged its further development (**11.20**). The exceptionally warm sea, 1 °C above normal, provided additional energy. The result was a category 4 hurricane with sustained winds of 230 km/h, gusts up to 280 km/h and a tidal surge of 3.6 m when it hit the Florida coast on 24 August.

The cost of this storm included 23 deaths, 180 000 people homeless, massive disruption to power and

■ **11.18** Damage caused by hurricane Andrew, 21–24 August 1992

■ **11.20** Satellite image of hurricane Andrew, August 1992

water supplies, telephone and other communication systems, and the inevitable aftermath of looting. Some of the damage suggests that even stronger winds might have been involved in association with an intense convection cell which was identified in the eye wall. Vortices of very strong winds might also have been caused by the effect of tall buildings disrupting the flow of Andrew's winds.

Nevertheless, thanks to accurate forecasting, the storm's relatively small size and the fact that neither of its coastal landing points was very densely populated, damage was to some extent limited.

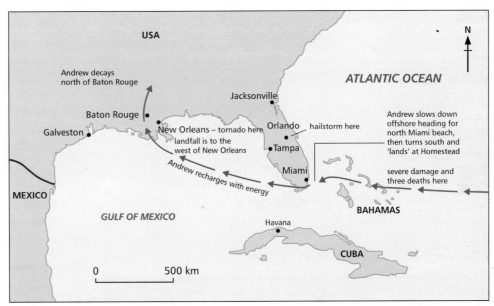

■ **11.19** Hurricane Andrew's track

9 Explain the annotation on **11.19** which describes variations in Andrew's intensity on its track from the Atlantic Ocean east of The Bahamas to its final decay near Baton Rouge.

10 What effect is global warming expected to have on such storms?

11 Keep a detailed record of a tropical revolving storm occurring during your A-level course; this will be a valuable resource bank on which you can draw to improve any examination answer.

11.7 **Microscale weather systems**

IT2

Hurricanes represent a formidable and as yet a seemingly uncontrollable hazard. In considering thunderstorms and tornadoes we are moving down a scale in terms of size, but the hazard element is barely reduced in intensity. All of these phenomena are associated with convection, an activity which can develop into a fully-fledged tropical revolving storm.

Thunderstorms

These storms may vary in size from a single cumulonimbus cloud which may develop over a heated surface, to a series of storms, often arranged in a line, which is termed a **multicell storm**. Thunderstorms can develop spontaneously in hot, humid air. Many of them may produce hail, dramatic temperature fluctuations, thunder and lightning, and yet they may still not be regarded as severe. In the USA, the National Weather Service classifies a thunderstorm as 'severe' when it is associated with 20 mm of hail and/or wind gusts of 93 km/h.

IT2

11.21 shows some of the distinguishing features of a more violent thunderstorm. Most significant is the balance between updraughts and downdraughts; this allows the storm to rumble on for several hours.

Hail is one aspect of the thunderstorm hazard; others include flash floods and lightning damage. Lightning can take many forms, but intra-cloud lightning is the most common. Of the 100 lightning flashes that are estimated to occur in the Earth's atmosphere each second, only 20 are cloud-to-ground strikes. This is inevitably the most dangerous type of lightning with more than 100 deaths, 1000 forest fires and upwards of $50 million of damage a year being directly attributable to this hazard in the USA alone.

■ **11.21** Distinguishing features of a severe thunderstorm

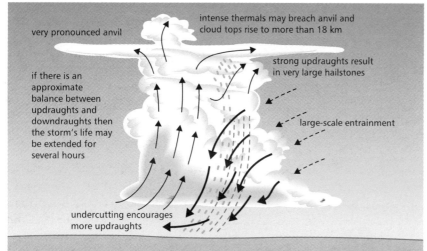

very pronounced anvil

intense thermals may breach anvil and cloud tops rise to more than 18 km

if there is an approximate balance between updraughts and downdraughts then the storm's life may be extended for several hours

strong updraughts result in very large hailstones

large-scale entrainment

undercutting encourages more updraughts

---

12 Why do you think Florida has the highest rate for deaths caused by lightning in the USA?

■ **11.22** Twin tornado funnels

Tornadoes

IT2

A tornado is a severe vortex of fast-moving winds surrounding an area of very low pressure – hence its alternative name of 'twister'. In some, the pressure difference may be as much as 100 mb, causing wind speeds on occasions to exceed 400 km/h. The funnel or trunk-shaped cloud which surrounds the vortex is usually no more than 600 m across and some are much narrower. There are larger versions and sometimes a tornado may contain several vortices (**11.22**).

In general, tornadoes travel at speeds between 35 and 75 km/h, but some can move a lot faster along erratic and unpredictable paths. They are as short-lived as they are unpredictable; most only last a few minutes and travel no more than a few kilometres while others defy the norm and survive for many hours and travel for hundreds of kilometres.

The spatial and temporal distribution of tornadoes within the USA (the country which suffers most from this hazard) is quite distinct. Their spatial incidence is such that Americans refer to 'Tornado Alley', running from the Gulf coast to as far as the Great Lakes. The conditions which favour tornado formation reach their optimum over these central lowlands during spring when markedly contrasting airmasses in the form of very warm, humid and unstable tropical maritime air from the Gulf meet the much colder, dry Arctic continental or polar continental air from northern Canada (**11.23**). This generates intense frontal activity, particularly along cold fronts, though the characteristics of the air in a vertical dimension are also significant.

Tornadoes represent one of the most severe, if localised, threats to human life and property. At present, the death toll from tornadoes in the USA is approximately 100 each year, but this represents a gradual reduction over the century. Occasional severe tornadoes, particularly those that occur in groups or families, can cause major destruction and loss of life. For example, in April 1974 an outbreak consisting of 148 tornadoes affected 13 states, killing over 300 people and causing $600 million worth of damage.

13 Read the following extract from *The Wizard of Oz*, which was written in 1898, and evaluate the extent to which it represents 'poetic licence' as opposed to accurate observation on the part of the author.

> The north and south winds met where the house stood and made it the exact centre of the cyclone. In the middle of the cyclone the air is generally still, but the great pressure of the wind on every side of the house raised it higher and higher until it was at the very top of the cyclone, and there it remained and was carried miles and miles away as easily as you could carry a feather.

Local winds

Two other small-scale weather systems are land–sea breezes and katabatic–anabatic winds. Neither of these systems has a significant hazard element, but they do influence the climate of many areas.

11.24 demonstrates that land and sea breezes constitute a daily system,

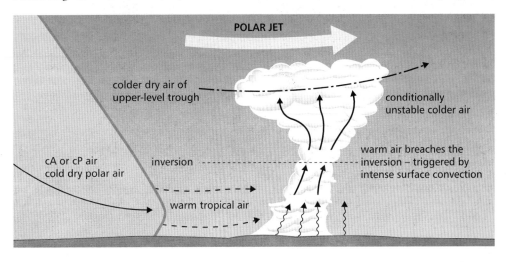

POLAR JET

colder dry air of upper-level trough

conditionally unstable colder air

cA or cP air cold dry polar air

inversion

warm air breaches the inversion – triggered by intense surface convection

warm tropical air

■ **11.23** The stage set for tornado formation

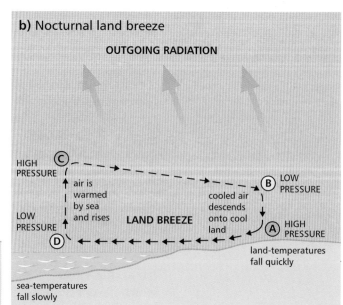

a) Daytime sea breeze

INCOMING SOLAR RADIATION

LOW PRESSURE Ⓒ

cooled air descends onto cool sea

SEA BREEZE

air is warmed by land and rises

Ⓑ HIGH PRESSURE

LOW PRESSURE

Ⓐ

HIGH PRESSURE Ⓓ

land-temperatures rise quickly

sea-temperatures rise slowly

b) Nocturnal land breeze

OUTGOING RADIATION

HIGH PRESSURE Ⓒ

air is warmed by sea and rises

LAND BREEZE

Ⓑ LOW PRESSURE

LOW PRESSURE

cooled air descends onto cool land

Ⓐ HIGH PRESSURE

Ⓓ

land-temperatures fall quickly

sea-temperatures fall slowly

■ **11.24** Land–sea breezes

with the onshore sea breeze dominating daylight hours and a reversal to offshore land breezes occurring at night. This system is spatially confined to a relatively narrow zone bordering the coast. The strength of the breeze will vary from day to day and from place to place for a variety of reasons and in this context it is important to note the direction of the gradient wind. Inevitably, if the direction of this is opposite to that of the land–sea breeze, then it may completely obliterate this mechanism. It should also be noted that land–sea breezes are comparatively shallow in vertical extent with 150m being the average upper limit for this type of flow. However, in tropical areas such breezes can be deeper and more frequent features, sometimes extending their influence up to 150–200km inland.

The climatic effects of this system can be quite pronounced. The arrival of the sea breeze leads to a noticeable fall in temperature, though the relative humidity

inevitably rises. This cooling is part of the moderating effect that water bodies exert on the climate of coastal areas. Thus the July mean daily maximum temperature at Great Yarmouth is 19.3°C, exactly two degrees lower than that for Norwich some 30km inland.

*In the following activities you will have a chance to construct **histograms**. A histogram is a graphical technique that is particularly useful for illustrating the distribution of values in a set of data. It is a graph of frequency distribution. Histograms deal with groups of data and these are shown by drawing bars or columns. It is an ideal technique to use to compare two sets of data, and these activities enable you to do this. Plot the frequency either in actual values or as percentage values on the vertical axis, and the groups of values on the horizontal axis.*

14 Use the data in **11.25** to construct wind roses for Entebbe (Uganda). These should be arranged in groups which will correspond approximately with the major compass directions (see below). Suggest reasons for the patterns revealed.

15 a Using the data in **11.26**, draw histograms to illustrate the wind direction at Dubai International Airport for **a** 0300 hrs, and **b** 1500 hrs in July.
b Carefully analyse the patterns illustrated by the histograms.

	N	NE	E	SE	S	SW	W	NW	Calm
0800 hrs	25	7	3	6	6	6	15	28	4
1430 hrs	1	1	7	39	34	12	2	2	2

■ **11.25** Mean percentage wind frequencies at Entebbe, Uganda, in July

Day in month	1	2	3	4	5	6	7	8	9	10	11	12	13	14	15	16
0300 hrs	50	180	180	160	170	70	60	90	110	100	170	160	140	160	160	151
1500 hrs	320	310	350	260	310	310	340	350	350	80	340	310	350	340	340	350

Day in month	17	18	19	20	21	22	23	24	25	26	27	28	29	30	31
0300 hrs	111	90	130	140	200	270	90	170	50	70	90	130	160	210	50
1500 hrs	30	320	300	310	81	140	350	350	10	10	331	350	330	340	30

■ **11.26** Daily mean wind direction at Dubai International Airport in July (by compass bearing)

■ **11.27** Katabatic and anabatic winds

Katabatic and anabatic winds are usually known as **down-valley** and **up-valley** winds (**11.27**). The most violent and persistent katabatic winds are encountered in Antarctica (see also section 12.5).

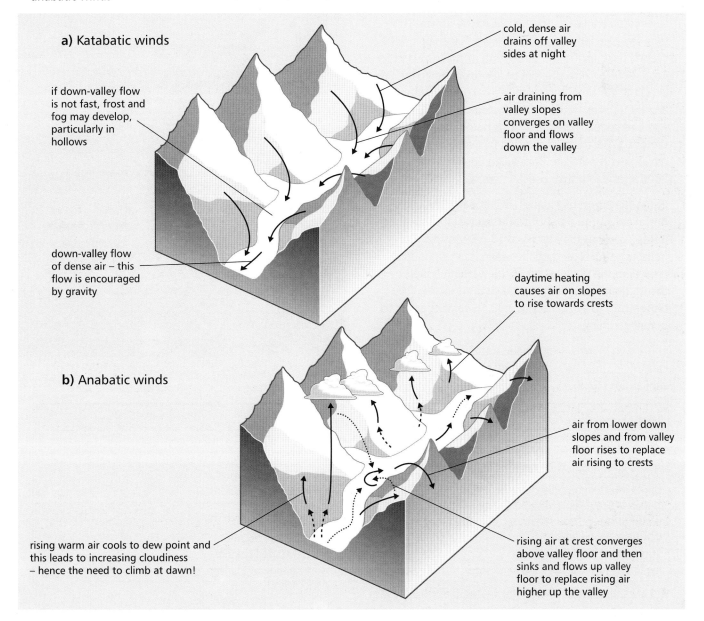

a) Katabatic winds

cold, dense air drains off valley sides at night

if down-valley flow is not fast, frost and fog may develop, particularly in hollows

air draining from valley slopes converges on valley floor and flows down the valley

down-valley flow of dense air – this flow is encouraged by gravity

b) Anabatic winds

daytime heating causes air on slopes to rise towards crests

air from lower down slopes and from valley floor rises to replace air rising to crests

rising warm air cools to dew point and this leads to increasing cloudiness – hence the need to climb at dawn!

rising air at crest converges above valley floor and then sinks and flows up valley floor to replace rising air higher up the valley

CASE STUDY

IT2

Storms over Britain

When the faithful churchgoers of Cwm-yr-Eglwys, Dinas, Pembrokeshire, had to abandon their evensong service on Sunday 25 October 1859 as storm-force northerly winds and heavy seas finally demolished their church (**12.1**), they did not immediately realise that they were the relatively fortunate victims of a severe weather event that was to become known as the Royal Charter Storm. This two-day gale led to the loss of over 100 ships on the Welsh coast, including the sinking of the iron-clad SS *Royal Charter* with the loss of approximately 500 lives. At that time, the storm was accepted without any thought as to the causal factors. After all, there had been equally violent storms before, such as the famous 1703 storm chronicled by Daniel Defoe which was reputed to have killed approximately 8000 sailors in British coastal waters.

When the storm of 15 and 16 October 1987, mistakenly termed a 'hurricane', devastated southern Britain, causing the deaths of 17 people and immense structural damage, apart from the outcry regarding the inadequacy of the warning issued by the Meteorological Office, there was also the temptation to attribute this violent weather event to global warming.

These two storms, though separated by over a century in time, nevertheless displayed amazing similarities (**12.2**).

■ **12.1** Cwm-yr-Eglwys before the storm of 1859 (top) and now

1859	1987
Developed off north-west Spain	Developed in the Bay of Biscay
Moved north-eastwards	Moved north-eastwards
Cyclogenesis resulting from contrasting airstreams	Cyclogenesis from a wave on a cold front
Upper-level trough present	Upper-level trough present
Tentative suggestion of the presence of a jet stream	Jet streaks present
Width of storm 300–500 km	Width of storm 300 km
Central pressure 965 mb	Central pressure 952 mb
Strongest winds 161 km/h	Strongest winds 172 km/h
Rapid pressure changes and wind shear	Pressure change of 25.4 mb in 3 hours and wind shear

■ **12.2** Comparison of two storms, 1859 and 1987

12.1 Increasing change?

IT2,8

These two weather episodes serve to remind us of the significance of abnormal and hazardous weather events. Even in the 20th century the atmospheric weather system can still produce surprises. We might also be tempted to believe that the occurrence of these similar events over a period of a century and a half suggests that sudden violent changes are simply part of the system. Earlier this century, there was an unshakable belief that climatic means calculated over a 30-year period provided a totally reliable base for predicting future climatic conditions.

Change is, of course, endemic to climate, and we recognise these changes on a variety of scales – diurnal and seasonal scales, for example. An abnormal event is perceived as essentially temporary. Thus we are certain that a snowy cold spell will end with a thaw and that a summer drought will eventually break down with a thunderstorm. While this degree of variation is accepted and the fact that the climate must have been very different in the distant past is recognised, until very recently there has been a reluctance to accept any idea of measurable change in contemporary climatic conditions.

Early warnings regarding the effect of human activity on the well-being of our planet were sounded as early as the 1950s by pressure groups such as Greenpeace. The effect on the atmosphere was quickly identified as an area of major concern. However, as with the activities of most pressure groups, it took some time before the message was clearly received in the corridors of power and by the public at large. Climatic change, and particularly that induced by human activity, is now so firmly ingrained in the consciousness that any unusual weather event is immediately heralded as an indicator that change has begun. In the autumn of 1992, the British government sponsored a series of television advertisements linking energy-saving to climatic change.

IT2,8

It is clear that change has always been a feature of the Earth's climate. Apart from the Pleistocene Ice Age, research has revealed the existence of a whole series of climatic trends on a variety of time scales (see section 7.7). There is also great certainty that human activity has the potential to modify climate. It has already been seen on a local scale (see section 8.1 and also section 12.5). Concern is now growing that this will happen, if it has not already begun, on a global scale. Students of the near future will probably grow up in a world increasingly threatened by the effects of climatic change. To date, weather hazards have been referred to as extreme but temporary departures from the norm. There is no doubt that climatic change will represent the greatest hazard that the human race has ever faced. In this chapter we discuss the evidence for change and analyse the natural and human factors being held responsible for initiating such change.

12.2 Evidence of change from the natural world

IT8

The study of geology inevitably involves one in an appraisal of past climatic conditions. While the Coal Measures of the Carboniferous period are an indication of hot, humid periods in the Earth's past, sandstones are proof of drier conditions. Glacial deposits are self-evident manifestations, while throughout geological time fossils of past flora and fauna provide further evidence of former climatic conditions. When, however, we consider more recent geological time, such as the Pleistocene era, the evidence becomes clearer and it is possible to build up a more detailed picture of climatic change by studying changes in sea-level, lake sizes, fossil landforms and glacial and fluvioglacial deposits (see Chapter 7).

IT8

The biological world is also a source of valuable clues. **Pollen analysis** is particularly useful, while **dendrochronology**, or the study of variations in tree-growth ring width, has been applied successfully, with bristlecone pines (*Pinus aristata*) proving to be particularly lucrative on account of its longevity. These trees, which are found mainly in the southern part of the Rocky Mountains in the USA, include stands of 3000-year old trees in Nevada, with one tree reputed to be 4900 years old. Some dead examples go back 8200 years! Since the width of tree-growth rings reflects the availability of moisture and temperature conditions, dendrochronology can provide fairly precise measures of past climates. In dating the age of fossil flora and fauna, **carbon-14 dating** is an even more precise methodology, since it forms a precise proportion of all carbon used for growth and as a radioactive isotope it decays at a fixed rate. It is thus a relatively straightforward and accurate test for gleaning information of earlier climatic conditions.

■ **12.3** Temperature trends over the last 8000 years

12.3 **Evidence of change from human records**

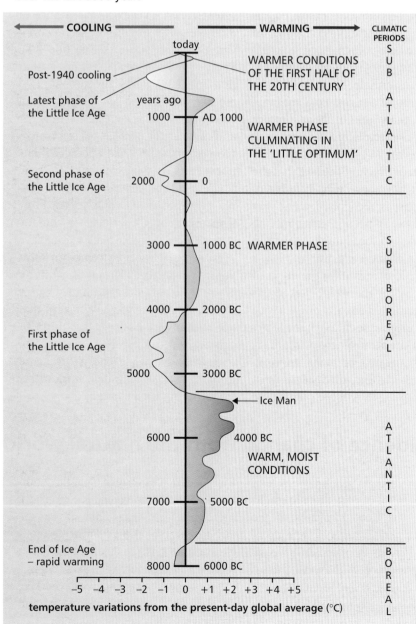

COOLING ← → WARMING

CLIMATIC PERIODS

today

Post-1940 cooling

WARMER CONDITIONS OF THE FIRST HALF OF THE 20TH CENTURY

S U B

Latest phase of the Little Ice Age

years ago

1000 — AD 1000

WARMER PHASE CULMINATING IN THE 'LITTLE OPTIMUM'

A T L A N T I C

Second phase of the Little Ice Age

2000 — 0

3000 — 1000 BC WARMER PHASE

S U B

4000 — 2000 BC

First phase of the Little Ice Age

5000 — 3000 BC

B O R E A L

Ice Man

6000 — 4000 BC

WARM, MOIST CONDITIONS

A T L A N T I C

7000 — 5000 BC

End of Ice Age – rapid warming

8000 — 6000 BC

B O R E A L

-5 -4 -3 -2 -1 0 +1 +2 +3 +4 +5

temperature variations from the present-day global average (°C)

Weather data recorded by instruments has an extremely short history. The first rain gauge was introduced in 1442, but it was not until the late 16th century that thermometers and barometers came into use. The 19th century saw the first tentative and scattered attempts to record some of the elements of weather on a systematic basis at weather stations. However, even a hundred years ago there was still only a very rudimentary and spatially uneven network of weather recording stations. Weather records in the developing countries of the tropics were only collected in quantity after 1945, while even today our knowledge is limited by information 'deserts', most of which, though not all, are oceanic areas (**9.2**).

Satellite technology and remote sensing have led to a rapidly expanding body of knowledge, but we still have a long way to go before we can refer to a valid and reliable global data bank. Even the data presently available is plagued by the uncertainty of its validity in respect of changing sites and instrumental reliability.

Human weather memories are invariably unreliable and relatively short-lived, though written and other evidence from the past does supply useful clues. For prehistoric times, a reliance is placed on archaeological discoveries, but written evidence from the Middle Ages onwards provides a more fruitful source. Thus documents record how Viking expansion and colonisation coincided with warmer conditions and a retreat of North Atlantic sea-ice. Several centuries later, at virtually the same time as Christopher Columbus was finding the New World, the Viking colonies in Greenland were being abandoned as the climate deteriorated and sea-ice advanced once more. Abandoned mine workings and cultivated fields at high altitudes in the Alps also point to the same climatic trend.

From all this evidence, it is possible to sketch a picture, which is initially hazy but then becomes increasingly accurate, of climatic change over the past 10 000 years (**12.3**). In general terms, the cooler periods were also accompanied by heavier totals of precipitation, greater storminess and increasing vulnerability of coastal areas to flooding. Conversely, the warmer periods were drier and generally more settled. It is important to remember that these only represent the average of long-term changes and it is also significant to note how modest the temperature vari-

ations have been. Nevertheless a change of only 1–2 °C in the average temperatures can make a significant difference to the actual climatic conditions experienced and it would undoubtedly have been the case that the actual changes experienced in certain areas would have been even greater.

A broad pattern of trends can be identified in **12.3**. However, weather events and climatic trends are far from predictable and the very hot summers of 1665 and 1666, which coincided with the last great advance of the bubonic plague and with the Great Fire of London respectively, are cases in point here. The danger of attempting to predict change using only a limited range of indicators has already been discussed. The atmospheric system is extremely complex and is controlled by a myriad interrelated mechanisms operating on a variety of spatial and temporal scales. Little wonder it sends out conflicting messages, such as a series of very warm years during the 1980s followed by the extremely cold winter of 1989.

12.4 **Causes of climatic change**

Before the middle of the 20th century, the vagaries of climate were not analysed for the purpose of discovering trends or changes. More recently, however, there has been a growing concern and an attempt to understand the underlying factors responsible for climatic change. A variety of such factors have emerged, some natural, but others ominously related to human activity.

Natural causes

Of the natural factors, astronomical changes in the Earth's orbit, taking place on a regular basis on different time scales ranging from 20 000 to 100 000 years, have long been known to affect global climates (**12.3**). Heightened sunspot activity is another known cause at work on a smaller time scale, whilst at the other extreme it is quite clear that the processes

of continental drift and plate tectonics have played a significant role in generating climatic change. The drifting of the continents from one latitudinal position to another will inevitably have climatic consequences (see sections 2.1 and 2.2), while the building of mountain chains will have encouraged greater accumulations of ice and possibly disruption of global wind systems. The relationship between volcanic activity and climatic trends has been much investigated. Links have tentatively been established between the sequencing of layers of volcanic ash in the Antarctic ice sheet and stages during the Ice Age. The Little Ice Age of 1250–1700 was a period of above average volcanic activity, though between 1500 and 1550 reduced activity correlated with less cold conditions. The first half of the 19th century was

IT3,8

Mount Pinatubo eruption

In June 1991, Mt Pinatubo erupted dramatically on a scale which placed it as the fourth largest volcanic eruption this century. After six centuries of dormancy, preliminary eruptions on 9 June sent a plume of debris and smoke 2 km up into the atmosphere, but by 14 June the scale of eruptions had increased noticeably with plumes now reaching 25 km. A massive eruption on 15 June sent debris almost 40 km high. In total, an estimated 10 billion tonnes of gas and dust were ejected, including 22 million tonnes of sulphur dioxide. The death toll was 500 and the climatic implications were ominous.

The ash, dust and the aerosol cloud formed from the ejections of SO_2 initially took three weeks to travel around the globe. As a massive eruption in a low latitude, the climatic repercussions are expected to be global in extent. Scientists predicted that the pollution would increase the chances of colder winters over the five years 1992–96, and that global temperatures could fall on average by 0.5–1.0°C. Thus Pinatubo will tip the global climatic system in the opposite direction to that resulting from any enhanced greenhouse effect. For several years, and at least until 1996, this eruption alone should be sufficient to offset any warming trend that is occurring. A very significant side-effect of this huge addition to atmospheric hydrogen sulphide will be a further depletion of the ozone layer, with a 10 per cent depletion being a conservative estimate.

IT8

colder again and was also characterised by increased volcanic activity.

Given their extent and the vital role they play in heat and moisture exchanges, it is clear that the oceans play a part in climatic change. Shifts in the broad pattern of oceanic circulation have been detected in the past and what seems to be emerging is that the oceans encourage negative feedback mechanisms. Thus the melting of Arctic ice approximately 11000 years ago had such a cooling effect on the North Atlantic Ocean that it initiated a 500-year cooling trend which led to the re-appearance of glaciers in the mountains of north-west Britain. In the Pacific Ocean, fluctuations in the El Niño effect are known to initiate quite signficant short-term changes in climate.

---

1 What types of feedback mechanism do severe volcanic eruptions cause?

2 Find out what is meant by the term 'a nuclear winter'.

IT8 ## Human causes

The chance discovery in September 1991 of the 'Ice Man' in the Similaun glacier on the Italian side of the Alpine border with Austria provided an opportunity to research in depth the circumstances of one of the earliest recorded weather victims. The preliminary scenario suggests that the 'Ice Man' was crossing this Alpine pass during a recognised period of more moderate climatic conditions (**12.3**), when he was caught on the return journey by worsening weather and subsequently froze to death, later to be encased within the glacier.

The Ice Man's contemporaries were not present in sufficient numbers, nor did they possess the technological know-how, to make much impact on atmospheric processes; for the most part they remained passive victims to climatic conditions. From the 18th century onwards, however, as the human population increased and gained technological expertise, their associated scale and range of economic activities and the need to dispose of ever-increasing quantities of waste in all forms led to an accelerating degradation of atmospheric quality and the upsetting of a variety of finely balanced atmospheric processes.

There are innumerable ways in which human activity has modified climatic conditions and it is possible to suggest several classifications of these

IT8

changes. They could be classified as to their source or their form (i.e. gaseous, liquid or solid), or in relation to the scale of the modification, and there is also a possible simple twofold division into intentional and unintentional modifications. In the remainder of this chapter, climatic change is classified by combining this last criterion with that of scale.

12.5 **Microscale change**

Examples of intended modification of climate at a local scale include cloud-seeding to increase precipitation, and the cultivation of shelter belts to reduce wind speeds. However, these deliberate attempts to engineer climatic change are insignificant compared with those changes inadvertently brought about by people.

---

3 a Find out why shelter belts have been used in the following locations: the lower Rhône valley, Kazakhstan (the Virgin Lands Programme), and along sections of the Trans-Siberian Railway.
   b Outline the benefits of shelter belts to farmers in semi-arid developing countries.
   c Why were hedgerows such a common feature of the British landscape ?
   d Summarise the arguments for and against hedgerow removal.

Any change in land use will affect the boundary layer of the atmosphere and thus the microclimate. Hedgerow removal, drainage schemes and different crop types generate modifications, but it is urbanisation that has had the most dramatic effect on microclimates. A great deal of research has been carried out in urban areas, particularly in the developed world. All these studies reveal a variety of processes and modifications to the air both over and to some extent downstream of urban areas.

The best-known modification is undoubtedly the generation of an **urban heat island** which can result in a steep thermal gradient between the central area and the surrounding suburbs and rural–urban fringe. This temperature difference can be of the order of 6°C and it tends to achieve its maximum at night during summer and early autumn, though it is present at all times of year. The factors contributing to this are:

- Heat is generated by energy use such as power stations, all types of buildings, transport and even human movement. It has been estimated that in German cities, such as Hamburg, coal-burning power stations produced more heat during the winters in the 1950s than was derived from the sun. Remember that even air-conditioning plants designed to cool building temperatures use energy and thus contribute to the urban heat island.

- The urban fabric is made up of building materials with generally high thermal capacities: that is, they absorb and store solar energy by day which is then released at night.

- Urban areas tend to produce an overall reduction in airflow, which means that less heat is lost and dissipated into any airstream moving across the area.

- The greatly increased pollutant content of the air tends to reduce losses through longwave radiation, so locally it enhances the greenhouse effect.

- The relative absence of plants and open water surfaces, together with the efficiency of urban drainage systems, mean that less heat is lost as energy required to evaporate water.

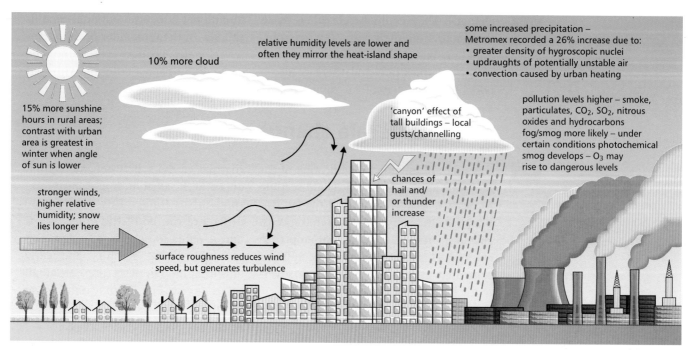

15% more sunshine hours in rural areas; contrast with urban area is greatest in winter when angle of sun is lower

10% more cloud

relative humidity levels are lower and often they mirror the heat-island shape

some increased precipitation – Metromex recorded a 26% increase due to:
• greater density of hygroscopic nuclei
• updraughts of potentially unstable air
• convection caused by urban heating

'canyon' effect of tall buildings – local gusts/channelling

pollution levels higher – smoke, particulates, CO_2, SO_2, nitrous oxides and hydrocarbons fog/smog more likely – under certain conditions photochemical smog develops – O_3 may rise to dangerous levels

stronger winds, higher relative humidity; snow lies longer here

chances of hail and/ or thunder increase

surface roughness reduces wind speed, but generates turbulence

■ **12.4** Urban modifications of climate

■ **12.5** Basic characteristics of a plume of modified urban air

Urban surfaces can modify climatic conditions in other ways too, and these are summarised in **12.4**. Thus any urban area of reasonable size will tend to modify atmospheric conditions to such a degree as to warrant the use of the term 'an urban climate'. These modifications have increased as urbanisation has accelerated. Milan, for example, with a population of 185 000 in 1860, was estimated to have created a local warming effect of approximately 0.6 °C, and by 1971, when the population had risen to 1 750 000, this temperature had doubled to 1.3 °C.

Urban climatic modifications develop to their greatest extent during spells of relatively quiet weather such as during anticyclonic conditions. Under these circumstances, urban heat islands may acquire depths of more than 1000 m. To an extent, the air stagnating over and acquiring the specific characteristics of an urban area may be regarded as a temporary small-scale airmass: an urban airmass. While the central urban area serves as its source region, this modified air may also spread and affect the climate of adjacent areas. This expansion is most likely to occur downwind of a large urban area, where a plume of modified urban air may lead to higher

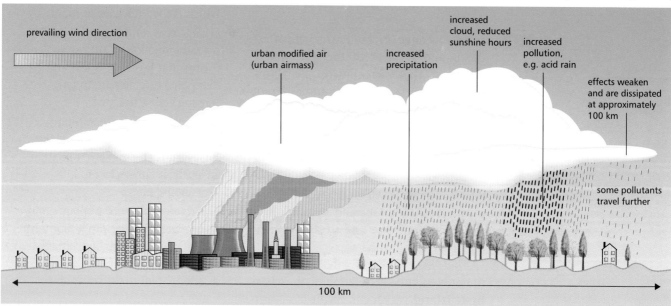

prevailing wind direction

urban modified air (urban airmass)

increased precipitation

increased cloud, reduced sunshine hours

increased pollution, e.g. acid rain

effects weaken and are dissipated at approximately 100 km

some pollutants travel further

100 km

CASE STUDY

Urban climate in Shanghai and Johannesburg

Most research on urban climates has inevitably concentrated on temperate latitudes, though with urbanisation accelerating in the subtropical world where pollution controls are comparatively relaxed, modifications are occurring here too.

Shanghai, China's largest city, displays a well-developed heat island and lower relative humidity levels than the surrounding countryside, and **12.6** illustrates its enhanced rainfall totals. This last modification is due to the presence of above-average concentrations of hygroscopic nuclei, the convective triggering effect of urban heating, and a suggestion that a barrier effect is created by the urban fabric which can cause weak fronts to be retarded in their movement; this can lead to longer and augmented rainfall events.

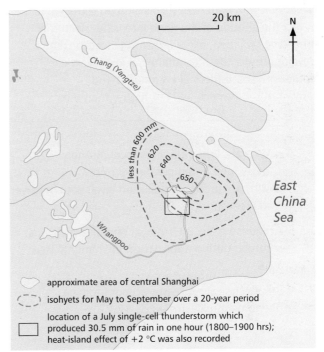

- approximate area of central Shanghai
- isohyets for May to September over a 20-year period
- location of a July single-cell thunderstorm which produced 30.5 mm of rain in one hour (1800–1900 hrs); heat-island effect of +2 °C was also recorded

■ **12.6** Some features of the precipitation pattern of Shanghai

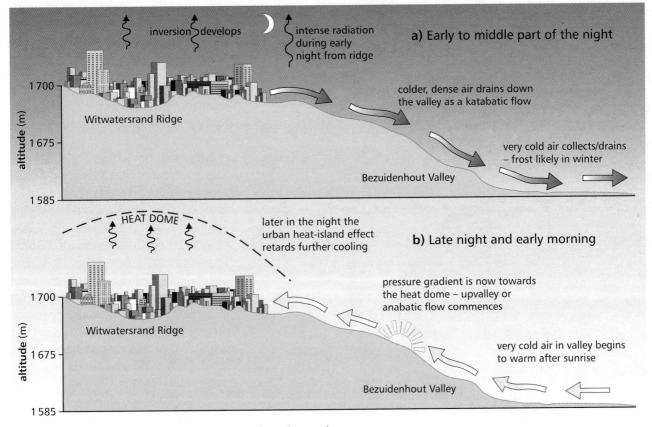

■ **12.7** The formation of 'country breezes' in the Johannesburg area

Johannesburg, South Africa's largest city, is located on the Witwatersrand ridge at an altitude of 1700 m. Nevertheless, it generates its own urban climate and in fact the altitude of the ridge intensifies nocturnal longwave radiation, allowing strong inversions to develop. Under these conditions, a low-level heat dome with sharp thermal boundaries and temperatures as much as 11 °C higher than the surrounding countryside can develop. Although rainfall totals are up to 25 per cent higher than adjacent lowland areas, it is difficult to differentiate between the altitudinal and the urban effect, though as in Shanghai some intense summer convectional showers appear to be the result of urban modification. Anabatic winds called 'country breezes' are another modification in Johannesburg (**12.7**).

4 a Why are urban climates most strongly developed in temperate latitudes?
  b Why are urban air pollution levels usually lower at weekends?

5 Account for the 30.5 mm of rainfall which was recorded during a July storm in Shanghai (see **12.6**).

6 What physical processes account for the phenomenon illustrated by **12.7**?

7 Record the pollution levels for SO_2, N_2O and O_3 published by the Department of the Environment; these are shown daily on Ceefax page number 404. Record this data for a period of one month and use it to construct air pollution maps and diagrams. You might wish to test for any relationship between the strength of two of these pollutants. You could also sample one summer and one winter month. This data together with the appropriate synoptic information could form the databank for an interesting individual study.

12.6 **Global climatic change – global warming**

■ **12.8** Proportions and annual growth rates of greenhouse gases

IT3,8

Causes

The causes of the enhanced greenhouse effect or global warming are by now well documented. Although its current annual rate of increase is less than any other greenhouse gas, the single most important greenhouse gas is CO_2. (**12.8**). Nearly 80 per cent of the human-induced or anthropogenic increase is due to the burning of fossil fuels, with the remainder being accounted for by deforestation which reduces the effectiveness of natural carbon cycling (see section 13.5). The global system has simply not been able to accommodate this huge increase in carbon over the past two centuries. It has only utilised 50 per cent of this increase through more rapid photosynthesis, particularly by trees and through absorption by oceanic plankton and by sea water itself. The net result has been a 25 per cent increase in the levels of atmospheric CO_2 since medieval times, with

IT3,8

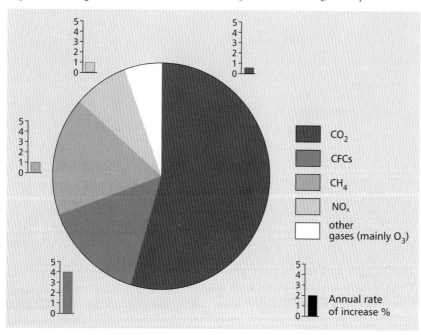

CO₂

CFCs

CH_4

NO_x

other gases (mainly O_3)

Annual rate of increase %

the Northern Hemisphere being responsible for 95 per cent of this, and the USA alone accounting for approximately 25 per cent.

12.8 reminds us of the significance of the other greenhouse gases, which though present in smaller quantities are growing at faster rates and are also more effective molecule for molecule than CO_2. CFCs, the well-known ozone depletors, represent the largest of this secondary group and their current rate of increase is alarming (see section 12.7). Methane is being released as the result of an expansion of rice cultivation, more intensive pastoral farming, burning vegetation and by leakages in coal and gas production. Nitrous oxides (NO_x) are released through the use of artificial nitrogenous fertilisers as well as by the combustion of wood and other fossil fuels. With a lifespan of approximately 170 years, this group of oxides has great potential as a greenhouse gas.

Consequences

The predicted effects of global warming will be more dramatic both in terms of their scale and their rapidity than any previous natural fluctuation (**12.9**). The present climate is expected to change in several ways with a variety of scenarios being suggested by large-scale computer models called **global circulation**

models (GCMs). The 'business as usual' scenario assumes that emissions of all greenhouse gases will continue to increase at present rates. This will lead to a doubling of CO_2 equivalent concentrations by the year 2030. On this basis, temperatures are expected to rise (and this rise may already have begun) by 1 °C by that date and by approximately 3 °C by the year 2100. Other estimates put the predicted rise much higher at 5–9 °C. This margin of error is due primarily to the uncertain effect of a variety of feedback mechanisms. Several feedback mechanisms will be important during any period of global warming. Thus increasing temperatures would result in increasing evaporation and an increase in water vapour, a naturally occurring and effective greenhouse gas. However, this positive feedback is likely to be countered by a predicted 10–15 per cent increase in cloud cover which is expected to produce an overall cooling trend, i.e a negative feedback reaction.

Another complicating factor will be the nature of the role played by the oceans and any effect there might be on existing vertical and horizontal transfers of oceanic water. Overall the oceanic effect will delay any warming-up process. However, other feedback mechanisms are more disturbing,

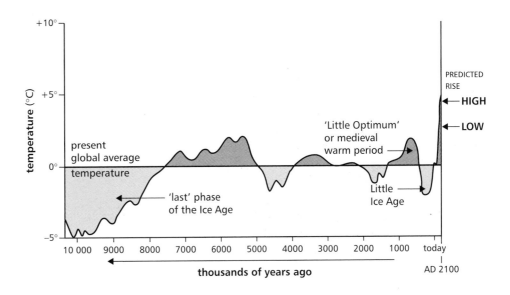

■ **12.9** Predicted global warming in relation to past climatic trends

IT3, 8

such as the 'runaway greenhouse effect' which would ensue from the release of huge quantities of methane at present trapped in tundra permafrost. This would increase the pace of global warming which in turn would accelerate the thawing process, thus releasing further quantities of methane.

There will be other climatic consequences. Global precipitation is expected to increase by 7 per cent but most of this will be accounted for by an increase in higher latitudes, while many areas in the tropics and subtropics are predicted to become drier. Climatic belts may shift and thus many believe that the climate of southern Britain will change from a marine west coast climate to a Mediterranean type. A final climatic consequence of global warming will be greater frequency of extreme, and thus hazardous, events. Droughts, floods linked with, for example, more frequent storm surges in the North Sea, greater storminess and extremes of temperature are to be expected.

IT5

These changes will affect economic and social well-being in many ways. What seems to be clear is that it is the subtropical and tropical countries of Brandt's South that will suffer most. When combined with increasing aridity, a modest rise in temperature will exacer-

bate problems such as desertification and adversely affect agriculture generally. Needless to say, it is in the South that nations will be least able to cope with the predicted rise in sea-level: think of the huge challenge that will confront Bangladesh with its millions of people presently living at or close to sea-level. Within the South the poorest people, particularly the urban poor, will suffer most because their hillside and floodplain shanty settlements will be most prone to extreme weather events such as heavy rain and flash floods. Flooding in some areas and drought in others may precipitate massive migrations of climatic or 'greenhouse' refugees. Emissions of greenhouse gases to date have already committed the world to a temperature rise of at least 1.6°C by 2030 and this emphasises the need for swift and effective strategies to combat this threat to global well-being.

IT5

Remedies

IT4

Without a doubt, it is energy use that is the key to controlling anthropogenic emissions of greenhouse gases and it will be vital to tackle these at source. There seems to be little hope of controlling demand, which seems certain to double by 2020. Even if we curb energy demand in the developed world this will be more than compensated for by a rapid increase emanating from the economic aspirations of an expanding population in the developing world (**12.10**).

The first strategy involves the use of fuels that emit less CO_2. Natural gas emits only 60 per cent of the CO_2 that coal does, while nuclear energy and that derived from renewable sources emit virtually none. (Small amounts are released as a result of the energy consumed in the construction of power plants and in the mining of uranium.) The problem here is that gas is a non-renewable resource and that the reserves of coal are 20 times those of gas, while despite the progress made in some countries, for example in France

■ **12.10** Trends in carbon dioxide emissions in six areas, 1960–85

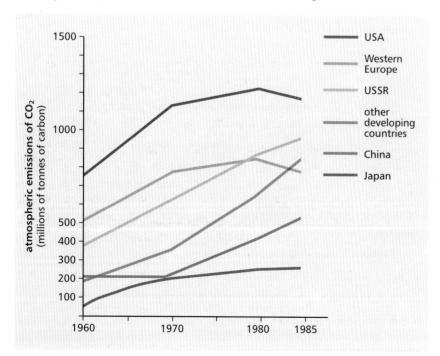

atmospheric emissions of CO_2 (millions of tonnes of carbon)

USA
Western Europe
USSR
other developing countries
China
Japan

where nuclear power plants account for two-thirds of the electricity produced, there are still concerns about the hidden costs and the environmental impact of this type of energy (see Chapter 27).

A second approach is to apply technology to ensure that we use the energy we need more efficiently. Technology is likely to make great advances in fuel consumption in transport, with energy-saving light bulbs and other domestic appliances and with combined heat and power-generating stations. Another important aspect of energy saving would be to improve energy conservation in all types of buildings.

A third useful approach would be to enhance nature's recycling of carbon

through a reduction in the rate of deforestation and by large-scale re-afforestation.

Reductions in emissions of other greenhouse gases will be important too. To date efforts have inevitably concentrated on the ozone-depleting qualities of CFCs, but the presently preferred alternatives, such as HCFCs and HFCs, remain powerful greenhouse enhancers. A reduction in emissions of nitrous oxides could be achieved through a reduced reliance on artificial fertilisers, while methane emissions could fall with an adoption of less intense cattle farming practices and by halting the clearance of forest by burning.

8 What types of feedback mechanism are illustrated here:
a temperatures rise → more polar ice melts → albedo rate falls → more solar energy is absorbed → temperatures rise
b increasing concentrations of atmospheric CO_2 → global rise in sea temperatures → rate of CO_2 absorption by oceans declines → increasing concentrations of atmospheric CO_2?

9 Evaluate the possible effects of global warming on the following:
a agriculture
b the water supply industry
c forestry
d health.

10 In any strategy designed to reduce emissions of greenhouse gases, what difficult decisions might have to be made in relation to:
a transport
b power generation?

[NB It has been estimated that motor vehicles will be emitting as much CO_2 as power stations by the year 2045.]

11 Study the data in **12.11** and then construct an argument in support of the continuing use of coal as a fuel for energy production.

12 How might the predicted climatic change for southern Britain affect the urban climate of London?

13 Who will gain and who will lose from the predicted outcome of the greenhouse effect?

1150 MEGAWATT POWER STATION	
Nuclear	**Coal-fired**
Requires 186 tonnes of uranium a year	Requires 5 million tonnes of coal a year
Produces 650 m³ of waste a year, of which over 15% is long-life radioactive material	Produces 1 million tonnes of ash, 11 million tonnes of CO_2 and 16 million tonnes of SO_2

■ **12.11** Comparison of emissions from nuclear and coal-fired power stations

oxygen molecules are split into individual oxygen atoms by UVR (O_2 + UVR → O + O) one oxygen atom combines with a molecule of oxygen to produce ozone (O + O_2 → O_2)

PRODUCTION OF OZONE

UVR varies seasonally and on a longer time scale in relation to sunspot activity; high sunspot activity in the late 1980s to1991 led to increased production of ozone

O Z O N E   L A Y E R

THE RESULT IS AN OVERALL BUT FLUCTUATING BALANCE

some ozone removed by rain

SO_2 from volcanic activity combines with H_2O to form H_2SO_2

DESTRUCTION OF OZONE

nitrous oxides from soil bacteria and oceanic upwelling

methane from swamps

■ **12.12** The birth and death of ozone in the atmosphere

12.7 **Ozone depletion – too much down here, too little up there**

Ozone, a minor gas in the atmosphere, is toxic and can constitute a health hazard in the lower atmosphere, but higher up it fulfils a vital function in screening the Earth's surface from harmful amounts of ultraviolet (UV) radiation.

The increasing concentration of ozone in some areas near the Earth's surface is now being balanced by a decline in the upper atmosphere. **12.12** illustrates how the ozone level can vary and that this gas is constantly being produced and destroyed by natural factors.

Early warnings in the 1970s regarding ozone depletion were largely ignored and thus 1985 is regarded as the date for the official discovery of the 'ozone hole' over Antarctica, although measurements suggest that 1975 marks the onset of serious ozone depletion in the area (**12.12** and **12.16**). This phenomenon is linked primarily with the increased usage of CFC gases in such things as aerosol cans and the manufacture of refrigerators. Cheap, non-toxic and non-flammable, they were hailed as a technological breakthrough when they they were invented in the 1920s. Their large-scale usage dates from the 1960s but it soon became apparent that their industrial benefits involved an environmental cost. **12.13** illustrates

how CFCs and halons cause devastating damage in the ozone layer, whilst **12.14** analyses how Antarctica with its unique geographical and atmospheric conditions provides the perfect setting for ozone depletion.

It is tempting to consider ozone depletion simply in terms of polar regions and undoubtedly it is over Antarctica that the springtime thinning has reached record levels (a 50 per cent loss was recorded in 1992). However, the 3 per cent annual global loss recorded between 1979 and 1990 includes increasing losses over populated temperate areas in North America, Europe and the Russian Federation. Small but significant losses are also being recorded in tropical areas.

Health risks – is a suntan really desirable?

In 1863 Admiral Fitzroy, a keen meteorologist, claimed that ozone 'improves the digestion and has a tanning effect'. Ultraviolet light does encourage the formation of vitamin D. However, a disturbing trend over the past half-century has been the increasing incidence of skin cancer, a simple

IT2, 8

IT2, 8

IT5, 6

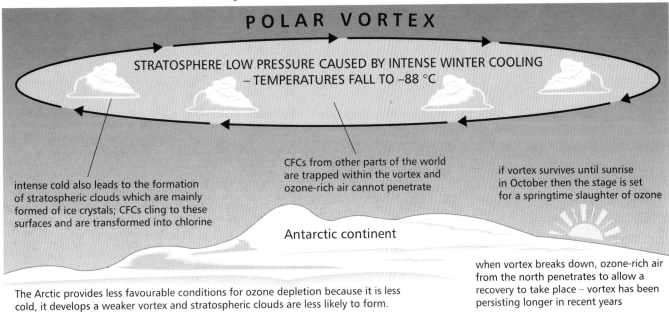

OZONE IS NOW BEING DESTROYED AT A FASTER RATE THAN IT CAN BE REPLENISHED

ULTRAVIOLET RADIATION

OZONE LAYER

OZONE absorbs **UVR**

chlorine atom from **CFCs** destroys ozone by taking one oxygen atom to form chlorine monoxide and oxygen

chlorine monoxide later combines with oxygen to form a new oxygen molecule and a chlorine atom; this destructive activity of chlorine can be repeated so that up to 10 000 ozone molecules are lost over a period of time

OXYGEN allows **UVR** to penetrate to Earth

CFCs
(foam, coolants in air-conditioning and refrigerators, propellant in sprays, etc.)

HALONS
(in fire extinguishers) release bromine which also destroys ozone

METHANE
from burning vegetation, increased rice production, intensive cattle farming

■ **12.13** How human activity destroys ozone in the atmosphere

IT5,6

classification of which appears in **12.15**. Although some believe that factors such as the use of oral contraceptives, oestrogens, exposure to fluorescent light and even diet may be responsible, the role of ultraviolet radiation in sunlight is of overwhelming importance. Sunlight may be the cause, but genetic factors affect the potential risk, with light-skinned, fair-haired, blue-eyed Nordic people being high on the risk scale.

Socio-economic factors are also significant. Office workers appear to be a high-risk group in developed countries, with cancer developing on the body trunk rather than on the head and neck. This group has a lifestyle with relatively little exposure to sunlight, but during

leisure time they may expose themselves to periods of intense sunlight and during holidays this exposure may be prolonged, with migration to lower or sunnier latitudes ensuring guaranteed sunshine. Fashion and peer pressure have over the past few decades dictated that a suntan is a desirable attribute. This desire has become an obsessive cult, with beachwear fashion trends permitting the exposure of more and more of the human torso to sunlight. Thus while in Mediterranean cultures the midday sun is deliberately avoided, affluent and largely fair-skinned people flock to such areas to deliberately expose themselves to the sun.

IT5,6

■ **12.14** The springtime 'slaughter' of ozone over Antarctica

POLAR VORTEX

STRATOSPHERE LOW PRESSURE CAUSED BY INTENSE WINTER COOLING – TEMPERATURES FALL TO –88 °C

CFCs from other parts of the world are trapped within the vortex and ozone-rich air cannot penetrate

if vortex survives until sunrise in October then the stage is set for a springtime slaughter of ozone

intense cold also leads to the formation of stratospheric clouds which are mainly formed of ice crystals; CFCs cling to these surfaces and are transformed into chlorine

Antarctic continent

when vortex breaks down, ozone-rich air from the north penetrates to allow a recovery to take place – vortex has been persisting longer in recent years

The Arctic provides less favourable conditions for ozone depletion because it is less cold, it develops a weaker vortex and stratospheric clouds are less likely to form.

Group or type	Malignancy	Incidence	Causal factors	Estimated % increase based on a 1% ozone depletion
Melanoma (known as malignant melanoma)	High (25% of cases result in death)	Males and young people	Associated with exposure to short bursts of sunlight, especially in early life; people who 'burn' rather than 'tan' are particularly prone	1 – 2
Non-melanoma skin cancers squamous cell carcinoma	High	Mainly older people	Associated with an accumulation of sunlight exposure hours; often develops on exposed areas of the body such as the head, neck or arms	3 – 5
basal cell carcinoma	Local	Generally	Also associated with an accumulation of sunlight exposure hours, and also develops in sun-free areas such as behind the ears – therefore could be trauma-induced, caused by wearing spectacles, braces or brassière	2 – 3

■ **12.15** A simple classification of skin cancer

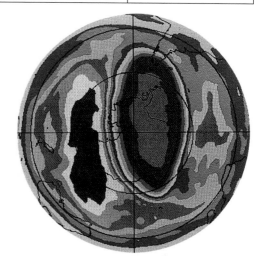

■ **12.16** Satellite map showing the extent of Antarctic ozone depletion in 1992. The oval pink area is the so-called 'hole' in the ozone layer

CASE STUDY

IT5

Skin cancer in Australia

Australia still holds the unenviable honour of being the world's league leader for the incidence of skin cancer. The data indicate clear links with skin pigmentation, with Aborigines and migrants from South-east Asia having lower rates than fair-skinned Australians. Length of residency is also significant, with migrants from Europe displaying lower rates than people born in Australia. Similarly with age, for it is the younger local people, reared on a 'sun exposure culture', who stand the greatest risk of developing skin cancer in later life. Thus young, fair-skinned immigrants are at greater risk than older immigrants. It is people who 'burn' rather than 'tan' who are at greatest risk. The occupational risk is also apparent, with outdoor workers being particularly prone to

developing skin cancer. Finally, there is an inverse relationship with latitude, with Queensland's death rate being double that of Victoria.

The fact that Geraldton, Western Australia, popularly known as Sun City, has the highest incidence of skin cancer in Australia – 1560 per 100 000 of 40–64 year olds compared with the national average of 1262 – indicates the predominant role that exposure to sunlight exerts. The high percentage of possible sunshine hours experienced throughout Australia provides ample opportunity for virtually anyone to enjoy outdoor leisure activities all year round. Economic development and physical factors have ensured a coastal concentration of population which means easy access to beaches for these leisure activities. Australia's demographic structure shows a large proportion of young/middle-aged people – the very groups who favour beach leisure activities. Finally, the rapidly increasing affluence and the increase in amounts of leisure time since 1945 have further encouraged the boom in coastal tourism such as is found along the Gold Coast of Queensland.

It is important to remember that skin cancer is not a new disease and that the chances of developing lung cancer remains seven times higher. However, both are generally avoidable diseases and most of skin cancer cases recorded in the post-war period were contracted before ozone depletion began, as there is a time-lag between exposure to ultraviolet B rays and the development of cancer. To a very large extent,

therefore, the present trends are a consequence of economic, sociological and physiological factors. The increasing rate and latitudinal spread of ozone depletion will make matters worse, but on current information this effect will probably reveal itself first in temperate latitudes and therefore in Australia an increase in the incidence of skin cancer is anticipated in Tasmania. It is estimated that a sustained 10 per cent depletion in ozone levels would result in a 26 per cent increase in non-melanoma skin cancer throughout the world, i.e. an approximate but conservative estimate of 300 000 cases, with an additional 4500 cases of melanoma.

IT5

Responses to ozone depletion

To date responses have been at two levels. First, there has been the preventive response to the medical threat as illustrated by the Australian jingle '*Slip* on a T-shirt, *slop* on some cream and *slap* on a hat!' We have become accustomed to the sunblocks and sunglasses worn by some Australian cricketers. In Australia, the government issues regular ozone alerts and public awareness is being raised by stressing the dangers of sunbathing during the middle of the day, and the need for adequate protection; for example, suncreams with a minimum protection factor of 15 are advised. In New Zealand, schoolchildren are urged to wear hats and eat school lunches in the shade, while in southern Chile schoolchildren are kept indoors at midday. While these measures reflect concern in the Southern Hemisphere nearest to the Antarctic thinning of the ozone layer (**12.16**), in recent years concern has become worldwide, with time warnings now being issued with the daily summer weather forecasts in the UK.

Secondly, there has been the response at the political level. The Montreal Convention (1987), initially signed by 46 nations, called for a 50 per cent reduction in CFC production by 1990. Later agreements urged a complete phasing out by 2000, whilst Germany has decided unilat-

IT5

erally to achieve this step by 1995. Worldwide consumption has dropped by 40 per cent from 1986 levels.

Several constraints will minimise the effectiveness of such measures. On the medical front, there is the psychological barrier to surmount, of a lifestyle where a suntan is seen as highly desirable, while on the political front there is the inevitable problem of achieving total international cooperation. There is a desperate need for the developed world to persuade and encourage developing nations to forgo the perceived benefits of using CFCs. Finally, the fact that CFCs and halons with their long, active lifespan are so effective as ozone depletors makes the need for action now rather than later very urgent. Without such action, US Vice-President Al Gore's comment, 'What will it do to our children's outlook on life if we have to teach them to be afraid to look up?' might well be a vision that comes true.

IT1,8

It is up to us as individuals to decide how far we want our governments to proceed with some of the difficult decisions that will have to be made if we are to sustain development throughout the 21st century. What is perhaps the most frightening aspect of all is that, even with the aid of computer and satellite technology, most experts assert that it will be at least a decade before we gain full understanding of the highly complicated and

14 Use the data in **12.17** to test the relationship between latitude and the incidence of skin cancer.
  a What conclusions do you reach?
  b How might melanoma death rates change in these locations by the year 2000?

15 Record high levels of chlorine monoxide were recorded in the atmosphere in 1992. Summarise the physical and human factors which may have contributed to this.

16 Use the data in **12.18** to construct a scattergraph. Insert best-fit lines and comment briefly on the trends.

17 a Why is it probably true to say that until recently the decreasing size of bikinis has been a more important causal factor than ozone depletion in accounting for the increasing incidence of skin cancer?
  b What would your proposals be for curbing the increasing incidence of skin cancer?

Country/area	Latitude where population was screened	Annual deaths from melanoma per million
Norway	61°N	10
Sweden	59°N	9
Scotland	56°N	4
England	53°N	6
France	48°N	1
Italy	43°N	2
North-east USA	42°N	9
California	37°N	12
Queensland	27°N	23
South Africa		
Transvaal	27°S	10
Natal	29°S	18
New Zealand		
North Island	39°S	12
South Island	45°S	8

■ **12.17** The incidence of skin cancer at different latitudes

Period	Female rate	Male rate
1930–34	0.5	0.7
1935–39	0.5	0.7
1940–44	0.8	0.8
1945–49	0.9	1.0
1950–54	1.1	1.4
1955–59	1.5	2.1
1960–64	1.8	2.4
1965–69	1.9	2.8
1970–74	2.0	3.0
1975–79	2.1	3.7
1980–84	2.2	4.0
1985–89	2.4	4.5

■ **12.18** Melanoma mortality rates for Australia, 1930–89

IT1, 8

increasingly vulnerable system we call the atmosphere. Continued research thus remains vital and several recent projects point to the significant role that the oceans play in climatic change. The Tropical Ocean Global Atmosphere research programme, based in Townsville, Australia, has focused on ocean–atmosphere interchanges in the western Pacific 'warm pool'. This is an area the size of the USA, where persistently high ocean surface temperatures of 28–30°C generate intense convection, building cumulonimbus tops reaching 18km and provoking an annual rainfall of 5000mm. This injection of vast quantities of energy into the upper atmosphere influences weather systems over the entire globe. Indeed, this warm pool may be regarded as the powerhouse of the atmosphere. A better understanding of ocean–atmosphere interactions is crucial, particularly since this pool is indisputably linked with the El Niño effect.

Similarly, early results from ice cores drilled in central Greenland indicate that the Earth's climate can change suddenly, sometimes within the space of a few decades, and it seems that alterations in the pattern of oceanic circulation may be significant here. Finally, there appears to be increasing scepticism about the global warming scenario. Some authorities now suggest that the oceanic uptake of CO_2 has been grossly underestimated, that tropical deforestation, especially in Amazonia, has been overestimated and that the role of regenerated temperate forests as a sink for CO_2 has been underestimated.

We still do not know with certainty whether or not the 0.3–0.6°C global increase in temperature recorded since 1890 is due to human interference. This rise lies easily within the bounds of natural climatic variability. What we can be certain about is that human activity is changing the composition of our atmosphere. Our interference with this system could be considered for a long time as unintentional, but over the past 30 years we must surely classify it as intentional. To interfere in this way thus seems to be at best foolish and at worst perilous, for it is certain that as far as our future on planet Earth is concerned, Nature will have the final say.

IT1, 8

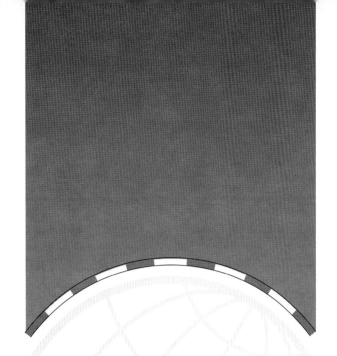

Ecosystems

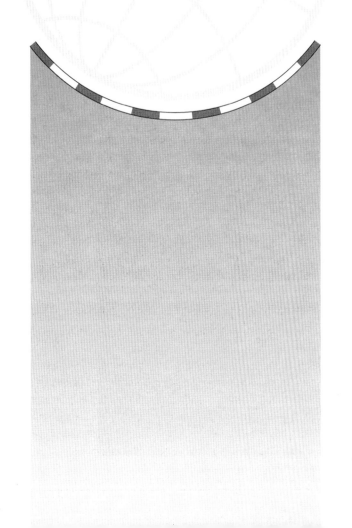

13.1 **Introduction**

An ecosystem is a basic functional unit of nature, consisting of living organisms (plants and animals) and their non-living environment (air, water, soil and rock). Balanced ecosystems vary greatly in size. They may be as small as a jam-jar of water containing microscopic algae (small green plants) and protozoa (single-celled animals), or a single tree and its dependents; or as large as the rainforests of South America – or even the whole of life on Earth. An ecosystem always functions as a whole unit and is a self-sustaining system, with the physical (or **abiotic**) components and the living organisms of that system all influencing each other. Both parts are needed for the development and maintenance of the system.

There are many types of ecosystem, even within a relatively small area such as the British Isles. Some are on land; others are aquatic. The oak tree shown in **13.1** may be considered as an example of a small ecosystem. The tree, the other organisms it associates with and the immediate physical environment all function together as a close-knit biological community or association. A tree may not appear to be doing very much at any given moment in time but, when it is in leaf, it is respiring, obtaining water and raw materials from its environment, manufacturing sugars (such as glucose), getting rid of waste, sensing and responding to changes in its surroundings. It may also be flowering or producing seeds (in this case acorns) or even starting to die and decay. The oak also alters the physical environment immediately around it by creating local micro-climatic effects such as shelter from wind and rain, shade, circulating water from the soil into the air by transpiration, and in countless other ways.

The physical environment provides the oak with all of its vital needs: living space, energy and raw materials such as air, water and minerals. A whole community of other living things – plants, insects, birds, mammals, fungi, bacteria and other micro-organisms – rely on the oak tree for their own survival. The tree produces their food and provides them with shelter. The tree, however, is dependent in its turn on the activities of many of these organisms. For example, squirrels and jays disperse its acorns by hiding them in the soil as a potential food supply for winter. Any acorns that are not recovered and eaten, germinate and grow up to become the next generation of oak trees.

Each autumn, an oak tree sheds its leaves to reduce the tree's demand for water. This is an adaptation to the climate in which this type of tree occurs. **Deciduous plants**, such as oak trees, survive freezing weather conditions in winter when water is not available to them in liquid form, by losing their leaves.

Not even an oak can live for ever, although some are known to have survived for 800 years. Trees are often damaged during gales, losing twigs and

■ **13.1** An oak tree – a small ecosystem

branches. Once the protective bark is cracked or broken open by strong winds or some other means (perhaps by a woodpecker), a whole army of organisms can move in to begin the process of disease and decay. Fallen leaves, twigs and branches are recycled by 'decomposer' organisms, which return the essential nutrients and chemicals of which the organic materials of the tree were made, to the soil, and the ecosystem is sustained for future generations of plants and animals.

13.2 The food factory

IT1

■ **13.2** The inputs and outputs of an oak leaf during photosynthesis

All ecosystems require energy in order to exist. This is provided by sunlight, with only minor contributions from other sources. Energy from the sun reaches the Earth's surface in two forms: heat energy and light energy. Heat energy cannot be IT1 used directly by plants and animals, but it warms the surroundings and speeds up chemical reactions. Light energy can be captured, however, but only by green plants during the process known as **photosynthesis**. The green pigment **chlorophyll** found within leaf cells is able to capture light energy and convert it into food energy by manufacturing **carbohydrates** (energy-storing chemicals) using elements such as oxygen, carbon and hydrogen as the 'building blocks'.

13.2 shows the inputs and outputs of an oak leaf during photosynthesis. The inputs are carbon dioxide from the atmosphere, water, minerals from the soil and heat energy from sunlight. These are combined during photosynthesis to build complex carbohydrates: sugars, starches, amino acids, proteins, fats and vitamins. As all of these organic materials are needed by animals for growth, movement and reproduction, green plants are the basis of all food chains.

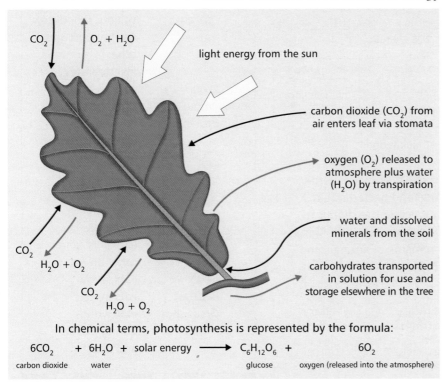

In chemical terms, photosynthesis is represented by the formula:

$$6CO_2 + 6H_2O + \text{solar energy} \longrightarrow C_6H_{12}O_6 + 6O_2$$

carbon dioxide   water   glucose   oxygen (released into the atmosphere)

13.3 Trophic levels and energy flows

By means of photosynthesis, green plants are the **primary producers** of food and energy for the whole ecosystem, passed from one organism to another along the **food chain**. Animals, along with a few groups of non-green plants such as fungi and some bacteria, are the **consumers**. Only about 1 per cent of the light energy falling on a leaf is converted into food energy and stored as carbohydrate molecules (**13.3**). Thus the total amount of energy available to the food chain is limited by the amount that can be trapped and stored during photosynthesis by the green plants.

Consumers include:

- herbivores (primary consumers) – eat green plants

- carnivores (secondary consumers) – catch and eat herbivores

- top carnivores (tertiary consumers) – prey on herbivores and other carnivores

- omnivores – eat both animals and plants

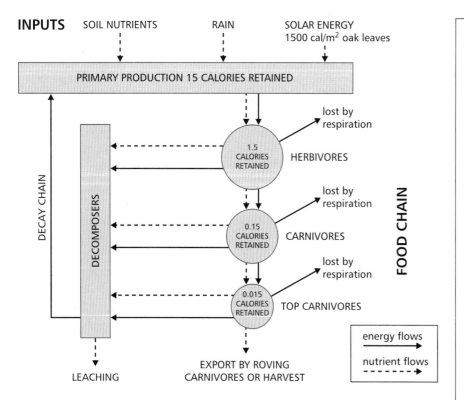

INPUTS

SOIL NUTRIENTS   RAIN   SOLAR ENERGY
1500 cal/m² oak leaves

PRIMARY PRODUCTION 15 CALORIES RETAINED

DECAY CHAIN

DECOMPOSERS

1.5 CALORIES RETAINED   HERBIVORES   lost by respiration

0.15 CALORIES RETAINED   CARNIVORES   lost by respiration

0.015 CALORIES RETAINED   TOP CARNIVORES   lost by respiration

FOOD CHAIN

energy flows
nutrient flows

LEACHING   EXPORT BY ROVING CARNIVORES OR HARVEST

■ **13.3** Energy and nutrient flows and losses in an oak wood

■ **13.4** Simplified food web based on an oak tree as a producer

■ decomposers – non-green plants, mainly fungi and bacteria, that release and recycle the chemicals contained within animal droppings and dead remains of animals and plants (**13.4**).

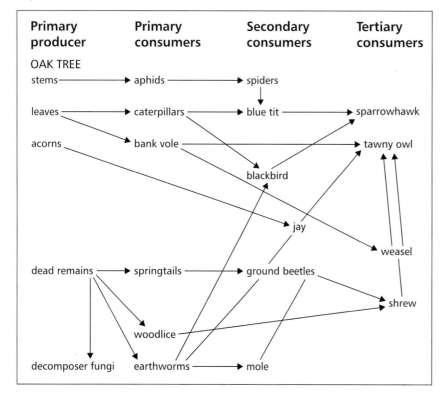

Primary producer	Primary consumers	Secondary consumers	Tertiary consumers
OAK TREE			
stems → aphids → spiders			
leaves → caterpillars → blue tit → sparrowhawk			
acorns → bank vole			tawny owl
	blackbird		
	jay		weasel
dead remains → springtails → ground beetles			shrew
	woodlice		
decomposer fungi earthworms → mole			

1 13.5 shows how the consumers in that food web occupy different links along the food chain, each link being referred to as a **trophic level.** What are the trophic levels of each of the following organisms? [Some may occur at more than one level.]

Tawny owl	eats small mammals, birds, earthworms
Mole	eats earthworms
Common shrew	eats insects, spiders, woodlice, earthworms and other invertebrates
Wood mouse	eats seeds, fruits, some insects
Brown rat	omnivorous – eats plants and animal matter
Bank vole	eats seeds, fruit and soft vegetation
Field vole	eats grass
Rabbit	eats grass and other plants
Finch	eats seeds
Redstart	eats insects
Great spotted woodpecker	eats wood-boring insects and nuts

When a plant is eaten by a herbivore, some energy is stored as living tissue in the animal's body, but the rest is lost as heat as the animal respires, moves and maintains its body temperature. If the herbivore is then eaten by a carnivore, the energy that was stored in the tissue of the herbivore is passed along the food chain into the carnivore. Thus the energy is transferred from one trophic level to the next. However, with each transfer more of the energy is lost as heat, as the carnivore also uses energy to respire, move and maintain its temperature. Imagine a bucket of water with a large hole in it being passed along a line of

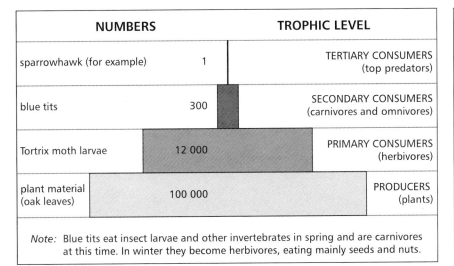

NUMBERS		TROPHIC LEVEL
sparrowhawk (for example)	1	TERTIARY CONSUMERS (top predators)
blue tits	300	SECONDARY CONSUMERS (carnivores and omnivores)
Tortrix moth larvae	12 000	PRIMARY CONSUMERS (herbivores)
plant material (oak leaves)	100 000	PRODUCERS (plants)

Note: Blue tits eat insect larvae and other invertebrates in spring and are carnivores at this time. In winter they become herbivores, eating mainly seeds and nuts.

■ **13.5** An energy pyramid: the figures represent the relative numbers of animals and leaves at different trophic levels

■ **13.6** A great spotted woodpecker

people. The people represent consumers at different levels in the food chain; the water leaking out is the energy lost by each consumer during respiration. After several transfers, the amount of water remaining in the bucket (representing the energy) will be very small. Therefore the shorter the food chain, the less usable energy is lost.

During a typical summer day in the UK, about 1500 calories of light energy fall on one square metre of oak leaves (**13.3**). Of this, only 15 calories (1 per cent) will be converted by photosynthesis into plant material. This is the **energy store**. When the leaves are eaten by herbivores, these animals will retain some 10 per cent of this (1.5 calories), stored as fat and body tissue. The rest is dispersed by respiration. If the herbivores are eaten by a carnivore, then the carnivore will retain only 0.15 calories. Of the original 15 calories stored by photosynthesis, 99 per cent have been lost as heat energy during movement and respiration

2 a Explain why there must always be a greater living weight (biomass) of plants than of animals in an ecosystem.

b Why must there always be fewer top predators than prey?

c In temperate climates, many trees and plants are deciduous, shedding their leaves in autumn in order to survive the adverse conditions of winter. Therefore they cease to manufacture food by photosynthesis at this time. What strategies for survival could the consumer animals adopt when their normal food supplies are no longer available to them?

d Explain why there is a loss of energy at each step along a food chain.

by animal consumers. The conversion efficiency may be even less than the example shown here.

Woodpeckers play an important role in the ecology of woodlands (**13.6**). With their chisel-like bills they hack holes in the bark and timber as they search for food, and excavate nest-holes. This allows fungi to enter, starting the decay process. Woodpecker nest-holes are later used as nesting and roosting sites by other species such as bats and other small mammals, birds and insects like wild bees.

13.4 **Natural recycling**

When fallen branches and the leaves shed in autumn decay, the energy from the sun that was stored during photosynthesis is released and escapes from the ecosystem in the form of heat energy – think of the heat generated by a compost heap! However, the chemicals obtained from water, air and minerals in

the soil are constantly recycled. Before they can be used again, they must first be converted back from complex organic compounds to their simpler chemical forms by **decomposers**.

When a tree is damaged, wood-destroying fungi can enter and start the process of decay and decomposition.

Fungal spores are blown by the wind, or accidentally carried by wood-chewing beetle larvae into their galleries. The spores incubate in the sheltered, moist conditions and fungal threads develop. As they spread, they rot the heart-wood of the tree. Other fungi, bacteria and a host of wood-boring insects and their predators follow. This concentration of insects attracts woodpeckers which create further entry points for fungi. After many years, the decomposers will have converted the wood and debris of the tree into a layer of humus on the woodland floor.

Large dead trees, both standing and fallen, are one of the most important components of a woodland or forest ecosystem, performing a variety of ecological functions by providing niches for animals, habitats for other plants and a source of organic material and nutrients to the soil that will be re-used by later generations. If timber is removed from the site, the nutrients and energy locked in it are also removed, and the whole system becomes impoverished. The cycle is broken and the system may no longer be self-sustaining.

13.5 **The carbon cycle**

Carbon and oxygen cycling are vital functions of ecosystems (**13.7**). It is estimated that each year the Earth's land plants extract some 120 billion tonnes of carbon in the form of carbon dioxide from the atmosphere. As we have seen, oxygen is a by-product of photosynthesis and this process is the means by which the essential supply of oxygen in the Earth's atmosphere is maintained at around 21 per cent of the atmospheric gases. However, during the process of respiration by living organisms and the decay of organic matter, photosynthesis is effectively reversed. Oxygen is taken from the air and used to release the energy and carbon dioxide stored by plant material.

Respiration in an organic cell is represented chemically as:

$$C_6H_{12}O_6 \; + \; 6O_2 \; \rightarrow \; 6CO_2 \; + \; 6H_2O \; + \; energy$$
glucose   oxygen   carbon dioxide   water

If respiration and decomposition were to cease, then much of the Earth's supply of carbon would be tied up in dead organic matter. Photosynthesis would slow down as a result, since insufficient carbon dioxide would be available for the process to take place.

In practice, there is a natural balance which maintains the approximate proportions of gases in the atmosphere. However, due to people burning fossil fuels, such as coal, peat and oil, the energy and carbon dioxide that was locked up during photosynthesis carried out by plants when they were living millions of years ago is suddenly released. This is then returned to the atmosphere in huge quantities, thereby upsetting the natural balance. Carbon dioxide is one of several **greenhouse gases**, and it is feared that its rapid increase in the atmosphere could be leading to global warming (see section 12.6).

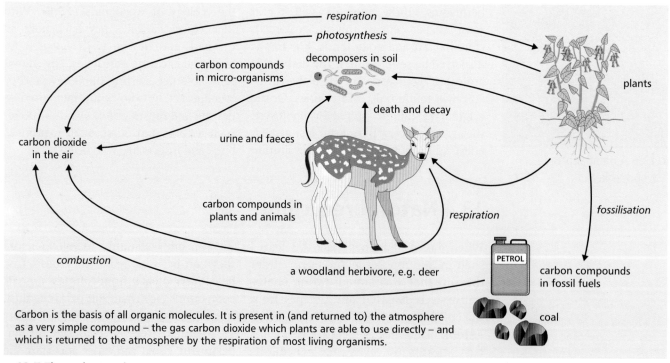

Carbon is the basis of all organic molecules. It is present in (and returned to) the atmosphere as a very simple compound – the gas carbon dioxide which plants are able to use directly – and which is returned to the atmosphere by the respiration of most living organisms.

■ **13.7** The carbon cycle

13.6 The nitrogen cycle

IT1

Nitrogen is an essential element in the composition of proteins. However, although this gas makes up 79 per cent of the Earth's atmosphere, it cannot be used directly by plants in gaseous form. It must be combined with hydrogen and oxygen before it can be absorbed by a higher plant such as a tree. Nitrogen-fixing bacteria are particularly important here because they are able to convert atmospheric nitrogen into ammonium ions and other nitrogenous compounds (**13.8**). They occur in nodules found on the roots of leguminous plants, such as clover and peas. Certain bacteria in the soil, as well as blue-green algae, perform a similar function.

IT1

In agricultural and forestry systems, the nutrients of which the plants are made are removed from an area when a crop is harvested. To compensate for this loss farmers must add artificial nitrates to the soil if its fertility is to be maintained. Such a system is only sustainable so long as a constant supply of fertilisers is brought in from outside the area. Artificial fertilisers are soluble in water, however, and much is leached into the groundwater or washed away by surface runoff into rivers, lakes and the sea, where the accumulation of nitrates and phosphates may cause unintended problems to these ecosystems due to over-enrichment.

■ **13.8** The nitrogen cycle

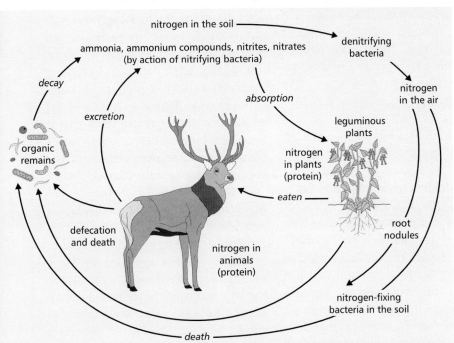

Nitrogen is present in the atmosphere as a very common gas comprising some 79 per cent of the air. Unlike carbon, this is not a form in which the producers can actually use it. They need it in the form of simple salts, especially nitrates. There are processes by which nitrogen is converted into nitrates. These involve living organisms, e.g. nitrogen-fixing bacteria and blue-green algae, as well as physical processes in the atmosphere.

3 a 13.8 shows the nitrogen cycle of an oak wood. At what point in the cycle is atmospheric nitrogen converted into nitrites and nitrates for use by plants?
b By what means is the nitrogen that is locked up in animal protein returned to the cycle?

13.7 Plant succession and soil development

IT8

It has been said that 'Nature abhors a vacuum' – that is, an empty space. A bare rock newly-exposed by erosion perhaps, or an expanse of freshly-erupted volcanic lava that has cooled and solidified, is soon colonised by algae and lichens. These simple, undemanding plants cling to the rock's surface, helping to corrode and weather it. As each generation of these **pioneer species** dies, a small amount of organic material is added as humus to the rock debris, form-ing a thin soil which allows the next wave of 'invading' plants to grow. These will be more advanced species, requiring more nutrients. In time these too will die, adding yet more humus and nutrients to the soil, increasing its fertility still further.

IT8

Plant succession of this kind is known as a **sere**, and invasion of a bare rock surface is described as a **lithosere**. As the soil conditions improve, a **succession** of more

■ **13.9** Lichen invading bare rock **IT8**

demanding, taller and deeper-rooted plants take over from the pioneer species. In the UK, algae and lichens are normally succeeded by grasses and herbs; short turf becomes a meadow, succeeded by a 'scrub' of shrubs such as hawthorn, bramble or wild rose (**13.9**). The meadow grasses and smaller flowering plants cannot withstand the increased shade created by the taller shrubs and the extra competition for space, water and nutrients. As the scrub stage in the sere matures, the seeds of trees arrive, carried to the site by wind or animals. The seeds germinate beneath the cover of the scrub, and the saplings eventually grow up to form a woodland. In time, the leaf canopy of the trees shades out the shrubs below that are unable to tolerate low light conditions.

As one seral stage succeeds another, the particular species that colonise an area are influenced by:

- local climatic conditions

- the physical and chemical properties of the rocks and soil

- the amount of usable water present

- the kinds of plants and animals available for colonisation

- the tolerance of the available species to local environmental conditions.

Eventually the vegetation cover reaches the stage at which it is in a state of balance for this particular set of conditions; the **climatic climax** vegetation or **biome** has been reached. No further changes take place other than the death of

senile plants and animals and their replacement by the next generation of that species. That remains the same until something happens that alters the conditions – climatic change, perhaps, or a natural disaster such as a volcanic eruption, or an outbreak of disease.

In north-west Europe and the British Isles, the climatic type may be described as cool temperate oceanic, with relatively mild winters, cool summers and rainfall during all seasons. The normal climatic climax vegetation for this climate is a broad-leaved deciduous forest, the actual species dominating the forest at any particular site being influenced by local soil conditions and minor variations in climate (see section 14.1). It is apparent, however, that woodland does not cover the whole area at the present time. This is because of the different seral stages that occur in the development of the vegetation towards the climatic climax and the presence of a number of **arresting factors** that prevent the vegetation from reaching it. Human activities are the most obvious of these.

Leave a garden untended for a few months, and weeds will soon invade the area and stifle the cultivated plants. Leave it for a few years, and a variety of shrubs and sapling trees will have taken over. The former garden will be well on the way to becoming woodland.

Although an area of cultivated land already has a soil, it will experience the same processes of plant **invasion** and **succession** if people stop cultivating it. By cultivating, farmers and gardeners halt seral progression, maintaining it at a **subclimax** stage. Crops, flowerbeds and pastures are only temporary **subclimax communities**, maintained by ploughing, digging, mowing or grazing. If these activities stop, invasion by other plants soon takes place. Similarly, such hazards as fire, or grazing by rabbits at a woodland edge, prevent the succession from progressing to the next seral stage, producing an alternative subclimax community known as a **plagiosere**.

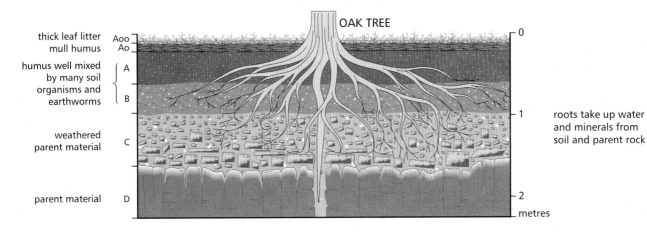

thick leaf litter — Aoo
mull humus — Ao

humus well mixed
by many soil
organisms and
earthworms — A, B

weathered
parent material — C

parent material — D

OAK TREE

roots take up water
and minerals from
soil and parent rock

■ **13.10** Profile of a brown earth

4 a What is a 'pioneer plant community'?
  b How and why does it differ from a climatic climax community?

5 The Burgess model of urban development makes use of a number of ecological concepts (see section 33.3). What similarities are there between the colonisation of an area by plants and the colonisation of urban areas by the invasion and succession of a series of human population types?

IT8 Plant succession goes hand in hand with the development of soil. **13.10** shows the typical soil profile that forms beneath broad-leaved deciduous forest in a cool temperate oceanic climate such as that in the British Isles. Such a profile is classified as a **brown earth**. The leaves shed by the trees each autumn accumulate on the surface, where they are decomposed by such organisms as fungi and bacteria into a slightly acidic humus or **mull**. This is mixed into the soil by large numbers of worms and other soil fauna so that the soil horizons (the layers) in a brown earth are not clear-cut and distinct. As precipitation (rain and snow) in this climatic type is usually greater than evaporation, there is a net downward movement of water through the soil which causes some leaching of soluble minerals, especially calcium and magnesium. IT8

6 a Find a suitable location and dig a soil profile. Are obvious horizons present in the soil?
  b Compare the texture and colour of the soil at different depths, and measure the pH.
  c Do they vary with depth (see section 13.9)?

13.8 **Sustainability**

IT4 On reaching the climatic climax, natural ecosystems have achieved a state of stability which is self-sustaining. Over time, the ecosystem has established a balance between its inputs – energy, water, oxygen, carbon dioxide, minerals from the rocks and soil – and its outputs – heat energy from respiration and decay, respired gases removed from the immediate area by atmospheric circulation, water vapour lost by evaporation and transpiration, minerals and water removed from the rocks and soil by leaching and runoff, and food within the bodies of migrating birds and other animals. IT4

If humans enter an ecosystem and harvest large areas of the natural vegetation, perhaps for timber, the harvested biomass is removed and transported to another area. This throws the natural system out of balance. Similarly, the original food chains in the system may be broken by clearance to make way for agriculture, or contaminated by pesticides. Precipitation received may become more acidic due to air pollution (**acid rain**). Water runoff from the area may be polluted by leaching of fertilisers, or by farm and industrial waste. When, for example, an area of forest is cleared, the amount of surface runoff and evaporation rates are increased over the area formerly occupied by the woodland. The removal of soil nitrates and other minerals from the system also accelerates, both as stream load and in solution, due to the increased runoff and, in some cases, faster chemical weathering by acid rain. Of course, the increased outputs from one area do not simply disappear – they become increased inputs to another, which may also be thrown out of balance. Increased nitrate levels in streams and lakes downstream from the deforested area may result in eutrophication and algal blooms.

As a result of human interference, the system is no longer able to support the natural vegetation for the area. Development has resulted in instability and is, therefore, unsustainable. In tropical areas, deterioration can be particularly rapid, since high temperatures accelerate chemical processes. This does not necessarily mean that all development by human populations is unsustainable. Wise management of ecosystems requires that development should only take place after careful analysis and evaluation of

the likely consequences of development and the range of land use options available (see Chapter 19). The management strategies chosen must be those that will keep environmental damage to a minimum.

The following quotation is one definition of **sustainable development**:

> Development should provide for the needs of the present without damaging the ability of future generations to provide equally for their needs, and it should not threaten the survival of other species. It is aiming at improving the quality of human existence whilst living within the means of the Earth's ecosystems forever.
>
> There are relatively few human activities that respect this principle, yet it is the only rational blueprint for survival.
>
> *BirdLife International Manifesto, 1993*

7 'In the long term, all development must be sustainable and firmly linked to the objectives of conservation.'

Write your own definition of sustainable development, and discuss the view expressed in this quotation.

8 Collect case studies from magazine and newspaper articles of development projects and consider whether or not they are sustainable.

13.9 Techniques: Investigating soils and vegetation

Investigating a soil profile

Soil profiles may be investigated by digging a soil pit. Choose a site where the soil is unlikely to have been recently disturbed.

Make sure you have the landowner's permission before you start.

1 Dig the pit about 1 metre deep – unless you hit hard rock – keeping the side you wish to examine vertical and as clean as possible. Do not remove more soil than is necessary. Lay the turf and spoil on a plastic sheet so that it is easy to replace.

2 Sketch the profile. Measure the depth of any distinct layers (horizons) in the profile and note their colour, depth, and pH.

3 Carefully refill the pit with the spoil and replace the turf.

Measuring soil texture

'Texture' is an indication of the coarseness of the soil, which reflects the proportions of clay, silt and sand particles present. The coarser the texture, the more quickly water will drain through the soil. Texture can be measured in different ways:

Sieving

Dry the soil and pass the material through a series of sieves with varying fineness of mesh – 2.0mm; 0.2mm; 0.02mm; 0.002mm. The amount of material 'caught' by each sieve is weighed and the amount expressed as a percentage of the total.

Feel

■ Gritty or sandy soil does not form a ball when squeezed.

■ Silty soil feels silky or soapy, and does form a loose ball.

■ Clay soil feels sticky when wet and is like plasticine that can be moulded into various shapes.

Sorting in water

Mix a sample of the soil with water in a beaker, shake the mixture thoroughly and allow it to settle. The coarser materials will settle more quickly than the finer ones, and the percentage proportions of each layer may be noted.

Measuring acidity and alkalinity – pH values

Water in the soil contains positively charged hydrogen ions (H^+ ions or cations). The greater the concentration of these, the more acidic is the soil. The level of concentration of H^+ ions is measured by the pH scale, a logarithmic scale from 0 to 14. The pH of the soil will be an important influence on the types of plant that can grow there.

■ A reading of pH 7 is neutral.

■ pH 6 is 10 times more acidic than pH 7, and 100 times more acidic than pH 8.

You can measure the pH of a soil sample with a soil-testing kit which contains Universal Indicator. If not available at school, soil-testing kits can be purchased from a garden centre. A colour card with the kit shows the colour that the Universal Indicator acquires at a particular pH value. Usually, yellow through orange to pink indicates increasing levels of acidity (pH<7), pale green is neutral (pH = 7) and shades of blue are alkaline (pH>7).

Sampling woodland structure and assessing the composition of plant communities

Systematic sampling using a point-line or line transect

Different woodlands, or even different parts of the same wood, have different

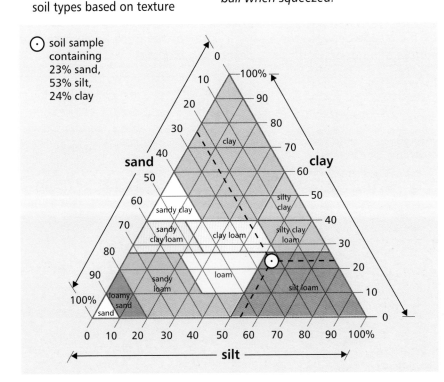

■ **13.11** Triangular graph to show the description of soil types based on texture

⊙ soil sample containing 23% sand, 53% silt, 24% clay

vertical structures. These may be investigated by sampling the vegetation at regular, predetermined intervals along a transect line. The greater the number of measuring points (i.e. the larger the sample size), the closer you will get to a true representation of the woodland structure along the chosen line.

You will need:

- Access to a wood for a transect-line of about 50 m. (Get the owner's permission first.)
- Some way of measuring distance along the ground and measuring or estimating heights. (Pacing, provided the stride-length is constant, will suffice for the former.)
- A clinometer, which may be used to calculate height of tall shrubs and trees, and a measuring staff or tape to measure smaller plants.

Method

At predetermined sampling points along the transect (perhaps every 5 m or other regular intervals) you should note:

- the species occurring
- the height of the plant.

Do these vary with:

- distance from the edge of the wood
- variations in soil type
- differences in drainage between the top and bottom of a slope?

The results may be recorded on a graph, plotting distance along the transect on the horizontal axis, and plant height on the vertical axis. (It is unlikely to be satisfactory to use the same scale for both axes as the height of the ground flora will not show up if the two scales are the same. It may be more satisfactory to use a logarithmic scale for the vertical axis.)

Quadrat surveys

These may be used to estimate the relative abundance of shorter plant species. A quadrat is a square of wire or wood for use in the field, 0.5 m per side being a convenient size. The quadrat is placed at random on the ground, the numbers of each plant species are counted or estimated as a percentage cover of the area of the square, and the results are recorded. If smaller plants are growing beneath taller varieties, for example lichens beneath heather, the resulting percentage cover may exceed 100 per cent.

Another method is to place the quadrat at predetermined intervals along a transect line. This is a useful technique when sampling the changes of vegetation that occur in a sand dune, for example, or a salt marsh at different levels.

Note: In order to obtain objective results it is important that the quadrat is placed genuinely at random, and not so that some rare species, such as an orchid, is deliberately included.

14.1 Broad-leaved deciduous forests

The prevailing cool temperate oceanic climate of the British Isles and Western Europe provides ideal conditions for the growth of a climatic climax vegetation consisting of such trees as pedunculate oak, beech and ash (**14.1**). These are the dominant species at lower altitudes, although alders and willows take over in damp, poorly drained places. In the mountainous areas of the west and north, exposed to the prevailing westerly winds which bring more rainfall and cooler conditions, sessile oak is more typical, with birch and Scots pine in the Scottish Highlands. The prevailing soil of these forests is the **brown earth**, characterised by mull humus, slight acidity and a profile of ill-defined horizons (see **13.10**).

As a broad-leaved deciduous forest develops it passes through five main **seral stages**:

Pioneer or *open stage* – dominated by lichens, mosses, grasses and herbs.

Scrub or *pre-thicket stage* – dominated by small shrubs, e.g. dog rose, bramble.

Thicket or *immature stage* – dominated by large shrubs and sapling trees, e.g. hawthorn, sallow willow, hazel or blackthorn with developing saplings of timber trees.

Mature stage – dominated by timber trees, e.g. ash, willow, beech or oak depending on the type of bed rock and local climate.

Senile or *over-mature stage*, in which the older trees die, and the space a tree occupied is re-colonised, creating a mini-succession.

Only the last two stages are the climatic climax vegetation for the area. The earlier stages in the succession are subclimax communities.

In a natural woodland all the stages in the succession can occur at the same time in different parts of the forest,

■ **14.1** Distribution of the world's major forest types

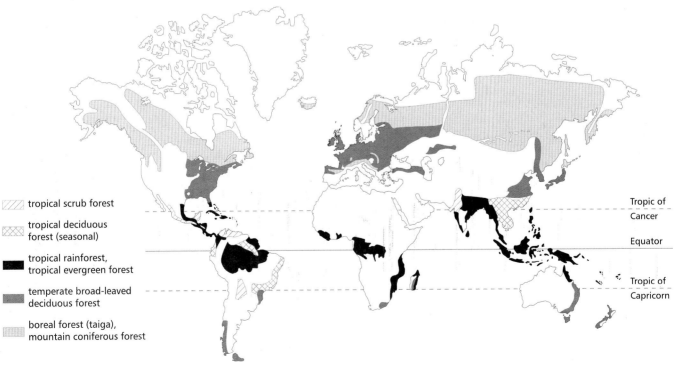

- ▨ tropical scrub forest
- ▧ tropical deciduous forest (seasonal)
- ■ tropical rainforest, tropical evergreen forest
- ▰ temperate broad-leaved deciduous forest
- ▨ boreal forest (taiga), mountain coniferous forest

Tropic of Cancer

Equator

Tropic of Capricorn

along with the animal communities that are associated with them. The time span over which a succession occurs will vary with the type of tree involved. For example, an oak woodland will take 150 years to reach maturity and a further 150 years to become senile. During the last 5000 years, however, humans have removed most of the original forest cover and are an **arresting factor** preventing its regrowth, so that forest is no longer dominant over most of the land area.

The history of broad-leaved deciduous forests in Europe

Some 12 000 to 15 000 years ago, the Pleistocene Ice Age came to an end. The climate became warmer and the last of the ice sheets melted. A wave of green vegetation spread slowly northwards into an empty landscape. This included the British Isles, which remained joined to the mainland of Europe until cut off by rising sea-levels formed the English Channel around 5000 BC. Scots pines and birch trees were probably the earliest colonists, the evidence for this being provided by the relative proportions of pollen grains preserved in peat bogs dated as having formed at this time. Some remnants of this ancient woodland still survive to the present day as the Caledonian Forest in the Scottish Highlands.

■ **14.2** Coppiced woodland with standards

Gradually the climate improved still further and, as the pioneer plants performed their role of improving soil quality, a larger variety of more advanced plant species were able to follow. These included shrubs such as field maple, hawthorn, holly and hazel, and broad-leaved trees – oak, ash, elm, lime and beech. As the forest spread so did the human population which depended on the forest for a living, by hunting wild animals and gathering nuts, berries, fruits and edible plants. At first, however, the numbers of people and their level of technology were very limited, and they had little more impact on the 'wildwood' than the wild boar, deer, wolves and brown bears that also lived there.

It was the change from a hunter–gatherer economy to the keeping of domestic livestock and the cultivation of crops that made a major impact on the forest ecosystem. Grazing by livestock prevented seedling trees from growing, checking the natural succession and regeneration of the forest. Leaves were cut for fodder and areas were cleared for settlement and cultivation of crops. But even as people cleared the wildwood, they were still dependent upon it for many of their everyday needs, especially fencing, building materials and firewood. As human technology improved – from primitive flint axes via bronze to iron – it became possible to clear the forest more quickly and efficiently. Simple ploughs, only effective on the lightest sandy soils, were replaced by the iron plough which could cope with heavy clay soils. Thus the speed at which the wildwood was destroyed rapidly accelerated.

The most ancient form of woodland management in the UK is **coppicing**. When a broad-leaved tree is cut down, it has the ability to sprout new shoots from its stump. While people remained dependent on the wildwood for many everyday needs, coppicing increased the productivity of useful wood. The small-diameter stems, or 'underwood', were cut in rotation every few years to provide firewood and charcoal, and to make fencing, hurdles and baskets. Hazel, ash, sweet chestnut, oak and hornbeam were the most widely used species. In most coppiced areas it was the practice to leave larger trees standing at intervals in order to provide larger building timber, a system known as 'coppice with standards' (**14.2**).

In the 20th century, the demand for coppice products has declined, with a consequent loss of ancient crafts and skills. Today, few woodlands are managed by coppicing. This is unfortunate, as many species of wild birds and flowering plants had become dependent on this system of management for their survival. Coppicing brings light to the woodland floor in the few years that follow clearance, enabling primroses, oxlips, bluebells and red campion to flourish. It also provides ideal conditions for scrub-loving birds. In spring, the coppiced woodland resounded to the songs of nightingales, blackcaps and other warblers but, with the decline of coppicing, the survival of these species is threatened and conservation organisations have had to re-learn the ancient coppicing skills in order to manage woodland effectively for wildlife.

Today, less than 10 per cent of Britain is wooded, and most of this shows little resemblance to the original wildwood. It is probable that there is no truly natural woodland left in the British Isles. All of today's woodland is, or has been, man-

aged in some way by humans. Most is secondary woodland, the result of natural succession from woods that were once coppice, or from cleared land that had previously been grazed by livestock or cultivated.

Of Britain's woodlands today, about half have been deliberately planted, consisting of extensive Forestry Commission or privately-owned plantations. These are rarely broad-leaved trees. Most are monocultures of introduced coniferous species, such as lodgepole pine and Sitka spruce, grown for their softwood timber. Unfortunately, these non-native conifers are of little value to native species of wildlife.

1 Suggest reasons for the decline of coppicing.

2 Identify the main causes of the loss of natural woodland over much of Western Europe.

3 Explain why conifers are planted in preference to broad-leaved trees.

Reading the following case study will help you to answer these questions.

CASE STUDY

Hayley Wood, Cambridgeshire

For many centuries Hayley Wood has been exploited by humans and its history has been recorded for over 700 years. The Domesday Book indicates that most of Cambridgeshire's original forest cover had been destroyed by the Anglo-Saxons, but that Hayley Wood escaped this clearance. It is one of the few remaining features of the county that would still be recognised by a local resident from the 11th century (**14.3**).

The wood is about 49 ha in area, with oak, ash, elm, maple, hazel and sallow willow as the main tree and shrub species. Much of the wood grows on a thick layer of chalky boulder clay and, although

Cambridgeshire is one of the driest areas in the UK receiving on average less than 650 mm of rain per year, the impermeable clay gives rise to damp ground conditions, especially in winter.

Hayley Wood's importance to past populations was as a source of large timber for building, and of smaller underwood, which was cut for firewood and other purposes. Most of the hazel and sallow willow was coppiced, with selected areas harvested at intervals of approximately seven years to provide suitable timber for the manufacture of wooden rakes, hurdles and wattle, pliant sticks that were woven together and daubed with mud to make the walls of buildings (**14.4**). Other trees, such as ash and maple, formed larger coppice to supply poles and medium-sized timber. But the largest 'standards' were mainly oaks, allowed to reach full maturity before being felled for timber, the branches being used for firewood after felling.

Hayley Wood was carefully fenced to exclude horses and other animals ' … to guard and protect it from bite, trampling and damage … which may be able to hurt the regrowth' (from a lease of Hayley Wood, 1584).

It was only after the construction of the railways in the mid-19th century that the importance of Hayley Wood as a source of timber to the local population began to decline. Coal became a cheaper fuel than wood, and metal substitutes became available as alternatives to timber products. The wood then became valued as a cover for game; foxes for hunting and pheasants for shooting were especially important. Fallow deer also arrived, probably accidentally, and a large herd remains in the wood to this day.

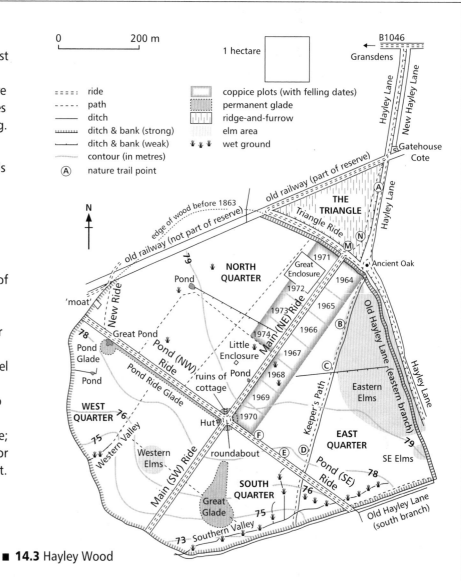

■ **14.3** Hayley Wood

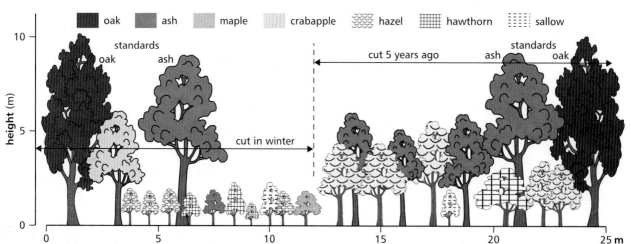

Woodland structure under classical coppice management: reconstruction of the profile of a wood such as Hayley Wood in the Middle Ages. Half the area was felled last winter; the other half has had five seasons' growth and is ready for felling if needed, though as this is Hayley Wood it will probably be allowed to stand for another couple of seasons.

■ **14.4** Cross-section of the coppiced area of Hayley Wood

Today, Hayley Wood is owned by the Bedfordshire and Cambridgeshire Wildlife Trust, and is managed as a nature reserve. The Trust has a detailed management plan, carefully designed and implemented to ensure that the wood's importance for wildlife is improved and maintained. It has been divided into several plots, some of which are coppiced in the traditional way. This is especially important for the survival of coppice-loving birds and wild flowers, notably the oxlip, a rare relative of the cowslip and primrose. Because of the great range of heights of woodland plants, it is possible to detect a number of vertical layers. Different woodlands, or even different parts of the same wood, often have different vertical structures (**14.5**).

Canopy
The uppermost layer formed of the branches, twigs and leaves of the larger trees

Shrub layer
Beneath the canopy a layer formed of smaller trees, shrubs and some of the climbers

Field layer
The taller non-woody plants, including both flowering plants and ferns – also sometimes called the 'herb layer'

Ground layer
Mosses and other very small or creeping plants growing on or very close to the ground

■ **14.5** Vertical structure of a broad-leaved wood

4 Having gained the necessary permission from the owner, sample the structure of an area of woodland by means of a line-transect and point sampling using the techniques described in section 13.9.

5 a If the vertical structure of the wood you have investigated does not resemble the structure depicted in **14.5**, what might be the reasons for this?

b Which layers are missing?
c Is it due to lack of light because of a very dense leaf canopy overhead in the summer months? (For example, beech woods seldom have a dense ground layer due to the density of the leaf canopy in summer.)
d Could it be due to the history of the wood and the way it has been managed by people?
e Could it be due to the presence of grazing animals, e.g. wild deer?

14.2 Coniferous or boreal forests

In contrast to the broad-leaved decidu-ous forests, there is a broad band of coniferous forest which lies nearer to the Arctic Circle, but to the south of the tundra (**14.1**). It forms a broad belt up to 2000 km wide, and extends around the globe in Northern Europe, Asia and North America. This biome, the largest tract of forest in the world, is usually called **boreal forest**, but is sometimes described by its Russian name **taiga**.

The trees of the coniferous forest are mainly evergreen and well adapted to this zone of long cold winters and short

14.6 The monotonous taiga landscape

coastal redwood becoming dominant on the Cascade mountains from Oregon southwards. To the east, lodgepole pine, balsam pine, tamarack, white spruce and black spruce become the dominant species of the Laurentian Shield.

6 Describe the essential features of the landscape shown in **14.6**.

While it is tempting to think of the coniferous forest as consisting only of trees, this is not the case. On flat ground, where drainage is impeded by permafrost beneath the surface, the forest floor becomes waterlogged in summer and sphagnum moss invades, accumulating acidic water. This, along with the lack of oxygen in the water, causes trees to die, with only the occasional lodgepole pine surviving due to its tolerance of the poor aeration of this muskeg-bog.

The soils of the boreal forest

summer growing seasons. Their needle-shaped leaves have a small surface area and thick waxy cuticles which keep water-loss by transpiration to a very low level. This is especially important to their survival when, because it is frozen, water is unavailable from the soil. Evergreen trees also have a distinct advantage over deciduous varieties in these conditions, as the leaves can begin to photosynthesise as soon as conditions become warm enough and there is sufficient length of daylight. Deciduous species must spend time growing a new set of leaves.

Coniferous forests are composed of only a small number of species (**14.6**). In Northern Europe, pine and spruce are dominant but to the east of the Urals these give way to Siberian fir, larch and stone pine. In North America, Sitka spruce, Douglas fir, cedar and hemlock predominate in Alaska and British Columbia, with

In this cold climate, in which precipitation exceeds evaporation, the needles and litter from the coniferous trees are slow to decay. When they do so, they form an acidic humus or **mor**. Rain and melting snow also contain dissolved carbon dioxide, forming a weak carbonic acid. As this percolates down through the top horizons of the soil, solution of humic acids also takes place. The resulting liquid is very acidic, with a pH as low as 4.5, which is able to dissolve and leach salts such as those of calcium, magnesium, sodium and potassium – a process known as **eluviation**.

The A horizon of a podsol, which lies beneath the litter and humus layers, becomes bleached to an ash-grey or whitish colour and is infertile, as many of the minerals needed for plant growth have been removed (**14.7**). This severely restricts the variety of plant species able to grow here. Those that do occur, such as conifers, are those species that require few nutrients. This limited plant diver-

14.7 Profile of a podsol

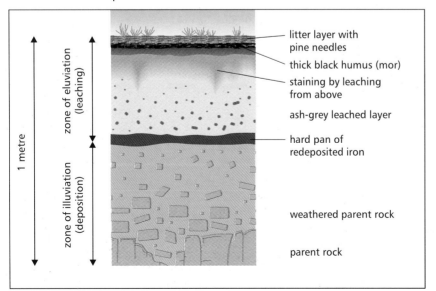

litter layer with pine needles
thick black humus (mor)
staining by leaching from above
ash-grey leached layer
hard pan of redeposited iron
weathered parent rock
parent rock

zone of eluviation (leaching)
zone of illuviation (deposition)
1 metre

sity in turn provides relatively few opportunities for exploitation by animals, and only a limited variety of birds and mammals are to be found.

Few soil organisms, including earthworms, can tolerate the cold, acidic conditions. Thus there is little mixing of the soil and the horizons that form in a podsol are usually clear-cut and distinct. Some of the leached minerals, particularly iron and aluminium, become concentrated in the lower B horizon and are deposited as a distinct dark layer – the process of **illuviation (14.7)**. This 'pan' may be hard and impermeable, causing waterlogging or a **perched water table**.

Podsols may also occur outside the main areas of coniferous forest in milder climates, where freely drained rocks such as sandstone occur and precipitation exceeds evaporation. In south-east England, for example, podsols occur on outcrops of the Lower Greensand and the Bagshot Beds. Here, they support an acid-tolerant heathland vegetation with gorse and heather, or woodland dominated by birch and Scots pine.

---

7 Compare the profiles of a brown earth and a podsol (**13.10** and **14.7**).
  a What differences are there between these two soil types?
  b How may the differences between the two be explained?

Logging in coniferous forests

Commercial forestry is an important economic activity in extensive areas of coniferous forest, and vast areas have been felled. Coniferous forests are the world's main source of softwoods, which are used for a variety of constructional purposes by the building industry. They are also used in the manufacture of fabricated board, plywood and veneers; they provide pit-props, railway sleepers, posts and fencing. One major use predominates, however: the production of wood pulp for the manufacture of paper. The large stands of a single tree species make harvesting and processing of the trees relatively easy.

There is much less concern over the harvesting of conifers than there is over tropical rainforests, as the boreal forest ecosystem, with its relatively low temperatures and rainfall, is more stable. Nutrients taken from the soil are returned by leaf fall and decay of dead wood. But as the temperatures and precipitation are much lower, and chemical reactions much slower than in the rainforest, much of the nutrient store is in the litter and humus. The deterioration of the soil due to loss of forest cover is, therefore, much less apparent. Relatively few nutrients are removed from the system by the harvesting of tree trunks for timber and, provided that the branches, bark and roots are left behind, trees will regrow with few problems.

---

8 a Make a list of the environmental consequences of forest felling.
  b Suggest reasons (other than those given above) why the harvesting of conifers gives rise to less concern than the felling of deciduous trees.

Most of the coniferous forest areas, in Western Europe particularly, have been felled and regrown several times, either by deliberate replanting or through natural regeneration. Many areas of coniferous trees are planted and managed exclusively for the commercial production of timber. Some of these, together with other forested tracts, may also serve as areas for recreation, or be used to control runoff and thereby prevent erosion and the siltation of reservoirs. However, many areas formerly occupied by forest have been cleared and converted to other uses such as agriculture, industry and urban growth.

IT8

Afforestation in Scotland

Under natural conditions, the native pinewoods of Scotland are dominated by Scots pines associated with birch trees. The trees are mixed in age, with dying trees and fallen timber plentiful, open spaces occurring side by side with thickly-wooded areas (**14.8**). Rowan with hazel, juniper, heather and bilberry cover the more open ground. Wild animals of this native woodland include red squirrels, wild cats and pine martens, with birds like crested tits, capercaillies and Scottish crossbills.

At their peak, around 6000 years ago, forests of this kind probably covered 20 per cent of Scotland, an area of some 1.5 million ha. This 'Great Wood of Caledon', the Caledonian Forest, stretched from Lochinver in Sutherland, southwards to Loch Lomond (**14.9**). However, people have cleared 99 per cent of the original forest. Widespread sheep-grazing followed by the Victorian passion for deer-stalking ensured that the pine forests did not regenerate. During the two World Wars there was further felling and burning to create farmland at a time when there was an urgent need to produce more food and to provide fuel and building timber. To overcome the timber shortage, many areas were replanted by the Forestry Commission as well as by private owners, usually with non-native species of tree, mainly Sitka spruce and lodgepole pine for commercial timber production. Forestry also brought much-needed employment to these remote upland areas, but these conifer plantations lack the variety of species and mixed age structure of natural woods.

By 1991 conifer plantations covered 961 000 ha, 12.5 per cent of the land area of Scotland. Less than 1 per cent of the original area of the Caledonian Forest remains in the Scottish Highlands (only 12 000 ha), confined to a few dozen scattered sites, and some of these have been threatened with clearance or replanting with non-native species (**14.9**). Over half of the surviving forest is of poor quality with thinly-scattered trees. Pine seedlings are eaten by red deer, especially in winter, so the remaining areas are ageing. The remaining natural forest needs long-term secure management, with careful control of deer numbers. If grazing pressures were reduced, woodlands could regenerate naturally. However, the exhortations of conservationists to the owners of sporting estates to reduce deer numbers have seldom been heeded. This is hardly surprising, as the value of estates is greatly enhanced by the numbers of red deer available for stalking.

New Forestry Commission guidelines no longer permit the planting of non-native tree species

■ **14.8** The Caledonian Forest, Abernethy

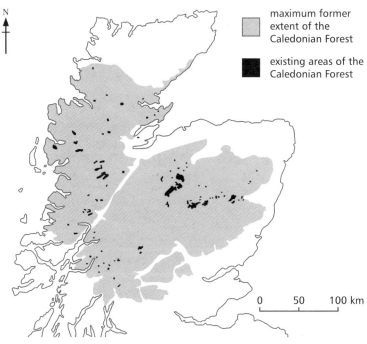

maximum former extent of the Caledonian Forest

existing areas of the Caledonian Forest

0   50   100 km

■ **14.9** The extent of the Caledonian Forest: today less than 1 per cent of the original area remains

among native Scots pines. If Scots pine is selectively harvested for timber, the replanted forest can better resemble the original natural woodland, supporting the growth of new Scots pine, heathers and other shrubs on which most of the wildlife depends.

In the 1980s, a huge afforestation programme of non-native conifers also took place on the moorlands and peat bogs of the Flow Country of Caithness and Sutherland in the north of Scotland, encouraged by the cheapness of the land, grants and tax reliefs. The areas most seriously affected were blanket bogs, an immensely important wildlife habitat of global scarcity and significance. Many sensitive wild species have been affected, especially rare birds like the golden eagle and the greenshank. By 1987, 79350 ha had been planted or were scheduled for planting, 67 000 ha of which were on blanket bog peat.

CASE STUDY

IT3

The problems of acid rain in mid-Wales

In recent years it has become evident that freshwater lakes and rivers in many parts of the world are becoming increasingly acidic. The cause is almost certainly acid rain. Large amounts of pollutants, especially sulphur dioxide (SO_2) and oxides of nitrogen, enter the atmosphere from industrial emissions, particularly from thermal power stations, domestic fires and car exhaust fumes. These gases dissolve in rainwater to form acids which are precipitated at the Earth's surface when rain or snow falls (see case study on page 100). The effects of acid rain have been noted in areas as far apart as Asia, North America and Europe, especially Scandinavia.

In Britain, 24 per cent of the total area of SSSIs (Sites of Special Scientific Interest), mainly in Scotland, the Lake District and Wales, are experiencing acidification. In England alone, 46 of 56 SSSIs – some 176000 ha – have been affected by emissions from industry and power stations (see section 8.5).

Although air pollution is the cause of acid rain, there is now evidence that its effects, when it becomes surface water, are made much worse by conifer afforestation. Acid rain is channelled to the ground by the needles and trunks of the conifers, concentrating the acidic pollutants around the roots, so that in extreme examples the trees may eventually be killed. Fallen conifer needles decay slowly and are themselves acidic. When these acids are leached into neighbouring streams and rivers their ecology is also affected.

Evidence comes from studies made by the RSPB and the University of Wales of the population fluctuations and distribution of the dipper – a bird that inhabits turbulent streams and rivers in mountainous areas (**14.10**). Dippers 'walk' beneath the surface of the water in pursuit of insects, especially caddis fly larvae and mayfly nymphs. These prey items are very sensitive to the quality of the water and cannot tolerate acidic conditions.

In mid-Wales, between 1958 and 1983, over half of the catchment area of the river Irfon in Powys had been afforested with conifers. In 25 years the acidity of the Irfon increased from pH 6.5 (near neutral) to pH 4.5 (very acid). Acid rain, running off the hills through the plantations of conifers, is thought to be responsible for this great increase in the river's acidity. This was accompanied by a severe decrease in dipper numbers which fell from nine pairs per 10 km to just two pairs. In contrast, the river Edw, which has not experienced afforestation of its catchment area, has remained near neutral at

■ **14.10** Dipper

around pH 7, and has experienced little change in its dipper population (**14.11**).

Studies of other Welsh rivers which seem ideal for dippers found that only 21 of 74 sites investigated were occupied by breeding pairs of these birds. Those without dippers were significantly more acidic than the occupied sites and the water also contained

higher concentrations of aluminium and mercury leached from the soils and surrounding rocks by acidic water, poisoning aquatic insect-life. The survey showed that all sites without dippers had low populations of aquatic insects so that it is not possible for dippers to feed and raise young.

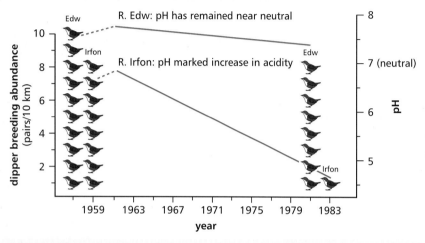

14.11 Trends in acidity and breeding dipper populations in two Welsh rivers

9 The population of dippers has been severely reduced by the effects of acid rain in some parts of the UK. After further reading on the subject of acid rain, make notes about **a** its origins, **b** the problems caused to the environment by acid rain, and **c** some possible ways of solving the problem.

14.3 **Tropical rainforests**

If an oak tree or Scots pine were to be transferred to an equatorial climate, it would be unlikely to survive for very long. The conditions are too hot and wet, and there would be too much competition from species better suited to this environment.

Under natural circumstances, areas close to the Equator are dominated by a dense blanket of tropical rainforest or 'jungle'. Such areas include the Amazon Basin of South America, parts of Central America and the Caribbean, the coastal areas of West Africa and the Congo Basin, and much of South-east Asia (**14.1**). Forest of this kind is often called **selva**, its local name in the Amazon basin.

High temperatures, averaging 26–29 °C throughout the year, high humidity and heavy rainfall, which may total 4 m or more annually, are the prevailing climatic conditions. There are no distinct seasons and as the soil never dries out, conditions

are always favourable for rapid plant growth and high levels of animal activity (see section 6.1).

Unlike northern Europe and other areas nearer to the poles, areas close to the Equator have experienced little or no climatic change for millions of years. The plants and animals here have had longer to evolve and adapt to the local conditions than anywhere else on Earth. As a result an immense diversity of species occurs here, with over 100 different types of tree found in a single hectare of forest. The Amazon selva alone is inhabited by at least 600 bird species; and there is an estimated 40 000 species of insect to a single hectare!

Although there is a huge variety of trees in a rainforest, they have many features in common – tall, straight trunks covered with smooth bark, and spear-shaped leaves with pointed 'drip-tips' forming a dense leaf-canopy 40 m above

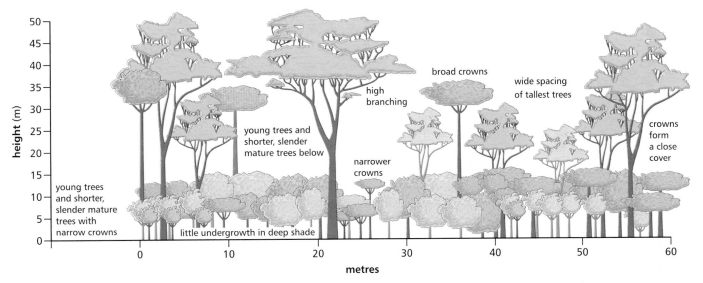

■ **14.12** Cross-section through a tropical rainforest

the ground (**14.12**). Every so often the crown of an isolated 'emergent' tree stands 10m higher than the rest, over-looking the canopy. Many of the largest trees have buttress roots – great flanges of supportive wood – which enable the trees to grow to great heights. Climbing plants, such as lianas and strangler-figs, entangle the branches of the canopy, along with the dangling aerial roots of tree-dwelling bromeliads, ferns, orchids and other epiphytic plants.

In the rainforests, most animal life is to be found high in the canopy, as the forest floor is in deep shade, dark and gloomy. The leaf-canopy intercepts most

of the incoming light, only 10 per cent reaching the forest floor, and traps some 80 per cent of rainfall. Thus at ground level, conditions are unsuitable for anything resembling the ground and herb layers of a cool temperate woodland. It is only when one of the giant jungle trees dies and falls that a shaft of sunlight can stab downwards to the forest floor, 'kick-starting' the growth of seeds and saplings. These struggle rapidly upwards in a life-or-death competition to reach the canopy, where they can receive all the benefits of full sunlight.

Trees in the tropical rainforest do not all shed their leaves at the same time, as there are no seasons here. Instead, each species has its own timing. Epiphytic mosses and algae are abundant, clinging to twigs and branches, but as such growth would clog their stomata and slow up photosynthesis, the leaves of trees have developed deterrent features – waxy surfaces and drip-tips, which act as spouts to shed water easily and permit rapid drying. The leaves also twist on their stalks during daylight so that the maximum amount of leaf surface is turned to face the sun, thereby increasing the rate of photosynthesis.

Rainforest soils

On seeing such a rich natural vegetation, the first European settlers in tropical areas gained the mistaken impression that the soils of the selvas must be

■ **14.13** Latosol or ferralitic soil profile

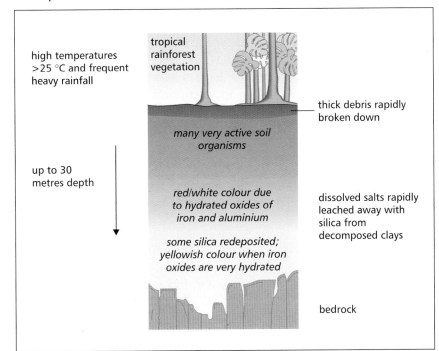

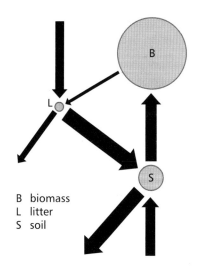

B biomass
L litter
S soil

Circles are proportional to the quantity of nutrients stored. The arrows represent the transfer of nutrients from one part of the system to another and are proportional to the amount of flow.

■ **14.14** The mineral nutrient cycle in a tropical rainforest

extremely fertile. However, plantation farmers who cleared the forest for crops soon realised their mistake.

Rocks in tropical rainforest areas are chemically weathered to great depths – often 20m or more – due to the high temperatures and heavy rainfall. Soluble minerals and nutrients are rapidly leached away by the percolating rainwater. The resulting soils are known as **latosols** or **ferralitic soils** (**14.13**). In its natural state the forest cover balances this leaching by providing copious supplies of fallen leaves and other organic material. These are rapidly broken down in these conditions by a host of decomposers – termites, earthworms, fungi and bacteria – releasing and recycling the nutrients the litter contains for instant re-use. Unlike temperate forests, in which the majority of the nutrients remain in the soil, a rainforest ecosystem holds about 70 per cent of the nutrients in the living matter (**14.14**).

---

10 In the tropical rainforest ecosystem most of the nutrients are stored in the vegetation (biomass). What would happen to the nutrient cycle if the forest cover was removed?

11 Compare and contrast the composition and structure of tropical rainforest with *either* broad-leaved deciduous forest *or* the boreal forest (taiga).

12 How can the differences you have described in question 11 be explained by differences between the climates and soils of the areas in which these forest types occur?

13 Compare the soil profiles illustrated in **14.7** and **14.13**. Explain the roles of **a** the prevailing climates, and **b** the dominant vegetation in producing these two different profiles.

Destruction of the rainforests – cause for concern?

It is estimated that before the arrival of humans, 14 per cent of the Earth's surface was covered with tropical rainforest – some 2 billion ha. Already, half has been destroyed, and the remainder continues to be felled and burnt at a rate of at least 7.5 million ha per year. This is equivalent to an area the size of Belgium, Luxembourg and the Netherlands combined or – if you prefer to think of it another way – an area the size of 20 football pitches is lost every minute of every day.

The indigenous human populations of the rainforests have evolved a way of life that depends on small-scale hunting and shifting cultivation. In the Amazon Basin, for example, local tribal groups possess an intimate knowledge of the forest. Small clearings are made in the jungle by **slash-and-burn** methods for growing crops. The cut vegetation is burnt to release potash and other minerals which act as fertilisers for crop growth. But the fertility soon declines in the hot, wet conditions and the cleared plot is abandoned after a few years. The soils and vegetation are then allowed to rest and recover for many years before being re-used. This gives the forest a chance to regrow and allows the soil to regain most of its lost fertility, and has proved to be a sustainable form of forest management.

In recent years, however, clearance of the rainforest has been allowed to happen on a massive scale, leading to widespread soil erosion and reduced biodiversity as species become extinct. This also threatens the very existence of the tribal peoples who have traditionally lived in the forest. In part, the pace of forest clearance has been accelerated by the huge rise in the human populations of such developing countries as Brazil and Indonesia. The construction of the Trans-Amazonian Highway has enabled the Brazilian government to encourage migration into rainforest,

■ **14.15** Flooding in the Philippines resulting from rainforest clearance

to wind, causes evaporation and upward movement of soil water with minerals in solution. At the surface, this water evaporates and the minerals crystallise out, forming a hard, impervious layer on the surface – a **laterite crust** – which greatly increases surface runoff. When it rains, the soil is subjected to rapid erosion and gullying (**14.15**). The land soon becomes useless for agriculture and has to be abandoned. Due to the changed soil chemistry it is seldom possible for secondary forest growth to take place, and a barren desert may be the end result.

Logging is an important economic cause of rainforest destruction (**14.16**). Some 3 billion m³ of tropical hardwoods are estimated to be harvested annually. The rights to fell timber on an area of land are usually held by a logging company for only a short length of time, perhaps five to ten years. As the logging companies are 'here today, but gone tomorrow', commercial logging is seldom carried out with any long-term concern for the environment or with future harvests in mind. To make matters worse, only about one in twenty rainforest trees, such as teak, mahogany and ebony, are of economic value. Unwanted trees may be fatally damaged during the felling of target trees, or are cleared to make way for tracks, roads and settlements. In some countries illegal logging also takes place.

areas but the new arrivals have little knowledge of tropical soils and sustainable methods of agriculture. They practise slash-and-burn, but on a much greater scale than the original tribal inhabitants. When a plot loses its fertility, too little time is allowed for secondary growth to take place and for soils to recover.

When large areas of forest are felled and removed, whether for forestry or agriculture, the natural supply of nutrients is also removed – the nutrient cycle has been broken. The surface of the soil is no longer protected by the forest canopy and roots from the direct impact of torrential rainfall. For the first time in millions of years the soil is suddenly exposed to the bright light and fierce heat of the tropical sun which, along with exposure

■ **14.16** A huge logging truck in rainforest in Brazil

This deforestation gives rise to a number of concerns. First, about half of all known species of living things come from rainforests. Many species have still to be discovered; their properties and potential benefit to mankind have not been investigated and evaluated. With the destruction of the forests, species become extinct each day and **biodiversity** is reduced. What drugs or other potentially useful chemicals did the genetic make-up of extinct species have to offer mankind? Has the potential cure for a disease such as cancer or AIDS already been destroyed?

The clearance and burning of the rainforests may also be the cause of irreversible global climatic change (see section 12.7). Huge amounts of carbon dioxide from the carbon that had previously been locked up in the biomass of the rainforests are suddenly released into the atmosphere. This traps out-going long-wave heat radiation from the Earth within the atmosphere, a process known as the **greenhouse effect**. This may be causing **global warming** – an overall increase in the temperature of the Earth's atmosphere. Sea-levels are likely to rise, since the volume of water in the oceans will increase due to the general expansion of water as the oceans become warmer and glaciers and polar icecaps melt.

Forest clearance also has far-reaching effects on global rainfall patterns, since water vapour is no longer passed into the atmosphere from the trees by evapotranspiration, but becomes surface runoff instead. The absence of atmospheric water vapour may cause the amount of precipitation to be reduced or bring lengthy periods of drought, which increase the likelihood of desertification.

14 Make a list of the reasons why we should be concerned about the rapid clearance of rainforest.

CASE STUDY

Illegal logging in the Philippines

Illegal logging has been a problem in the Philippines for many years. In 1930, tropical rainforest covered 17 million ha of these islands, but this has been reduced to just 7 million ha. In 1991, when typhoon Thelma struck the central Philippines, illegal logging operations on the islands of Negros and Leyte almost certainly contributed to the deaths of about 6000 people. Flash flooding and huge mudslides in the town of Ormac followed the torrential rainfall, claiming at least 3000 victims. Deforestation of the hill slopes probably made them unstable. There is legislation to control logging in the Philippines, but the government finds it difficult to enforce (**14.15**).

Japan is the world's major consumer of tropical hardwoods, importing about a third of the total produced each year. In 1988, Japan's official statistics for timber imports from the Philippines indicated 1.5 million m³, yet statistics from the Philippines government show that only 0.5 million m³ of timber were exported to Japan. This disparity can only be accounted for by illegal logging activities, perhaps serving to indicate its huge scale.

CASE STUDY

'Amazon tree-felling racket is halted'

On 13 August 1993, under the above headline, The Daily Telegraph reported that an illegal logging operation had been uncovered in the Amazon rainforest on the reservation of an Indian tribe, the Kaiapo. A total of 4500 trunks of prime-quality timber, including mahogany destined for the British furniture industry, had been impounded by the Brazilian Environment Institute. After the USA, Britain is the world's largest importer of mahogany. The Kaiapo tribe had been supported by the pop star

Sting and the Body Shop. Brazil nuts and bead bracelets had been purchased from the tribe to help them make a living without felling the rainforest. They had also recently negotiated with the Brazilian government a £1.7 million healthcare programme for the Kaiapo. The Body Shop has expressed their extreme disappointment with the tribe's leaders for letting down the 3500 Kaiapo who, until this racket was exposed, had been regarded as leaders among Brazil's indigenous peoples.

The scandal has strengthened calls by the environmental protection groups Greenpeace and Friends of the Earth to impose a complete ban on the trade in mahogany until the illegal logging crisis has passed. They want companies and local councils not to buy mahogany. They say that a ban would benefit both the environment and the Brazilian economy, as it is estimated that smugglers remove timber worth £830 million from the Amazon every year without paying taxes or logging dues.

Solving the problem

A number of potential solutions to the problem of rainforest destruction have been suggested. Since commercial logging is a major cause, a change of attitude to the rainforests by the logging companies must be a starting point. The forests must come to be regarded as a sustainable source of timber and other valuable products.

Up to now, most commercial loggers have been robbing the forests, taking the timber with no thought for the future. Commercial logging companies must be allocated longer concessions, perhaps 60 years or more, so that it will be in their own best interests to protect the forest from illegal and indiscriminate felling activities. They will need to be properly policed and the companies encouraged to harvest only the most mature trees, reducing sapling damage to a minimum. Replanting harvested areas would also be encouraged.

Indigenous tribal communities need to be allocated large areas of unexploited forest as tribal reserves in which they would be permitted to continue their traditional sustainable existence without interference. Compensation for not felling the forest might be offered in the form of healthcare and similar schemes.

Stands of virgin rainforest must be carefully preserved and remain untouched. Many such areas can become wildlife reserves and national parks.

They may have tourist potential, providing valuable income for a developing nation if such development can be achieved without damage to the forest. If core areas of virgin forest are left adjacent to carefully managed logging areas, displaced plant and animal species should be able to recolonise the logged forest after operations have finished.

Sawmills must be reduced in scale to decrease the damage to soil caused by heavy concentrations of activity and the use of motor vehicles. Portable sawmills, light enough to be transported into the rainforest by canoe and assembled temporarily at the felling sites, are being developed and will be a key factor in the establishment of sustainable logging. Better use of the wood taken must also be encouraged by developing the market for timber species that have not so far been regarded as 'commercial'.

The international trade in other non-timber forest products such as nuts, fruits, medicinal plants and, in the case of Amazonia, latex must also be increased, and their value built into the economic equation, so that the true worth of intact forest is realised.

Another potential solution is what have been called 'debt-for-nature' swaps. At the heart of such a scheme is the fact that many developing nations are crippled by foreign debt. The reckless exploitation of the rainforests and the sale of tropical hardwoods to developed countries such as Japan generates badly needed hard currency to help repay loans and interest. The cleared land can also be used for a few years to produce an income from cash crops or cattle ranching. Debt-for-nature schemes allow international conservation organisations to provide a debtor country with some relief from, and

rescheduling of, their debt burden in exchange for guarantees that some of the money that would otherwise have been used for debt repayments is used instead for conservation schemes and projects to protect the environment. This idea is spreading rapidly and initial fears and criticisms by some developing countries that such schemes amounted to 'interference in the nation's internal affairs' are dwindling.

CASE STUDY

IT4

The Gola rainforest, Sierra Leone

Rainforests are estimated to have covered some 60 per cent of the land area of Sierra Leone but today only about 4 per cent remains (**14.17**). This valuable remnant is threatened by farmers who convert the virgin forest to 'farmbush', clearing the trees to grow their crops, then leaving the land fallow so that scrub and degraded woodland returns. Uncontrolled logging is another serious threat, while many rare animals are hunted as 'bushmeat'.

The Royal Society for the Protection of Birds (RSPB) is working with BirdLife International and the government of Sierra Leone in West Africa to establish a 750 km² rainforest reserve for wildlife in Gola Forest near the town of Kenema. The aim is to manage forest exploitation on a sustainable basis – to allow its use to earn money from the forest, but to avoid its destruction.

Gola is one of the most outstanding areas of rainforest and wildlife left in West Africa. Several rare and endangered bird species are dependent on it, as well as important species of mammal. These include at least seven species of monkey and the rare pygmy hippopotamus. The majority of West European breeding birds that spend the winter in Africa either pass through the area on their way further south, or spend the winter in the region – hence the RSPB's interest in the Gola Forest. The government is responsible for managing the forest, but local people depend on it for their livelihood, and to ignore their needs would be a disaster. The RSPB hopes to work closely with both.

There will be several stages to the project. The first is to prepare management plans for the reserve areas. These will specify where logging may take place and how much timber may be removed. Other areas will be strictly protected as nature reserves where neither hunting nor logging will be allowed. The next stage will be to mark these areas on the ground, and provide patrols to enforce the rules. Training of the staff in forestry and wildlife management is essential. A research station for ecological studies will be set up. An environmental education programme for the local people has also been established so as to raise awareness in local communities and schools of the need for sound forest management and conservation, and ensure a long-term sustainable future for the reserve.

■ **14.17** Gola Forest, Sierra Leone

15 a Describe the causes and consequences of the depletion of tropical rainforest resources.

    b Examine the relative merits of methods that might be used to prevent or control this depletion.

16 Identify what you think will be some of the difficulties associated with implementing the Gola Project.

14.4 **Tropical seasonal forests**

Typical tropical rainforest, as described in the preceding sections, only occurs where the climatic conditions provide high levels of rainfall and high temperatures throughout the year (**14.1**). However, the climate alters with changes in altitude, increased distance away from the Equator towards cooler latitudes and increased distance from the coast into continental interiors. Conditions are sufficiently different to cause tropical rainforest to give way to other forest types. For example, if there is a season of drought – a period of the year during which rainfall is unreliable or less than in tropical rainforest areas – then the vegetation must overcome the problems caused by this period of water deficiency if it is to survive. The plants must be adapted in some way to overcome the problems of drought.

IP2

As in temperate areas, one adaptation is for trees to be deciduous, losing their leaves during the dry season to reduce transpiration. In India, Myanmar (Burma) and Thailand the natural forest vegetation is referred to as 'monsoon forest', although much of it has been removed. Many of the tree species are deciduous, losing their leaves from around December when the dry season arrives until the monsoon rains burst in June/July (**14.19**).

There are a great many variations within India due to differences in the amount of rainfall, temperatures, altitude and soil conditions. Along the coast there may be long stretches of coconut palms, with mangrove swamps along river deltas and creeks. In the Western Ghats, a line of mountains and hills extending from north-west India to the south, rainfall is sufficiently high to support a tropical evergreen forest, although the trees are not as tall as in the true selvas. In contrast, the Indus plain covering most of Pakistan and much of north-eastern India suffers from extremes of temperature and an unreliable monsoon rainfall, which may be as little as 50–200 cm per annum. Here, monsoon forest gives way to grasslands and even

desert. Isolated clumps of acacia with an understorey of thick thorn scrub grow along river banks.

IP2

Another threatened forest resource

IP2, IT7

As with other forest ecosystems, the great majority of India's forests have been felled. Less than 7 per cent of the original forest cover of the Indian sub-continent remains – a sharp decline from over 40 per cent at the beginning of the 20th century. The pressures are not just from logging. Much of the clearance has been due to the demands of agriculture. Over half of the world's water buffalo, and a seventh of its cattle and goats, are found in India. There is not enough fodder produced to meet the demands of this huge mass of livestock, and so they are forced into the forests to graze. This damages saplings and damages tree growth as a result of foliage removal, thus helping to decrease the forest cover.

Other causes include the felling of trees for fuelwood for cooking. Even in the urban areas of India, over 50 per cent of cooking stoves are still heated by wood. Because of the exploitation of the forests, many women in rural villages are now forced to spend over six hours a day in collecting their headloads of sticks for fuel, each walking an average of 1700 km per year (**14.18**). Villagers desperate for cash are cutting down trees such as banyan and mango that were previously protected on religious grounds and for their fruit. Woodland under the control of the Forest Department is also being degraded by excessive pressure from fodder collection and fuelwood collection. The current rate of wood consumption far exceeds the regeneration capacity of the remaining areas of forest, a situation which is clearly unsustainable.

The clearance of monsoon forest, tropical and temperate, on the steep slopes of the Himalayas has greatly

■ **14.18** An Indian woman with a headload of fuelwood

increased surface runoff during the torrential monsoon rains. When trees are present they act as a natural buffer against erosion and floods. Surface flow is slowed; rainwater infiltrates the soil by way of root channels; the leaf canopy protects the surface of the soil from the impact of large raindrops; and their root systems bind the soil particles.

Forest clearance may be the cause of widespread soil erosion in areas such as Nepal, and of landslides that have devastated villages and swept away terraces on the slopes that were once used to grow hill rice and other crops.

a) Dry season

b) Wet season

■ **14.19** Seasonal contrasts in Sanjay Ghandi National Park, Bombay

17 Collecting fuelwood – usually carried out by women in developing countries – is a back-breaking and time-consuming activity. Find out what development agencies and aid organisations are doing to reduce the demand for fuelwood (see section 27.5). What alternatives are there in developing countries?

18 In what ways do the pressures on Indian rainforest differ from those experienced in Brazil?

CASE STUDY

Deforestation and flooding in Bangladesh

Downstream from the Himalayas, uncontrolled runoff caused by deforestation in the catchment areas of the rivers, and increased silting of river channels as a result of soil erosion, may have contributed to the disastrous and widespread flooding in Bangladesh. Bangladesh is situated at the confluence of the floodplains and the deltas of the rivers Ganges, Meghna and Brahmaputra (**14.20**). There have been 15 major floods in the area this century, drowning thousands of people and their livestock and devastating crops (see the case study on page 46).

However, the evidence that forest clearance is the main cause of flooding is not conclusive. Some scientists point out that much of the forest cover in the Himalayas is still intact, and in many places villagers have been actively replanting trees. The most disastrous floods have occurred when the monsoon rains have been exceptionally high in the catchment areas of all three rivers at the same time, resulting in peak flows reaching Bangladesh all at once. In most years, there is an interval of up to four weeks between the flood peaks of the Ganges and the Brahmaputra, and flooding is less severe (**14.21**).

The Himalayas are also still an active orogenic area, experiencing numerous earthquakes which result in increased erosion and heavy loads of sediment for the rivers to carry. The increased incidence of flooding in Bangladesh may therefore be the result of several contributory factors, of which deforestation in the Himalayas is but one. Further research is needed to increase understanding of the causes and to find possible solutions and ways to

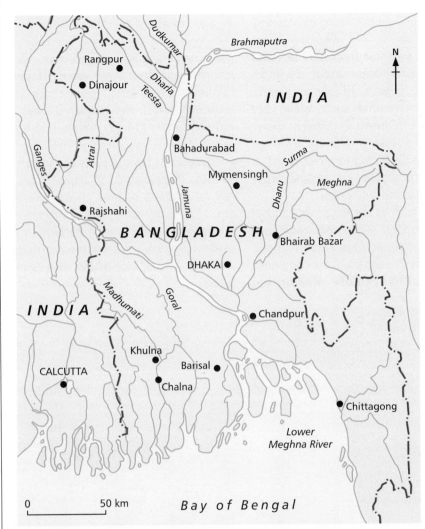

■ **14.20** The delta area of Bangladesh

ameliorate the problems caused by the floods.

Proposals have been made by the Bangladesh government to construct up to 3500km of embankments along the banks of the Ganges and Brahmaputra rivers as they enter the delta area in Bangladesh (see also the case study on page 46). This Bangladesh Flood Action Plan, if it goes ahead, will cost the World Bank some $5 billion, but it is now being seriously questioned. While it aims to prevent flooding of cities such as Bangladesh's capital Dhaka, and enhance crop production, the embankment scheme would also cut off large areas of wetland, important as fish-producing areas, from their water supply. Fish provide the people of Bangladesh with their major supply of protein. It is also suggested by some critics of the scheme that although the embankments may control flooding for some years, silting eventually reduces the capacity of the channels, causing them to overflow and breach the embankments. Thus, in the long term, the embankments could actually increase the risk of inundation of large areas.

The scheme would also do little for those who live on the seaward end of the delta, the so-called 'char-lands'. These, it is argued, would suffer an increased risk of flooding. The problems caused by flooding in Bangladesh might be reduced by spending the money on better flood forecasting and warning schemes, improved flood shelters and emergency services to help flood victims.

■ **14.21** Flooded street in Dhaka

19 Devastating floods are an all too common event in Dhaka, the capital of Bangladesh. In what ways might overpopulation and unsustainable human impact on natural ecosystems be the cause of these floods?

20 Weigh up the pros and cons of the Bangladesh Flood Action Plan. Do you think that the potential benefits outweigh the likely costs?

14.5 Techniques: Monitoring vegetation change

Satellite images are becoming increasingly familiar to us in our everyday lives, especially in weather forecasts. Satellites can record information about the landscape using sensors of various kinds. Photographs are one such image but other sensors, sensitive to different wavelengths of radiation in different bands of the spectrum (including infrared, which is invisible to the human eye), provide different data about the land below.

Satellites such as the American Landsat or the French SPOT send information back to Earth in a digitised form at set intervals, where it can be analysed by computer. The results of this **remote sensing** can be used to assess the type and quality of the vegetation of an area. For example, the combinations of reflected wavelengths sent back from areas of virgin rainforest are different from those from secondary forest. Newly cleared areas are different again (**14.22**). Vegetation maps can quickly be produced in this way for even the most remote parts of the Earth's surface. Comparisons of a given area at regular intervals of time enable monitoring of a wide variety of environmental phenomena, and such methods have made it possible to assess the distribution and rate of clearance of the world's rainforests.

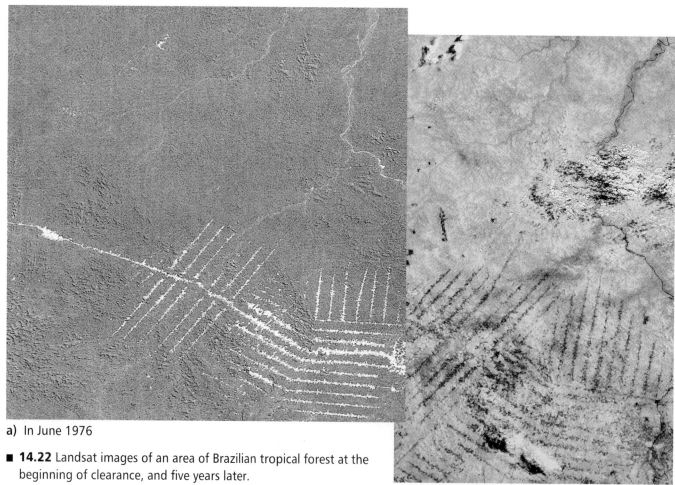

a) In June 1976

■ **14.22** Landsat images of an area of Brazilian tropical forest at the beginning of clearance, and five years later.

b) In September 1981

15.1 Tropical grasslands

Typically, **savannas** are tropical grasslands, but this is an extremely varied ecosystem, ranging from plains covered by tall grasses dotted with trees, through unbroken grasslands with arid thorn bush, to a final merging into the desert. Savanna is therefore a transition zone between true tropical forest at one extreme, and desert at the other. Savannas begin to occur as rainfall declines with increasing distance from the sea. Average temperatures and evaporation rates are high, and there are long dry seasons. The savannas form a wide belt on either side of the Equator, located between the tropics of Cancer and Capricorn (**15.1**). The largest areas are found in Africa, but they are also found in northern Australia, the Campos and Llanos of Brazil, other parts of South America and the Caribbean. Much of southern Asia, particularly India, is also savanna.

Tropical savannas cannot be said to be a true climatic climax vegetation. Undoubtedly, their character is partly accounted for by aridity – unreliable rainfall and seasonal drought – but isolated stands of trees exist within extensive areas of grass as a result of local variations in drainage and soil quality (see also section 6.2). Fire may be a major causal factor. Savanna is more extensive in Africa than in any other continent, and this may be due to the long-established presence of people here. In the tall-grass savannas of Africa, cattle herders burn the old dead growth during the dry season to encourage the growth of young grass when the rains arrive.

Many of the plant species present are **xerophytes**, which have become adapted during their evolution to withstand arid, drought-ridden conditions. Trees typically possess a thick, corky bark

■ **15.1** Distribution of the world's grasslands and deserts

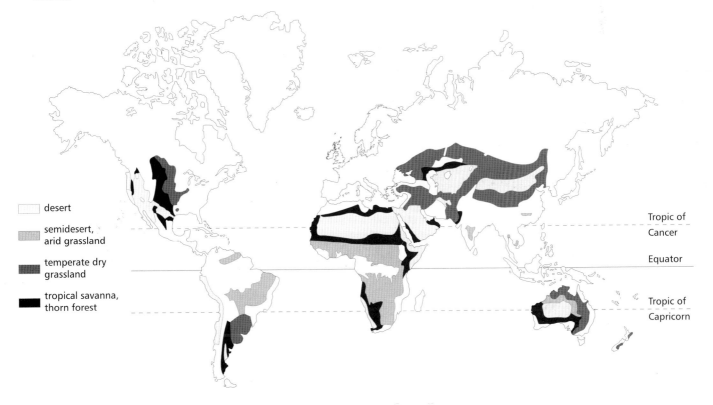

- desert
- semidesert, arid grassland
- temperate dry grassland
- tropical savanna, thorn forest

Tropic of Cancer

Equator

Tropic of Capricorn

15.2 Savanna vegetation with acacia trees, East Africa

and have bulbous trunks made of spongy wood which stores water. The extraordinary baobab tree is a good example. But these adaptations for coping with drought also make them resistant to fire, enabling these plants to survive when others would be wiped out. Savanna grasses can also survive drought and fire. Their leaves may be burnt by the flames, but their long, fibrous, water-seeking roots are not so easily damaged. Growth is from the base of the leaf so that grasses can also tolerate frequent grazing. Many common savanna plants, such as acacias, are covered in thorns – also an effective deterrent against grazing (**15.2**).

In areas where the human population is small, huge herds of herbivorous animals, including elephants, zebras, wildebeest, gazelles and antelopes, roam

across the African plains (**15.4**). Carnivores, such as lions, cheetahs and leopards, prey on the grazing herds, along with scavenging jackals, hyenas and vultures. Some species are becoming scarce owing to farming, poaching and other human activities.

Savanna soils

The soils of tropical grasslands are strongly influenced by the lengthy droughts that alternate with wet seasons. These conditions create **lateritic soils**, with a characteristic hard, cemented layer (**15.3**). This crust lies beneath a thin surface layer of dead grasses which quickly decay to make humus. Capillary action during the dry season causes the upward movement of water, containing minerals in solution. High evaporation rates concentrate these minerals, forming the laterite crust, which is mainly composed of sesquioxides of iron and aluminium, giving the soils their characteristic red colour.

1 a Make a checklist of the ways in which savanna soils and plants are adjusted to climatic conditions.

b Find out ways in which the animals of the savanna seem to have adjusted to these conditions.

15.3 Laterite soils form where temperatures are high, with seasonal droughts and little shade

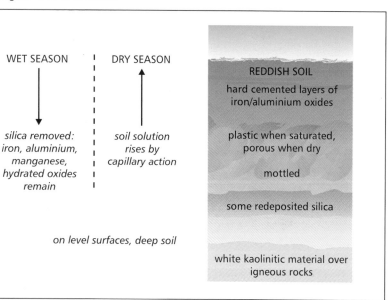

WET SEASON | DRY SEASON

silica removed: iron, aluminium, manganese, hydrated oxides remain

soil solution rises by capillary action

on level surfaces, deep soil

REDDISH SOIL
hard cemented layers of iron/aluminium oxides

plastic when saturated, porous when dry

mottled

some redeposited silica

white kaolinitic material over igneous rocks

Game reserves

 IT4,6

In order to conserve the biodiversity of some of the most important areas for wildlife, large areas of tropical grassland in Africa and India have been declared 'national parks'. The Serengeti Plain in Tanzania is one of the best known; it experiences spectacular migrations of wild animals, notably of 1.2 million wildebeest (**15.4**). Rain falls unevenly across the Serengeti. It is driest in the south-east, with the result that by May the more palatable grasses

■ **15.4** Migrating wildebeest IT4,6

IT4,6

in this area have been grazed low. Columns many kilometres long of wildebeest, gazelles and zebra trek the 200 km towards Kenya to the north-west in search of greener pastures. The grazing animals are ruthlessly pursued by lions, which ambush stragglers – the weak, young calves and the elderly. By November, the rains break in the south-east and a return migration takes place.

Serengeti and other African parks, for example the Masai Mara, Tarangire, Tsavo and the Ngorongoro, have become important earners of foreign currency for their countries from the tourist trade, owing to the current fashion among people from developed countries for safaris and 'green tourism'. To preserve the wildlife populations, strenuous efforts have been made to reduce the slaughter of animals by illegal hunting and poaching, especially of elephants for their ivory, and of rhinoceros for their horn, which is said to have aphrodisiac properties. In recent years a worldwide ban on the trade in ivory has substantially reduced elephant poaching.

The creation of these huge national parks, however, has not been without its critics. The indigenous peoples of the African savannas, such as the Masai, are traditionally nomadic cattle herders. Over many centuries, they have developed a lifestyle that is in balance with the natural environment. From an ecological point of view this is the most sustainable way of using the pasture in these areas of scarce and irregular rainfall. However, some game-park managers and government officials concluded that these pastoralists were in direct competition with the wildlife for food, water and living space. As a result, whole tribes have been forbidden to hunt and graze their cattle within the parks, some of which cover an area the size of Wales.

IT4,6

To compensate, deep boreholes have been sunk outside the protected areas by international development agencies to make water available locally for both people and livestock. But these have had a number of unforeseen side-effects. Attracted by the water, and also the shops, missions and dispensaries that developed around the boreholes, the nomadic cattle herders have adopted a more settled existence. However, the abnormal concentrations of cattle have over-grazed the surrounding areas and, since the pastoralists are highly dependent on wood for cooking and building, there has also been a severe impact on trees. Their destruction is the main cause of desertification in the arid areas of Africa.

It is now argued by some that the tribal peoples and their nomadic way of life are an integral part of the natural ecosystem – part of the biodiversity that conservationists are trying to save for future generations. They say that the rights of indigenous peoples to use the land in traditional ways should also be preserved within the protected areas.

In the Amboseli Park, Kenya, successful attempts have been made to resolve this conflict by providing direct compensation to the displaced people for their loss of land rights and by the building of facilities such as schools and clinics at the park's margins, all paid for from tourist income. As the tribal peoples have benefited from this income, so the poaching of wildlife has also decreased. The wildlife is now perceived by these people as a valuable asset.

2 a Construct a balance sheet itemising the costs and benefits of designating large areas of the savanna as national parks.

b In your opinion, do the benefits outweigh the costs?

3 Wildlife populations can be adversely affected by human development and drought in semi-arid areas. However, tourism based on 'wildlife spectaculars' can be a valuable source of income to such areas. Collect examples of advertisements for 'green tourism' from newspapers, holiday magazines and TV programmes. What precautions do you think tour operators should take to ensure that tourist pressure does not damage wildlife and natural habitats?

Desertification

In Africa, to the south of the Sahara Desert, the savanna grasslands form part of the Sahel, a zone that is prone to drastic climatic fluctuations with prolonged droughts. Since the late 1960s the situation has worsened, and droughts and famine have affected much of sub-Saharan Africa (**15.5**). These have been responsible for appalling human suffering, especially in Ethiopia and the Sudan. However, many of the plants of this zone are well adapted to withstand the strains and stresses imposed by this unpredictable climate. The plants are xerophytic, with small, thick leaves to reduce transpiration, but which can be shed in prolonged dry periods so that the plants become dormant until the next rains arrive. They are often protected by thorns or by distasteful chemicals which make them unpalatable to grazing animals such as goats and cattle.

As the human population has increased, the scrub has been cleared – cut for firewood and overgrazed by domestic animals – thus altering the local microclimates. This has allowed the desert to encroach southwards into areas of former savanna. Indeed, it is the growth of the human population that has been blamed for the recent climatic change and famine of the Sahel. The increasing frequency of droughts has coincided with the losses of forest and bush to agriculture. As rivers have dried up, so the demand for wells and boreholes has increased, progressively lowering the water table, and further aggravating the water shortage.

Some scientists have suggested, however, that there is little evidence that the rainfall of this arid zone has decreased overall. They point out that such areas have always experienced major variations in rainfall from year to year. The drought, they say, is simply part of a normal long-term cycle. Drought has not caused the problems, merely revealed them.

Whatever the truth, there is no doubt that the removal of the natural vegetation cover has also led to increased soil erosion by both wind and the infrequent falls of rain. The result is that over many areas of Ethiopia and the Sudan, people have migrated from the worst-hit areas. Sand dunes have encroached on villages and farmland at the desert's margins. Unsustainable management of the land has been the 'trigger' for short-term human misery and disaster.

■ **15.5** Drought problems in the Sahel

IT2,8

It remains to be seen whether these changes, described as **desertification**, are permanent and irreversible or just a temporary phase (see also Chapter 12). It is also the case that in Africa, famine areas such as Ethiopia, the Sudan and Somalia have experienced periods of civil war and acute poverty.

4 a Explain how desertification might result from natural causes.

b Draw an annotated diagram to explain the possible links between people and desertification.

15.2 Temperate dry grasslands

Large areas of temperate dry grasslands are found to the south of the great coniferous forest belts, and within the temperate continental interiors of Europe, Asia and North America (**15.1**). Similar grasslands include the Canterbury Plains of New Zealand, the plains of the Murray–Darling to the west of the Great Dividing Range in Australia, and the Pampas of the eastern coastal areas of South America.

Temperate dry grasslands differ from the tropical savannas in several ways. The grasses are not as tall, seldom exceeding a metre in height, and they grow more slowly owing to the dry climate (annual rainfall 300–500 mm), and severe winters experienced in most of these areas. There are, however, some similarities. The grassland plants have various adaptations for resisting drought. They include succulents and others with narrow or spine-like leaves with waxy or downy surfaces, and most have long, water-seeking roots.

Animal life is not as rich as in the tropical savannas, probably because of the cold winters and less productive vegetation. In North America, these grasslands were once grazed by huge herds of bison or buffalo which were exploited to the verge of extinction during the spread of settlers, mainly of European origin, into the Midwest and Great Plains. There is a great variety of insects, several reptiles and much interesting birdlife, many species being migrants which are able to over-winter in warmer climates. Many rare species now require special conservation measures.

Soils of temperate dry grasslands

The soils that develop beneath temperate grassland have their own distinctive characteristics. With the onset of winter, the grasses above the surface die off and accumulate as a dense turf. There is a dense network of roots beneath the surface which also decay, helping to build up a thick layer of nutrient-rich humus or **mull** (**15.6**). As the grasses take up such minerals as calcium, these important nutrients are concentrated and returned to the soil in the mull humus. They are then available to be taken up again by plants in the following spring when growth recommences.

■ **15.6** Chernozem soil profile

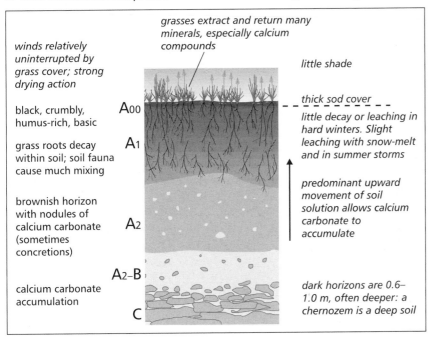

winds relatively uninterrupted by grass cover; strong drying action

black, crumbly, humus-rich, basic

grass roots decay within soil; soil fauna cause much mixing

brownish horizon with nodules of calcium carbonate (sometimes concretions)

calcium carbonate accumulation

A00

A1

A2

A2–B

C

grasses extract and return many minerals, especially calcium compounds

little shade

thick sod cover

little decay or leaching in hard winters. Slight leaching with snow-melt and in summer storms

predominant upward movement of soil solution allows calcium carbonate to accumulate

dark horizons are 0.6–1.0 m, often deeper: a chernozem is a deep soil

Wind and summer sun cause rapid evapotranspiration from the surfaces of the soil and grasses. Even though summer is the wettest season, rain seldom percolates below root depth. The only season during which downward leaching can take place is following snow-melt in spring. The mull supports a rich soil fauna with a variety of earthworms and other invertebrates which thoroughly mix the soil materials together. The resulting soils are black in colour, rich in calcium and other basic nutrients, and have indistinct horizons due to the mixing. They are classified as **black earths** or **chernozems**.

CASE STUDY

IT8

The Hungarian *pusztas*

Today, the *pusztas* of Hungary are an excellent example of the temperate dry grassland biome, strongly resembling the Russian steppes and the prairies of North America, dominated by vast areas of feathery grasses with a rich variety of spring and summer flowering plants (**15.7**). *Puszta* is a Hungarian word meaning 'empty' or 'barren'. However, the *pusztas* are not a natural ecosystem, but are the result of invasion by humans into the eastern fringes of the European broad-leaved deciduous forest.

The first invasion was during the 9th century, when the Magyar peoples expanded their territory eastwards, burning and felling the original sparse forest cover and draining the marshy river valleys. Later, in the 13th century, there was a second invasion when plundering Mongols, practising a 'scorched earth policy', invaded and destroyed almost everything in their path, reducing the area to *puszta*, a flat, empty plain dominated by grasses. During the less disturbed centuries that followed, the grasslands were extensively grazed in traditional ways by livestock – cattle, horses and sheep.

Since the 1950s, however, traditional livestock grazing has declined, and much of the area of *puszta* has been ploughed up and planted with cereals, sunflowers, lucerne and rape. This is now threatening the internationally important wild bird populations that are adapted to live in the dry grassland regime. Species such as bustards, plovers, larks and cranes have experienced a dramatic decline.

Today, strict conservation measures are being provided by the Hungarian government to protect some of the core areas of *puszta* by the establishment of 'biosphere reserves' such as the 15 200 ha Hortobagy National Park. There is also an urgent need to establish strict rural planning laws to cover the remaining areas, with the adoption of environmentally sensitive farming systems.

> **5 a** Account for the major similarities and differences between the flora and fauna of the tropical grasslands or savannas and those of the dry temperate grasslands.
> **b** Describe and account for the problems that the major grassland biomes of the world have experienced as a result of expansion of the human population. How might some of these problems be solved?

■ **15.7** *Pusztas* landscape, Hungary

IT4,8

Agricultural development in the American Midwest

When, in 1805, the American explorers Lewis and Clark travelled across the High Plains of America's Midwest, which includes the Dakotas, Nebraska, Kansas, Oklahoma and the west of Texas, they found arid, prairie grasslands grazed by millions of buffalo which were preyed upon by Native American peoples, wolves and grizzly bears. If they traversed the same area today they would find a very different scene.

Following the Homestead Act of 1862, European colonists travelled here in their covered wagons to settle. Each staked a claim to an area of 160 acres (65 ha) of land which, despite the uncertainty of the climate with its frequent droughts, they attempted to farm. They ploughed the treeless grasslands and reduced the huge herds of buffalo to the brink of extinction. At first, yields of the main crops – wheat, maize and cotton – were high. While farm animals were used to pull farm machinery, a certain amount of nutrient replacement took place. Dry spells brought some wind erosion of soils and crop failure but, when rainfall improved, the plains once again appeared lush and fertile. However, with the introduction of farm machinery, the fertility of the soil was soon exhausted and yields began to decline rapidly. In the 1930s, years of drought were accompanied by high winds and the depleted soils, without the protective surface layer of grasses, were swept away. Millions of hectares were reduced to a 'dust-bowl'. When the rains returned in later years, torrential downpours led to spectacular sheet and gully erosion.

During the 1930s thousands of farmers were forced by the drought, increasing poverty and debt to abandon the land. They migrated west to the growing state of California in the hope of finding employment in agriculture or new industries which were trying to establish themselves there, in spite of the depression. The story of one displaced Oklahoma family is vividly told in John Steinbeck's *The Grapes of Wrath*.

Soil conservation methods have now been successfully applied in the eastern part of the High Plains (**15.8**). These include:

- the use of terracing and contour ploughing on slopes to prevent soil being washed downhill
- crop rotation and strip-cropping with leguminous clovers and lucerne to increase the nitrogen content
- planting of tree belts to provide windbreaks
- the retention of straw and crop litter to protect the surface from raindrop impact.

The 1950s also saw the increasing use of irrigation by pumping water from the huge aquifer that underlies the High Plains, but there are fears that in the long term the levels of the aquifer will drop rapidly, especially in years of drought and as a result of over-exploitation. Indeed, in some areas in the west of the region where the rainfall is least, land has been abandoned. It has been suggested that these areas should follow the example of the Oklahoma Nature Conservancy which is purchasing land and restoring it to original prairie grassland on which herds of buffalo will be re-introduced. If this happens, the area will have reverted to its original, sustainable ecosystem.

■ **15.8** Soil conservation by 'contour ploughing' along the line of slope

15.3 **Hot deserts**

More than a third of the Earth's land surface is desert (**15.1**). Such areas are characterised by a low or almost non-existent precipitation of less than 25 cm per year and high evaporation rates. However, deserts are not all classified as hot deserts. The driest parts of the temperate dry grasslands are really a midlatitude desert, and there are also cold or high-latitude deserts, such as Turkestan and the Gobi Desert in Asia, and the Great Basins of the USA. These have hot summers but freezing winters.

Hot deserts constitute about a fifth of the total area of the world's deserts (**15.1**). Although the popular image is of vast areas of barren sand dunes, there are also large expanses of bare rock and gravel (see sections 6.4 and 6.5). Daytime temperatures are very high, 58 °C having been recorded as a shade temperature in the Sahara. However, due to the lack of cloud cover, temperatures at night fall rapidly, often dipping below freezing point. A true hot desert is characterised by having no month averaging less than 6 °C. They are located between 15° and 30° north and south of the Equator as follows:

- on the western coasts of continents – the Atacama in South America, the Kalahari and Namib Deserts in southern Africa, the Sonora and Mojave in North America
- in the centre of Australia

- the majority of northern Africa, the vast Sahara Desert, extending eastwards into Arabia as the Rub' al Khali – the 'empty quarter' – and on into the Indian subcontinent as the Thar Desert.

The causes of deserts

Deserts have several physical causes. The areas between 15° and 30° of latitude lie some 1500 km north and south of the Equator and are areas of constant high pressure, as they are beneath the descending air of the Hadley cells within the Earth's atmospheric circulation (see section 11.4). Subsiding air is increasingly compressed and becomes drier and warmer as it sinks. Thus it has a low relative humidity and clouds are seldom able to form.

Those deserts lying to the west of such mountain ranges as the Andes, Rockies and Great Dividing Range are rainshadow areas within the trade wind belts. These winds blow towards the south-west in North America and to the north-west in the Southern Hemisphere.

The west coast deserts have yet another cause. Cold ocean currents offshore cool the winds blowing towards the land so that the air's ability to hold water vapour is greatly reduced. Thus little rain falls on the adjacent land, although there are often advection fogs in places like the Atacama and Kalahari Deserts (see section 10.5).

Desert soils

Owing to the lack of moisture and vegetation in hot desert areas there has been little true development of soil, the surface simply consisting of drifted sand, pavements of bare rock, gravel or boulders (**15.9**). However, on the rare occasions when rain does fall, minerals are dissolved from the rocks. These are concentrated and redeposited as salt crystals on the surface when the water evaporates in the high temperatures, particularly where

■ **15.9** Hot desert landscape

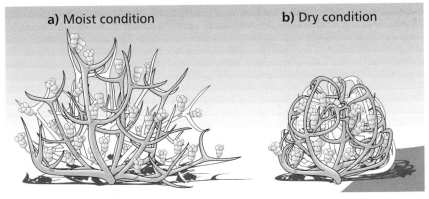

a) Moist condition

b) Dry condition

■ **15.10** The Rose of Jericho plant (*Anastatica hierochuntica*)

■ **15.11** The fennec fox is well adapted to hot desert conditions

water has been concentrated in a wadi or as a lake within a desert basin.

Sheets of water washing across the surface and torrents in wadis and gullies also carry large amounts of sediment (see sections 6.4 and 6.5). But this surface water quickly evaporates and sinks into the ground. The surface becomes a hard saline or alkaline surface crust. Similarly, artesian water coming to the surface at an oasis, as at the Qarun–Faiyum Oasis in the Sahara, for example, may also carry salts in solution, which are deposited as the water evaporates. Saline and alkaline crusts are a local characteristic of some desert soils, referred to as **aridisols**.

The ecosystem of hot deserts

The large diurnal temperature range, high evaporation rates and extreme aridity of hot deserts cause major problems to the plants and animals that live there. Not even grass can survive such extreme conditions. Organisms living in hot desert areas therefore possess a wide range of xerophytic adaptations.

At best, vegetation cover is scanty. Cacti and other succulents predominate in some places, with swollen stems for storing water, waxy cuticles, and leaves reduced to thorns to reduce evapotranspiration and deter grazing. The huge, branching saguaro cactus of Arizona, which may be 15 m tall, is just one example. Most desert plants have stomata (the pores through which evapotranspiration takes place) which close in response to high evaporation rates. Their long, deep roots, often bulbous, take maximum

advantage of the rare occasions when rain falls, and of any mist, dew or frost that forms during the cool desert nights.

The creosote bush of the North American deserts has a dense network of tiny rootlets near the surface which are able to gather tiny amounts of dew with great efficiency. An individual creosote bush needs a large area just to supply its own needs, so it is not possible for other plants to grow close by. The bush grows outwards from its original base, and the inner parts die off. After several years of this process, it forms a large hollow ring.

Other plants are ephemerals, only bursting into life when rain falls, flowering and producing seeds which may then lie dormant for years until the next rain falls. The Rose of Jericho, a plant of the Middle East and eastern Sahara, rolls itself into a tight, protective ball after its fruits have ripened (**15.10**). It only uncoils to release its seeds when it is thoroughly soaked. Several other species have similar adaptations. Some break off at the original root and winds roll them across the desert's surface to ensure maximum seed dispersal. Another problem that desert plants must cope with is the high concentrations of salts and alkalis in the aridisols. Many desert plants, such as salt bush, are **halophytes**, able to tolerate these saline conditions.

Animal life must also be adapted to withstand the extreme physical conditions imposed by the hot desert ecosystem. The species present vary from one desert to another, but the general range of adaptations to help them avoid the problems of desiccation are similar. Many insects, reptiles and smaller mammals seek shelter during the heat of the day, beneath boulders or in burrows where it is cooler and more humid. At night, they become active and emerge under the cover of darkness to hunt for their food requirements. Small mammals such as gerbils and jerboas feed on seeds and dry vegetation. In the Sahara they are hunted by the fennec fox which has huge ears and superb hearing (**15.11**).

The large range of insects are hunted in their turn by lizards, geckos and, in some places, toads. The spadefoot toads of Arizona survive times of drought by burying themselves deep beneath the surface, not emerging again until it rains, when they take advantage of the temporary puddles to feed and to spawn. Their eggs hatch and tadpoles develop very quickly, for they too must be ready to bury themselves by the time the puddles evaporate and disappear.

The camels of northern Africa and Asia are, perhaps, exceptional. Their large, splayed feet prevent them from sinking too far into sand. They can close their nostrils during sandstorms, and store great quantities of water in their stomachs so that they can go for days without drinking. They can eat even the most thorny desert plants and the food energy is stored in their humps as fat.

Desert-living birds must also be suitably adapted for survival. In Arizona and Mexico, the extraordinary road-runner chases across the ground like an Olympic sprinter, in pursuit of lizards and snakes which provide these birds with both their food and their liquid requirements. Adult road-runners allow water from their digested food to trickle from their beaks into the gaping throats of their young. In Africa, male sandgrouse often travel 40 km or more to collect water for their chicks. When they reach an oasis they wade into the water and fluff-out their belly feathers which absorb water like a sponge. They then fly back to their nests where the chicks gather round to suck the water from their parent's feathers.

6 a Describe three ways in which
 i plants and **ii** animals are adapted to save or store water in a desert ecosystem.
 b Describe three ways in which living things can obtain scarce water in a desert ecosystem.

CASE STUDY

IT8

'Desert Storm'

The desert ecosystem is fragile and easily disturbed. When, in 1990, Iraq invaded Kuwait, the ensuing Gulf War resulted in a major disturbance of the region, with pollution and erosion of the desert soils and their sparse vegetation by the military explosions and the movements of tanks and other vehicles.

A particular feature of the surface of long-established areas of hot desert is the presence of a surface coating called 'desert varnish', a dark-coloured layer of ferromanganese, just a few thousandths of a millimetre thick. The bare surface is also occupied in many places by a microfloral crust, the roots of ephemeral plants, which only burst into life following rain. These varnishes and crusts, which may have taken 5000 years to form, help to stabilise the desert surface and restrict further movement of wind-blown material. But they are easily broken, by explosions and the tyres and caterpillar tracks of vehicles (**15.12**). The tracks from the movements of vehicles during the Gulf War will probably remain visible for many centuries, and it is feared that the incidence of dust and sandstorms will increase as a result. Since the Gulf War, there have been heavy sandstorms in Arabia, just as there were exceptional sandstorms in North Africa during and following the desert campaigns of the Second World War.

■ **15.12** Damage to the desert duricrust

The effects on wildlife have also been severe. Many rare and endangered species, especially birds, were seriously affected by oil slicks in the Gulf and by the immense pollution caused by burning oil following the destruction of Kuwait's oilfields as the Iraqi Army retreated. But it is the vegetation, and its associated mammals, birds and insects that have been most badly affected, damaged by noise, habitat destruction and the laying of mines.

It is still too soon to assess the full effects of the Gulf War, but although 50 years have elapsed since the Second World War damaged the Sahara Desert, so far only 35 per cent of the vegetation that was destroyed has recovered. The presence of minefields and thousands of unexploded shells and bombs in the desert will go on causing the destruction of individual animals, including humans, for a long time to come. Ironically, however, they may also have a beneficial impact on the desert ecosystem since, until they are finally cleared, they will inhibit human occupation, serving to reduce overgrazing, thus helping to preserve the environment.

CASE STUDY

IP2, IT8

The Indira Gandhi Canal

Much of north-west India and parts of Pakistan are occupied by the Thar Desert. It is known from archaeological evidence that this area was a 'green and pleasant land' 1500 years ago, fed then by the legendary 'River Saraswati' which was said to flow from the Himalayas into the Rann of Kutch. Why the river dried up is not fully understood. But since 1958, at a cost of 500 billion rupees, one of the world's longest irrigation canals, the Indira Gandhi Canal, has been constructed (**15.13**). It is some 680 km long, and carries water from the Harika Barrage in Punjab deep into west Rajasthan, irrigating thousands of hectares of former desert. Rice is the principal crop, but oilseeds, cotton, groundnuts and cereals are also grown.

The development has not been without its problems, however. As with so many irrigation schemes in desert areas, evaporation of the water has led to salinisation – a concentration of salts and alkalis as water is drawn to the surface and evaporated. In places waterlogging of the soil is also a problem. After a few highly productive years yields are greatly reduced.

The construction of the canal has also disrupted the nomadic lifestyles of the Rajput camel herders, as rough grazing has been reduced and traditional routeways disrupted by fences and canals. The population is rapidly increasing, and with this has come a breakdown of traditional village communities and an increase in crime rates.

■ **15.13** Indira Gandhi Canal

7 The Indira Gandhi Canal was constructed to carry irrigation water to some desert areas of Rajasthan in India. What are **a** the potential benefits, and **b** the possible disadvantages of such schemes?

8 Collect evidence to support the idea that the desert is a fragile ecosystem.

9 'Grasslands and deserts that are the result of human activities and mismanagement of the environment rather than natural physical conditions are found in many parts of the world.' How far do you consider this to be a true statement? Give examples in support of your discussion.

16.1 **The Arctic tundra**

The harsh climate of the high latitudes around the poles prevents the growth of most plants. Indeed, the very word **tundra** means 'a treeless plain'. It is only where rocks appear through the ice and snow that any plants are able to grow during the short summer. In the Northern Hemisphere, tundra vegetation occurs on the arc of land that lies to the north of the boreal forest or **taiga** but, in the Southern Hemisphere, the ice-covered continent of Antarctica experiences even colder conditions than the north, so that there are almost no areas on which tundra plants can grow before the ocean is reached. Tundra also occurs in mountainous regions away from the polar areas, where similar climatic conditions prevail owing to high altitude (see section 7.6).

In the most exposed areas of the Arctic tundra, little can grow other than the most hardy lichens and mosses, but they can form a layer several centimetres thick if they are not grazed. Even in midsummer only the top few centimetres of ground thaws out and beneath this it is permanently frozen – **permafrost**. In addition to lichens and mosses, which are the basic 'building blocks' of the tundra ecosystem, a range of grasses and sedges with dwarf and creeping plants such as dwarf willow, dwarf birch, Arctic heath, bilberry and crowberry, are to be found in more sheltered places. Flowering plants include saxifrages, which survive as tightly-packed rosettes and cushions, and Iceland poppies, which must germinate, grow, flower and produce their seeds during the short summer that lasts just six to eight weeks (**16.1**). It is only at this time that conditions are warm enough for plants to grow, but they can take advantage of the long hours of summer daylight that permit almost continuous photosynthesis and growth. There are also extensive areas of bog or **muskeg**, very similar to the muskeg that is found within poorly drained areas of taiga. Indeed, tundra has been described as 'boreal forest without trees'. These bogs are dominated by cotton grass and sedges with bog moss or sphagnum.

Living things in the tundra are really only active in the summer. During winter, the factors limiting growth are darkness and the physiological drought, the result of a period of up to eight months during which temperatures are well below freezing and most of the surface is snow-covered. This is made worse by strong winds that can still abstract water from plant tissues at low temperatures. As the soil is completely frozen, this moisture cannot be replaced, and any plants exposed to the wind for long periods will die. This helps to explain why so many tundra plants are low-growing, and die back completely in winter, surviving only as rhizomes or bulbs beneath the surface, or are quick-growing, seed-producing annuals.

Under natural conditions, the tundra vegetation was grazed by large migratory herds of caribou and reindeer. But for many centuries the Lapps of northern Europe have domesticated the reindeer, shifting their herds across northern Scandinavia and into the former Soviet

■ **16.1** Tundra landscape in summer

■ **16.2** Polar bears are ideally suited to tundra

■ **16.3** An emperor penguin colony

the boggy tundra pools are alive with insect larvae, which are food for large colonies of these migratory birds. The larvae emerge as clouds of midges, making a visit to the tundra in summer a most uncomfortable experience.

The seas of the polar regions are also rich in plankton because cold water contains more dissolved oxygen than warm water. In the Southern Ocean around Antarctica this plankton is food for prolific numbers of krill, shrimp-like creatures that attract large numbers of fish, whales, seals and penguins.

One of the most remarkable of these is the emperor penguin, adapted to withstand the Antarctic cold by a thick layer of blubber and a fine covering of feathers. Like all birds, they must come to land to lay and incubate their eggs. These birds spend the summer at sea feeding, but come ashore shortly before the onset of winter. They gather in large colonies, or 'rookeries', where the females lay their eggs which are then left to be incubated by the male penguins (**16.3**). Throughout the darkness and extreme cold of the Antarctic winter they huddle together, each with a single egg balanced on his feet, kept warm in a feather-lined pouch below the stomach. For nearly four months the males cannot feed, but survive on the energy stored within their body fat. After 60 days the chicks hatch and are fed on the tiny amounts of food that still remain within the males' stomach and which they regurgitate. At last, having spent the winter at sea, the females return, shuffling and tobogganing on their front over many kilometres of snow and pack-ice. At the rookery they find their now emaciated, starving mates and feed the young on the stomachful of fish which they have carried with them.

Union in search of suitable grazing, while in Asia and America, Eskimo (Inuit) communities have traditionally hunted the migrating herds of wild caribou and reindeer.

Other grazing animals of the tundra include the musk ox, which survives the cold by means of an extremely thick coat. Predators include polar bears (**16.2**) and the Arctic fox, which is largely dependent on the huge numbers of ground-nesting birds that migrate to the tundra to breed during the short summer. Among them are several species of geese, other wild-fowl and wading birds. When ice-free,

Penguins are not found in the Northern Hemisphere, but the Arctic oceans are similarly rich in plankton and fish. Seals are numerous, and these are preyed upon both by the Eskimos and by polar bears which find the seals' breathing holes in the pack-ice or which stalk the seals when they come ashore.

16.2 **Tundra soils**

The climatic conditions that prevail in tundra areas mean that the subsoil remains permanently frozen as permafrost. Only the surface layer thaws in summer, and it is at this time that most precipitation occurs. Although this is not heavy, it is sufficient to make the surface layer waterlogged since water cannot percolate through the impermeable permafrost. The lack of oxygen in these waterlogged conditions restricts bacterial action so that the remains of the tundra vegetation only partly decompose and accumulate as a layer of peat, stained black by acid humus.

Below the peat a layer of bluish-grey clayey mud is found, containing unoxidised ferrous iron compounds (**16.4**). Only when exposed to the air and oxygen will these change to a rusty brown ferric state. Tundra soils of this kind are referred to as **gleys**, but gleys are also found in other climatic regimes where conditions are waterlogged.

However, a particular characteristic of tundra gleys is the presence of angular rock fragments throughout the soil profile, caused by the breaking of rock by freeze–thaw action, and the upward movement of these due to frost heave (see section 7.6). When water changes from its liquid state to solid ice it expands, contracting again when it melts. Lenses of ice often form beneath rock fragments, lifting them towards the surface where they are stranded. On slopes of less than 4°, these stones may form rings or polygon-shaped patterns (**16.5**) which on steeper slopes become stone stripes owing to the pull of gravity. The movement of the surface layer caused by frost heave is referred to as **cryoturbation** and this layer is described as the **active layer**.

■ **16.4** Tundra gley soil profile

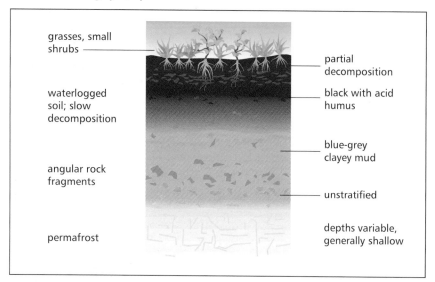

- grasses, small shrubs
- waterlogged soil; slow decomposition
- angular rock fragments
- permafrost
- partial decomposition
- black with acid humus
- blue-grey clayey mud
- unstratified
- depths variable, generally shallow

■ **16.5** Stone polygons caused by cryoturbation

CASE STUDY

IT2, 8

Coping with the problems of permafrost

Permafrost is major feature of tundra areas (see section 7.6). From a human point of view, however, it is a difficult phenomenon to cope with because the depth at which the permanently frozen ground is encountered beneath the surface varies from season to season and from place to place. Often ice lenses form within the **active layer**, creating spaces which are filled with silt or gravel when they thaw. It is this freezing and thawing of the active layer that causes problems when humans try to construct roads, buildings and pipelines across it.

Under natural conditions, most of the surface is covered with a layer of moss which, so long as it remains intact, reduces the depth of thawing. Tracked vehicles can strip off the moss cover, causing deeper thawing which results in subsidence and the formation of gullies. Even the colour of construction materials can alter the depth of the permafrost. An area of pale-coloured concrete, for example, reflects insolation with the result that there is little thawing of the surface beneath it in summer. Such an area will be less badly disturbed than one where a dark surface, which absorbs insolation, allows warmth to be transferred to a greater depth, increasing the depth of the active layer and causing the surface to sink, crack or break up. Similarly, a heated building can cause major problems, often leading to distortion and subsidence.

Several solutions to these problems have been found. One is to ensure that the foundations of buildings in the tundra are based on solid bedrock and not permafrost. Another, especially suited to houses and small buildings, has been to construct them on stilts, allowing freezing air to circulate beneath the construction so that the stilts remain firmly embedded in the permafrost. All water supply and waste-pipes are well insulated and kept clear of the surface to avoid disturbing the balance.

The oil pipeline constructed from the wells in Alaska to the terminal at Valdez crosses some 1300km of permafrost, and a number of ways of ensuring that it is not fractured by variations in the active layer have been built in (**16.6**). Since it carries hot crude oil it is well lagged to prevent heat loss and is raised

■ **16.6** Alaskan pipeline elevated above the permafrost layer

for most of its length on stilts embedded in the permafrost, the pipe itself being supported by cradles covered with a Teflon coating, allowing some movement due to expansion and contraction. Movement can also be experienced during earth tremors, for Alaska is an earthquake zone. Great care has been taken in constructing 'underpasses' and burying some sections of the pipeline to allow the unimpeded migration of caribou (see also case study on page 79).

---

1 Describe the physical conditions of the world's tundra regions.

2 How have **a** plants, and **b** animals adapted to survive these conditions?

3 a Explain what is meant by a gley.
   b How does a gley differ from a podsol?

4 How do humans cope with tundra conditions?

16.3 **Ice over all**

IT7

There are some areas of the globe – the Greenland ice-cap and Antarctica, for example – where conditions are so cold that plants are not able to grow and, therefore, few animals are found away from the coasts and surrounding seas (**16.7**). The coastal areas are immensely rich in life, however, especially in Antarctica with its immense numbers of

seals, whales, penguins and other sea birds – all part of a food chain based on the abundance of plankton and krill that live in these icy seas.

IT7

Antarctica has been described as 'the world's last great wilderness'. It covers 13.5 million km², one-tenth of the Earth's land surface, and is covered by a huge ice-cap averaging

■ **16.7** Antarctic ice-cap

IT7

2000 m deep. In winter, when the seas around Antarctica freeze, the area of the continent is nearly doubled. Even the coastal areas experience average temperatures of –15 °C while in the centre of the continent around the South Pole, average temperatures are –40 °C.

It is known that the rocks beneath the icecap are rich in minerals, including oil and coal. Many people fear that due to global pressure and demand for scarce resources, this wilderness could be damaged beyond repair if exploitation were allowed to proceed. The International Antarctic Treaty of 1959 agreed that Antarctica should only be used for peaceful purposes and that there should be freedom of scientific investigation and research, with shared knowledge of the results. But there is concern at the debris and litter accumulating in this remote environment from the 1000 and more scientific and support personnel who populate Antarctica at any one time.

Even more alarming, however, is the indiscriminate exploitation of the krill, whale and fish stocks of the Southern Ocean. The huge quantities of plankton in the Southern Ocean feed krill and fish, which are an important link in the food chain supporting sea birds, seals and other marine mammals, and larger fish. It is feared that if the stocks are severely diminished the whole food chain will collapse, destroying this ecosystem.

IT7

Another problem, recently identified, is the possible damage to wildlife in the Antarctic caused by seasonal holes in the ozone layer in the upper atmosphere. The ozone hole over the Antarctic may be caused by pollution of the atmosphere with such gases as chlorofluorocarbons (CFCs). The hole reduces the filtering effect that ozone has on ultraviolet (UV) light, so that increased UV intensity is experienced at lower levels. It is known that this can cause skin cancers in humans, but recently it has been shown that phytoplankton in the Southern Ocean may be at risk. This could seriously affect the krill, and the rest of the dependent food chain. There is evidence that the eyes of seals and penguins are also being affected by increased UV intensity (see also section 12.7).

IT6, 7

A recent trend has been a significant increase in the number of cruise ships visiting Antarctic waters. Although no one is suggesting that hotels might one day be built on the continent, the growing numbers of tourists being landed for day visits gives rise to some concerns, such as the disturbance of seal and penguin breeeding colonies, the discarding of litter and the inadvertent introduction of alien species, diseases and viruses which could threaten the polar ecosystem. There are many who feel that Antarctica should be left as the world's last wilderness. That effectively means keeping people out.

---

5 Weigh up the arguments for and against exploiting the resources of the Antarctic.

6 Is the case for the protection of the Arctic regions any less than that for the Antarctic? Justify your viewpoint.

CHAPTER 17 Marine Ecosystems

17.1 The diversity of the world's marine ecosystems

Water covers 71 per cent of the Earth's surface, and 97 per cent of this is found in the oceans. The oceans play a key role in the maintenance of Earth's life-support systems. Not only do they help redistribute solar energy by the circulation of ocean currents and evaporation within the hydrological cycle, they are also a massive reservoir of dissolved oxygen and carbon dioxide, helping to regulate the balance of gases in the atmosphere.

The oceans and seas are dominated by waves and tides produced by the gravitational pull of the sun and the moon. Tides are a significant influence on life at the edges of the land, the vertical tidal range varying from as little as 30 cm in landlocked seas such as the Mediterranean, to as much as 20 m.

Sea water is salty, with an average salinity of 35 parts by weight of salts to 1000 parts of water, i.e. 35‰. About 27‰ is sodium chloride, the remaining 8‰ consisting mainly of salts of magnesium, calcium and potassium.

There are as many as 250 000 species of marine animals and plants. These are divided into two major groups: **pelagic organisms** that are adapted to live in the open salt waters of the world's seas and oceans, and **benthic organisms** that dwell on the ocean floor. However, most of the fixed (**sessile**) benthic plants and animals have a pelagic stage as part of their life cycle, often forming part of the marine plankton.

Plankton consists of microscopic, usually single-celled, floating plants and animals (**17.1**). Plant plankton are known collectively as **phytoplankton** and, like land-based plants, produce food by photosynthesis, obtaining their carbon from atmospheric carbon dioxide dissolved in ocean water and fuelled by the sunlight, which only penetrates the surface layers of the oceans. It is their use of carbon dioxide and production of oxygen that gives plankton a vital role in maintaining the oxygen balance of the Earth's atmosphere.

Phytoplankton, along with the marine algae (seaweeds), form the basis of marine food chains and webs, with the exception of the food chain based on the chemosynthetic bacteria – see page 215. The main consumers are largely microscopic animals, zooplankton. Plankton exists in huge quantities – a cubic metre of sea water may contain 200 000 individuals. Larger animals feed either on plank-

■ **17.1** Plankton (× 16 magnification)

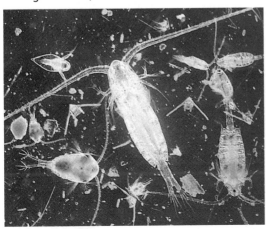

■ **17.2** Seaweed on rocks: note the zonal distribution

ton (or the detritus from dead plankton) or are larger carnivorous **secondary consumers**, ranging from fish such as sandeels and herrings and even the huge basking sharks and whales (marine mammals), to the fixed-location filter-feeding sea anemones and shellfish.

The larger multicellular algae or seaweeds are important 'producers' in limited areas, especially near the shore (**17.2**), but there are few oceanic herbivores that perform a role similar to grazing animals on land.

---

1 Identify the different ways in which the oceans are important to life on this planet.

17.2 **Zones of the ocean**

Oceans may be divided into two major zones (**17.3**):

■ The **oceanic zone**, which lies beyond the continental slope, reaching depths as great as 600 m.

■ The **coastal zone** (sometimes referred to as the *neritic zone*, meaning 'near shore'), which extends to the edge of the continental shelf, at which point the ocean floor drops steeply down the continental slope.

The oceanic zone

The oceanic zone may be divided into three vertical layers, rather like altitudinal zones on high mountains:

■ The surface or **euphotic layer** – sunlight penetrates through this zone and so it supports photosynthesising phytoplankton and their consumers, including zooplankton, fish and shellfish. These in turn support a diversity of seabirds and mammals such as whales. Many of the fish, such as sardines, anchovies, herrings and tuna, are commercially important.

■ The **bathyal layer**, starting some 200 m below the surface, is much colder and insufficient light penetrates to this depth for photosynthesis to take place. Thus there are no 'producers', so animal

■ **17.3** Vertical zonation of the oceans

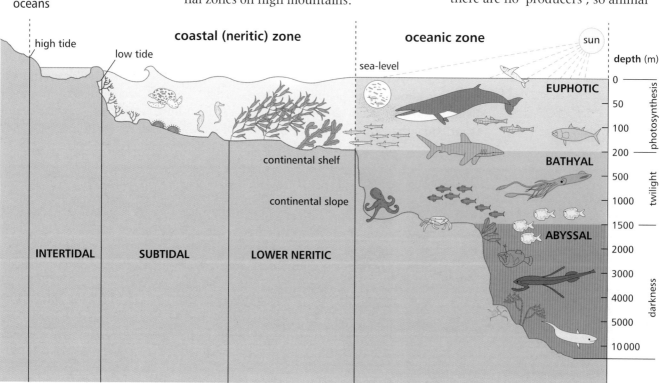

17.4 Decapods such as this live in the north-east Atlantic at a depth of 1000 m

communities living at this depth are mainly scavengers and their predators, dependent on the productivity of the sunlit zone above.

■ The **abyssal zone** is deeper still, below 1500 m. Here, it is pitch-dark and only a little above 0°C with very high pressures caused by the depth of water above. This zone supports a diversity of decomposers, including bacteria, that survive on the detritus 'rain' of dead plants and animals that sink from the euphotic and bathyal layers above.

Within the abyssal zone, strange life-forms based on sulphur rather than carbon have recently been discovered around the mid-ocean ridges. These ridges are the edges of diverging tectonic plates where the water is warmed by upwelling hot magma. It is thought that hydrogen sulphide gas rising from these vents is converted by highly specialised bacteria into chemical energy without the help of sunlight, a process known as **chemosynthesis**. These bacteria form the basis of an extraordinary food chain consisting of strange-looking worms, gastropods and crustaceans specially adapted to withstand the immense pressures experienced at these great depths (**17.4**).

The coastal zone

In contrast to the ocean depths, the coastal zone is one of shallow water, bathed in sunlight, relatively warm and rich in nutrients, extending from the high-tide mark on land to the edge of the continental shelf. Although the coastal zone represents only 10 per cent of the total area of the oceans, due to the availability of light for photosynthesis it contains 90 per cent of its plant and animal life and is the location of major commercial activities, including fishing. Coastal habitats are diverse and include cliffs, wave-cut platforms, rocky shores, beaches of deposited sand and shingle, sand dunes, estuaries, intertidal mudflats, salt marsh, mangrove swamps, islands and coral reefs (see Chapter 5). Together, these habitats form a natural chain but they are becoming increasingly fragmented by human development.

When the tide is out a section of the coastal zone is exposed to the air. Organisms living in this intertidal zone must be specially adapted to cope with a variety of problems, the chief of which is to avoid being dried out while the tide is out, but able to tolerate immersion in salt water when the tide is in. They must also be able to withstand varying degrees of heating and cooling and, in exposed locations, an extreme battering by waves.

Immediately above the high-tide mark there is another zone which is soaked by wave splash when the tide is in.

Between the tide marks, the length of time that part of the shore is exposed to

17.5 Zonation of a typical rocky shore showing zones of seaweed and barnacle species

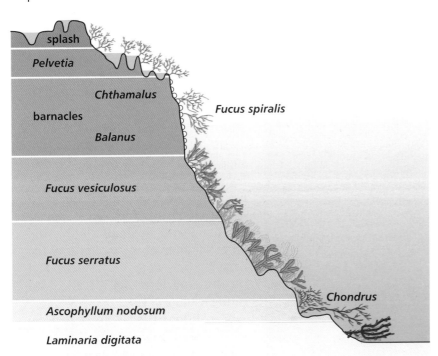

splash

Pelvetia

Chthamalus

barnacles

Balanus

Fucus spiralis

Fucus vesiculosus

Fucus serratus

Chondrus

Ascophyllum nodosum

Laminaria digitata

■ **17.6** Differences in features of the dog whelk

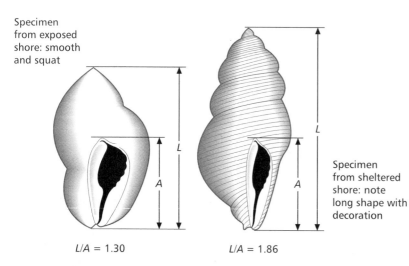

Specimen from exposed shore: smooth and squat

L/A = 1.30

Specimen from sheltered shore: note long shape with decoration

L/A = 1.86

the air has a great influence on the communities of plants and animals that can survive there. This produces a marked zonation of species up and down the shore between the high and low-tide marks (**17.5**).

There are further influences on shore life, including the nature of the lithology forming the coastline. Rocky shores provide a firm base to which seaweeds and shellfish, such as limpets, may attach themselves, but such coasts are often exposed, and may suffer from extreme battering and scouring by wave action, especially during storms. Sand and mud provides no such firm base, but many creatures can survive on such shores by burying themselves in the soft material when the tide falls, emerging to feed, or extending a syphon to the surface to filter-feed on plankton and detritus when the tide comes in (**17.6**).

17.3 **Commercial fishing**

IT4

Fish and shellfish supply people with a significant source of animal protein, about 91 per cent of the catch coming from seas and oceans. Over 99 per cent of the fish caught are taken within 370 km of land. Many kinds of fish make up the catch, which is mainly consumed by humans, but increasingly fish caught are used for making fish meal, which is fed to domestic animals such as broiler chickens.

It has been estimated that if the harvest of food from the sea is to be sustained, the total catch that may be taken each year should not exceed 100 million tonnes. However, modern methods such as sonar to locate fish shoals, the attraction of shoals by lights and electrodes, and the use of fine-mesh nets and fish-factory trawlers, have led to increasing annual catches which are fast approaching the sustainable limit (**17.7**). Indeed, in some areas overfishing has already resulted in the exhaustion of stocks, with inadequate mature fish remaining to maintain supplies. In the 1970s, the Peruvian anchovy became commercially unviable owing to a combination of overfishing and the shifting of the shoals away from the cold Peruvian Current.

The seas around the British Isles support a rich marine flora and fauna. For many centuries this abundance has been the focus of an important fishing industry. They also support an abundance of sea birds and other wildlife. Mismanagement of the fisheries puts both the livelihood of the fishermen as well as the fish-eating wildlife at risk.

Over-fishing has become a problem in the north-east Atlantic since the 1960s, caused by rapid modernisation

IT4

■ **17.7** A modern crab fishing vessel

of the fishing fleet, which is increasingly effective in catching fish. The first serious collapse was the herring stock during the 1960s and 1970s so that, in 1975, a complete ban on their capture was introduced.

Today, there are similar fears for sandeels and sprats in the North Sea and the Scottish waters around Orkney and Shetland, which are harvested as a prolific source of fish meal and oil. Catches fell rapidly during the late 1980s and early 1990s, with a knock-on effect on the sea-bird colonies of these northern islands which have been unable to catch sufficient sandeels to feed their young.

It is also estimated that the catch rate for cod, haddock, plaice and herring from the Atlantic is at least four times higher than the sustainable limit. The problem of the conservation of fish stocks has resulted in much bitter argument among the partners of the European Union (EU). The Common Fisheries Policy was only established after years of bitter negotiation, which has established quotas (the 'total allowable catch') for each species which are allocated to the fishing nations of the EU. A 200-mile (322 km) limit within which non-EU countries are excluded has also been imposed.

The Common Fisheries Policy also regulates the mesh size of nets, minimum landing sizes of fish and other technical aspects, all designed to conserve stocks. However, many regard these measures as totally inadequate and it is likely that catches will have to be reduced still further. Already the fishing industry is experiencing major hardship as a result of these restrictions, and falling catches because of depleted stocks and over-capacity in the fishing fleets.

One solution may be to set up compensation schemes for fishermen to encourage the decommissioning of vessels, thus reducing the size of the fishing fleets. There are also proposals to limit the number of days fishing fleets can spend at sea, and for each fishing boat to be allocated an individual, transferable quota for types of fish its crew wishes to catch, possibly sold to fishermen by government auction. But arguments continue, and some say that there is a fundamental weakness in the scheme owing to discrepancies between the strictness with which individual member states enforce the conservation regulations.

CASE STUDY

Whaling

Whales are marine mammals ranging in size from porpoises (1 m long) to the 15–30 m blue whale. An International Whaling Commission has been established as a result of concern over sharp declines in commercial whale species, with some species being brought close to extinction. The Commission has regulated hunting quotas and imposed bans to ensure a sustainable supply. However, the methods used, mainly based on harpoons, are regarded by many as inhumane, and many environmental organisations have campaigned vigorously to put an end to all commercial whaling. Nevertheless, there is a loophole that permits killing whales 'for the purposes of research', and some nations, notably Iceland, South Korea, Japan and Norway, have got around the ban by increasing their 'research' catch.

2 The efficiency of modern fishing techniques and vessels has been blamed for declining fish stocks in many parts of the world. If you were the government minister responsible for the conservation of fish stocks, what proposals would you suggest to prevent over-fishing and to ensure a sustainable future for the fishing industry?

3 'As many species that once lived on Earth have become extinct by natural processes, we should not be concerned about the extinction of some wild species, such as whales, due to human exploitation.' How far do you agree or disagree with this statement? Justify your view with examples and reasons.

17.4 **Estuaries**

Estuaries are river mouths, where tidal action causes the mixing of salt and fresh water, creating a range of complicated conditions for living organisms. The salinity of sea water may be greatly diluted by inflowing streams and rivers when the tide falls, only to be replaced by saltier water as the tide rises. Silt carried by river water or by coastal currents and longshore drift is deposited in the shelter of the estuary, leading to the formation of sand and mudflats which may be exposed at low tide (see section 5.4). Thus estuary organisms must be able to survive desiccation, wide variations in salinity and the instability of the deposited silt.

Plants that can withstand saline conditions are termed **halophytes**. Many are succulents, possessing water-storing tissues and formidable networks of rhizomes or roots which stabilise the mud deposits.

CASE STUDY

IT7

Strangford Lough

Strangford Lough in Northern Ireland is an excellent example of an estuary ecosystem. It is a sheltered marine inlet of some 150 km² located in drumlin country in County Down. It is virtually landlocked, but connected to the Irish Sea by the Strangford Narrows (**17.8**). At the southern end the salinity of the water is similar to the Irish Sea, but at the northern end it is diluted by several inflowing streams, with a consequent variation in plankton and other life.

The intertidal habitats of Strangford Lough are variable. Those exposed to wave action and currents consist of banks of pebbles and gravels; more sheltered areas are composed of fine sands and muds. These areas of sand and mud deposits are being invaded by salt-marsh plants. Typical of the pioneer plants is glasswort (*Salicornia* sp.). It is succulent and its branching root network helps to stabilise the mud, paving the way for salt-marsh grasses to invade, followed by such plants as sea lavender, sea aster and sea plantain. Where this plant succession has built up the salt marsh to the point that it is only occasionally immersed by salt water, rushes and reeds more commonly associated with freshwater marshes occur. The zonation of these species strongly reflects the length of time and frequency with which the marsh is inundated by salt water, and there is a tendency for the freshwater species to be more abundant furthest from the open sea.

The open waters of the lough provide abundant fish including sandeels, herring and mackerel, pursued by sea birds including terns and auks and an

■ **17.8** Strangford Lough, Northern Ireland

internationally important population of seals. Due to the high plankton turnover in this area of concentrated tidal flow, the lough bed, particularly in the Strangford Narrows, has unique populations of filter-feeding organisms such as sponges, sea anemones and cool-water corals and their predators such as brittle starfish.

The open intertidal gravels, sand and mudflats are rich in invertebrate animals such as lugworms and ragworms along with tellins, cockles and other bivalve shellfish. The tiny spire shellfish, *Hydrobia* – no larger than a grain of rice – is also extremely abundant. These invertebrates attract huge, internationally important numbers of wading birds and wildfowl, especially in winter and during their spring and autumn migrations between their Arctic breeding grounds and their winter quarters to the south (**17.9**). Commercially important within the lough are lobsters, crabs, Dublin Bay prawns and scallops.

Species	Strangford Lough counts	% of Irish population
Mute swan	214	13
Brent goose	13 455*	67
Shelduck	2 185	18
Wigeon	1 890	2
Gadwall	985	2
Pintail	220	11
WADING BIRDS		
Oystercatcher	4 585	7
Golden plover	9 080	9
Lapwing	13 885	7
Knot	9 825*	39
Bar-tailed godwit	1 057*	5
Redshank	3 100*	12

* numbers of international importance

■ **17.9** Important wildfowl and wading birds on Strangford Lough

As with so many other ecosystems, a variety of development threats and issues must be addressed at Strangford Lough (**17.10**). These include the following:

■ *Commercial fishing* – whether by trawling, dredging, netting or potting – damages the bed of the lough which, in many places, shows extensive scarring and ecological damage.

■ *Fin-fish farming* (for salmon, for example) – so far

applications for permission to establish caged salmon farming in the lough have been refused. Strangford Lough is an attractive site for such development, with its clean water and sheltered conditions. But experience in Scotland and elsewhere has demonstrated a variety of problems including:

□ unsightly cages

□ pollution of the adjacent area with uneaten food and waste produced by the fish

□ algal blooms resulting from nutrient enrichment

□ conflict as a result of the attraction of fish-eating wildlife

□ damage caused by chemicals used to control fish diseases and parasites

□ escaped fish interbreeding with wild stock producing genetic contamination and reduced viability of wild fish

□ competition for space with recreational activities.

■ *Shellfish farming* for Pacific oysters, mussels, king scallops and Manila clams is being trialled in the lough (**17.11**). These activities have some visual impact, and there are concerns over potential pollution from accumulation of organic waste; disturbance to bird populations and a conflict of interests, since natural predators of shellfish are attracted to the culture sites; and severe reductions in the plankton populations from artificially dense concentrations of filter-feeding shellfish. There is also the risk of 'alien' shellfish species introduced to the lough 'escaping' and becoming established, thus competing with the ecologically important indigenous species.

■ **17.10** View across Strangford Lough

■ **17.11** Shellfish farming

■ *Recreational developments* – the sheltered waters of the lough and attractive scenery make it an idyllic setting for recreational and competitive boating. There are over 2000 sailing boats, large numbers of sailing dinghies as well as motor cruisers using the lough, especially in summer (**17.12**). There are increasing numbers of windsurfers, and jet-skiing has a small but growing following. The problems from further development of these interests include physical disturbance to the surroundings from noise and boating activities and to the lough-bed and

■ **17.12** Sailing on Strangford Lough puts pressure on the environment

shores from moorings and anchorages; loss of habitat from building of slipways and construction of marinas; and damage to marine life from anti-fouling chemicals, oil and fuel spillage, dumping of refuse and discharge of toilets. As much of the shoreline is muddy, the lough is not particularly attractive to bathers, but recreational divers exploring wrecks, observing and collecting shellfish and spear-fishing could be a potential problem.

■ *Wildfowling* – this is a traditional activity at Strangford Lough, from the shore and islands. However, in recent years the numbers of some wildfowl and wading bird species have declined sharply, and it is thought that this is partly due to increased disturbance. Refuge areas have been established.

■ *Waste disposal and pollution* – there have been considerable problems caused by fly-tipping of rubbish on the foreshore of the lough and litter from boats, although the tipping of domestic waste is forbidden. There is also some direct discharge of sewage effluents from seven settlements around the lough, although all effluents receive some treatment before discharge. Local nutrient enrichment from this source has led to excessive algal growth. Discharge of toilets from boats has already been mentioned. Leaching of fertilisers and pesticides from surrounding farmland and spillage of farm slurries are other potential sources of pollution.

> **4** Considering the ecological importance of Strangford Lough, draw up a list of regulations that you would suggest to ensure the sustainable development of the lough and its surroundings.

CASE STUDY

IP1, IT7,8

Reclamation in Tokyo Bay

In many parts of the world, estuaries and other coastal ecosystems are subjected to a range of human development pressures ranging from pollution from industrial effluents and spillage of fuel from vessels to reclamation for urban expansion, industrial growth, and recreation (**17.13**). This is especially true of areas in developed countries such as Japan. Tokyo Bay provides an excellent example.

Since the end of the Second World War, Japan's economy has expanded rapidly, maintaining a faster growth rate than almost anywhere else on Earth. Such rapid expansion, coupled with an affluent and growing population, requires space, especially for housing. Prices of development land have soared. Part of the solution has been reclamation of coastal wetlands to expand Tokyo's metropolitan area, now a conurbation of more than 20 million people.

Ecological losses of salt marsh, intertidal mudflats and other marine wildlife communities have been considerable (**17.14**). In addition, housing developments on low-lying coastal land are exposed to a series of hazards. Japan lies in a major earthquake zone which reduces the load-bearing capacity of the reclaimed sands, silts and clays as well as placing developments at risk from tsunamis (huge waves set up by an earthquake's seismic vibrations) and tidal waves generated by typhoons (high-velocity revolving storms that, in summer, sweep along the shores of the East China Sea and the western Pacific). Reclaimed land may also be subject to subsidence and shrinkage, placing property at risk of damage and flooding during storms and high tides.

However, reclamation around Tokyo Bay has helped solve another problem – waste disposal. Affluent urban populations produce huge amounts of solid waste, and much has been used for landfill in low-lying areas, helping to raise development sites above the flood-danger level and providing an 870 ha base for runway extensions at Tokyo's Haneda airport. By extending the runways into Tokyo Bay, noise problems have been reduced as aircraft now land and take off over water. There are disadvantages, however. Solid waste often contains a range of toxic chemicals from industry which may be leached from the infilled site, polluting the waters of the Bay.

Conflict may also arise from recreational development. Reclaimed land may be used for the construction of golf courses and other facilities for formal recreation. But the loss of coastal habitat destroys recreational opportunities for bird-watchers, walkers and others who require a natural environment in which to pursue their leisure interests.

5 Discuss the potential conflicts that may arise from the reclamation of sites of ecological value. What are the economic benefits of developments on reclaimed land?

■ 17.13 Coastal reclamation around Tokyo Bay

■ 17.14 Tokyo: the block-shaped areas are reclaimed land. Can you identify this area on the map?

IT7

Cardiff Bay – a study in conflict

Cardiff Bay is the tidal estuary of the rivers Taff and Ely as they join the Severn estuary. During the 19th century the shores of the bay were heavily developed with industry, docks, warehouses and poor-quality housing for the working population. However, due to industrial decline in this century, the area has experienced widespread economic problems, high rates of unemployment and dereliction. Plans have recently been produced for the redevelopment and regeneration of the area.

In spite of its former industrial development, and pollution of the Taff and Ely rivers, Cardiff Bay has areas of intertidal mud that are used by thousands of wading birds, wildfowl and other estuarine life, of sufficient importance for the area to be designated as a Site of Special Scientific Interest (SSSI) and, as such, an area that is subject to special protection. However, a major controversy has arisen as a result of the proposed redevelopment plan for Cardiff Bay (**17.15**). A main feature of the proposed scheme is to construct a barrage across the mouth of the Bay at a cost of more than £100 million. This would create a fresh-water lake of more than 160 ha that would hide the intertidal mud which the developers consider to be unsightly. They claim this is necessary to attract new residents and jobs to the area and to increase the potential for investment.

A public enquiry and a parliamentary enquiry have been held, hard fought by those for and against the scheme. The arguments are set out below.

The case FOR the scheme

- The barrage and lake is required to attract £2000 million of public and private investment to the area, for housing, recreational and modern industrial development. The lake will make great improvements to the landscaping and scenic qualities of the Cardiff Bay area, thus creating the superlative environment necessary to attract inward investment.

- 24 000 new jobs will be created over 15 years, many a result of the construction work offered by the building of the barrage itself.

- 6000 homes will be built, many commanding high prices owing to the high quality of the surroundings and the recreational opportunities for sailing that will be provided by the lake.

- The risk of flooding will be *reduced*, as storm-driven high tides will be excluded by the concrete barrage.

- The freshwater lake created will provide a new wildlife habitat. A fish-pass will be included in the scheme, so that salmon and sea trout will have access to their spawning grounds upstream. An alternative feeding area for wading birds will be created some 6 km away at Wentloog.

The case AGAINST the scheme

- The creation of a permanent lake will cause groundwater levels to rise, affecting 1000 homes in the area and possibly affecting the pitch in the international rugby stadium at Cardiff Arms Park.

- The cost of the barrage could be as much as £150 million. This expenditure is unnecessary, as the rest of the redevelopment scheme can still go ahead without the construction of the barrage. The developers have not proved that the barrage will attract the additional investment that they claim, and it will not be used to generate electricity or create new road links.

- Most of the new homes built will be far too expensive for local people.

- Jobs created by the construction of the barrage will only be temporary, and many would be for construction workers from outside the area, already employed by the construction firms.

- The barrage would *increase* the risk of flooding as floodwaters could exceed the storage capacity of the lake and mechanical faults in the sluices could delay their opening, thus blocking floodwater behind the barrage.

- The Cardiff Bay SSSI will be destroyed, and wading birds displaced are unlikely to use the alternative areas that are proposed as it will take many years for the ecology of the new areas to develop and provide the food required

- The lake will be highly polluted, with the danger of contamination by sewage and dead animals washed down by the rivers. Sporting activities such as sailing could not be permitted owing to the risk of disease to anyone falling in the polluted water.

6 Consider the arguments for and against the Cardiff Bay Barrage Scheme. Prepare a letter that might be sent to your MP expressing your views on whether or not the development should go ahead, giving the reasons for your choice.

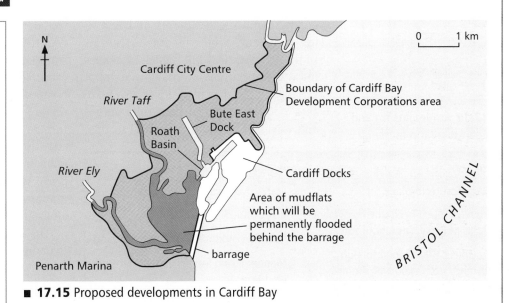

■ **17.15** Proposed developments in Cardiff Bay

17.5 **Mangrove swamps**

Mangroves grow in tropical estuaries, where they perform the same task as pioneer plants of other estuaries – that of trapping and anchoring mud. Worldwide, there are 15.8 million ha of mangrove swamps, the greatest concentration being found in South-east Asia.

Mangroves are trees and shrubs that are well adapted to exist in these surroundings by the development of a horizontal raft of roots that extends across the mud (**17.16**). Some taller mangrove species send out aerial roots which curve

■ **17.16** Mangrove swamp

down to act as props. Others have a series of vertical spikes on the roots nearest the water which act as a 'breathing tube' for the exchange of carbon dioxide and oxygen.

Mangroves also spread by means of highly specialised seeds, which germinate while they are still hanging on the branches of their parent. These develop a long spear-like root and shoot before they are released, dropping into the mud below or floating away on the tide until cast up in a sheltered spot where the root embeds itself in the mud and a new tree is established. Because the seedling can photosynthesise while floating it can drift for more than a year, covering hundreds of miles before reaching a suitable site to become established.

Many shellfish, shrimps, crabs and fish live among the thick tangle of mangrove roots. One of the strangest is the mudskipper whose front fins are adapted as a pair of primitive legs so that it can wriggle and crawl across the open mud. It retains a chamber full of water for respiration in its gills, returning to the water for a refill when its dissolved oxygen runs out.

The mangrove swamp ecosystem plays an important part in maintaining water quality, removing pollutants and retaining sediment, while producing humus from its own leaf-fall which supports many aquatic animals at the lower end of the food chain. The mangroves also serve as a natural barrier against tidal surges and wave damage during tropical storms.

Mangrove swamps are important breeding grounds for immense numbers of shrimps which in many tropical countries form the basis of important commercial operations. In Ecuador, for example, shrimps are farmed by the creation of shallow lagoons which replace the mangroves that formerly formed a protective fringe along the coastline. The shrimp fry are collected wild from the few remaining mangrove swamps, but the removal of the mangroves has produced a host of environmental problems.

The dilemma for countries such as Ecuador is shown in **17.17**.

■ **17.17** Arguments for and against shrimp farming

For	Against
Uses local technology	Mangrove ecosystem destroyed
Provides much-needed employment (2.5% of Ecuador's labour force)	Risk of flooding increased
Provides badly needed foreign currency from export of shrimps – 20% of Ecuador's foreign earnings from exports in 1988	Pollution produced by shrimp farming
	Mangroves no longer there to remove pollution
Temporary timber available for fuel and construction as mangroves felled	Loss of sustainable source of timber, crabs and other seafood as mangroves cleared
	Loss of potential tourist attraction as much wildlife destroyed
	Wild shrimp supplies for stocking of shrimp farms diminish as swamps are drained

7 Should the development of commercial shrimp farms be continued in areas of mangrove swamp such as those of Ecuador? Justify your answer.

17.6 **Coral reefs – an endangered ecosystem**

Coral reefs occur between latitudes 30° N and 30° S, but only in shallow tropical seas not more than 90 m in depth, although reefs also extend to the northern ends of the Red Sea and the Gulf of Iran, and around Bermuda, owing to the high sea temperatures there. Corals require sea temperatures that are constantly warm, never falling below 18.5 °C.

Coral reefs are built by colonies of polyps, simple marine organisms that are close relatives of sea anemones. These organisms secrete a hard skeleton around themselves by converting calcium salts in solution into solid calcium carbonate. The polyps have tentacles to seize free-swimming plankton from the water.

Different coral species produce irregular masses, 'heads' and branching tree-like structures, often of different colours, so that coral reefs are ecosystems of great beauty (**17.18**). Numerous single-celled algae, zooxanthellae, live within the tissues of the coral polyps using energy from sunlight to photosynthesise and produce food which is used both by the algae and to some extent by the coral polyps.

There are three main types of reef:

■ **fringing reefs** which, as their name suggests, grow outwards from the fringes of the shores of landmasses and islands

■ **barrier reefs**, such as the Great Barrier Reef off Australia, which form some way offshore, separated from the land by a broad channel

■ **atolls** which are rings of coral around a sheltered, shallow lagoon.

Coral reefs support a great abundance of fish and other marine life due to the availability of food and shelter. Parrot fish eat the polyps, biting off pieces of

■ 17.18 Coral reef

Huge shoals of brightly coloured fish graze on algae or filter plankton from the water. Others, like the sinister-looking moray eel, lie in wait in crevices to prey on other fish passing by. Reefs are also natural breakwaters, protecting nearby land from the erosive forces of the sea (**17.19**). Their colour, beauty and biodiversity also attract tourists, and they have become important recreational areas.

Unfortunately, the future of coral reefs is becoming a major concern of marine scientists throughout the world. Many reefs have become damaged, or are showing signs of stress, from both natural and human causes. Hurricanes and storms can cause extensive damage and the corals may be subject to diseases such as 'white band' caused by bacteria, or attack by predators such as the crown-of-thorns starfish (**17.20**), which has reached plague proportions along the Australian Great Barrier Reef. In some places there has also been a decline in zooxanthellae in the coral tissues. This so-called 'coral bleaching' may be a symptom of small but significant temperature increases resulting from global warming.

coral with sharp beak-like teeth, while starfish pour digestive enzymes into the coral chambers to feed on a 'polyp soup'.

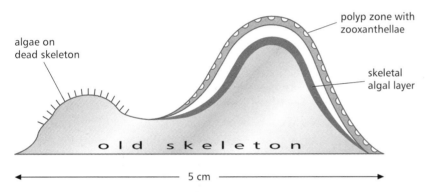

algae on dead skeleton

polyp zone with zooxanthellae

skeletal algal layer

old skeleton

5 cm

■ 17.19 Cross-section through a coral polyp colony

But there are also other human causes of damage. Sewage input into the waters around reefs, mining of coral and dredging activities, exploitation of fish and other food sources living among reefs, coral gathering for souvenirs and decoration of aquaria – all are contributing to the deterioration and decline of the world's coral reefs. After research and marine assessments, the establishment of a range of coastal management schemes is required for the conservation of these unique ecosystems.

8 Examine the conflicts that arise between the development of tourism and the survival of coral reefs. How might these conflicts be resolved?

■ 17.20 Crown-of-thorns starfish

The Baltic Sea – victim of marine pollution

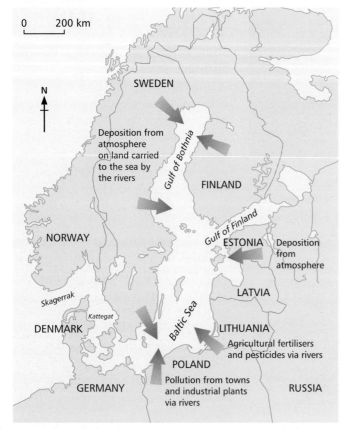

0   200 km

N

SWEDEN

Deposition from atmosphere on land carried to the sea by the rivers

Gulf of Bothnia

FINLAND

Gulf of Finland

NORWAY

ESTONIA   Deposition from atmosphere

Skagerrak

Kattegat

LATVIA

Baltic Sea

DENMARK

LITHUANIA

Agricultural fertilisers and pesticides via rivers

POLAND

Pollution from towns and industrial plants via rivers

GERMANY   RUSSIA

■ **17.21** The Baltic Sea: the sources of its pollution

The Baltic Sea and its wildlife populations face an uncertain future. It has an area of 374 000 km^2 and an average depth of only 60 m (**17.21**). As it is virtually landlocked, with only a narrow link to the North Sea via the Skagerrak and Kattegat, which permits a very limited water exchange, the Baltic is particularly vulnerable to the build-up of pollutants, especially the toxic organic pollutants used in agriculture and released by industry, washed in by such rivers as the Oder and Wista.

The Baltic is also a cold sea and, being less salt than the oceans (2–10 ppm compared with the Atlantic's 34 ppm), it is prone to freezing. Indeed, the Gulf of Bothnia is frozen over each year from December until May. This limits the number of species able to survive in these conditions, and the food chains are extra-sensitive to disturbance.

The problems first came to light in the 1960s when the build-up of such insecticides as DDT and DDE within food chains in the Baltic caused huge declines in fish and sea birds, and of predators such as the white-tailed sea eagle that feeds largely on fish. Then came PCBs (polychlorinated biphenyls) which are a waste product of the plastics industry and used in electrical equipment, sealants, etc. Like DDT, PCBs also build up along the food chain, causing the deaths of many birds, as well as mammals such as seals and otters that have become sick and sterile as a result of PCBs. The grey seal population in the Baltic declined from around 100 000 in 1900 to fewer than 1500 in 1990.

There are continuing fears at the long-term effects of brominated flame retardents, used in everything from TVs to curtain fabrics, and the deadly dioxins, which have been found in large quantities in fish such as herrings. Other pollutants entering the Baltic are fertilisers resulting from the runoff of artificial nitrates and phosphates from agricultural land, which could lead to over-enrichment and eutrophication.

> **9 a** Examine the physical conditions which seem to exacerbate the pollution problem in the Baltic Sea.
>
> **b** Identify some of the difficulties likely to be encountered in any attempt to reduce the levels of pollution.

18.1 The variety of wetlands

The variety of inland freshwater ecosystems is immense. They range from still waters – small ponds, deep or shallow lakes of varying size, artificial reservoirs and flooded mineral pits, peatbogs and marshes – to the flowing waters of rivers, streams and ditches. The organisms that make up the living part of the ecosystem vary from place to place depending on the prevailing climatic conditions, the depth of water, the amount of oxygen dissolved in the water and its **trophic status**.

The trophic status of a freshwater ecosystem refers to the pH of the water and the amount of nutrients dissolved in it that are available for plant growth. There are two extremes:

■ **Eutrophic**, from the Greek *eu*, meaning 'good'. This refers to water bodies having alkaline pH values and that are rich in dissolved nutrients such as nitrates, phosphates and calcium carbonate derived from the rocks and soils beneath and around the wetland. These are further increased if runoff is received from agricultural land which has had fertilisers added to it.

Eutrophic waters are most common in lowland areas, especially areas of chalk and limestone, and are identified by the prolific amount of vegetation growing in them, usually with a natural succession or hydrosere (see next section) at their margins. They are also rich in animal life and are often cloudy owing to large amounts of plant and animal plankton suspended in the water (**18.1**).

■ **Oligotrophic**, from the Greek *oligos*, meaning 'little'. Typically these have acidic pH values, contain few plant nutrients and are characteristic of mountainous areas (**18.2**), where large amounts of precipitation are received and the rocks are often of igneous or metamorphic origin, therefore acidic in nature. Oligotrophic wetlands support very little life. The lack of nutrients restricts plant growth and the water is relatively clear owing to the absence of plankton. Open areas of oligotrophic water are often distinguished by their bare, stony shores and absence of a succession of fringing vegetation.

There are many variations between these two, and these are referred to as **mesotrophic wetlands**.

1 Compare the appearance of the lakes shown in **18.1** and **18.2**. Account for the differences you have noted.

■ **18.1** Eutrophic lake: Colemere, Shropshire

■ **18.2** Oligotrophic lake: Loch Coruisk, Skye

18.2 **Plant succession in a wetland – a hydrosere**

Many lakes, ponds and flooded gravel pits in the British Isles are eutrophic and have a succession of plants growing around their margins. A typical lake-margin succession is shown in **18.3**. In the open surface waters, there are such free-floating plants as duckweed and the water fern, *Azolla*. However, the true pioneer plants are the submerged species such as Canadian pondweed, water milfoil and *Potamogeton*, along with those rooted in the lake bed but with floating leaves such as water-lilies. The roots and remains of these plants trap and stabilise mud and silt on the floor of the lake, building its depth layer by layer.

As the water becomes more shallow, emergent species such as the swamp reed, *Scirpus,* and fen-forming plants such as the *Phragmites* reed and sedges, take over. These play their part in 'drying out' the lake margins, eventually making conditions suitable for invasion by scrub and tree species like willow and alder that form a damp-loving 'fen carr'. Each species in the succession acts as a 'pump' and, if the succession is allowed to continue for a sufficient length of time, conditions will become sufficiently dry for the climatic climax woodland species of the area to invade and dominate.

In the water, plankton (algae, cyclops and water-fleas) are plentiful. These support a huge variety of animal life – insects and other invertebrates, and vertebrates including frogs, toads, small fish and the larger predators such as pike. Wetlands are another example of a complex but balanced, interdependent food web.

The abundance of plant and animal life in the water attracts other animals, which may include otters and a huge variety of birds – ducks and other wildfowl, kingfishers, herons and many more which come to feed here. Many species also nest among the bankside vegetation, including reed and sedge warblers which hunt for insects among the reeds.

The balance of the ecosystem is a delicate one, however, and easily disturbed. Excessive amounts of nutrients, usually as runoff containing fertilisers from farmland, sewage or industrial effluents, can pollute the water. These extra nutrients may over-enrich the water, encouraging the prolific growth of algae – 'algal blooms' – that use up all of the available dissolved oxygen, causing mass die-offs of insects, fish and other animals further along the food chain. Other aquatic plants can also be killed as they are coated and smothered by the algal bloom (**18.4**). Such imbalance due to excessive amounts of nutrients entering the water is termed **eutrophication**.

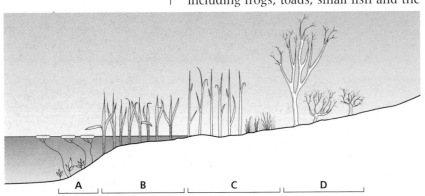

A submerged and floating-leaved communities: *Potamogeton, Elodea, Nymphaea*

B reed swamp: *Scirpus*   C fen: *Phragmites, Carex, Filipendula*   D carr: *Alnus, Salix*

■ **18.3** Cross-section through a hydrosere

■ **18.4** Algal bloom

Other problems, as we have seen in the case study on page 185, result from acidification of water as a result of air pollution. In Sweden, for example, nearly 14000 lakes have suffered acidification, with a fall of 0.6 or more in their pH since the Industrial Revolution. This has reduced the diversity and number of species, especially in phytoplankton and snails, bivalve molluscs and crustaceans. In some areas, lakes and streams are being limed in order to counteract the effects of acid deposition.

2 How does 'natural' eutrophication differ from that caused by humans?

3 Do any bodies of water in the area in which you live suffer from eutrophication caused by human activity? If so, what measures are being taken to correct this situation?

18.3 **Lowland peatbogs**

Originally peatbogs covered 7 per cent of the land area of the United Kingdom. Peat mainly consists of the undecayed remains of sphagnum mosses, and forms in waterlogged anaerobic conditions where the decay of dead vegetation is slowed by the lack of oxygen.

There are three main types of peatbog:

- **Blanket bogs**, which form in upland areas where the climate is wet enough for peat to form as a thin mantle covering the surface. Since rainfall is the main source of the water, conditions are oligotrophic, acidic and sterile. Few plants can grow in these conditions apart from sphagnum mosses, cotton grass and such plants as sundew and butterwort, which compensate for the lack of nutrients in their environment by catching and digesting insects.

- **Intermediate bogs**, which are mostly found in wet lowland areas that are marginal for the development of blanket bog.

- **Raised bogs**, which are domed areas of peat found in lowland areas.

In the remainder of this section, we are dealing mainly with the raised peatbogs of the UK (**18.5**). They usually occur above a shallow hollow in the ground originally excavated by a glacier (**18.6**). When the ice melted at the end of the Pleistocene Ice Age, the waters of the resulting lake usually contained dissolved nutrients and were, therefore, eutrophic or mesotrophic, supporting the growth of reeds, sedges and other fen plants. The remains of these accumulated and the lake gradually became infilled with plant remains, forming sedge peat.

■ **18.5** Raised peatbog

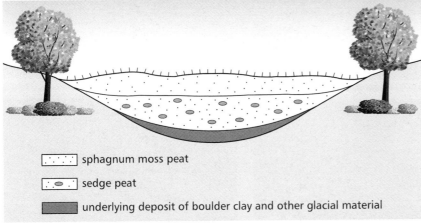

[...] sphagnum moss peat

[. ⬭] sedge peat

▮ underlying deposit of boulder clay and other glacial material

■ **18.6** Cross-section to show the development of a raised bog over a period of 10 000 years

■ **18.7** 'Pete Marsh' (bog man), who has been preserved for 2500 years in the peat

vegetation and climatic conditions. Weapons, tools, boats and even well-preserved human remains have been found, contributing to our knowledge of the lifestyles of our ancestors (**18.7**).

Unfortunately, raised peatbogs in the UK are one of the most rare and threatened habitats in Europe. At their maximum extent they probably covered some 95000ha, about 5.3 per cent of the total peat area of the UK. Just 6000ha remain in the UK today, and little of this is sufficiently intact to be actively laying down peat. Raised bogs have been drained and converted to agricultural use and commercial forestry, and for many centuries peat has been dug from both raised and blanket bogs, dried and used as a domestic fuel. In Ireland today, many homes are still heated by peat as an alternative to coal, using turf cut from Ireland's extensive blanket bogs (**18.8**). Peat has also been used as a 'litter' to cover the floors of stables for horses and other domestic livestock. But in recent years the major uses for peat have been as a soil conditioner and as a growing medium in horticulture and gardening. Extraction techniques have also changed considerably. Originally, all peat was dug by hand – a tiring and back-breaking job. But machines have now been developed for digging peat. Some are mechanical diggers such as Hi-Macs, but in recent years huge milling machines have come into operation (**18.9**). Deep drains are cut

Later the bog acquired its dome shape due to the growth and accumulation of sphagnum mosses. As these are fed entirely by rainwater, the surface becomes oligotrophic, with extremely acidic and sterile conditions. Layer by layer the moss accumulates as a blanket of moss peat, burying the sedge peat in the hollow below, slowly raising the surface of the bog above the surrounding areas of land.

The very sterility of the habitat means that only highly specialised plants such as the sphagnum mosses can grow here, along with the insectivorous sundews, butterworts and bladderworts. However, these bogs attract a great variety of rare insects and birds, the overall mixture making the raised bog habitats unique and valuable places for wildlife.

Raised bogs are also of immense interest to the archaeologist, since a rich archive of human and other information lies preserved in the peat. Preserved pollen grains provide evidence of past

■ **18.8** Hand-dug peatbog, Ireland

■ **18.9** Peatbog excavated by a massive milling machine

in the sudden release of carbon dioxide back into the atmosphere, thus contributing to the greenhouse effect.

The survival of the few remaining raised peatbogs, and the unique assemblage of wildlife species that they support, is dependent upon the development and use of peat alternatives by gardeners and the horticulture industry (**18.10**). The industry, encouraged by a consortium of conservation organisations, is carrying out research into alternatives based on composts made from recycled organic waste from parks and gardens and on imported coconut fibre pith, or coir. Everyone is being urged to provide effective protection for the remaining bogs, especially those that have been scheduled as SSSIs (Sites of Special Scientific Interest).

IT7

through the bog and the surface vegetation is removed to expose the peat below. The machine then skims a few centimetres from the surface over an area of several hectares and the process is repeated every two or three months until the peat supply is exhausted. The peat gathered in this way is easily dried, ready for bagging and for sale. The raised bog is completely destroyed over the area from which the peat has been extracted and the deep drains that are necessary cause neighbouring areas of bog to dry out, whether or not they are scheduled to be dug.

Since they contain the accumulated organic materials formed from the carbon dioxide and other minerals converted by photosynthesis over thousands of years, peatbogs are 'carbon sinks'. Drainage of the peat and its decomposition from use in horticulture or burning as fuel results

4 Compile a list of regulations that you think would protect wetlands but allow some to be used for recreation and sustainable developments.

5 Write a letter to your local newspaper urging gardeners *not* to use peat to improve their soil or as a growing medium, giving reasons why you think remaining areas of peatbog should be conserved. What peat alternatives might gardeners use?

CASE STUDY

IT8

Thorne Waste and Hatfield Moors – peatlands in danger

Thorne Waste (1900 ha) and Hatfield Moors (1400 ha) are the largest lowland raised peatbogs in Britain. However, for several centuries they have been progressively drained and worked for the extraction of peat. It is only in recent years that this peat has been used for horticulture.

Drainage of Hatfield Moors began as early as the 17th century when, in 1626, Cornelius Vermuyden, a Dutch drainage engineer, began a three-year drainage project. Incoming rivers were blocked off and water courses canalised. This was further developed in the 18th century and steam pumps were installed in the 19th and 20th centuries.

In the early years the main use for the peat was as turf, which was burnt as fuel. Production remained small but increased rapidly during the latter half of the 19th century when peat was mainly used for animal litter in stables (horses were a major means of transport at this time). Throughout this period the peat was hand cut (hand graving) and the blocks piled up to dry. At least 10 years passed before an area was re-cut, allowing for some regeneration of the bog vegetation. **18.11** indicates the dramatic changes that took place following the introduction of milling machines to the bogs in 1985 (**18.12**).

Technique used	Area of patches ha	Length of cuttings m	Distance of bare peat from intact vegetation m	Mean time between re-cutting
Hand graving	20–40	<200	5	10+ years
Machine (from 1965)	0.5–80	200–400	10–20	2 years
Machine (post-1975)	up to 200	up to 3000	100–200	1 year
Milling (post-1985)	200–400	1000–3200	500–2000	1–2 months

■ **18.11** Cutting methods and their scale at Thorne Waste and Hatfield Moors

1950 to 1980

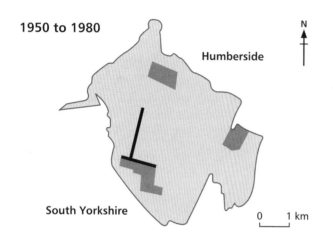

Humberside

South Yorkshire

N

0   1 km

Species	Number of birds present	
	Late 1970s	1991
Merlin (wintering)	5	2
Hen harrier (wintering)	6	2
Teal (breeding)	50 pairs	30 pairs
Snipe (breeding)	50 pairs	2 pairs
Nightjar (breeding)	43 pairs	35 pairs
Whinchat (breeding)	30 pairs	18 pairs
Lapwing (breeding)	1 pair	2–3 pairs

■ **18.13** Changes in bird species at Thorne Waste and Hatfield Moors

1980 to 1990

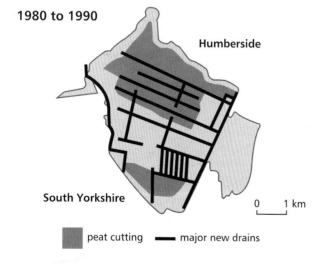

Humberside

South Yorkshire

0   1 km

▮ peat cutting   ▬ major new drains

■ **18.12** Destruction of peatbog at Thorne Waste and Hatfield Moors

6 Using **18.11–18.13**:

a What impact do you think each of the extraction techniques for peat will have had on the landscape and peatbog ecosystem?

b Which technique produces the largest area of bare peat?

c Which would be the most sustainable method of peat production?

d At what date do you think conservationists started to express concern about the future of the Hatfield Moors raised bog ecosystem? Give reasons for your answer.

18.4 Pressure on wetland ecosystems

IP2, IT7

Keoladeo Ghana National Park, Bharatpur, India

The Keoladeo Park at Bharatpur, Rajasthan in India, is an area of some 29 km² (**18.14**). It is an artificial wetland, created during the 1890s by diverting water from a nearby irrigation canal into a marshy depression in which rainwater collected during the monsoon. It was the brain-child of the Maharaja of Bharatpur who hoped to provide his guests with some excellent shooting. He succeeded, as the area now attracts some of the many thousands of wildfowl from northern Russia that over-winter in India.

In the first half of the 20th century, extravagant shooting parties were held for visiting British and Indian dignitaries, and enormous numbers of birds were shot (**18.15**). The record 'bag' was taken in 1938 during the visit of the Viceroy, Lord Linlithgow, when 4273 birds fell on one day to just 41 guns.

In 1956 the area was declared a sanctuary, not only for the wildfowl but also to protect the many other bird species that came to breed or over-winter at Bharatpur – over 350 different kinds (**18.16**). Bharatpur had also become one of the two known wintering sites of a globally endangered species, the Siberian crane.

— metalled roads

— tracks

— canals

lakes/marshes

:•: villages

1 Prince of Wales Gate
2 Sotion-Ka-Mandir
3 Forest Lodge
4 Forest HQ & Rest House
5 Sita Ram Bani
6 Sapan Mori
7 Keoladeo Temple
8 Aghapur Gate
9 Irrigation Rest House

0   1   2 km

■ **18.14** Keoladeo Ghana National Park

Traditionally, the villagers around Bharatpur had been permitted to graze their domestic cattle and water buffaloes there, to harvest the *khus* grass – a type of reed used for thatching and from which a valuable scented oil is extracted – and to collect fuelwood and fodder. However, with the rapid increase of the human population in India, pressure on the sanctuary was beginning to destroy the habitats on which the wildlife depended. In order to control these problems the area was designated a National Park in 1981. A boundary wall was built around the park, the villagers were ordered to remove their cattle and buffaloes, and told that they could no longer harvest the *khus*.

But the concept of a wildlife sanctuary that could not be used by the local people 'just to protect animals' was an alien one. In 1982, the deprived villagers decided to take matters into their own hands. With nowhere else to graze their livestock, because the surrounding areas are cultivated or overgrazed, the villagers, driven by poverty and hunger, broke down the wall in an attempt to return their cattle to the park. Seven people were killed as the police opened fire to prevent this invasion.

■ **18.15** Plaque at Bharatpur

No wildlife reserve can survive for long if the local people are hostile to it, and at last attempts are being made by the authorities at Bharatpur to reduce the problem. An educational programme has been developed; land has been acquired as a buffer zone or 'green belt' around the park within which the local people may gather fuelwood and fodder; the villagers are being permitted to harvest the *khus* on a controlled basis as part of a management plan for the park.

However, a number of conflicts remain. There are concerns at the increased use of pesticides on farmland in the vicinity of the park, and high amounts of pesticide residue are being recorded in the eggs of nesting birds. Indeed, pesticides have been blamed for recent breeding failures among some of the park's birds of prey.

But the most pressing problem is the competition for water. Most is still obtained from the irrigation reservoir and there is an increasing demand for its use by agriculture. In recent years there have been several failures of the monsoon, with relatively little rainfall being received. Farmers find it difficult to understand why their crops should be allowed to whither and die while the small reserves of water in the reservoir are diverted to maintain the water supplies in the park for the wildlife.

■ **18.16** Bharatpur wetland after the monsoon

7 What advice would you give to the manager of the Keoladeo Ghana National Park in India that might help reduce the hostility of the local population to the existence of the park? You might find it helpful to list **a** the reasons for restricting access to the park by local people and their livestock, and **b** the possible benefits they could derive from the park.

CASE STUDY

IT6, 7

The Coto Doñana wetlands, Spain

While the conservation problems of an area such as Bharatpur in India have been created by a rapidly increasing human population and poverty, many of the problems facing the Coto Doñana are caused by affluence and the increasing demand for seaside holidays and recreational facilities from tourists to Spain.

The Coto Doñana is a large area (77 260 ha) of marshland – the famous *marismas* – formed by the delta of the Guadalquivir river, south of Seville in south-west Spain (**18.17**). It is one of the world's most important wildlife areas, a national park, and designated as a World Biosphere Reserve by the UNESCO 'Man and Biosphere Programme'. These marshlands, with dunes, scrub and Mediterranean woodland in the south, are home to thousands of rare birds, mammals, reptiles, insects and plants, including the Spanish imperial eagle and Iberian lynx (**18.18**). But this immensely important ecosystem has been threatened by development pressures from several sources.

It has already experienced several major ecological problems, caused largely by agricultural activities and over-exploitation of the groundwater that formerly maintained the water levels of the *marismas*, as it is siphoned off for use in industry and agriculture. The water table is known to have dropped by 20 m in places.

In 1986, 30 000 water birds died from contamination by pesticides sprayed on neighbouring farmland in an effort to control mosquitoes during the visit of a government official. Illegal poaching is also a problem, but a more subtle threat has been the introduction of an American crayfish which is competing with local species. The habitat has been further degraded by nearby reclamation for rice paddies and irrigated farming, fish farming, disturbance, pollution and the falling water table. In 1970 there were more than 200 000 ha of wetlands in Donana; today only 27 000 ha remain.

But new developments also threaten the site, including the proposed construction of a new holiday resort, 'Costa Doñana', which would house 32 000 tourists, and the creation of a new golfing complex which, if implemented, would become the largest in Europe. The nearby tourist resort of Matalascañas is also expanding, already catering for over 40 000 people (**18.19**). These developments create a huge demand for water, which is obtained by pumping groundwater from beneath the Coto Doñana. This demand is not just for drinking water, baths and showers, however. Enormous amounts are also needed for watering the lawns, gardens and golf courses of the area and supplying neighbouring farmland with water for irrigation.

On hearing the news of the proposed developments the outspoken conservationist David Bellamy remarked:

> This violation of a key World Biosphere Reserve and of the new international ethic of conservation and environmental care must not be allowed to happen.
> … I have cancelled a proposed family holiday to Spain and will, if the development [of Coto Doñana] is allowed to proceed, campaign for others to follow suit.

Fortunately, there are signs that international outrage at the development proposals and the protests of many individuals have caused the authorities, who had previously backed the development, to think again. A report, published in 1992, has recommended total protection of the area, rejecting building operations that would destroy its ecology and landscape, and advising that a new irrigation scheme should be scrapped and a full investigation made of water use in the region.

The European Union is also prepared to intervene to protect the area, and new jobs may be created from EU funds. The Spanish Ornithological Society has recently opened a visitor centre on the edge of the park to raise awareness and understanding of the ecological importance of the Park, while access to the area is being carefully controlled. 'Green tourism', allowing local people to benefit from the protection of the wildlife as an economic asset, could be the solution.

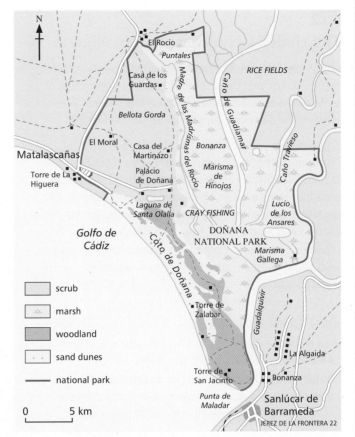

■ **18.17** Coto Doñana

■ **18.18** Flamingos at Coto Doñana

■ **18.19** Tourist development at Matalascañas

IT4

The Hadejia–Nguru wetlands, Nigeria

The Hadejia–Nguru Wetlands are in northern Nigeria, some 200 km east-north-east of Kano, at the southern edge of the Sahel, an arid region on the southern edge of the Sahara, with unreliable rainfall (**18.20**).

The wetland's seasonal floods attract thousands of water birds that over-winter in the area from Europe. Due to drought and human population increases the area faces acute water shortages, although the appalling human tragedy that has occurred at the eastern end of the Sahel has, fortunately, not been repeated here. Nevertheless, the area is experiencing widespread and continuing losses of natural vegetation and desertification of what was once savanna grassland with scattered trees.

Although it is referred to as a 'wetland', much of the area is dry for part or all of the year. The actual extent of the flooding varies according to the amount of rainfall received during the rainy season, which begins in June, and by the amount of water released from upstream dams or abstracted for irrigation.

Two groups of people live in the area:

■ **The Hausa**, who are traditionally cultivators, occupying small, permanent mud-hut villages

built on sandy ridges (fossilised sand dunes, some 10–30 m higher than the floodplains) between the areas of seasonal flood. In the rainy season these higher 'tudu' areas around the village are used to grow crops of sorghum and millet. As the floods recede, the newly uncovered areas, called 'fadama-land', enriched by silt deposited during the floods, are farmed for crops such as rice, peppers and tomatoes, irrigated by networks of channels linked to the tiny plots, each divided by a low, hand-built mud wall (**18.21**). These cash crops are taken to be sold at the nearest market. Fishing is also possible when the land is flooded.

■ **18.21** Hausa cultivation and irrigation

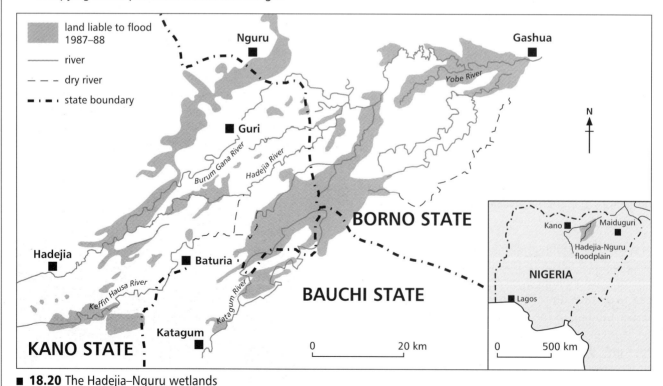

■ **18.20** The Hadejia–Nguru wetlands

■ **18.22** Fulani cattle herder

■ **The Fulani**, semi-nomadic cattle, sheep and goat herders who live in makeshift camps in the wetlands for part of the year, but return northwards to the desert for the rainy season (**18.22**).

The traditional farming economy of the area is a sustainable system, since the cattle and other livestock of the Fulani only move into the cropped areas of the Hausa after the main period of growth is over, the dung from the cattle helping to fertilise the ground.

However, major changes are taking place, which threaten this situation, and will damage the important wildlife that is found here. These are:

■ Population increase, which increases the demand for fuelwood and food production.

■ Urban influences, which are changing the traditional culture and values.

■ Improved access to the floodplains, which is bringing regional and national marketing patterns to the area.

■ More intensive agriculture, with fences and barriers erected to prevent cattle damage. These inhibit the Fulani's nomadic movements.

A series of major irrigation schemes is proposed. Damming the rivers would prevent the seasonal flooding of the current wetlands, and large-scale irrigation would bring a monoculture of wheat, requiring high inputs of artificial fertilisers. It would also displace substantial numbers of people, who would be forced to drift to the already over-burdened cities.

There is, however, a major conservation project under way in the area which aims to minimise the effects of these changes and prevent the proposed irrigation schemes. It hopes to conserve the Hadejia–Nguru wetland area of Nigeria as a productive ecosystem in which the indigenous peoples, birds and other wildlife can continue to exist by means of the traditional land uses, on a sustainable basis.

The Hadejia–Nguru Wetland Conservation Project involves the Nigerian government and state agencies, IUCN, WWF, BirdLife International and the RSPB, and the Nigerian Conservation Foundation. The Project involves a range of activities aimed at finding solutions to the problems. Research is taking place into the hydrology, ecology and social structures of the area. Local people are being trained as wildlife officers, while villagers and children are participating in educational programmes which encourage sustainable practices and a greater understanding of ecology and the environment (**18.23**).

Small sustainable farming and fuelwood conservation projects are experimenting with new methods of sustainable production for fish, poultry, honey, fruit and fuelwood.

National and local decision-makers are important target-audiences for the project, especially those responsible for the control of water-use developments in Nigeria. A major cost–benefit analysis has been carried out which indicates that the current patterns of use in the wetlands for agriculture, fuelwood and fishing contribute more to the region's and Nigeria's economy than would be gained from massive investment in expensive dam and irrigation projects, introducing unsustainable wheat production which damages the ecosystem.

■ **18.23** Sustainable fruit farming

IT8

The Aral Sea

Drainage of wetlands can result in a variety of unforeseen and unintended problems. A tragic example is provided by the Aral Sea in central Asia, which lies partly in Kazakhstan and partly in Uzbekistan within the former Soviet Union, and was one of the world's largest salt lakes.

Largely due to the demand for increased production of cotton by irrigation of desert land, some two-thirds of the lake's former water supply from the rivers Amudar'ya and Syrdar'ya has been diverted. The schemes were paid for by state funds during the Communist regime. Now, over 27 000 ha of the Aral Sea's former area are dry land (**18.24**). This has left the former fishing port of Muynak high and dry and it is now nearly 50 km from the lake's shore (**18.25**).

The former bed of the sea has become a salty desert, strong winds blowing sand and salt crystals as dust storms into the neighbouring irrigated areas, damaging crops and causing health problems to the local people. There have also been changes to the local climate, as the ameliorating effects of the formerly large area of water have been reduced. As a result, there have been hotter summers and lower temperatures in winter.

■ **18.25** Fishing boat beached on the shore of the shrinking Aral Sea

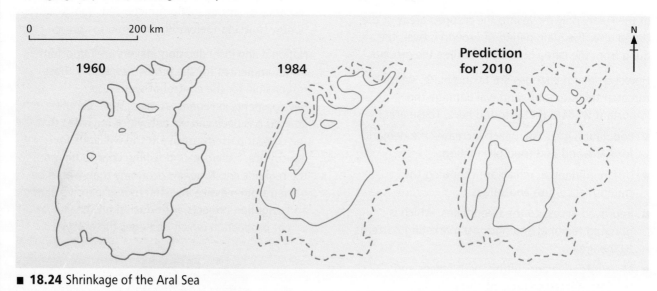

■ **18.24** Shrinkage of the Aral Sea

The foregoing case studies illustrate threats to wetland areas on a global scale.

8 Write an account of the ecological importance of wetlands. Why should they be conserved?

9 a What are the main threats to wetlands?
  b How do those threats in developing countries such as India and Nigeria differ from those experienced in developed countries such as the UK, Spain and the former Soviet Union?

10 Describe attempts that are being made to reduce the pressure on wetland ecosystems.

The final chapter of this unit examines a selection of issues arising from the use and management of ecosystems at a more local level. Five of the eight studies relate to the UK, but that is not to suggest that the problems discussed are, in any way, peculiar to that country. Indeed, the studies bring into focus principles and questions which have a much wider geographical relevance. Most offer hope in the sense of highlighting good practices and pointing to possible solutions. Equally, most offer dire warnings if appropriate actions are not taken.

19.1 **Lowland heath**

IT7

In the UK there are three distinct types of heathland – maritime, upland and lowland. Their different geographical locations and climatic conditions create ecological differences between them, and they support different plant and animal communities. Lowland heath occurs mainly on sandstone outcrops such as the Lower Greensand and Bagshot Beds in the southern counties of Britain, with major areas in Dorset and Hampshire, and smaller amounts in Cornwall, Devon, Berkshire, Surrey, Sussex and Suffolk. Lowland heath is a globally scarce habitat, and the UK has 40 per cent of the world's total.

Characteristically, lowland heathland consists of open ground that is not cultivated (**19.1**). The soils are low in nutrients, usually acidic and dominated by heather and other low-growing shrubs. Heathland developed where woodland was cleared by people in the Bronze Age, 3600–3000 years BP.

At first a few crops were grown, but nutrients were quickly leached from the sandy soils, which soon became very acidic and podsolised, with a strong resemblance to the soils that form beneath boreal forests. Crops were replaced by grazing animals which prevented the regeneration of woodland, and plants were harvested for thatch and fuel. Heather (*Calluna vulgaris*), gorse (*Ulex* spp.) and wavy hair grass (*Deschampsia flexuosa*) came to dominate large areas. Where open heather and gorse predominate, such rare animals as the sand lizard and smooth snake may be found, along with birds such as the Dartford warbler, nightjar, woodlark and hobby. The silver-studded blue butterfly may also be found here. **Subclimax vegetation** such as this is maintained by fire and grazing but if these factors are removed, open heaths are quickly invaded by self-seeding birch and conifers.

Lowland heath was once far more widespread than it is today. Human activity first created the heaths but, especially since the Industrial Revolution, people have been responsible for their decline. Between 1830 and 1980 the area fell by 72 per cent (from 143 000 ha to just 39 450 ha), nibbled away by agriculture, forestry, mineral extraction, urban development and the

IT7

■ **19.1** The contraction of Dorset heathland between 1934 and 1987

0   10 km

N

1934   1987

■ **19.2** Decline of lowland heathland in Dorset, 1934–87

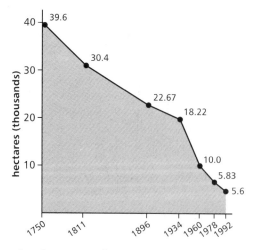

39.6
40
30.4
30
22.67
18.22
20
10.0
10
5.83
5.6

hectares (thousands)

1750 1811 1896 1934 1960 1978 1992

■ **19.3** Lowland heath landscape with invading Scots pine

abandonment of 'commoners' rights'. In Dorset alone, over 80 per cent of the area of heathland has been lost in the same period (**19.1** and **19.2**).

Most of the losses took place between 1950 and the 1980s. Urban development, especially of the Poole–Bournemouth conurbation, has had a major impact, and this represents a particularly serious threat due to the irreversible nature of this form of habitat loss (**19.4**). Small pockets of sand, china clay and ball clay extraction have caused further disturbance and fragmentation of heaths. Elsewhere encroachment by birch and conifers has taken its toll by dramatically altering the habitat (**19.3**), with the result that the rare plants and animals listed above can no longer exist there. This encroachment is due in large measure to the fact that people living in villages in the heathland areas today no longer exercise their commoners' rights to graze stock on the common land.

Not only has lowland heath been directly destroyed, but the remaining areas have become increasingly fragmented, making it difficult for rare species to regain a foothold if, for any reason, they are eliminated from a particular site.

It is unfortunate that lowland heath, despite its beauty and unique assemblage of flora and fauna, is so often perceived as having little economic value. Although many heathland sites have been designated as Sites of Special Scientific Interest (SSSIs), this statutory designation is no guarantee of their protection. Planning permission has all too often been granted to such developments as the construction of the M3 motorway, the laying of pipelines and the extraction of ball clay. The development of housing estates both directly destroys heath and leads to degradation of remaining areas by increasing access and subjecting this fragile habitat to pressures such as motorcycle scrambling, horse riding and picnicking.

Canford Heath in Dorset once stretched westwards from Bournemouth towards Dorchester. Thomas Hardy wrote of it as 'Egdon Heath, a vast tract of unenclosed wild'. Today, it is one of the largest areas of heathland that remains outside a nature reserve. In recent years,

■ **19.4** New housing encroaching on heathland

Canford Heath has been threatened by the rapid expansion of Bournemouth and Poole, one of the fastest-growing conurbations in Europe. In spite of its designation as an SSSI, housing, commercial developments and a relief road have been allowed across the heath. Fortunately, it seems that the remaining areas are now safe. Dorset County Council have agreed on a Dorset Heathland Strategy for the conservation, protection and management of heathland.

It is for such habitats as lowland heath that **environmental impact assessment** and **strategic environmental assessment** (see section 19.9) could play an important role in enhancing their protection and conservation. This would be particularly significant if national policies relating to the extractive industries, housing and urban development, and road construction – all of which have had a major impact on lowland heath – were strategically assessed for their environmental impact.

1 Is there a 'heath' place-name somewhere near you? If you live in the southern half of England, there is a good chance that there is. Hampstead Heath and Heathrow are two London examples.

2 Should the remaining heathlands in the UK be protected from further human development on account of their value for wildlife? Give reasons for your opinion.

19.2 **Crofting in the Outer Hebrides**

Among the wet and boggy coastal grasslands, lochs, hills and moorlands of the Outer Hebrides, the traditional method of farming known as **crofting** is in decline (**19.5**). Typically, this was small-scale, often part-time, farming that created a mosaic of land uses – of small arable fields planted with such crops as oats, potatoes, turnips, cabbages, hay and silage. Sheep and a few cattle grazed the pastures and moorlands. A few hens and goats provided eggs, milk and cheese. Traditional part-time employment by which crofting communities supplemented their income included fishing, weaving and knitting as well as pottery and other crafts, bed and breakfast accommodation and hotels for tourists.

In recent years, however, there have been marked changes in these crofting areas. Cattle numbers have declined but the sheep population has greatly increased. As farming has become less profitable many crofters have left the land, and their small-holdings have been sold as holiday homes or to 'incomers' escaping from the city life. The amount of silage grown has greatly increased, while haymaking and the planting of other crops has declined.

This has produced many changes in the Outer Hebrides, and brought problems for the varied wildlife populations that had become adapted to the traditional farming methods used on crofts. For example, the crofting areas have become the main stronghold for the corncrake, one of the three globally threatened bird species that is found in the United Kingdom, and

■ **19.5** Crofting land in the Western Isles

IT4

IT4 which is now a rare and endangered creature. Only 60 years ago, the corncrake was a relatively common bird of hay meadows and unimproved pastures throughout the west and north of the British Isles (**19.6**). Its decline has gone hand in hand with the spread of intensive grassland management, with highly fertilised swards dominated by planted, more productive, species of grass. This is cut mechanically for silage, often as early as late June or in July, well before the corncrakes that nest in the fields have had a chance to raise their young. As a result many nests and chicks are crushed or chopped up by the blades of the mowers. If the corncrake is to be saved from extinction along with other wildlife species that currently depend on the habitats of the Outer Hebrides, traditional crofting methods must also be safeguarded and encouraged to survive. They are interdependent.

So what are the solutions? The Scottish Crofters Union and conservation organisations such as the RSPB recommend that future agricultural and social policies should be combined with environmental objectives. Through reform of the European Common Agricultural Policy (CAP), sustainable agricultural practices such as traditional crofting should be rewarded financially for sound management of the countryside and conservation of wildlife, and not just for the production of food.

3 By further reading, learn more about crofting as the traditional farming system of north-west Scotland. How far could crofting be described as a 'sustainable' farming system?

19.3 **Wildlife in towns: Bedford**

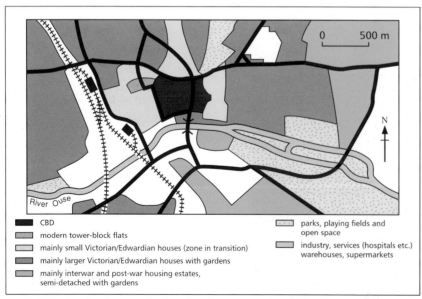

■ CBD	□ parks, playing fields and open space
▤ modern tower-block flats	▨ industry, services (hospitals etc.) warehouses, supermarkets
▤ mainly small Victorian/Edwardian houses (zone in transition)	
▤ mainly larger Victorian/Edwardian houses with gardens	
▤ mainly interwar and post-war housing estates, semi-detached with gardens	

■ **19.7** Generalised map of urban land-use zones in Bedford

Urban geographers are familiar with a range of models of urban land use, ranging from the concentric ring theory of Burgess, through the sectors proposed by Hoyt to the multiple nuclei of Harris and Ullman (see section 33.3). What these models all agree on is that there is a range of different land use types in a town or city which are a reflection of the human ecology of the area.

Where shopping or commerce prevails we have the CBD, characterised by multistorey buildings and office blocks to which shoppers and office and shop workers commute from the surrounding residential areas. In these suburbs there are different building styles, and the size of gardens varies with the date of

■ **19.8** Pigeons in the CBD, Bedford

development and the affluence of the residents. There are also industrial zones, parks, golf courses, recreational areas and areas dominated by transport such as railway sidings.

It is not only the human ecology that forms these zones. Each type offers different opportunities for wildlife to live, feed and breed. Bedford in the south Midlands provides a typical example. It was located originally on a fording point across the river Ouse, now bridged. The CBD is located to the north of the river, with the Harper Centre and a range of department stores and other shops both large and small (**19.7**). There is little obvious wildlife to be seen in this zone, but birdlife is visible in the form of town pigeons in large numbers, particularly in the traffic-free streets where they are often fed scraps and enjoyed by shoppers

■ **19.9** River Ouse, Bedford

and visitors (**19.8**). Town pigeons often nest on ledges and in holes in buildings, which strongly resemble the cliff ledges where their wild ancestors would have nested. Starlings and house sparrows are also found in this zone.

Away from the CBD, especially to the west, there are closely-packed terraced houses, with backyards rather than gardens, typical of the 'zone in transition' and homes of 'blue-collar workers'. Properties that are in a poor state of repair will have starlings, sparrows and town pigeons nesting in the roof, and there could be such unwelcome residents as rats and house mice, especially in those houses near the railway line.

To the north, along such tree-lined streets as De Parys Avenue and on out to Brickhill, there are houses with large gardens. The ages of the buildings vary, from Georgian houses in some areas, to Victorian villas and those built in the 1930s and post-war years. Immediately a greater variety of wildlife is to be seen. Town pigeons are replaced by wood pigeons and collared doves; there are blackbirds and song thrushes, robins and blue tits, and the ubiquitous magpie. These are really woodland birds, but large gardens with flowerbeds, lawns, shrubs and trees must strongly resemble open woodlands as far as these species are concerned. There is also the added attraction of a free food supply at bird tables. Grey squirrels and hedgehogs can be seen here too, and it is not unknown for foxes to be glimpsed at dusk or early in the morning, sometimes raiding dustbins in their search for food. Butterflies and moths feed on the flowering plants in the gardens.

Alongside the river Ouse with its parkland there is an even greater diversity of birdlife, with swans, ducks, coots and moorhens using the river, and Canada geese on open water and in other parks with lakes (**19.9**). Even the occasional heron and kingfisher may be seen, while overhead there is often a hovering kestrel. There are damsel flies and dragonflies, frogs, toads and newts.

There are a number of large schools within Bedford's built-up area. These have extensive playing fields with large areas of mown grass. These especially attract black-headed gulls in winter, while short mown grass and asphalt playgrounds are particularly attractive to pied wagtails, which chase after insects. Rooks and crows search the playing fields for grubs, and even flocks of lapwings and golden plovers have been seen from time to time.

One of the more interesting habitats is the area of land alongside the railway and the shunting yard. Here there are large areas of open space, weed and scrub growth and a few buildings, some of which are derelict. A great variety of birds, insects and other wildlife inhabit these areas. Flocks of finches search the weeds for seeds; foxes, rabbits and even badgers live along embankments.

Throughout the UK, railway lines provide a green corridor along which wildlife can move, often into the heart of a city.

The wildlife of towns therefore often reflects human land use patterns, influenced by the feeding opportunities available and the adaptations of the particular species. Those that are highly specialised in their habitat requirements are less likely to be seen in the urban situation, but many species are able to live alongside the human population and benefit from our wastefulness.

---

4 To what extent do you think that town planning has an obligation to protect and promote wildlife?

19.4 Management of habitats for wildlife: Titchwell RSPB Reserve, Norfolk

IT4

When a conservation organisation such as the RSPB purchases an area of natural or semi-natural habitat in order to establish a wildlife reserve, it is tempting to imagine that all that now happens is to put a fence round it, erect 'Keep Out' signs and, perhaps, build a hide or two so that a few bird-watchers can enjoy their hobby in peace. Nothing could be further from the truth.

The habitats of most wildlife reserves require constant management to maintain ideal conditions for wildlife. As we have noted in section 13.7, plant succession, if left unchecked, will eventually change the existing reedbeds or salt marsh into the climatic climax vegetation of the area. In the case of Titchwell, this would be broad-leaved woodland. The objective of the reserve's management plan is to prevent the succession from taking place by manipulating the different habitats, and holding them at a particular stage in their seral development. However, management is also carried out to improve conditions for certain species, and to add to the wildlife interest and conservation importance of the reserve.

The RSPB's Titchwell Marsh Reserve is on the north Norfolk coast. The 200 ha were purchased in 1972, which consisted at that time of five natural habitats – reed marsh, salt marsh ('aster marsh'), sand dunes, shingle and foreshore. However, although the site was already important for wading birds and wildfowl in winter, it was realised that there was great potential for creating new marshland habitats which would attract additional species to the area, including such rarities as avocets, bitterns and marsh harriers. These would also provide better conditions for wading birds and wildfowl.

Another factor that the RSPB considered when creating the Reserve's management plan was the increasing number of bird-watchers visiting Norfolk, putting pressure on the few existing wildlife reserves and endangering their conservation value. By creating car parking, proper footpaths, interpretation and viewing facilities at Titchwell, the RSPB could provide an alternative wildlife spectacle that could be enjoyed by the specialist bird-

IT4

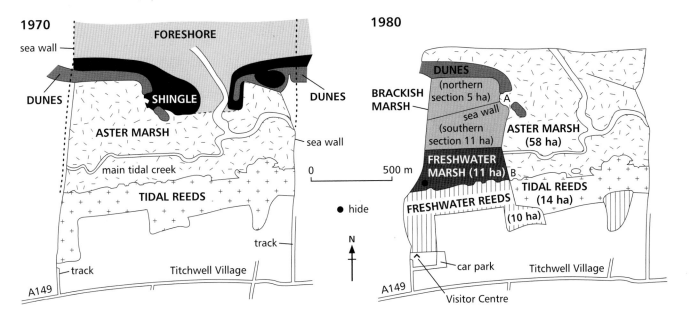

■ **19.10** Titchwell RSPB Reserve showing the creation of new habitats between 1970 and 1980

watcher and general public alike. With careful management this could be achieved without harming or disturbing the birds.

With all this in mind, the first step was to build a new sea-wall and other embankments so that salt water would be excluded from some areas and new areas of freshwater marsh created. A series of ditches and sluices was created so that it became possible to control water levels to provide ideal conditions for the growth of marsh plants. Areas of brackish marsh were also created. These changes can be seen by comparing the maps in **19.10**.

The management of the site has achieved its objectives. There are now some 50 breeding pairs of avocets as well as bitterns, marsh harriers and other reedbed birds at Titchwell, while huge flocks of wild geese and various species of ducks and waders are attracted in winter. It has proved to be a winner with the public too, visitors to the reserve increasing from just 500 in 1973 to over 100 000 in 1993.

5 Do you think that the conservation of wildlife habitats should be left to voluntary organisations such as the RSPB or is it the responsibility of government? Justify your viewpoint.

19.5 Recreational pressure on the Yorkshire Dales National Park

National parks were first created in England and Wales in 1949 following a report, written in 1945 by John Dower, entitled *National Parks in England and Wales*. The objective of designating such areas was to preserve the landscape of some of the most beautiful parts of the country that were the product of '… nature and human use'. The idea was to ensure that traditional farming and land uses continued in the designated areas by keeping the land in private ownership, while providing car parks and other amenities so that the general public would be able to enjoy the natural beauty and wildlife of the parks in their leisure time.

There are 10 national parks, plus the Norfolk Broads which is not designated as such but has equal status. Each is the responsibility of a national park authority (**19.11**). However,

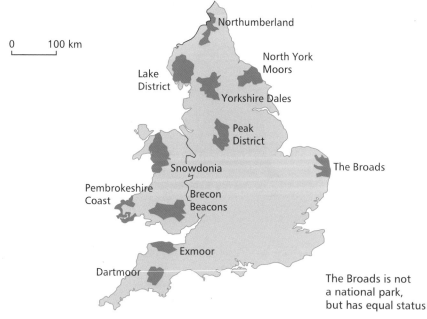

■ **19.11** National parks in England and Wales IT6

The Broads is not a national park, but has equal status

District by the building of motorways – the M6, for example.

The problems of the Yorkshire Dales National Park are typical of those experienced by the parks. Within the total area of this national park, some sites – Malham Cove, for example – are 'honeypots' which attract more than their fair share of the park's visitors (**19.12**). Although Malham and its attractions such as the Cove, Janet's Foss, Goredale Scar and Malham Tarn only account for some 0.5 per cent of the total area of the Dales Park, it receives at least 12 per cent of its visitors. This results in overcrowding on fine days, especially at weekends and bank holidays; excess litter; erosion of footpaths; trampling of vegetation; and wear on areas of geological and geomorphological interest such as the limestone pavement above the Cove. This destroys much of the purpose in visiting Malham by detracting from its peace and natural beauty. Even the area's popularity as a venue for geographical fieldwork contributes to these problems.

there is increasing criticism of their management. Because the land remains in private ownership, park authorities often have to battle against inappropriate developments and to gain access rights for the general public for walking and climbing. Because access is limited, the public pressure on those footpaths and land that are open is enormous, leading to erosion of footpaths, queues at stiles, traffic congestion on roads and at car parks. There are many complaints of deteriorating environmental quality.

In part, the problems of excess visitor pressure on the national parks has been the result of the rapid increase in ownership and use of motor cars, along with improved access from the industrial conurbations to areas such as the Lake

■ **19.12** Approaching Malham Cove

6 Imagine you have been commissioned by a national park authority to carry out an assessment of the impact of visitors on a honeypot area within a national park.
  a What criteria might you select for measuring the physical impact of visitors to the site?
  b Draw up a questionnaire from which you might assess how much visitors enjoyed their visit to the site, including the factors that might have contributed to, or spoiled, the quality of their visit.

7 What would be your suggestions to the government for solving the problems of visitor pressure on the national parks in England and Wales?

19.6 **An isolated island ecosystem: Galapagos**

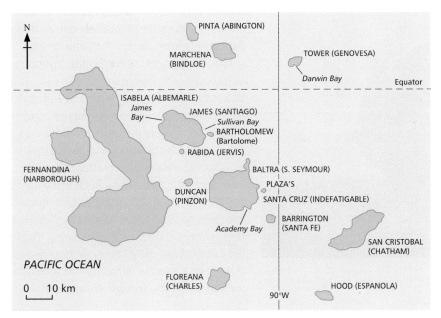

■ **19.13** The Galapagos islands

The Galapagos islands are an isolated group of volcanoes in the Pacific Ocean, some with peaks 3000m above sea-level. They lie roughly on the Equator, just under 1000km due west of South America (**19.13**). Because of their extreme geographical isolation, a unique community of species has evolved, which provided much evidence for Charles Darwin's theory of evolution which he published in 1859.

The islands have a low rainfall supporting a semi-desert of succulents and cacti, some of which are protected by formidable thorns, with more lush vegetation only on those islands with high volcanic peaks where there is sufficient moisture provided by mist and low cloud. Some of the Galapagos islands are so dry that they resemble deserts. The soils also vary from island to island.

Darwin discovered that the birds, notably Darwin's finches, and reptiles, such as iguanas and tortoises, while showing a strong family resemblance to those on mainland South America, vary slightly from these and from one island to another. They have adaptations of their physical features and feeding behaviour that equip them to cope with the particular conditions of their individual island.

On the mainland, iguanas climb trees to eat leaves. On those Galapagos islands with no trees the iguanas live on the rocky seashore and eat seaweeds, having evolved long sharp claws so that they can cling to the rocks (**19.14**). The giant tortoises of Galapagos show such marked differences from one island to another that it is possible to say from a quick look exactly which island a particular type comes from. Those from the driest islands have long necks and shells with a high peak at the front so that they can reach up for cactus branches and leaves. On wetter islands they can graze on ground vegetation and so have short necks and a curved front edge to their shells. Similarly, there are variations from island to island between the finches.

From such observations Darwin surmised that each group had evolved, in isolation over millions of years, from common ancestors, separated from each other by a few kilometres of ocean. 'Natural selection' was the process he thought to be at work. If a chance mutation produced features that enabled survival in particular conditions, then those characteristics were passed on to the offspring.

There are many examples of unique species evolving on remote islands. There are several reasons for this. Physical conditions may vary, as between the islands of the Galapagos group, for example, or there may be an absence of predators such as cats, so that the advantages provided elsewhere to birds by their ability

■ **19.14** Marine iguana, Galapagos

■ **19.15** Artist's impression of a dodo

to fly, may not be needed in the new situation. Flightless birds, therefore, are often a feature of the ecosystems of remote islands.

Best known was the dodo of Mauritius in the Indian Ocean (**19.15**). The dodo, a fat, flightless pigeon, became extinct in the 18th century when they were hunted for food by visiting sailors, who also introduced rats, cats and pigs to the islands. As a result of this new competition the ground-nesting dodo was soon eliminated.

On Galapagos there is the flightless cormorant, a species unique to the islands. The iguana has also evolved a different lifestyle on these islands which are free from land predators. For this reason the Galapagos islands are subject to rigorous conservation measures. Rats and cats, which had been introduced by people, had eliminated the iguana completely from some islands by catching the young and eating the eggs. These predators have now been removed and other conservation measures introduced, paid for with the income from tourists.

8 Why do unique species evolve in geographically isolated groups of islands such as the Galapagos?

19.7 **Conservation problems of a sand dune ecosystem: Wissant, France**

An extensive area of coastal sand dunes, known as La Dune d'Aval, lies near the village of Wissant between Cap Gris-Nez and Cap Blanc-Nez in northern France (**19.16**). In recent years, these dunes have suffered serious erosion as a result of human activities, but a scheme for their conservation has been successfully implemented.

Coastal sand dunes provide excellent opportunities to study a particular type of plant succession known as a **psammosere**. At low tide, sand dries out and is blown inland by onshore winds. The wind-blown sand is dropped when the wind speed is reduced by the friction caused by pioneer plant species growing in the dunes.

A typical succession is shown in **19.18**. Marram grass and other dune plants are well adapted to survive the particular conditions imposed by this dry, loose growing medium. The adaptations of marram grass include a long, branching network of roots, which binds the loose sand, and a rolled leaf. This forms a tube which encloses the stomata of the leaf through which the grass transpires.

IT8

■ **19.16** The location of La Dune d'Aval in northern France

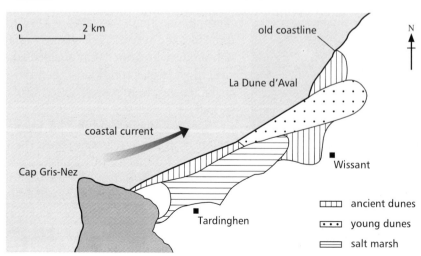

■ 19.17 Cross-section of a blade of marram grass (*Ammophila*). Stomata are restricted to the protected surface

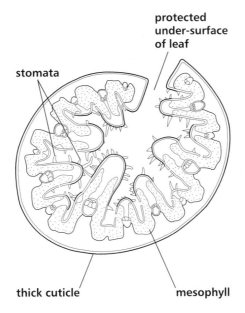

protected under-surface of leaf

stomata

thick cuticle

mesophyll

The outer surface of the leaf has a thick waxy surface which prevents evaporation. While conditions are dry the leaf is tightly rolled, keeping water-loss by transpiration to a minimum.

The pioneer species, such as marram grass that grows on the foredunes, or 'live dunes', closest to the sea, pave the way for others by stabilising the sand and adding water-retaining humus and nutrients to form a thin soil (**19.18**). Such species as sand sedge and fescue grasses may now invade, along with rosette-leaved plants such as dandelions and hawkbits, or heathland species such as heather. These form the more stable communities of the fixed dunes, leading eventually to a cover of shrubs and woodland.

The problems of the Wissant area began in 1974 with sand and gravel extraction off-shore in Wissant Bay, bordering the English Channel, which reduced the amount of sand available to form new dunes and permitted some encroachment by the sea. In 1980 a new housing estate, built largely to house summer visitors, was established on the inland side of La Dune d'Aval. The development provided a point of access for the residents and holiday-makers who needed to cross the dunes to get to the beach. The dunes were also used as a site for Moto-cross. The resulting trampling and disturbance, coupled with salt spray from the sea during a huge storm experienced in the winter of 1980/81, helped to destroy the protective covering of marram grass and other vegetation on both the fore and fixed dunes, thereby exposing the surface of the sand to the wind once again, and destabilising the whole dune system. La Dune d'Aval at Wissant became a 'sea of sand', which blew freely into the new housing estate where it buried many of the new homes (**19.19**).

The local authorities acted quickly to overcome the problem. The loose sand was anchored and the dunes re-stabilised. Windbreaks were created

■ 19.18 Cross-section of a sand dune to show plant succession

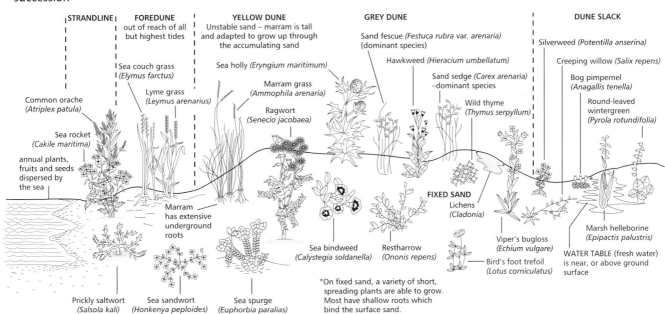

STRANDLINE

FOREDUNE
out of reach of all but highest tides

YELLOW DUNE
Unstable sand – marram is tall and adapted to grow up through the accumulating sand

GREY DUNE

DUNE SLACK

Sea couch grass (*Elymus farctus*)

Sea holly (*Eryngium maritimum*)

Sand fescue (*Festuca rubra* var. *arenaria*) (dominant species)

Silverweed (*Potentilla anserina*)

Lyme grass (*Leymus arenarius*)

Marram grass (*Ammophila arenaria*)

Hawkweed (*Hieracium umbellatum*)

Creeping willow (*Salix repens*)

Common orache (*Atriplex patula*)

Ragwort (*Senecio jacobaea*)

Sand sedge (*Carex arenaria*) –dominant species

Bog pimpernel (*Anagallis tenella*)

Sea rocket (*Cakile maritima*)

Wild thyme (*Thymus serpyllum*)

Round-leaved wintergreen (*Pyrola rotundifolia*)

annual plants, fruits and seeds dispersed by the sea

FIXED SAND
Lichens (*Cladonia*)

Marsh helleborine (*Epipactis palustris*)

Marram has extensive underground roots

Sea bindweed (*Calystegia soldanella*)

Restharrow (*Ononis repens*)

Viper's bugloss (*Echium vulgare*)

WATER TABLE (fresh water) is near, or above ground surface

Prickly saltwort (*Salsola kali*)

Sea sandwort (*Honkenya peploides*)

Sea spurge (*Euphorbia paralias*)

*On fixed sand, a variety of short, spreading plants are able to grow. Most have shallow roots which bind the surface sand.

Bird's foot trefoil (*Lotus corniculatus*)

■ **19.19** House buried by sand at Wissant

using branches and lines of nets and, by replanting marram grass over a wide area, the plant succession was successfully re-created. Carefully signposted board-walk pathways have been built across the dunes, and newly planted areas have been fenced off and 'Accès Interdit' signs erected to prevent further damage by trampling. Harmful activities such as Motocross are now banned.

The fragility of the dune ecosystem and the need to protect it have been heavily publicised locally and a programme on the topic introduced into schools throughout the Nord-Pas de Calais. So far the scheme has proved successful, but a watchful eye must constantly be kept on the situation to avoid a repetition of the problem.

9 Examine the problems caused by public access and trampling in fragile habitats such as sand dunes. How can such problems be solved?

19.8 Malaria in North Borneo – problems caused by interfering with an ecosystem

The problems created by human interference with an ecosystem are dramatically illustrated by the World Health Organisation's programme in 1955 to eliminate malaria from the former North Borneo, now Sabah and the Sultanate of Brunei in South-east Asia. The malaria parasite is carried by the anopheles mosquito. The programme consisted of spraying people's homes and the swamps and other places in which the mosquitoes bred with the persistent pesticide Dieldrin, a chemical in the organo-phosphorus group. Malaria was successfully eliminated but, unfortunately, the programme set off a series of unintended knock-on effects.

In addition to killing mosquitoes, many flies and cockroaches were also killed by Dieldrin. This severely reduced the food supply of house lizards and geckos, so that they starved, but there was also a build-up of pesticides in their bodies from eating the many insects which had already been killed by Dieldrin. The island's cats then died as a result of consuming large numbers of poisoned lizards. This resulted in a plague of rats in the villages, which infected many people with Sylvatic disease, which is carried in rats and transferred to humans by fleas, a problem only solved by introducing large numbers of healthy cats.

The problems did not end here, however. The Dieldrin had also eliminated a parasitic wasp that laid its eggs in a caterpillar that lived in thatch. The population of caterpillars exploded causing the destruction of many thatched roofs.

Interference with natural ecosystems, upsetting the natural balance, can result in numerous unintended effects. It is important, therefore, that development projects of all kinds are carefully thought through and that environmental impact assessments are carried out before commencing.

10 After some further reading, write an essay on 'The problems caused to the environment by the use of pesticides'.

19.9 Techniques: EIA and SEA

Environmental impact assessment

The aim of environmental impact assessment (EIA) is to reduce or eliminate likely damage to ecosystems by new human developments. By attempting to predict and evaluate the impact that a proposed development would have on the selected site, its wildlife populations and the wider environment, an EIA provides decision-makers with information which will help them to reach their decision as to whether or not the project should be given permission to proceed, or should be scrapped or modified. Usually EIAs are a part of the planning process for individual development proposals such as new transport routes, housing estates, power stations or oil refineries. European laws have demanded in recent years that all major development projects are subjected to an EIA before they are allowed to proceed.

The first step is for an audit to be made of the present condition of the site in which it is proposed that the development should take place. This includes the site's flora and fauna; its physical characteristics such as landscape features, soils, water, air and climatic factors; and human features including those of archaeological and architectural value.

The nature of the proposed development, its production processes and operational features, along with possible alternatives, are then reviewed and an attempt made to predict:

■ the significant effects on the future state of the environment if the development is permitted to proceed – destruction or damage to wildlife populations and habitats, the use of natural resources, emissions of pollutants and other hazards

■ the future state of the environment if development does not take place.

By comparing the differences between the two predictions, the environmental impact of the project, both during and after construction, may be assessed.

Methods of reducing or eliminating the undesirable effects can then be considered and, finally, decisions made as to whether or not the proposed development should be allowed to proceed. If the development does take place, the actual impacts of the project should then be monitored.

Many countries now have EIA systems established through their national regulations and, depending on the nation involved, may be carried out by government officials or private companies and organisations. Less developed countries are not as likely to carry out EIAs as developed nations because of the high costs involved. The decision as to whether or not a project is allowed to proceed following EIA procedures will depend on a wide range of factors, and the findings of an EIA could be ignored if national defence considerations, economic interests or powerful vested interests are deemed to be more important by the planning authorities than the environmental considerations.

The techniques used in EIA are still being developed. There is a great need for more testing of the predictions made by an EIA against the actual impacts of the development in order to refine the techniques used.

Strategic environmental assessment

A more recent development of environmental impact assessment is strategic environmental assessment (SEA). This is used to assess the consequences for the environment of planning strategies – the background policies, plans and programmes that influence many planning decisions at national or even international levels. It has the advantage of taking account of the cumulative effects of many projects. It is therefore one way in which the concept of sustainability may be implemented by maintaining the condition and ability of the environment to perform its various functions over time.

19.10 **The way ahead**

The basic message hopefully conveyed by this unit, and this chapter in particular, is that the future of many of the world's ecosystems lies in the balance, because they are under threat from a multiplicity of pressures. The future of the global ecosystems can only be assured through better knowledge and understanding, particularly of their workings and the ways in which they respond to human interference. That knowledge and understanding needs to be acquired and applied by users, decision-makers and managers alike. This is crucial if we are to achieve sustainable development and the conservation of threatened habitats and species. The much wider use of techniques such as EIA and SEA offers some hope. However, the bottom line is simply that we are all citizens of fragile Earth; we all have responsibilities to ensure that our natural heritage is passed to the next generation, intact rather than in tatters.

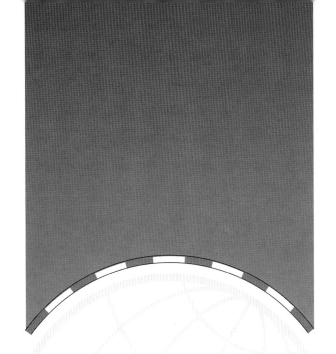

Population

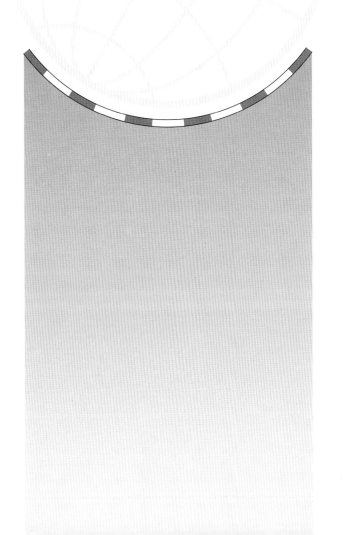

20.1 **Definition and distribution**

I keep six honest serving men.
(They taught me all I knew);
Their names are What and Why and
When and How and Where and Who.

Rudyard Kipling

Rudyard Kipling was able to summarise even the most complicated ideas. To him, the art of understanding any subject was to ask the right questions, and to express the answers as carefully as possible. The former is the main aim of this unit; the latter should be the main aim of the student.

The subject of population geography is a complex one, but by investigating it in a systematic fashion it is hoped that a clear picture will emerge of its major aspects, namely distribution, structure, change and associated issues. Kipling's 'honest serving men' can be employed to give an understanding of the scope and meaning of population geography.

What?

Population geography generally investigates the location, amount and change in human population at a variety of scales. It deals with spatial distribution (as shown on a map, for example) and with change of location (as shown by a flow line). It also studies structure: the numbers of people in particular age groups, the composition of the total population from different ethnic or religious groups, and its sex composition. As will be seen by the end of this unit, however, even this is an oversimplified description of the subject matter of population geography.

Why?

Numerous techniques are applicable to the study of population. They range from choropleth maps (**20.1**) to map distortions (**20.2**). One of the other aims of this book as a whole is to enable readers

■ **20.1** Choropleth map of world population distribution, by region

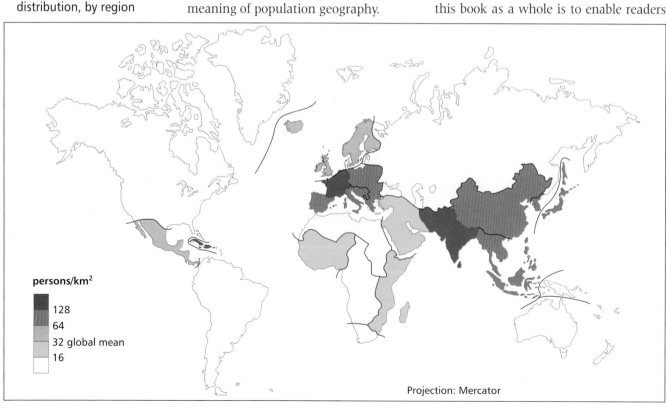

persons/km²

128
64
32 global mean
16

Projection: Mercator

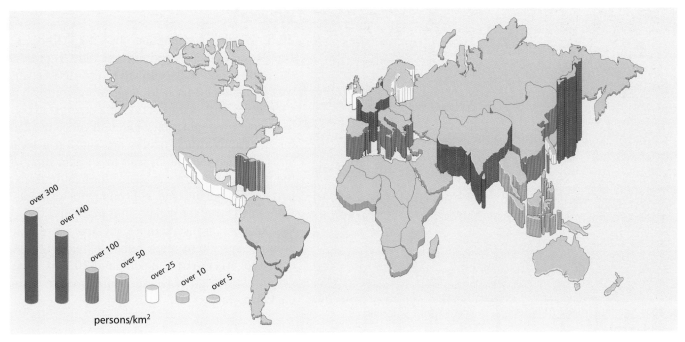

over 300
over 140
over 100
over 50
over 25
over 10
over 5

persons/km²

■ **20.2** World population density map using 'depth'

■ **20.3** Population issues revealed in newspaper headlines

both to interpret such maps and diagrams and to compile them for themselves. This is the response to Kipling's second question. The subject is studied here in order to enable the reader to understand both the subject itself and the way in which it is portrayed. Hardly a day goes by without a front-page item in the newspaper relating directly to population. A selection of such references is shown in **20.3**. A very important aim of this text is to arm readers with an understanding of the subject sufficient to enable them to see behind such headlines and take an informed position themselves.

When?

The study of population has long been important to governments. Britain started counting its entire population in 1801 when the first national census was held. Well before that, however, counts were made both on a local and a national basis, usually as an aid to tax collecting. For example, the Old Testament chronicles major migrations and there are references in the New Testament to population counts, one of them at the time of Jesus' birth. The Domesday Survey in 1086 enumerated land holdings, populations and wealth for large areas of Great Britain, while Malthus' essay on population was written as long ago as 1798 (see

section 24.2). All of this suggests that population study has been important for a long time. Data exist for many countries and areas over considerable time spans, and these allow us to study population change over time.

How?

The methods of studying population have also evolved. At one time, methods were largely descriptive. Although Malthus' ideas have been given the appearance of quantification, they were largely concepts born of perceptions rather than accurate data. Later, especially after 1801, reliable data became available and more accurate mapping, measurement and prediction became possible. Now there is the possibility of monitoring the location and movements of people by remote sensing (**20.4**). Population forecasts, as a basis for governmental planning, are now the product of powerful computer programs. The first County Monitor, giving the breakdown of population figures for the Isle of Wight, was available in May 1992 following the British census held in April 1991. This rapid turnaround was only possible using the latest techniques. While huge flows of refugees, caused by famine or conflict, can appear overnight, such techniques are indispensable if major disasters are to be avoided or managed.

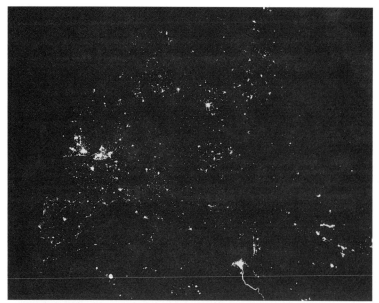

■ **20.4** Satellite image of Europe and North Africa showing settlements

Where?

20.5 is the explanation by the Office of Population Censuses and Surveys (OPCS) of how the information they collected in the 1991 census was going to be used in a planning context. It suggests why it is important for a country to collect accurate population figures in order to plan for the future. Such figures are vital on a local basis because they often lead to an allocation of the national resources available for health, transport developments and education, for example. The same is true for regions that make up a country. Regions are sometimes created on ethnic grounds and these often reflect religious differences. Nigeria is a case in point and **20.6** explains why a knowledge of where people live can be of vital importance.

Who?

Collecting personal details of individuals can be a very emotive issue. The ethnic data gathered by the 1991 British census, for example, could be viewed with great suspicion by the very people it was aimed at helping, and the explanation of the reason (shown in **20.5**) might have a very hollow ring to it. Unless it is collected, however, there is little way that effective planning of educational provision can be made. Unfortunately, there have been examples in the past of the misuse of sensitive data such as ethnic origin. The 1992–94 conflict in Bosnia–Hercegovina (see case study on pages 292–94) is an example where **ethnic cleansing** at least partly resulted from a knowledge of the composition and distribution of the population. Personal details can only be stored in de-personalised form in the United Kingdom. Nobody could tell the details of an individual by looking at census returns. If this were possible, then people would rebel against such collection methods. Legislation, such as the Data Protection Act, ensures the rights of individuals in the UK to know what data are stored on them, and by whom, and enables them to insist on the deletion of any information they do not wish to be stored. There has been a revolution in the way that data from a wide variety of sources can be collected, stored, recalled and used. This has been effected by computers and complex software programs which allow, for example, the fusion and overlaying of different data sets to create and manipulate maps. These systems are known as **geographic information systems (GIS)**.

Why is this information needed?

The Census provides essential information for central and local government, health authorities, and businesses. Here are some examples of how this information is used.

PEOPLE
An accurate count of people in your area helps central government work out how much money to grant to your local authority and health authority. In turn these authorities use Census information when planning services within their areas.

HOUSING
A count of dwellings and the people in them shows the amount and the type of housing in your area. This information will help plan how much housing might be needed in the future.

EMPLOYMENT
The Census will show how many people work in different occupations and industries in each part of the country. This will help government and businesses to plan jobs and training.

TRANSPORT
The Census shows how people get to and from work. Together with information on the availability of cars, this helps plan roads and public transport. It is also used to estimate how many cars will be using the roads in the future.

ETHNIC GROUP
This question is included in the Census for the first time. It will help assess the extent and nature of racial disadvantage and what needs to be done to overcome it.

HEALTH
This information will help local and health authorities plan services and facilities for long-term sick and elderly people.

Surveys after the Census:
A very small sample of people and households will be asked to take part in one of several **voluntary** surveys. One survey will help the Census Offices check how well the Census itself worked. The other surveys will gather fuller information than it is possible to collect in a Census. Information gathered in any such survey will be handled entirely within the Census Offices. It will be treated in the same strict confidence as information given on the census form.

REMEMBER

Sunday 21 April 1991 is Census day

Office of Population
Censuses and Surveys
(The Census Office
for England and Wales)

■ **20.5** Part of the publicity sent out by the OPCS just before the 1991 British census

Census may spring surprise

Up to 30m may not exist

Nigerians are about to hear just how many of them there are. Prepare for a surprise, say government officials, who will soon release the first results of last November's national census. "Africa's most populous nation" may well have far fewer than the 110m to 120m generally estimated – nearer to 90m, rumour has it.

Nigerians may react with equanimity to this revelation. What they particularly wish to know is where they all live, for the 30 states' share of Federal Government revenue is partly determined by population.

"People are aware that they are going to gain more from the central purse by falsifying the head count, and they do just that," commented the weekly magazine *West Africa*. How many live where, however, may not become public information for many months, and the reception accorded those details will provide the most difficult test of the census.

In the meantime, it seems, Nigerians will have to settle for a basic population count.

That in itself is no mean achievement, given the controversies of the past. There have been 11 attempts at an acceptable national census since 1863 and on each occasion the exercise has ended in failure, the journal noted.

The 1952 census, which put the total population at 33m, was believed to have been an underestimate because it was widely assumed the British were counting heads to increase revenues. In 1962, the results were not published because leaks led to political controversy.

In the 1963 count the then Western and Eastern regions alleged that the Northern region had inflated its own figures to ensure the federal dominance of the Northern People's Congress. The north responded angrily: under-populated areas in the south had been overcounted to give the southern regions an unfair share of federal revenue, it alleged.

Ten years later General Yakubu Gowon's military government had a go – and failed. Nigeria by then had been divided into 12

states, and the count for the six northern states – 51.4m – hugely outnumbered the six southern states' 28.4m.

It was decided that since the 1963 census had produced the least unacceptable results it should provide the base for subsequent population figures which have assumed a growth rate ranging from 2.5 to over 3 per cent.

The man in the hot seat this time around has been Alhaji Shehu Musa, a former secretary to the Federal government regarded as a potential presidential candidate. His job as chairman of the National Population Commission has been easier than that of his predecessors. The government defused potential religious and ethnic tensions by omitting questions on these subjects from the questionnaire.

It was nevertheless a monumental exercise involving $\frac{1}{2}$m staff during the three-day exercise across 225,000 enumeration areas.

Michael Holman

■ **20.6** From a *Financial Times* Special Report on Nigeria, 1992

If you are working through this section in order to write course notes on population geography, be sure to write side headings to remind you at a later stage what the notes are about. You should also consider writing notes on case studies apart from answering the questions, so that you can remember the most important facts to illustrate an examination answer. Your first side heading, for example, should be *Definition*.

1 After reading the information on the scope of population geography, write your own definition of the subject.

2 How have recent developments in computer hardware enabled more accurate and responsive studies of populations to be made?

3 Describe how the choropleth map of world population (**20.1**) has been drawn. Does it give a clear picture of the distribution of world population or does it have drawbacks? [Look at the scale, map projection, availability of data and distribution within countries.]

4 In what circumstances might you choose to use a 'distorted' map such as **20.2** rather than a choropleth map? [Think of the point you are trying to stress and the range of differences you can show in both techniques.]

5 The headlines in **20.3** come from just two pages of one edition of a national newspaper. Conduct a similar exercise on one specific day using one of the national 'broadsheet' newspapers. As a result of your exercise, how important do you consider a knowledge of population geography is to an understanding of world affairs? Justify your answer, listing all the activities reported in the paper that have links to population issues.

6 List the reasons a government would have for conducting a census. Which do you think most important, and why?

7 You decide to conduct a census in your school to collect information on mobility (the movements of families in the recent past). The questions must be short and clear (because you are asking them of Year 7 upwards). You are allowed to ask 10 questions in all.
  a Write the questionnaire, including an introduction to explain what you are doing.
  b What sort of problems do you expect to encounter, and how will you overcome them?
  c If possible, conduct a small sample exercise to check whether you were correct in the predictions you made (a 'pilot' survey) – but remember to obtain clearance from a suitable member of staff before doing so.

8 What problems did the Nigerian government encounter in trying to obtain accurate figures upon which to base its planning (**20.6**)? How were they overcome?

9 How does the Nigerian experience reflect on the information shown in **20.1**?

10 Write an essay of about 750–1000 words (three or four sides of A4 paper) entitled: 'Ask the right questions and you will get the right answers – population geography needs a basis of accurate facts'.

20.2 Population density and distribution

The total population of an area is measured by means of a census (see above). This overall measurement allows the computation of population **density** figures by comparing it with the size of the unit involved in the census. Population density is the number of people per unit area. For example, the population density of the UK is about 234 people per km². By itself, however, this figure conveys very little. It says nothing about variations between densely-populated areas in inner cities and almost unpopulated areas in Highland Britain. The scale of the study can hide significant variations in population density (**20.7**). Some might be described as 'overpopulated', whilst others would be 'underpopulated'.

Population **distribution** describes the way that people are located within an area. Maps of population distribution can reveal places where a lot of people live and others where there are few people. Atlas maps of settlement location are one type of distribution map. Reference to the key for such maps will reveal that different sizes and shapes of symbol are used to indicate towns of different sizes. They show fairly crudely how population is distributed in that area. However, they cannot show how houses are situated close together in the inner cities and more widely apart in the

■ **20.7** Some population data for selected countries

Country	Population in 1990 millions	Area '000 km²	Population density in 1990 persons/km²	Estimated mean annual growth 1990–2010 %	Estimated population in 2010 millions
Australia	16.53	7682	2.1	1.0	20.34
Bahrain	0.48	1	694.6	2.4	0.82
Bangladesh	104.53	144	725.9	2.6	188.20
Belgium	9.92	33	299.7	0.1	10.04
Botswana	1.21	588	2.2	3.3	2.44
El Salvador	5.11	21	242.0	2.4	8.49
Finland	4.95	338	14.6	0.2	5.13
Gabon	1.20	268	4.5	2.6	2.09
Hong Kong	5.68	1	5304.4	0.7	6.74
Macau	0.44	<1	25882.3	2.5	0.78
Malta	0.34	1	1076.0	0.4	0.38
Mauritania	1.92	1031	1.9	2.8	3.55
Mongolia	2.09	1565	1.3	2.8	3.89
Poland	37.86	313	121.1	0.5	42.56
Puerto Rico	3.29	9	369.8	1.1	4.62
Singapore	2.65	1	4288.0	0.7	3.12
Spain	39.05	505	77.4	0.3	41.83
UK	57.08	244	233.8	0.2	57.56

suburbs. That can only become clear on maps of a suitable scale. Scale can also be misleading in showing distribution, as in the case study of London (see below).

Population density and distribution are used as a basis for many measurements of the relationship between population and resources. If the measurements are used sensitively, they can be very useful, for example for planning purposes. If, however, they are used in the wrong way, they can be dangerous. For example, they have been used in the past when it was perceived by countries that their optimum population had been exceeded. The immigrant or minority sector of the population is often selected as being 'surplus to requirement' if the resources of the country are under strain (see case study on pages 290–92). Population distribution characteristics (such as 'they tend to group together and not integrate into the community') are quoted to support the fact that there are not enough resources to go round. The identified group is put under pressure, given fewer employment opportunities and even persecuted in extreme cases. This applied to Asians in Idi Amin's Uganda (1960s), Jews in Germany (1930s and 1940s) and the Kurdish population in Iraq at the end of the Gulf War (1991). The measurement of population density and of population distribution in particular is therefore extremely important, but also controversial. Misinterpretation from maps of the wrong scale can lead to the wrong conclusions and may even give fuel to racist behaviour. The case study below, of population density and distribution in London, highlights some of these points.

CASE STUDY

TECHNIQUES

Measuring population density and distribution in London

This case study shows how the use of maps at different scales can reveal significantly different patterns of population density and distribution to those expected from first sight. 20.8 seems to show where there were comparative concentrations of five different minority groups in London in 1981 and 1984. It appears that there were strong concentrations in certain areas, few of which overlapped. The concentration of Jews was mainly in three boroughs in central and north-west London. Many of the Bangladeshis lived in Tower Hamlets. Cypriot concentration was in north London. Caribbean centres were more dispersed, but with a major concentration in inner south London; one area overlapped with the distribution of Irish-born citizens and one with Jews. Irish concentration was otherwise in a corridor running west from Westminster. The evidence at this scale is of marked concentrations of different ethnic groups.

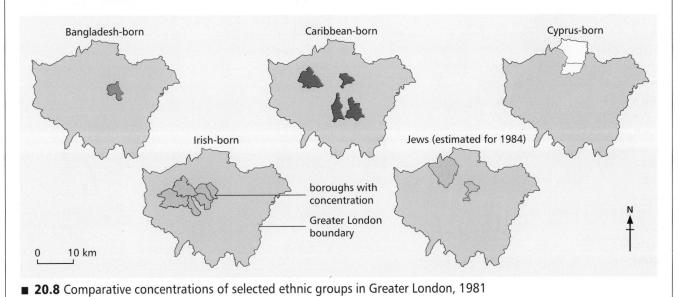

■ **20.8** Comparative concentrations of selected ethnic groups in Greater London, 1981

Scale and the interpretation of distribution maps

It is possible, however, that apparent concentration in some areas is imagined rather than real. **20.9a** shows how a distribution which appears to be segregated (concentrated in one particular area) may in fact be just as evenly distributed as the rest of the population. On the other hand, **20.9b** suggests that a distribution which may appear to be even can have concentrations within it. The distribution of minorities in London deserves a closer look.

20.10 seems to suggest that **20.8** was correct in picking out the places where Jews were concentrated, but a closer look at Hackney, one of the areas shown to have a concentration, reveals that it was only certain subdivisions (wards) of the

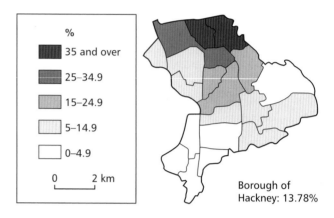

■ **20.11** Jews as a percentage of total population in Hackney, by ward, 1971

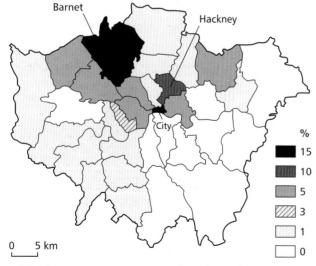

■ **20.9** Population distribution at different scales

■ **20.10** Jews as a percentage of total population in Greater London

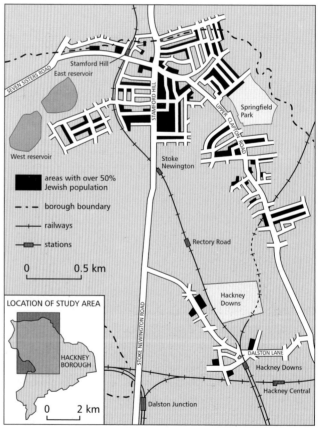

■ **20.12** Distribution of Jews within a Hackney ward, 1971

borough which had high figures (**20.11**). Even then this is not the whole picture. **20.12** shows that concentrations occur even on the street level within wards. Different pictures are revealed by looking at density and distribution at different scales and this example should serve to warn against hasty descriptions and conclusions from inadequate data. At least be aware of the scale of the map and treat it with due caution.

---

11 a In what ways could the population density figures shown in **20.7** be misleading?

b Classify the countries shown in **20.7** into two groups according to their population growth rates. What conclusions can you draw from your classification?

c Draw bar graphs to represent present population and that in the year 2010. Try to arrange them so that the final diagram shows those which are gaining most at one end of the *x*-axis, and those gaining least at the other end.

Label your graph to comment on the relationships you have found in activity 11b.

12 Explain the difference between population density and population distribution.

13 Select one population distribution or density map from a textbook or an atlas and describe:

a how it has been drawn

b what it shows, and

c some of the things it does not show about the population distribution or density.

20.3 Population size: a real or imagined problem from a 'Northern' viewpoint?

IT5

It has already been suggested that many news items and television discussion programmes centre around population as an issue. Population size is one aspect that creates much debate. It is easy to be given the impression that this is the major problem faced by the world today. It could be that population growth is, for example, leading to environmental degradation. Below is a list of facts and predictions about world population.

IT5

■ **20.13** The North–South Divide

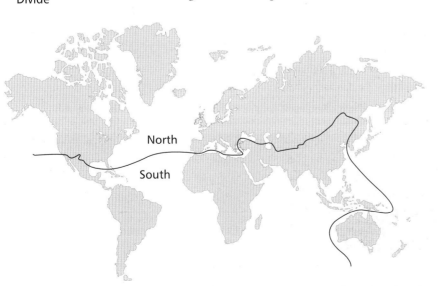

North

South

Some population facts

■ The developed 'North' consists of 33 countries, the developing 'South' of 127.

■ In 1992 there were an estimated 5.5 billion people on Earth, 1.2 billion of whom lived in the North.

■ Individuals in the North consume, on average, around 20 times more than those in the South. The North is industrialised, the South less so.

■ 97 million people were born in 1992, 90 per cent of them in low-income countries.

- By 2050, the North will still consume twice as much as the South.

- The disparity between North and South is growing annually. The South is tied in to debt repayment so much that Carlos Fuentes, a Mexican commentator, wrote in the early 1990s: 'Every Mexican baby is born owing $1000 to a Northern bank'.

- The difference between the mean income of the top 20 per cent and the bottom 20 per cent of the world population expressed in 1989 US dollars grew between 1960 and 1989 from $1864 to $15 149.

- At the end of the 1990s, there will be an extra billion mouths to feed from a starting point in 1990.

20.14 Is it numbers that are the problem, or the unequal share of resources?

- By 2050, UN estimates are that the population of the South will double to 9 billion people.

- World population as a whole will stabilise at some 14 billion by around 2050.

14 Read the list above and then decide for yourself whether population size is the most important issue. Might it be that it is being used as an excuse by those in the North who do not wish to give up their mass-consumption way of life in order to give a better share of resources to the South? What evidence do you have for your conclusion?

15 Divide a page into three as shown below. Decide what general point is being made in the 10 statements above and write suitable notes for each under the heading you have suggested – one example has been done for you.

General point	The North	The South
Definition	33 rich countries, developed and industrialised	127 poor countries, developing and lacking in industrial development

20.4 Techniques: Population mapping

Choropleths

*A choropleth is a map showing different densities by means of shading (see **20.23**). It is one of the most commonly used techniques in population geography. Decisions on what classes to use in order to show differences in density and what colour or shading scheme to use are very important. You are presented here with some data which illustrate the decisions that have to be made (**20.16**).*

Distorted maps

*There are many ways in which maps can be 'distorted'. They can be drawn according to time or cost scales as opposed to distance scales, thus distorting the resultant shape. Another way of distorting them is to give areas 'depth' according to some factor, such as density of population (**20.17**). Examples are shown in **20.2** and **20.18**. This gives a good idea of relative densities whilst maintaining true size or shape of area (depending on the map projection used).*

Country	Population density persons/km²
Austria	7.61
Belgium	9.92
Denmark	5.13
Finland	4.95
France	55.87
Germany	77.87
Greece	10.01
Ireland	3.54
Italy	57.44
Luxembourg	0.37
Netherlands	14.76
Norway	4.20
Portugal	10.41
Spain	39.05
Sweden	8.44
Switzerland	6.62
UK	57.08

■ **20.16** Population densities in West European countries

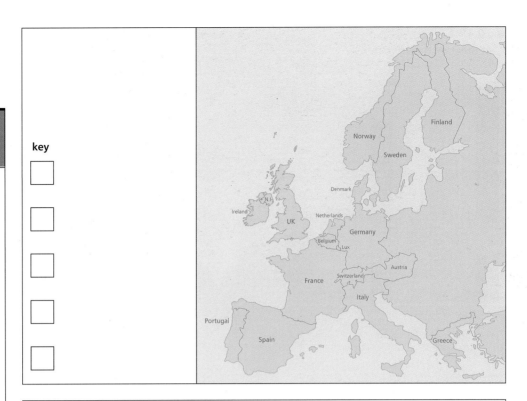

■ **20.17** Technique for drawing 'height' maps to show population density

1 Draw a square grid over the base map.

2 Transfer the map from the square grid to a piece of isometric drawing paper. This is known as a **transformation**.

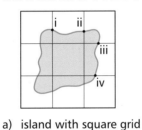

a) island with square grid

isometric grid —

b) the same island transferred to isometric drawing paper

3 Now trace the transformed outline on to a good-quality tracing paper. With a very soft lead pencil (BBB), shade lightly *on the reverse side* of the tracing paper wherever you have traced a line.

4 Work out the 'height' of the area by the usual means (e.g. 1 mm = 10 people per km²). Then draw vertical lines on the western and eastern ends on the base map produced in (2).

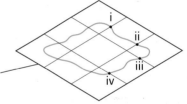

4.2 mm   4.2 mm
W   island   E
          A

5 Take the tracing of the island made in (3) and place it over the base map so that points W and E lie at the top of the vertical lines you have drawn. Draw round your tracing of that island and you will get an exact replica of the original, 4.2 mm above it.

4.2 mm   4.2 mm
      island
        A

6 If you are drawing a 'height' map for an area like that shown in **20.15**, repeat the process for all the countries. Complete the map by shading the areas which are shown, avoiding overlaps.

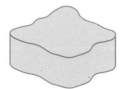

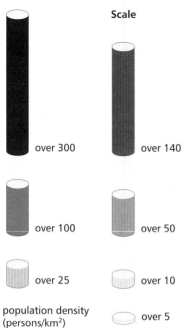

■ **20.18** A 'depth' map of population densities in Asia

Scale

over 300

over 140

over 100

over 50

over 25

over 10

population density (persons/km²)

over 5

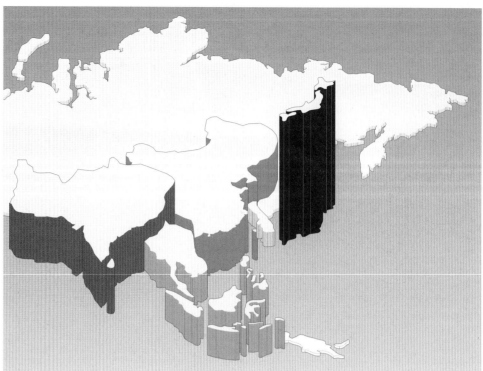

16 The base map of Western Europe (**20.15**) shows the divisions within which the population density figures were estimated (**20.16**).
  a Decide on five density classes to be shown on the finished map.
  b Select appropriate colours and shade in a copy of the base map to illustrate population densities.
  c Comment on the technique used and how useful it is in illustrating population densities in Europe. You may like to look at an atlas, in particular at physical and industrial maps, to help you make your comments.

17 Look at **20.18** and comment on the way that it has been used to show population density in Asia.

18 Compare **20.18** and your completed version of **20.15**. Which one do you think gives the best impression of population density and why?

19 Look through an atlas or geography textbook at the population density maps. What other techniques are used and which, in your view, are most successful?

Topological maps

The most well-known topological map is that drawn to represent the London Underground system. If you sit on a tube train and follow your progress between one station and the next on such a map, you may well be looking at a straight line whilst feeling the train going round a steep curve. Topological maps are true to one element, but make few concessions to the others. The Underground map is true to the relation between stations. It is not the right shape and the distance between places is distorted. The same idea can be used to draw population maps. Countries can be shown relative to their population size, whilst making only a few concessions to their true shapes and positions with respect to one another.

20.19 is a topological map showing world population. Each of the squares on the map represents several million people (there are 57 million people in the UK, for example). The squares have been assembled in such a way as to suggest the true shapes of the countries whilst giving a very good visual idea of their relative populations.

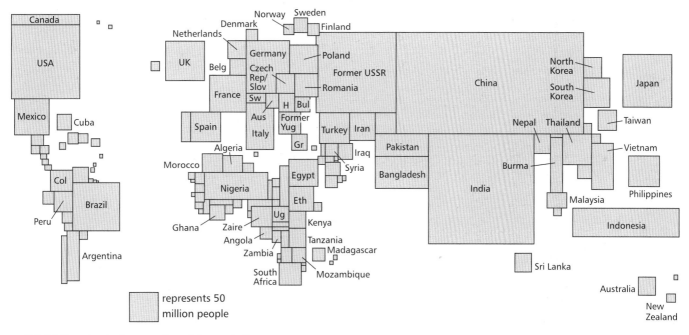

■ **20.19** Topological map of world population

20 You are to draw a topological map of Europe to represent total population of each of the countries named in **20.16** (the smallest countries have been omitted). Do so by following instructions **a** to **c**.

a Select a scale so that the smallest unit can be shown by at least one square on squared paper and the largest does not take up too much room. [Round the figures in order to make this easier.]

b Referring to a political map of Europe, start with the most westerly country (Ireland) and shade (lightly in pencil) the squares needed to represent it. The squares should be shaded to represent, as nearly as possible, the true shape of the country.

c Work eastwards from this country until the map has been completed. Draw lines around each shaded area and tidy the map by rubbing out the shading.

d Comment on the technique you have used, mentioning any drawbacks it may have and for what purposes it would be especially useful.

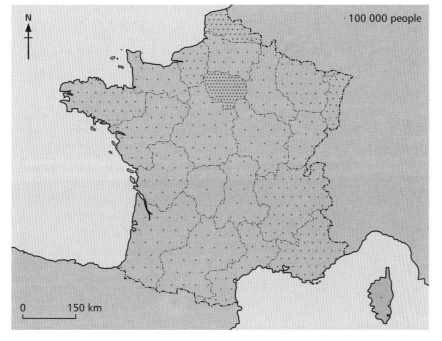

· 100 000 people

0   150 km

Dot maps

Another way of showing both density and distribution is to use a dot mapping technique. **20.20** *is a dot map of population in France. The population figures have been scaled so that one dot represents 1 million people. Dots have then been located evenly by département. A further refinement would have been to locate them more densely where the largest towns are and less densely where the physical features preclude high densities of population. All the dots are the same size, but more complex distributions could be*

■ **20.20** Dot map of population distribution in France

Region	Population 1990 '000s
Arnsberg	3685
Berlin (East)	1279
Berlin (West)	2130
Brandenburg	2641
Bremen	638
Braunscheig	1614
Darmstadt	3491
Dortmund	1850
Düsseldorf	5168
Freiburg	1935
Giessen	981
Hamburg	1626
Hanover	2032
Karlsruhe	2484
Kassel	1188
Koblenz	1377
Köln	3963
Lüneburg	1467
Mecklenburg-Vorpommern	1964
Mittelfranken	1566
Münster	2438
Niederbayern	1057
Ober-Bayern	3721
Oberfranken	1056
Oberpfalz	991
Rheinhessen–Pfalz	1847
Saarland	1065
Sachsen	4901
Sachsen-Anhalt	2965
Schleswig–Holstein	2595
Schwaben	1594
Stuttgart	3610
Thuringen	2684
Trier	478
Tübingen	1590
Unterfranken	1235
Weser–Ems	2170

■ **20.21** Population data for the regions of Germany

■ **20.22** Base map of Germany

shown for other data by using different colours. A student drawing a dot map by hand should use one stroke of the pen to make the dot rather than trying to make a large dot by a circular motion of the pen nib, which is a method that makes it very difficult to keep all the dots the same size.

21 Population data for Germany are given in **20.21**. Copy the base map in **20.22**, then draw a dot map to show both the density and distribution of population as follows:

a Select a scale so that each division has enough dots to show differences, but not too many to make the exercise a very long one.

b With reference to an atlas, indicate lightly in pencil on your base map (so that these lines can later be rubbed out) the areas of densest population and those of sparse population.

c Locate the correct number of dots in each division to illustrate both the density and distribution of population.

d Complete the key.

e Comment on the use of the technique. How could its accuracy be improved?

20.5 Preparing an examination answer

Population density and distribution in Egypt

QUESTION: *Describe* and *explain* the **density** and **distribution** of population in Egypt.

In planning your answer to this question, four elements must be considered. The two 'command' words are in *italics*, and the two 'subjects' are in **bold** type.

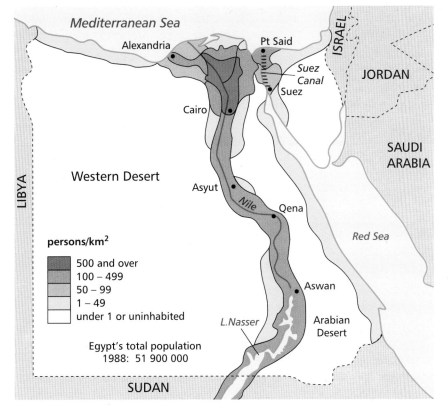

■ **20.23** Population densities in Egypt

persons/km²

	500 and over
	100 – 499
	50 – 99
	1 – 49
	under 1 or uninhabited

Egypt's total population
1988: 51 900 000

Answer checklist

- *Describe* **density**
  - What are the greatest densities and where are they?
  - What are the lowest densities and where are they?
  - How are they spaced?
- *Describe* **distribution**
  - Are there any shapes to the areas of different densities? If so, what?
  - Are they linear, nucleated or evenly distributed?
- *Explain* **density**
  - Are the areas of different density associated with any of the following:
    physical factors:
    relief, climate, soils, water?
    human factors: communications, resources, farming, industry?
  - If so, how are they linked?
- *Explain* **distribution**
  - Are the patterns made by the areas of different density associated in any way with physical or human factors?

If the exam question is presented with a map (**20.23**), the checklist can be used to produce the answer set out below. Headings are included for planning purposes – they must not be included in exam answers (unless they are asked for).

'Describe and explain the density and distribution of population in Egypt.'

Introduction

Egypt, in the north-east corner of Africa bordering the Mediterranean Sea, has some of the most densely populated and some of the least densely populated areas of the world.

Describe density

The highest density of population (over 500 people per km²) is found in the area around Cairo and northwards along the two main distributaries of the river Nile towards the Mediterranean Sea. High densities of over 100 per km² are found in the rest of the delta and inland along the Nile valley. Densities of up to 50 people per km² are found along the Red Sea and Mediterranean coasts and the Suez Canal. There are large areas of very low population density both west and east of the Nile valley. There is a sudden division between the high densities of the Nile valley and the low densities which are found on either side of it.

Describe distribution

In terms of distribution, the high-density population areas form linear zones through the country, along the Nile itself, along the banks of the Suez Canal and along the coasts of the Red Sea and the Mediterranean Sea. The lowest-density areas form continuous zones across the rest of the country.

Explain density

The high-density areas are principally explained by the presence of fertile soil or by communications and trade routes. Along the Nile valley, farmland is particularly productive. The relief is flat, the soil is alluvial (deposited by the Nile in flood and full of minerals) and therefore rich, and there is a constant water supply (even if irrigation is a laborious chore in the growing season). The climate is hot all year and allows for up to three crops annually. Consequently there is a high concentration of farmers in these areas. Along the Nile itself, which is a major waterway, trading settlements have been established. This is also the case on the Mediterranean coast, the Red Sea coast and in the Suez Canal area. These developments lead to moderate population densities. The low-density areas represent the high lands of the Arabian Desert, and the Western and Arabian Deserts themselves. In these areas there are extreme temperatures, little available water, difficult rocky and sandy terrain and few natural resources. Where these do occur, as in the oilfields along the Red Sea coast and west of Alexandria and in the oases (e.g. Kharga and Dakhla Oasis west of Luxor), population densities are slightly higher. The greatest population densities of all are now found in the major towns where industry (Cairo), trade (Suez) or tourism (Giza) have led to concentration.

Explain distribution

The linear distributions of high-density population are linked to the communications and agricultural activities along the river Nile, the trading artery of the Suez Canal and the developments along both the Mediterranean and Red Sea coasts. The large areas of relatively low population correlate with the inhospitable desert areas and the abrupt break between high and low-density distributions reflects the limits imposed by nature on further human development given the present level of technology, especially in water exploitation. Attempts have been made to expand the area under cultivation, for example by using water from Lake Nasser (impounded behind the Aswan High Dam), but these have only emphasised the sharp break between densely populated farming regions and almost unpopulated desert.

The large areas of low density are explained by the climatic conditions prevailing there. The deserts coincide almost exactly with the areas of lowest density, but this is relieved in a few places where other attributes, such as trade routes, the availability of water or oil deposits, make it worth while for people to live in the area, even though they have to pay heavily for imported water and foodstuffs (except in the case of oases).

Conclusion

Egypt has a very well-defined distribution of areas of different population densities. It also has large areas which, given the technology, could be populated in the future. However, with the predicted accentuation of dry areas (due to warming under the greenhouse effect), the distribution is likely to continue to reflect great differences.

Administrative division shown on 20.24	Population density persons/km²
1	72
2	154
3	93
4	309
5	106
6	135
7	153
8	467
9	302
10	309
11	1687
12	1078
13	5430
14	3310
15	197
16	264
17	278
18	197
19	191
20	159
21	195
22	472
23	1300
24	310
25	304
26	564
27	4640
28	645
29	373
30	228
31	176
32	118
33	271
34	336
35	257
36	201
37	546
38	267
39	116
40	969
41	360
42	382
43	249
44	195
45	151
46	196
47	540

■ **20.25** Population data for the divisions of Japan

22 A base map of Japan is provided in **20.24**. Population statistics for the administrative divisions are listed in **20.25**.

a Use the data to create a diagram illustrating population density in Japan, choosing your method from any of those given in this chapter, or one you have found from another source.

b Describe the pattern revealed by your map.

c With reference to an atlas, give some of the reasons for the pattern you have found.

[This activity asks for descriptions and explanations of the density and distribution revealed by your mapping exercise, so the headings to assist in your answer can be found in the checklist on page 267.]

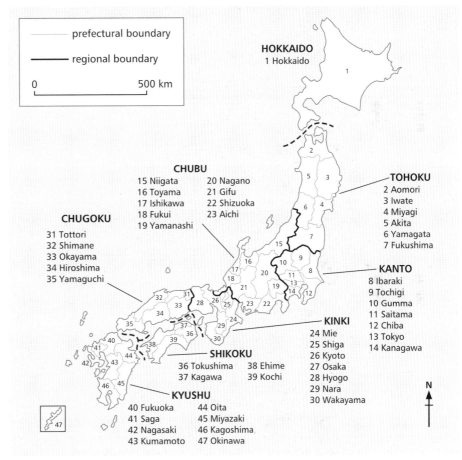

HOKKAIDO
1 Hokkaido

CHUBU
15 Niigata
16 Toyama
17 Ishikawa
18 Fukui
19 Yamanashi
20 Nagano
21 Gifu
22 Shizuoka
23 Aichi

CHUGOKU
31 Tottori
32 Shimane
33 Okayama
34 Hiroshima
35 Yamaguchi

TOHOKU
2 Aomori
3 Iwate
4 Miyagi
5 Akita
6 Yamagata
7 Fukushima

KANTO
8 Ibaraki
9 Tochigi
10 Gumma
11 Saitama
12 Chiba
13 Tokyo
14 Kanagawa

KINKI
24 Mie
25 Shiga
26 Kyoto
27 Osaka
28 Hyogo
29 Nara
30 Wakayama

SHIKOKU
36 Tokushima
37 Kagawa
38 Ehime
39 Kochi

KYUSHU
40 Fukuoka
41 Saga
42 Nagasaki
43 Kumamoto
44 Oita
45 Miyazaki
46 Kagoshima
47 Okinawa

prefectural boundary
regional boundary
0   500 km

N

■ **20.24** Base map of Japan

21.1 **Components of population change**

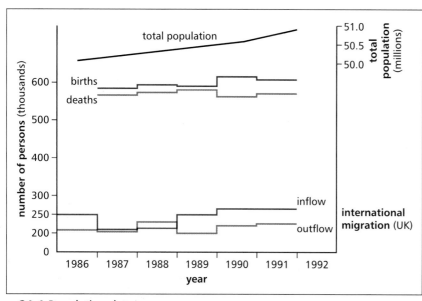

■ **21.1** Population data for England and Wales, 1986–91

for England and Wales for a recent period. During that time, the total population changed as a function of the four rates, all of which are illustrated on the graph.

The way that births and deaths operate to control the population rate of change may be likened to water-level changes in a bath (**21.2**). With the plug out, one tap left running fast would lead to a small amount of water building up in the bottom of the bath. This would represent a high birth rate (the fast-running tap) and a high death rate (the open plughole). The result would be a low total population (the water level) which tended to remain stable, but with a high turnover.

21.3 shows the results of immigration and emigration (mobility) as well as natural population change. Mobility is the third important aspect of population change and is dealt with in detail in Chapter 22. **21.4** gives the total population for the UK recorded by each census since 1901. Only a small part of each intercensal change is accounted for by mobility.

IT1 If population totals are an important issue with which the world will have to grapple, then an understanding of how these numbers are reached must be critical if the issue is to be treated sensibly. The population of any area changes as a function of births and deaths, as well as the movement of people into and out of that area. **21.1** shows some population data

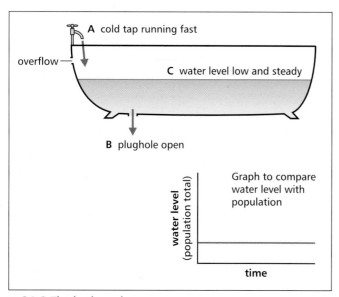

■ **21.2** The bath analogy

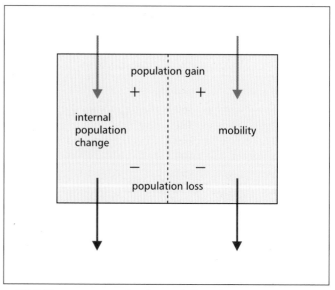

■ **21.3** The components of population change

Census date	Total population millions	Intercensal change millions
1901	38.2	–
1911	42.1	3.9
1921	44.0	1.9
1931	46.0	
1941	48.2	
1951	50.6	
1961	53.0	
1971	55.7	
1981	56.3	
1991	57.4	

1 a Describe the trend in the total population of the UK between 1986 and 1992, as shown by **21.1**.
b With reference to the four other sets of data shown in the graph, explain the population trend.

2 For each of the following instances, draw diagrams similar to **21.2** showing both the situation within the bath and its impact on the population graph:
a The plughole is left open whilst the tap is turned down, the bath having first been filled.
b Both taps are left running fast, and the plughole remains open.
c The plug is put in to partially block the drain and the tap runs slowly.

3 How might immigration and emigration be portrayed in the bath analogy? Draw a diagram to illustrate your answer.

4 In terms of the four rates shown in **21.1**, what combinations of events could lead to:
a an increase in the population of an area
b a decline in its population?

5 a Complete **21.3** by adding the following labels in the correct places: births, deaths, immigration, emigration.
b Illustrate your answers to activity 4 by drawing diagrams similar to **21.3**.

6 a For **21.4**, work out the intercensal changes in population (changes between censuses). The first two have been done for you.
b Plot them on a line graph.
c What trend do the figures show?

21.2 **Measuring fertility**

Several different measures can be used to illustrate the level of fertility in a population. The simplest is the **crude birth rate** which shows the number of births per 1000 people, including all age groups. This measure does not take into account the possible fluctuations to be expected if the population structure is unusual. For example, if there is a larger than average older population, the birth rate will be low. Similarly, if there is a 'baby boom', then another will be expected later on when this 'bulge' of population reaches child-bearing age (**21.5**). The article on the 'baby boomers', however, shows that prevailing social and economic conditions can also influence this.

To eliminate the effects of the size and structure of the population on the crude birth rate, the **age-specific** birth rate is sometimes used. It is computed by expressing the number of births to mothers of a particular age as a percentage of all women of the same age in the population. If these age groups are added for all child-bearing age groups, the **total fertility rate** is produced.

7 Read the article in **21.5** on page 272.
a What three factors does the author think affected the increase in birth rate?
b Give some examples of the way that business has taken advantage of the increased number of babies.

Yuppie puppies make their mark on the second baby boom

THE United States is experiencing a severe outbreak of babies. An estimated 4,125,000 babies were born in America in 1991. This is only the second occasion since the classic Baby Boom years of 1948–1964 that more than four million infant Americans arrived in one year. The previous time was the year before last, 1990.

Is this a passing epidemic, or a permanent shift with significant implications for American society and politics? A decade ago America was bemoaning the collapse of its birth-rate (down to 3.1 million babies at its trough in 1975). But since around 1985 – and dramatically since 1989 – the US has been going through a second baby boom.

The demographers' explanation of the surge in procreation is three-fold. First, there has been a huge, nationwide litter of so-called "Yuppie Puppies", the last-chance offspring of the children of the original Baby Boom, now in their mid-thirties to early forties. The lives of these late-entrant parents can be traced with acronyms.

In the 1970s, they were the original Yuppies (young urban professionals). In the 1980s they married to become Dinkies (double income no kids). Before they realised it, they became Grumpies (grown-up mature professionals) and finally, just before it was too late, they had children. There is no generally recognised nickname for their new state, but it could be something like Dappies (Doting Ageing Parents of Precocious Infants).

By its nature, this part of the demographic "bubble" will burst soon, as the female half of the Baby Boom generation passes beyond child-bearing age. Gregory Spencer, Chief of Population Projections at the US Census Bureau, says: "These are people who had been concentrating on their career, on getting MBAs, getting rich, travelling the world, enjoying themselves. They said all along that they were going to have children but we demographers didn't believe them.

Mark Phillips, 43, is a TV reporter, with a daughter of six and son of two. "What I've learned from the broken sleep over the last six years is that our bodies were designed to reproduce in their late teens and early twenties, not late thirties and early forties," he says.

"Our generation mortgaged its fifties and sixties and cashed in its twenties and thirties, not just in the physical sense, but in the financial sense as well. College tuition is something like $15,000 (£8,000) a year. I hate to guess what it will be 20 years from now, just as I might be planning to retire."

This is a lesson already taken to heart, it seems, by the next generation of Americans. Those born after the Baby Boom, sometimes called "baby busters", have settled into a more traditional pattern of earlier marriage, and earlier, more frequent, child bearing. This is the second factor, say demographers, in the baby surge.

The Baby Boomers delayed marriage and kids because they could do so. They were the first generation to have easy access to birth-control, abortion and – in the case of women – interesting jobs. The next generation, now in its middle to late twenties, is returning to "traditional values and family patterns", according to Professor Thomas Espenshade, a respected demographer at Princeton University.

The US fertility rate has climbed from 1.8 babies per woman in the mid-1970s to 2.1 per woman – exactly the number needed to keep the US population stable without immigration. Professor Espenshade says the latest statistics show the climb is partly due to a trend to earlier child bearing among middle-class Americans in their twenties.

The third factor in the new baby boom is the high number of babies being born to immigrant mothers. Demographers say this factor is the most difficult to track into the future. There is also a continuing torrent of children born to children in inner cities: but here, thankfully, the numbers are relatively stable.

Equally difficult to track is the political significance of the sudden growth in America's family. The middle-class trend away from having children coincided, in the 1970s and 1980s, with a political trend towards ignoring children's concerns and, consequently, a raw time for many children. Much rubbish was spoken in the 1980s about family values.

One in five American children now lives in poverty; one in five lives in a household without an adult male; three in five will live in a one-parent home at some time in their childhood. Government spending on children – at federal and state level – has been falling behind spending on adults and far behind spending on old people. Standards in schools have been collapsing and the cost of college education has been soaring.

The catalogue of children's misfortunes helps to explain many of the country's woes, from crime to lack of skilled workers capable of competing with Europe and Japan. Here is something that both conservatives and liberals can agree on: but not on what to do about it.

The US has socialised old age but not childhood, partly because old people vote and children do not. Old people in America can look forward to pensions and heavily subsidised health care. But the welfare and tax provisions for children are the most niggardly in the industrial world. In other words, the structure of US tax and welfare systems makes it sensible to be childless and allow other people's children to earn the money to pay the taxes to look after you in your old age.

The problem is that the uneven demographics of the last 30 years – and the poor educational standard of many Americans – may make it economically and politically impossible for next century's adults to keep retired Baby Boomers in style.

The second baby boom has already caused cultural echoes of the first: a surge of full-length Hollywood cartoons, from *Who Framed Roger Rabbit* to *Beauty And The Beast*; a revival in sales of the station wagon; the transition from *Dallas* – in which children always disappeared from birth to 18 – to *thirtysomething*, which is about Baby Boom parenting angst.

Professor Espenshade says there is no evidence that the rising birth-rate has raised awareness of children's issues. But he says this may be the effect in the long run – partly because people with children are more likely to think about the future and because the increased birth-rate represents a turning away from "now and me" ideals towards more traditional values.

■ **21.5** A report in *The Independent on Sunday*, 5 January 1992

21.3 **Aspects of the birth rate**

| IT5 |

	Total fertility rate
Europe	1.9
North America	1.9
Former USSR	2.3
Oceania	2.7
Latin America	4.4
Africa	6.5

■ **21.6** Average birth rate by continent, 1990

	Total fertility rate
England	1.8
USA	2.0
North Korea	2.7
Indonesia	3.3
Sri Lanka	3.4
Mexico	4.6
Bangladesh	6.5
Kenya	8.0

■ **21.7** Average birth rate by country, 1990

■ **21.8** 'The ideal family'

21.6 shows that the world average birth rate was around 3.9 children per woman in 1990, but that this figure was subject to enormous variation. The highest rate overall was in Africa, where a rate of 6.5 was more than three times that in either Europe or North America. By country, the range of birth rates was revealed to be even greater (**21.7**). A number of factors influence the birth rate.

'Tradition' is sometimes suggested as being important in determining family size. It is said that large families reflect the social standing of the parents and that various pressures from society determine family size. If these conditions have prevailed for some time, the term 'tradition' is used to explain it. More accurately, however, the term should be broken down into it constituent parts. It is important in many parts of the world to ensure that there is an offspring, preferably a working male, to look after parents in their old age. For this reason, especially in rural areas of India and Africa for example, families are large. Since death rates, particularly infant death rates, are high in these areas, birth rates need to be high to fulfil this aim. However, large families are not necessarily a good investment for small farmers. So if life expectancy for infants increases (due to medical advances or better hygiene), then other measures may be taken to limit family size once the insurance aim has been achieved. One measure is birth control (see section 21.4) but even more radical solutions are sometimes used, as in India (see case study on pages 275–79).

Social pressure includes the perception of people, particularly women, about what is expected of them.

	Ideal number of children wanted	
	by mothers aged 45–49	**by daughters** aged 15–19
Africa	7.8	6.6
Asia and Pacific	4.9	3.3
Latin America and Caribbean	5.5	3.3
Middle East	5.9	4.2

Country	GDP per capita US$	Birth rate per 1000
South Africa	2490	31.7
Algeria	2250	40.2
Ivory Coast	710	50.9
Burkina Faso	180	47.2
Ethiopia	120	43.7

■ **21.9** The relationship between economic conditions and birth rates in the early 1990s **IT5**

Research has shown that there is a tendency in many parts of the world for women to choose to have fewer children than before. One way in which this is shown is in the different aspirations of mothers and their daughters (**21.8**). With greater life expectancy and improved education, younger women are beginning to limit their 'ideal family' at lower figures than before and birth rates are therefore falling.

Economic conditions are also very influential on the birth rate. In general, the lower-income countries have higher birth rates than the high-income countries (**21.9**). Reasons for this include the need for old age 'insurance' described above, but also the supply of labour for the family and the lack of education about health and contraception which keeps the birth rate high. The distribution of wealth within the country is also very important in this respect. Where the share is unequal, as in Kenya (**21.10**), birth rates remain high. Where, on the other hand, income is more equitably shared, birth rates are lower. Birth rates are, however, a symptom of wealth distribution rather than a cause of it. Poor families would not necessarily be better off if they had fewer children. For example, in Bangladesh boys are on average producing more than they consume by the age of 10 and have 'repaid' all their parents' investment in them by the time

■ **21.10** Wealth and birth rates for selected countries

Country	Per capita income $	% of wealth owned by richest 10%	Total fertility rate
Kenya	340	45.8	8.0
Sri Lanka	340	28.2	3.4
Mexico	2240	40.6	4.6
North Korea	2010	27.5	2.7

■ **21.11** The case of Ameera from Pakistan – **IP2**

AMEERA, PAKISTAN

My mother-in-law would never allow it

I had my first child one year after I got married. Then I had a baby every year after that until I had five girls and three boys. My husband sells fruit on the streets of Lahore. I have no idea of what he earns, but he gives me about 1500 rupees ($86) a month to run the house. Two of my sons are working too and they bring in about 300 rupees a month each.

I wish I'd had fewer children – if I'd known the way prices would go up … It's so difficult to manage on what my husband and sons bring home. When they get married I'll tell them to use family planning because prices get higher every day and it's impossible to support a large family. Myself, I never thought about using birth control before because my mother-in-law would never allow it. She believes that children are a blessing from God and we shouldn't do anything to stop them. So when I did do it was in secret.

I found out about it from one of my neighbours. She was using condoms and advised me to do the same. I can't read or write so I don't know if there were posters or books about it. There are no health visitors in this area, so if my neighbour hadn't told me I still wouldn't know anything about it. I don't know whether my husband knew either. But when I asked him for permission he just agreed.

The doctor at the hospital told me about the pill, but said you have to take them regularly, and if you forgot even once, then you'll get pregnant. Anyway, I was sure my husband would forbid me to use the pill, so I thought it was better to use condoms. They were five or ten rupees a packet and they hurt a lot and I had some internal injuries. So I went back to the lady doctor and she gave me a cream and some tablets.

My in-laws didn't know – I didn't tell them. My mother-in-law was suspicious and asked us, so we had to tell her we were using condoms. Then there was a big fight and she said I mustn't use them ever again. My husband was on my side – he wanted us to use family planning. But in the end it was all for nothing, because I got pregnant anyway. So then I went secretly to have an abortion, and my mother-in-law found out about that too. So there was another huge fight.

Recently I've heard that there have been advertisements on the television and people say the doctors give you 50 rupees if you go for the sterilisation operation. I think it's a sort of bribe they have to offer because otherwise the people won't go, and they want to control the population. That's why they give you the money instead of making you pay. Men have the operation too, but it's mostly the women. I've seen it with my own eyes. They do the operation and keep the woman there for about an hour then give her 50 rupees.

Maria del Nevo

they are 15. By contrast, in the USA rich families are certainly better off if they have fewer children, since it costs on average $100 000 (excluding college fees) to raise a child to the age of 18. American families are therefore limited by economics in a way that Bangladeshi families are not.

Cultural pressures have already been alluded to above. The 'yuppie puppies' (**21.5**) provide a good example of the influence of cultural pressure on the birth rate. Probably of greatest importance on a world scale in this respect are religious factors. For example, a Papal Encyclical in 1993 re-affirmed the opposition of the Roman Catholic Church to any form of artificial birth control. The case of Ameera from Pakistan (**21.11**) examines other cultural influences on the birth rate that also pertain in Bangladesh.

Political factors also operate to influence birth rates. In China, draconian measures are brought to bear on families exceeding the quota (taxes are increased, housing subsidies removed, etc.), and in

India, government incentives are used to encourage the use of birth control measures, including sterilisation. In other countries, such as France and to a certain extent the UK, encouragement is given to people to have children by use of variations on the family allowance theme. Whereas one factor may be of overall importance in the case of one particular family, it is usually a mixture of factors which influences the birth rate in the population as a whole.

8 In your notes, write a classification of the causes of differences in the birth rate between countries.

9 In **21.11**, what pressures were acting on Ameera on the one hand to use contraception and on the other to avoid it?

21.4 **Birth control and abortion**

Some people in the developed world look on birth control, and possibly even abortion, as a means of controlling the 'oncoming human tide' of some of the less developed areas, for example Africa. Others throughout the world see both as a contradiction of God's basic laws. The following information is not intended to take sides, but rather to look at some of the facts and issues involved.

Most areas of Africa, although they have high birth rates, are also 'underpopulated'. On most measures of the term, there are both room and resources to support much larger numbers in nearly all the constituent countries. The fact that Africa in general has such high birth rates should not therefore be taken as a threat or as a wanton disregard by Africans for the future of their environment. In any case, birth rates in Africa are falling. Among the reasons are education and the availability of birth control. Compared with some areas of

Europe, for example, pollution and environmental degradation are less and population densities are lower.

People in developing areas (probably the same proportion of people as in developed areas) act rationally in deciding on the size of their family. Decisions are made with respect to circumstances. Forces such as religious belief may lead to large family size, just as they do in the developed world. Once birth control measures are available to them, they add them to their armoury. **21.12** shows the extent to which modern contraception was used in various countries, including two in Africa, by 1982. Religious and social conditions affected the uptake in Egypt, and availability was the major limiting factor in the Kenyan countryside in the period shown. The rates in both are now higher as contraception is seen as a priority in both countries in population planning.

Country	Period	Average annual population change	% using modern contraception
Egypt	1974–82	1.0	34
Kenya (rural)	1967–78	0.2	8
Jamaica	1975–79	4.2	55
Mexico	1976–79	2.8	39
Bangladesh	1976–79	1.4	13
Thailand	1969–81	3.8	59
USA	1965–76	0.4	68
Japan	1971–81	0.3	56
Hungary	1966–77	0.7	74

■ **21.12** Uptake of contraceptive measures by 1982   IT5

Population control schemes are sometimes put in place by governments with scant regard for the wishes of individuals. The Chinese and Indian examples fall into this category. Having been 'paid' with transistor radios or cash to be sterilised, people often feel cheated at a later date, particularly if their own family circumstances change. A better approach is to persuade people to take family planning decisions themselves in the light of information provided.

Abortion, the artificially stimulated rejection of a foetus, is legal for a variety of reasons in many countries of the world. Amongst the reasons for allowing it are the physical health of the mother, her mental health, and identified abnormalities in the foetus. Some religions, however, argue that abortion is a sin. Until 1895, the Catholic Church taught that the soul entered the male foetus 40 days after conception and the female foetus 80 days after the event. Thus abortions before these times were tolerated. In 1895, however, the Church moved to its present position that the soul is infused at conception, effectively banning abortion. Abortion became a subject of heated debate as it became more widely available in many countries, with the 'pro-life' lobby pitched against those demanding the right of women 'to have control over their own bodies'. The debate in developed countries is, therefore, often at a moral level. The practical level is perhaps more important in less developed areas.

IT5

CASE STUDY

IP2, IT5

Some aspects of population control in India

India's population is growing at about 1.8 per cent per annum. The population in 1988 was 796 million. Allowing for a gradual decline in the annual percentage growth rate, the total in 2010 will be 1225 million. India and China will then both have populations over one billion.

The population balance is lopsided in India. In recent years, for every 100 girls, 116 boys are being born (**21.13**). This statistic is very telling as it highlights the social and economic pressures on parents. Indian women have a relatively high fertility rate of 4.3. With the huge overall numbers involved, it might be expected that the male : female ratio would be in balance. The surplus of boys is, therefore, surprising.

The first reason for the imbalance is that girls can be seen very much as 'second best' in India. Despite the fact that it is usually women who do a lot of the work, they are seen as expensive. For example, whereas young girls must have saris, young boys can make do with a loincloth. Throughout girls' lives,

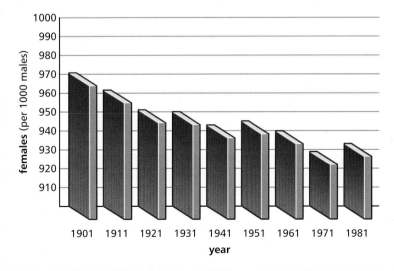

■ **21.13** Male : female birth ratios in India

there are ceremonies which must be undertaken with as much ostentation as possible. First, there is the ear-piercing ceremony, for which a ritual feast must be provided by the family. Then there is the coming-of-age ceremony, again requiring lavish supplies of food. Eventually, there is the marriage ceremony which is potentially the most financially crippling of all (**21.14**). When women are married in India, tradition demands that they supply a dowry. This can be worth up to 15 times the annual income of the family and often leads to borrowing and lifelong debt. If a family cannot supply sufficient dowry, the woman may suffer the ultimate social stigma and remain single. Sometimes, young females commit suicide to avoid being a financial burden on their parents. Although dowries were made illegal in the 1960s, they are still demanded and are becoming more lavish. There is said to be 'dowry inflation' in India. They remain so important that they are a principal means of wealth transfer in the country.

For example, in the village of Pilana, western Uttar Pradesh (north of Delhi), Ram Pal Tyagi's daughter was married in early 1993. Her dowry consisted of a moped, a fridge, a television, a double bed, a sofa set, an iron safe, clothing, household utensils, cash, gold and ornaments. Her father, 'a man of average means', is a sugarcane farmer.

The average rural Indian family, therefore, feels that to raise a girl is 'to water a neighbour's land'. One result of this is that in certain rural areas, female children are killed soon after they are born. Often the first female child survives, but poor families think seriously about keeping a second since she could lead to bankruptcy later on. The traditional approach

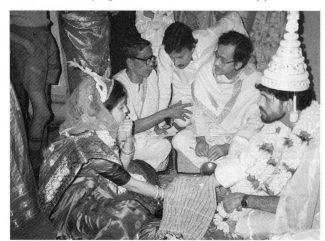

■ **21.14** A lavish Indian wedding ceremony

to this is for the mother-in-law to administer some sort of poison in the child's milk. One reason for the imbalance, therefore, is the extreme one of infanticide. It is estimated that four in ten girls are killed at birth in some rural areas of India.

Since girls are seen as far less valuable in the long run, they are often less well nourished than boys and when they fall ill, a poor family may not seek expensive medical advice for them whereas a boy will usually be well looked after. For example, out of ten young children in an intensive care unit in a village in south-west India in 1993, nine were boys. This constitutes another reason for the population imbalance. Female infant mortality rates are higher than amongst their male counterparts.

It is now possible to determine the sex of a foetus after about 12 weeks of pregnancy, using techniques originally developed to detect foetal abnormalities. For example, ultrasound scanning equipment, relatively cheap and portable, was widely used throughout India to determine the sex of unborn children. Another technique, amniocentesis, a chemical test which was equally easily portable, was also used for this purpose. The application of these techniques to sex determination is now illegal, because the discovery that a foetus is female could be as good as a death warrant. Women whose unborn child was 'diagnosed' as female often decided on an abortion. The high cost was offset by the very high perceived cost of bringing up a girl. As many as 3000 female foetuses were aborted every day in India.

Hinduism, the religion of large areas of India, determines that a son must look after the soul of his parents. He is the guarantee that they will reach Nirvana by lighting their funeral pyre. Boys are highly valued, not only for their low cost, their earning power through dowries and the social kudos they convey, but also for such religious reasons. The pressures on families to produce boys are, therefore, huge.

Several methods have been tried in order to redress the current situation, which had led to a 'shortfall' of 25 million women in India by 1993. As stated above, dowries are illegal. It is also illegal to kill female children, but neither measure is always effectively policed in such a vast country with so many remote corners. Where local campaigners, such as strong chiefs of police or the emergent women's groups, do take a strong line and education is brought in as a weapon against female infanticide, incidents are fewer. A second line is to raise the value and earning power of women and girls. Educating them to produce craft items for world sale, and to organise on a cooperative basis, is one way to achieve this.

A third way is to 'bribe' the families not to kill their female children. A goat used to provide a suitable bribe. However, by 1990, with the spread of knowledge about consumer goods, partly by satellite TV which now reaches most corners of India, this was no longer the case. A survey by the Indian Market Research Bureau showed that 77 per cent of the 800 or so villages surveyed received television transmissions, and that these were an important influence on consumer trends. At least 60 per cent of the villages, for example, had shops which sold soap, detergent and batteries. Toothpaste is now used almost as frequently as the traditional Indian method of using a twig from the neem tree. This makes people demand more modern goods, and bribery is now being priced out of the options.

A fourth way is proving fairly successful in some rural areas: this is to leave cots outside the local health centre. Female children who would otherwise have been killed are left there in the knowledge that they will be taken into care in orphanages.

If all of this sounds difficult to believe, similar problems, including infanticide, exist in other countries (**21.15**). It should also be remembered how important it is to many people in Britain to produce a male heir. Just take a look at the local shops: how many examples of 'J. Smith *and Daughters*' can you find? **21.16** helps to put some of this case into perspective.

Postscript

It is by no means all of India that has the problems mentioned in this case study. Some states have taken strong measures to combat the problems. Kerala, in south-west India, has achieved a considerably better overall position for women; although the dowry system still exists there, some of the wealth has been created by men working in the Gulf and sending money home. **21.16** shows some of the comparisons between Kerala, India and other countries, including low-income countries (LICs). The Kerala government has addressed the problems of women, but many of the underlying prejudices still remain. Nevertheless, a more educated female population must, in the end, lead to the closing

GIRLHOOD: A PERILOUS PATH

PREBIRTH
Tests that tell the gender of a foetus are used by parents in India and China to abort unwanted females. Of 8000 foetuses aborted in a Bombay clinic during the late 1980s, only one was male.

BIRTH
An unwanted girl baby may be killed at birth or allowed to die when she falls ill. In parts of Hunan Province, China, 60 per cent more girls die than boys.

INFANCY
Girls are biologically more resilient than boys but shorter breastfeeding and less health care threaten girls' survival chances. In Jordan 100 girl infants die for every 85 boy deaths.

EARLY CHILDHOOD (1–5 years)
Less food and care for girls leads to illness and stunted growth. Girls in Tunisia are twice as likely as boys to die of diarrhoeal infection.

CHILDHOOD (6–12 years)
Child labour and domestic duties rob girls of childhood and disrupt their education. Girls as young as eight commonly go into domestic service in Nepal and Bangladesh.

ADOLESCENCE
Girls who are unschooled and an economic burden are married off at an early age, by arrangement and sometimes for cash. Half the girls in Bahrain are married by the age of 15.

TEENAGE MOTHERHOOD
Babies born to girls younger than 18 are often born too early, are too small, and cause extra health risks to their mothers. A quarter of the 500 000 women who die in childbirth annually are teenage girls.

■ **21.15** It's not just India

of the huge gaps between the control that men and women each have over their lives, and those of their children.

Although a Muslim country, many of the observations made in this case study about birth control and attitudes to girls also hold true for Bangladesh.

■ **21.16** The Indian situation in context

10 a List the pressures that lead to female infanticide in India.
b List the remedies that have been tried so far.
c How would you suggest overcoming the problem? Is there anything that the richer countries could do to help?

LIFE AND HEALTH

People in Kerala live longer – thanks to better nutrition and state health-care provision. Far fewer children die before they reach 12 months of age.

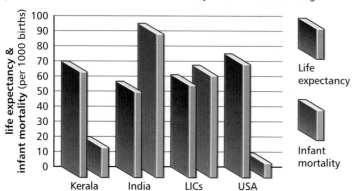

● Fair-price shops and ration cards ensure that two-thirds of the subsidised basic foods go to the poorest 30 per cent – and 99 per cent of Kerala's villages have a fair-price shop within 2 km.

WOMEN AND SOCIETY

The position of women is generally better than in other parts of India or other low-income countries, because they are better educated and have fewer children.

● 94 per cent of primary-age girls and 99 per cent of primary-age boys are in school.
● There are more females than males enrolled in arts and sciences pre-degree, degree and graduate courses – a total of 82 538 women and 73 516 men in 1990–91.

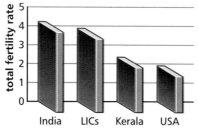

QUALITY AND ECONOMY

Kerala's quality of life is comparatively high.

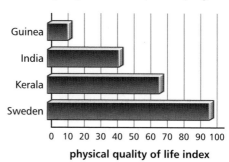

But in conventional economic terms it is a poor state – lagging behind the rest of India.

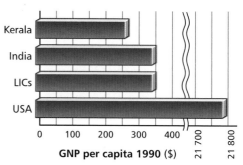

● Kerala manages to maintain high consumption and low productivity thanks to remittances from workers in the Gulf which are equal to 20–25 per cent of the state domestic product. Only 2 per cent of this is invested in commercial ventures. Most of it is spent on land, houses, cars or jewellery.

21.5 **Death rates**

IT5 Just as crude birth rates have been shown to be a poor measure of fertility, so crude death rates (the number of deaths per 1000 people) are a poor measure of mortality, even though they are frequently used. **21.17** is a world map of crude death rates for 1980–85. The map shows a poor correlation between level of development and crude death rate. This is partly explained, as was **IT5**

deaths per 1000 persons

- 17
- 14
- 11 global average
- 8

■ **21.17** World crude death rates by region, 1980–85 [IT5]

Rich countries	15
Middle-income countries	25
Poor countries	129

■ **21.18** Infant mortality rates per 1000 live births

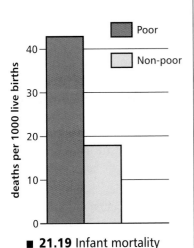

■ **21.19** Infant mortality rates in Porto Alegre, Brazil, 1980

the case with birth rates, by population structure. A preponderance of young people, for example in Central America, will almost inevitably lead to lower mortality figures as measured by crude death rates. But this does not necessarily mean, because it shows relatively high crude death rates, that the society is healthy any more than the society with a preponderance of old people is unhealthy. Access to health care is also a most important determinant of death rate.

Another measure is life expectancy at birth. This relates better to the level of development of a country: those with life expectancy currently over 75 years include Japan, the UK, the USA and Canada, France and Australia. Life expectancy in all of those countries is also increasing (see Chapter 24). In countries such as Zaire, Benin, Peru and India, however, the figure is less than 50 years.

Infant mortality rates are another means of measuring the effect of mortality on the population balance in a country. **21.18** shows that the figures vary enormously and that they do so partly as a result of the economic status of the area.

It is tempting to think that a high infant mortality rate is a blessing in disguise, keeping population totals low. However, try projecting it on your own

family. The loss of a child is a devastating event. It is also a fact that, while death rates remain high, family size is maintained at a high level to ensure that there are children to look after parents in their old age. Only when death rates, and infant mortality rates in particular, decline does the birth rate also decline. [IT5]

11 a Describe the pattern of distribution of crude death rates shown by **21.18**.

b To what extent does there appear to be a correlation between level of development and crude death rate?

12 a What is the link between individual wealth and infant mortality as shown in **21.19**?

b How does this information affect your answer to activity 11b?

However they are measured, death rates are seen to change over time. In many areas of the world they have been declining as medical advances have been made or introduced and as [IT5]

Year	IMR	Year	IMR
1541	194	1761	191
1546	203	1766	185
1551	166	1771	181
1556	216	1776	165
1561	240	1781	187
1566	166	1786	179
1571	164	1791	170
1576	152	1796	174
1581	144	1801	179
1586	164	1806	162
1591	182	1811	168
1596	168	1816	167
1601	165	1821	158
1606	149	1826	154
1611	170	1831	149
1616	173	1836	153
1621	154	1841	152
1626	192	1846	156
1631	161	1851	156
1636	178	1856	151
1641	194	1861	147
1646	163	1866	152
1651	167	1871	153
1656	191	1876	144
1661	180	1881	139
1666	209	1886	145
1671	198	1891	151
1676	176	1896	156
1681	234	1901	138
1686	208	1906	117
1691	186	1911	110
1696	191	1916	91
1701	171	1921	76
1706	176	1926	68
1711	179	1931	62
1716	172	1936	56
1721	203	1941	50
1726	203	1946	36
1731	239	1951	27
1736	181	1956	23
1741	209	1961	21
1746	183	1966	18
1751	175	1971	17
1756	170	1976	13

■ **21.20** Estimated infant mortality rates (IMR) for England, 1541–1976 (per 1000 live births)

diets and public health have improved. A good example is shown by infant mortality rates for England (**21.20**).

Long-term trends may be interrupted by unnatural events. At times of famine, for example, it is usually the most vulnerable, the young and the old, who die first. Wars tend to be selective of males of fighting age, though it is estimated that 150000 children aged under 16 were either killed or disappeared in the war in Bosnia up to mid-1993. Disasters, either natural or caused by people, can have a major influence on the annual death rate.

Date	UK	India	Japan	New Zealand	Netherlands
1971–75	11.8	15.5	6.4	8.4	8.3
1976–80	11.9	13.8	6.1	8.2	8.1
1981–85	11.7	n.d.	6.1	8.1	8.3
1987	11.3	10.8	6.2	8.4	8.3
1988	11.4	11.0	6.5	8.3	8.4
1989	11.5	10.2	6.4	8.2	8.7
1990	11.3	n.d.	6.7	7.9	8.6

■ **21.21** Death rates (per 1000 people) in selected countries

13 a Draw a graph of 20-year moving means (the mean of data for five consecutive figures) to illustrate the data in **21.20**.
  b Describe what your graph shows.

14 a Describe the trends in crude death rates in the UK and India (**21.21**).
  b Why should the trends differ? [Think in terms of population structure.]
  c Using evidence from **21.21**, what differences would you suggest exist between developed and less developed countries?

15 Using a source such as *The Guinness Book of Records*, list the 15 largest world disasters you can find. Which of these was 'natural', and which the result of human action (or perhaps inaction)? Which would most easily be avoided in the future?

21.6 **Demographic transition**

Both birth and death rates change over time, as indicated above. Observations of the ways in which these changes relate to one another have led to the generation of a model, known as the **demographic transition model** (**21.22**). The changing relationship between births and deaths is portrayed as proceeding through four stages.

1 The high stationary stage – fertility and mortality levels are high and subject to short-term fluctuations. Deaths due to natural checks such as famine, disease and war are the most significant influence on population growth, which tends to be relatively small. The stage is associated with the largely undeveloped societies relying on primitive technology and minimal subsistence.

2 The early expanding stage – population begins to grow at an accelerating rate as a result of the birth rate being sustained at a high level and of the death rate falling quite dramatically in response to the introduction of modern medicine, better diet and more sanitary living

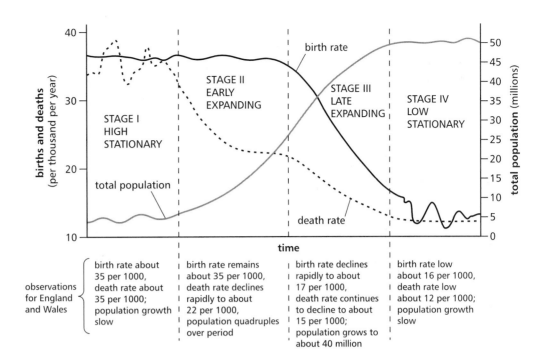

| observations for England and Wales | birth rate about 35 per 1000, death rate about 35 per 1000; population growth slow | birth rate remains about 35 per 1000, death rate declines rapidly to about 22 per 1000, population quadruples over period | birth rate declines rapidly to about 17 per 1000, death rate continues to decline to about 15 per 1000; population grows to about 40 million | birth rate low about 16 per 1000, death rate low about 12 per 1000; population growth slow |

Year	Birth rate per 1000	Death rate per 1000	Total population millions
1700	36.0	30.5	4.8
1710	33.0	31.0	5.0
1720	35.5	34.0	5.0
1730	36.0	38.0	5.0
1740	38.0	36.0	5.0
1750	39.0	30.5	5.1
1760	36.5	30.0	5.5
1770	38.0	30.5	6.2
1780	38.0	29.0	6.4
1790	40.0	26.0	7.0
1790	40.0	26.0	7.0
1800	38.5	22.0	9.0
1810	37.0	20.5	10.0
1820	36.0	20.5	12.0
1830	35.0	21.0	13.0
1840	31.0	20.0	15.5
1850	32.5	22.5	17.5
1860	34.0	22.5	20.0
1870	34.5	22.0	22.0
1880	33.0	20.0	26.0
1890	30.5	18.5	29.5
1900	28.0	17.0	32.5
1910	25.0	14.5	36.0
1920	20.0	12.5	37.0
1930	17.0	12.0	40.0
1940	14.5	13.0	41.5
1950	16.0	11.0	44.0
1960	17.5	11.5	46.0
1970	16.5	11.0	48.5
1980	14.0	12.0	49.5
1990	14.0	11.0	50.5

■ **21.23** Demographic change in England and Wales, 1770–1990

IT8

conditions. During this phase, economic developments might include the emergence of commercial agriculture and the initiation of industrialisation.

3 The late expanding stage – the rate of population growth begins to slacken as the death rate stabilises and the birth rate declines (traditions and taboos weaken and more people practise birth control). During this stage, society becomes significantly industrialised and urbanised.

4 The low stationary stage – this occurs when both fertility and mortality levels are low, but with the birth rate more prone to fluctuate. Population growth is minimal, if there is any at all. Society at this stage enjoys considerable economic wealth and a high standard of living.

The rate of demographic change varies from country to country. The length of time it took for the cycle to occur in England and Wales (**21.23**) is not necessarily reflected in other countries. Even in Europe, the transition process started at different dates. Whereas nearly all European countries are now in stage 4, England and Wales entered stage 3 around 1870, France around 1840 and Denmark around 1920. Less developed countries often had health improvements introduced from elsewhere suddenly, so that death rates began to decline very rapidly from that time and the whole transition process was foreshortened.

The demographic transition model is a generalisation based on observation. Particular countries can be expected to deviate from the pattern suggested in the scheme, perhaps missing out stages altogether. The model describes what has occurred so far in the history of demographic change. It is sometimes used to predict the likely demand for resources in a country in the future. However, it finishes at stage 4. The preceding work should suggest that different patterns could occur in the future, for instance in the more developed countries where death rates may now start rising as a function of population structure.

16 a Data for England and Wales from 1700 to 1990 are given in **21.23**. Use the data to construct a graph to show how the two rates and the total population changed over the period.

b Look at **21.22** which has been constructed from observations such as those of the population changes for England and Wales. Look at the graph you have constructed in **a** and draw the boundaries of the four stages as shown in the model. Label the stages carefully on your drawing.

21.7 **The UN Population Conference, 1994**

In September 1994, a major population conference was convened in Cairo. Held every 10 years, the UN conferences take stock of the current situation and attempt to reach a consensus about population policy for the future. The 1994 conference raised heated debate about family planning, especially pitching the Vatican and certain Muslim nations against the others. In the end, consensus was reached, even though no population targets were set either for the world or for individual countries. However, the developing nations showed their determination to reduce the average number of children per couple. Amongst the most forward-looking of the delegations was the one from Iran which stressed 'the empowerment of women, socially and politically' and greater access to family planning in the country. It also stressed that its comprehensive programme, which includes use of the pill, condoms, sterilisation and abortion laws, owed very little to imported ideas from the developed nations and much more to decisions made within the country to suit local conditions. It seemed that much of the running on world population control was being made by the developing nations, and that the revised UN estimate of a global population growth rate of 1.59% compared with 1.72% in 1992 owed a lot to progress in these countries.

22.1 **What is mobility?**

Migration is one of the mechanisms by which population change occurs. It may lead to the redistribution of population within an area, but may equally lead to a net outflow or inflow of people. It may serve to magnify changes that are already occurring in the natural population balance (births minus deaths) or it may help to redress that balance. This situation is expressed by the equation:

$$PC = NI + NM \text{ or } (B - D) + NM$$

where PC = population change
NI = natural increase
NM = net migration
$(B - D)$ = births minus deaths

Migration is the term used to describe the movement of people from one place to another who then take up residence in that new administrative area. As such, it is distinct from **circulation** which describes short-term and reciprocal movement, such as commuting, pastoral nomadism or holiday-making. Migration and circulation are both types of **mobility**.

There are various other ways to classify mobility. The criteria upon which mobility may be subdivided include the distance over which the movement takes place, whether it is national or international, whether it is forced or voluntary, and whether it involves large numbers of people or individuals. One attempted classification is shown in **22.1**.

■ **22.1** A classification of mobility

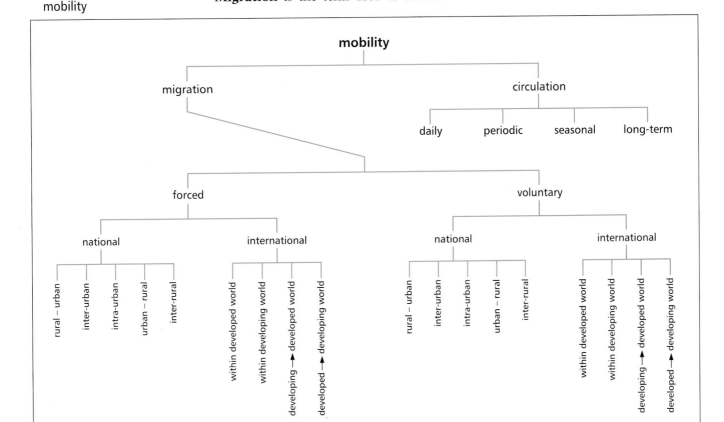

■ **22.2** Examples of mobility

1 a Use the information in **22.2** to write examples against the categories identified in **22.1**.

b For the categories which still have no examples, research the media (including television and newspapers) to complete the picture.

c Were there any examples which could have fitted more than one category? If so, explain how you resolved the situation. In either case, suggest how the classification could be improved.

2 Using the classification in **22.1**, attempt to list the factors which might lead to a person moving from one place to another. Place these factors in two columns, one headed 'Repelling from home area' and the other headed 'Attracting to another area'.

The factors identified in the answer to activity 2 are better known as **push** and **pull factors**. The former are those tending to repel people from their home area and the latter – pull factors – are those tending to attract them to another place. The way these factors influence migration is suggested in **22.3**.

As can be seen, factors may encourage an individual to leave the original area (A). These could include lack of work, poor living conditions, lack of promotion potential, hazards, or hunger. In the distance may be a goal (C) where each of these conditions is either known or perceived to be better. These factors therefore become pull factors. The two sets acting together may initiate a move. Even one set by itself could cause migration to occur, as in the case of someone who is doing quite well in a job, has a nice home, but still thinks a move somewhere else would lead to a better standard of living. Between A and C might involve covering a great distance (for example, migration from Britain to Australia in the 1950s), rugged relief (the Rockies on the trail west from the developed

IT2

a) Boarding the Japanese bullet train

b) Kurdish refugees

c) Turkish workers arriving in Munich

d) Camp for Ethiopian refugees

e) Enjoying a day on the beach

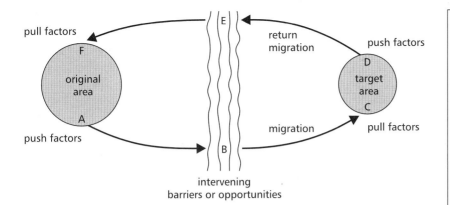

■ **22.3** Push–pull model of migration

IT2 USA to developing California in the early 19th century) or difficult climate (movement from south-west to south-east Australia before the railway was built). Consideration of these obstacles may deter migration. Alternatively, there may be intervening opportunities (B) on the migration route. Economic migrants from the developing world frequently end up in a place other than that to which they were heading. If they find work in an intervening place, they will make the best of it and stay. Exactly the same reasoning may later apply to a return migration from D to F.

Lee (1966) has modified the model of migration to take into account the fact that the start of the cycle and the target region have both push and pull factors associated with them (**22.4**).

■ **22.4** Lee's model of migration

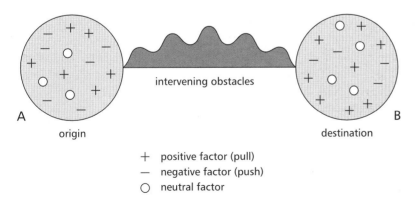

+ positive factor (pull)
— negative factor (push)
○ neutral factor

3 a What do you understand by the term 'neutral factor' in Lee's model? [Remember that the decision to move is often an individual one.]

b Why, in the case illustrated by Lee's model, might an individual tend to leave A for B?

4 a Push and pull factors fall into four main groups: physical, economic, social and political. Make a copy of the table below, and place two different items from the following list in each of these categories:

■ Freedom of speech
■ Poverty
■ Harsh climate
■ Fertile soils
■ Heavy taxes
■ Promotion
■ Good wages
■ Marriage
■ Political asylum
■ Persecution
■ Discrimination
■ Bereavement
■ Planning decision
■ Natural disaster
■ Attractive climate
■ Relatives and friends

	Push	**Pull**
Physical		
Economic		
Social		
Political		

b Try to add further examples of your own to the table to complete a thorough classification of push and pull factors.

22.2 **Explaining migration**

It is possible to generalise about migration movements even though, as suggested above, they are usually the result of individual decisions. This is because many of the factors which influence an individual are also at work on other people. For example, political unrest in an area will quickly lead to the movement of large numbers of people, each making a similar decision in light of the circumstances.

The basic laws of migration were suggested by E. G. Ravenstein in the late-19th century. Within his analysis of migration, he said that:

- most migrants travel short distances and with increasing distance the numbers of migrants decrease
- most migration movements produce a compensating counter-movement
- migration occurs in stages and with a wave-like motion
- the major direction of migration is from agricultural areas to centres of industry and commerce
- large towns grow more by migration than by natural increase
- migration increases in volume as industries and commerce develop and transport improves
- most migrants are adults, and families rarely migrate out of their country of birth
- women are more migratory than men within their country of birth, but men more frequently venture beyond it, and town dwellers are less migratory than country dwellers.

In succeeding years, these laws have been modified in the light of observation and changing circumstances, but they laid an important framework for the study of the subject. Two of the laws in particular may need some revision. The first of these is the one explaining volume of movement. Ravenstein argued that areas which were close to a migration magnet were likely to generate more migrants than those that were further away. As with many generalisations in geography, this is an example of **distance–decay**. The law was modified somewhat by Zipf (1946) who formulated the inverse distance law:

$$M_{ij} = 1/d_{ij}$$

where M_{ij} is the number of migrants moving between places i and j and d_{ij} is the distance between them. A graphical idea of what this formula describes is shown in **22.5**.

The curve shows a negative exponential relationship in that the further the distance from the goal of migration, the fewer the migrants, who decrease at a decreasing rate with distance. Zipf's model did not take into account the sizes of the original populations involved and if this is included, the **gravity model** results:

$$M_{ij} = p_i, p_j/d_{ij}^2$$

where M_{ij} = volume of migration between i and j
p_i = population of place i
p_j = population of place j
d_{ij} = distance between them.

The second of Ravenstein's laws which needs some further exploration is the one that states that migration occurs in stages and with a wave-like motion. What he meant was that migration tends to take place from one level of the urban hierarchy to the next and the vacuum left tends to draw in people from further down the hierarchy. The migration may be progressive, or an individual may decide to settle after a single move if the opportunities are great enough (**22.6**). This phenomenon is know as **stepwise** or **staged migration**.

The processes shown in **22.6** have been noted widely, but the explanation of them has been progressively modified. In 1960, Stouffer suggested that it was not just the size of the settlement and intervening distance which were at work in creating staged migration. The perceived opportunities at the two places involved (e.g. A and B in **22.6**) and in the journey between them were said by

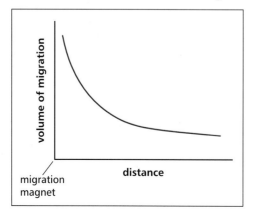

■ **22.5** Zipf's distance–decay relationship

■ **22.6** Stepwise or staged migration

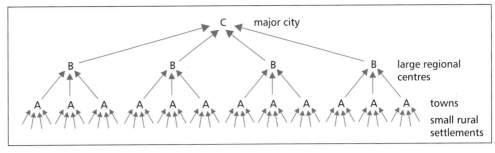

■ **22.7** Population pyramid for migrants to Kuwait, 1980

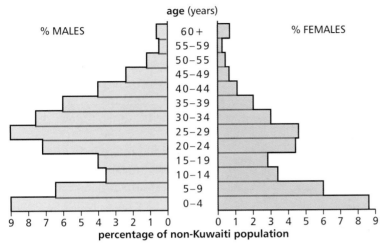

Estimated population represented in diagram – 830 000

Stouffer to be more important influences than size and distance. The idea of **intervening opportunities** introduces into Ravenstein's model a restraining influence, a friction, which may lead to lower than expected movements between places at different stages in the hierarchy, because people have found what they were looking for in between.

22.3 **Who migrates?**

The last three items in the list of Ravenstein's laws of migration suggest that it is only certain elements of the community who tend to move. **22.7** is a population pyramid for the migrants to Kuwait in 1980, well before the Gulf War. The migrant population represented in the diagram was 830000 out of a total population of 1372000. The immigrant workers were largely Pakistani, Palestinian and Lebanese. The pyramid clearly shows that it is the males of working age who form the majority of the migrants, to be joined later by their wives and only at a much later stage by older relatives, by which time children may also have been born to them. This imbalance of age and sex groups at the receiving end is also reflected at the places from which the migrants have come. Villages in India are often very short of manpower as the active 15–30 year olds have moved to the cities to seek their fortune or improve their lot.

5 The age–sex structures of the capital of Peru, Lima, and of one of the poor departments in the Peruvian Sierra from which people migrate to the capital, are shown in **22.8**.
  a Describe the main differences in the age–sex structures of the two areas.
  b Account for the differences you have described.

6 a With reference to **22.9**, comment on the education levels **i** in Apurimac **ii** in Lima **iii** of the migrants to Lima from Apurimac.
  b To what extent does this example support the idea that areas from which migration takes place are impoverished by the people they lose?

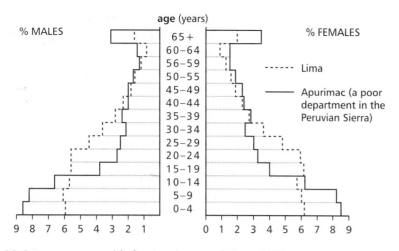

% MALES   age (years)   % FEMALES

- - - - Lima

——— Apurimac (a poor department in the Peruvian Sierra)

■ **22.8** Age–sex pyramids for Apurimac and Lima, 1981

Level of education reached	Education levels of total population (%)		Education levels of migrants to Lima from Apurimac (%)
	Apurimac	Lima	
No formal education	48.7	3.4	9.1
Primary	38.1	32.6	46.9
Secondary	10.4	45.0	34.3
Further education	2.7	16.9	6.0
Unknown	0.1	2.1	3.7

■ **22.9** Peru – levels of education of people 15 years or over, 1981

This phenomenon has placed strains at both ends of the migration path and governments have had to try to cope with it. At the receiving end, hostels have sometimes been built to house the single-sex migrants (as in South Africa or Germany – see page 290). Unfortunately, word of this accommodation soon spreads back to the rural area from which the migrants often come and the problem is exacerbated. The best way to stem the migration, particularly if it is draining the villages of manpower, is to improve the situation in those villages. This means not only improving housing and services, but also encouraging useful and meaningful work. There is often a pool of very highly skilled labour in rural communities and if it is given an outlet, it will flower into just the sort of enterprise that can act as an overriding pull factor. In India, for example, the Community Development Programme has been encouraging local weaving skills, woodworking and pottery industries, and providing new ideas and equipment to bolster local carpentry and blacksmithing skills. Villages have begun to produce a surplus of manufactured goods which are then sold via cooperatives or on the world market by such organisations as Traidcraft. Similar rural development programmes are under way in Brazil, Nigeria, Malaysia and Romania. Along with other former communist East European countries, Romania is beginning to suffer from greater mobility because expectations have been raised and political objections to movement have been dropped.

22.4 Organising migration

Up to this point, emphasis has been put on the decision of the individual to migrate. One of the ways that decisions are made easier, or even forced, is by government policy. The ways in which this policy may be organised are shown in **22.10**. Such policies may lead to very large-scale movements of population, or the almost total absence of movement.

---

7 Look at the photo-montage (**22.11**). You may recognise some of the people shown, but even if you don't, you will be able to do the activity. All the people shown are UK citizens.
   a List the ways in which ethnic minorities have influenced the life of Britain.
   b In what ways does the fact that Britain is a jigsaw of many racial and cultural groups affect the variety of experiences available in the country?
   c In your opinion, is this a good or a bad thing?

Type	Example
Political restraint	The Berlin Wall – built to stop those who had become disillusioned with the communist system in East Berlin from crossing to the West
Political encouragement	The settling of eastern Finland in the 1960s to ensure that the USSR could not easily legitimise any invasion
Economic dissuasion	The tax incentives that were offered by the British government and the EC to keep people and employment in the peripheral areas, e.g. the Highlands and Islands of Scotland
Forced movement for economic reasons	Asians in Idi Amin's Uganda – the Asians who ran many of the economic enterprises in Uganda had their property confiscated and pressure was put on them to emigrate; eventually, after resistance, they were expelled
Forced movement for political reasons	Palestinians were expelled from the Occupied West Bank territories in Israel in 1992 in response to violent activities against the occupying Israelis
Economic encouragement	European immigration to Australia in the 1950s through the Assisted Passage Scheme

■ **22.10** Government influences on migration

■ **22.11** Some British citizens

22.5 **Racial diversity – benefits to society**

IT7

The UK has a rich cultural heritage. The islands have been subject to invasions from Romans, Saxons, Vikings and Normans and in more recent times a refuge for Poles, Bangladeshis and East African Asians, amongst others. The early invasions were so long ago that the net result of the intermixing of the groups and their descendents came to be called the 'British race'. The later influxes occurred so recently that there has not yet been a full assimilation. Each of the groups, however, has greatly influenced the life of the nation.

Despite the enrichment of the life of the country (artistic, theatrical, sporting, commercial, administrative and industrial, for example) brought about by immigrants, resentment and even anger can be directed at such groups by those who see themselves as 'long-standing' citizens. Such behaviour is called **racism**. It is often directed at easily identifiable groups, especially Black people. Racist behaviour unfortunately seems to be an expression of individuals' basic desires to defend their territory, a normal piece of biological behaviour, but one which could be described as being at the 'animal' level. Easily identifiable threats to that territory, whether they are local and

IT7

personal (for example, at the street level) or perceived at a larger scale (the country at large) can therefore be targets for individual anger. This in itself can cause tension in a community, but real problems arise when groups of similarly-minded people get together and organise their racist behaviour on a larger scale. Out of such processes are born movements such as the British National Party, demanding 'Britain for the British', the similar Front Nationale in France and the neo-Nazis in Germany and South Africa.

Although it has been described as the reaction to a basic biological drive, racism is nevertheless on the level of unin-

formed, animal behaviour and is not to be excused by the fact that it is a 'gut reaction'. When the facts are twisted to support a particular belief, bigoted behaviour follows. Everything is then seen in the light of that belief. Racism holds that immigrants (however long-standing they might be) are a threat to the well-being of the nation (**22.12**). They may, therefore, be encouraged, by one means or another, to leave. The fact that many of the targeted groups have as much right to live in that country as the person propounding the theory is neatly forgotten. If a person holds a British passport, for example, was born and registered in Britain or has been officially given British citizenship, then he or she is legally British. The length of time this qualification has been held makes no difference in the eyes of the law. One of the responses of the immigrant communities has been to raise the general awareness of their cultural and commercial achievements (**22.13**). Racism, of course, is by no means a solely British phenomenon. It may be found wherever there are large communities of people of different cultural backgrounds.

■ **22.12** A British National Party march in London

■ **22.13** Mural on a wall in Reading

Racism in Germany in the 1990s

In 1990, Germany was re-unified after the division into East (communist) and West (democratic) Germany at the end of the Second World War in 1945 (**22.14**). Prior to re-unification and following the Second World War, West Germany performed an 'economic miracle'. It was at this point the strongest economy in Europe, leading the way in many branches of industry and technology. Its products, from modern and efficient factories, were exported all over the world and its currency, the Deutschmark, was one of the few currencies against which the strength of other currencies was compared. East Germany, on the other hand, had suffered nearly half a century of economic stagnation and structural decay. Upon re-unification, the powerful West

■ **22.14** The division of Germany before unification in 1990

German economy was expected to support development in the East. The modernisation of factories, rebuilding of cities and development of infrastructure were all extremely expensive and led to dissatisfaction in the West because resources were seen to be diverted to other areas and the standard of living did not increase at the rate to which West Germans had become accustomed. In the East, improvements were nowhere near as fast as the people had convinced themselves they would be. The result was a very dissatisfied nation. In the wake of this, in 1992, there was serious racial conflict in several cities, one of which was Rostock (**22.15**).

Germany has long had a policy of encouraging guest workers into the country. In the West, the largest group consists of Turks who generally live in large hostels within urban areas and work at major industrial complexes such as Volkswagen in Wolfsburg. In the East, many Vietnamese were encouraged to live and work in the cities. Vietnam, a fellow Communist state when the policy was put in place, provided workers as a mirror to what was happening in the West. The Vietnamese were innocent people caught up in the Rostock violence (**22.15**). The Romanians were refugees from the corrupt, economically bankrupt Communist regime in that country. Romanian gypsies had been persecuted in the Second World War, when they were one of the targets for Hitler's concentration camps. They became one of the weakest groups in the post-war Communist state, so when the chance came for them to escape to a friendly state which promised a better life, they did just that. West Germany, as a reaction perhaps to the worst excesses of racism in the Second World War, had very liberal immigration and asylum rules in its Constitution up to 1992. These rules had been exploited by up to a quarter of a million people per year, but when economic difficulties presented themselves, the new arrivals became the focus of blame for the problems.

Celebration at 'festival' lit by fires of racism

John Eisenhammer writes from Rostock about the East German families who went shopping by day and cheered attacks against foreigners by night

Even the sea breeze cannot blow away the sharp smell of charred walls and stairs. Nor the cloying scents of frustration, embarrassment and hatred still hanging in the air. Look to one side, as you stand on the grassed area in front of the massive blocks of council flats where the refugee hostel is, and you'll see families laughing as they return from shopping or work. Look to the other side and you see the blistered, blackened vestiges of a xenophobic orgy.

It is like day and night. By day, since Saturday, those same families with children and food would gather before Block 18 on the estate, eager to see the latest goings-on around the hostel. And by night they clapped and cheered as youths tanked up with beer began their assaults on the terrified foreigners inside with rocks, fire and smoke-bombs. It was like a Volksfest, a popular festival. But it resounded to the cheer of Germany for the Germans, illuminated by the fires of racism.

For four nights hundreds of police and special riot units tried to contain what has been the worst explosion of violence against foreigners since unification. The local police chief, Siegfried Cordus, said he had never seen such viciousness and brutality. 'People clapped at every stone which hit a policeman,' said a bystander. Lothar Kupfer, Interior Minister of the state of Mecklenburg, in which Rostock lies, spoke of a 'civil war'.

In the end, for all the water-cannon, tear gas and truncheons, the police lost. Late on Monday night they withdrew, apparently to regroup or change shifts, leaving the hostel at the mercy of the hooligans. Some were just kids, most from the estate and Rostock, reinforced by neo-Nazis from far and wide, hardened by street battles. They were well organised with petrol containers in nearby bushes from which they filled up beer cans, once drunk, to make fire bombs. The crowd of onlookers, some 3,000 strong, bigger than on either of the previous four nights of rioting, egged them on. Once inside the building the youths smashed everything on two floors. A few jagged bits of porcelain are all that is left of the toilet. Water drips everywhere from broken pipes.

The hostel was destroyed despite the fact that, in desperation, the authorities had evacuated all the 200 residents, mainly Romanian gypsies, on Monday afternoon, busing them to temporary hostels in other towns. But there were about 100 Vietnamese families with children in the adjoining block. Not refugees, but still living and working in Rostock since their guest-worker days under the Communists. Terrified, they barricaded themselves in their flats as flames leapt from the windows nearby. For well over an hour the fire service looked on from afar, terrified by the rioters. The police were still re-grouping. Finally the Vietnamese were slipped to safety over the roof. The fires still burnt.

'And the fires will continue burning wherever they take these so-called asylum-seekers. People here are fed up,' says Dietmar, gesticulating wildly. He is one of the small groups that continually forms in front of the scarred building. 'It was disgusting, the way they sat around here, rubbish everywhere,' say 15-year-old Alex. 'The city dump is paradise compared to this shit heap. They had to be got rid of.'

The hostel which served as the refugee distribution centre for the entire state of Mecklenburg, is situated in the heart of the massive Lichtenhagen housing estate, a desolate Communist-built concrete zone which is home to 20,000 people. Real unemployment is around 50 per cent, since the harbour and the shipyards, the city's mainstay, barely function. The disillusionment and frustration, the anger of the bored youth groups that have sprung up everywhere, found an easy target in the foreigners' hostel. 'They get housing while we cannot find any; they get money for sitting around all day,' says 19-year-old Werner.

The pressure grew as ever more refugees flooded in, Germany's liberal asylum laws powerless to stop them. Over the summer, 80 a day were arriving in Lichtenhagen. Often they could not be distributed quickly enough, so they camped in the open. 'No other country in the world would tolerate this influx. It is unmanageable,' says Heike Buhrow, who works at the hostel. Overall, 46,000 arrived in Germany in July, a new record. The national total this year has already surpassed the 256,000 of 1991. In towns across the country tension is reaching breaking-point.

It broke in Lichtenhagen. 'These were not only neo-fascists at work here. The anger of ordinary people, built up over months, suddenly exploded,' says 65-year-old Franz Bartl.

■ **22.15** Extract from *The Independent*, 26 August 1992

8 Read **22.15** which describes the problems in Rostock in 1992.

  a List the factors as reported in the article which contributed to the attack on the hostel.

  b In your opinion, what was the main contributory factor to the attack? Explain your answer.

  c To what extent do you think that newspaper reports encourage such behaviour?

9 Read 'The Few' by Billy Bragg (**22.16**).

  a Give an example from the German case study of 'the simplicities of bigotry'.

  b In what ways does the poet believe that the country turns a blind eye to racism?

  c How does Billy Bragg think racists twist the evidence to fit their case?

  d 'What do they know of England who only England know?' (a quote from Rudyard Kipling) suggests one possible antidote to racist views. Explain what this might be.

At night the Baby Brotherhood* and the Inter City Crew*
Fill their pockets up with calling cards
And paint their faces red white and blue
Then they go out seeking different coloured faces
And anyone else they can scare
And they salute the foes their fathers fought
By raising their right arms in the air
Oh look out my country's patriots are hunting down below
What do they know of England who only England know?
From the stands of the Empire Stadium
Come the heralds of the New Dark Age
With the simplicities of bigotry
And to whom all the world's a stage
These little John Bullshits know that the press
Will glorify their feats
So that the general public fear them
And the authorities say give 'em all seats
And the wasted seed of the bulldog breed
Is chanting 'ere we go
What do they know of England who only England know?
Our neighbours shake their heads
And take their valuables inside
White my countrymen piss in their fountains
To express our national pride
And to prove to the world that England
Is just as rotten as she looks
They repeat the lies that caught their eyes
At school in history books
But the wars they think they're fighting
Were all over long ago
What do they know of England who only England know?
And the society that spawned them
Just cries out Who's to blame?
And then wraps itself in the Union Jack
And just carries on the same
Oh look out, my country's patriots are hunting down below
What do they know of England who only England know?

From the album *'Don't Try This at Home'*

* The Baby Brotherhood and the Inter City Crew are 'football supporters' who hold strong racist views, and many of their number belong to the British National Party

■ **22.16** 'The Few' by Billy Bragg

10 a Using all the information in this section, attempt to write your own definition of 'racism'.

  b In your opinion, how should racism be confronted? [Think about leadership by well-known figures, groups of people, e.g. 'Rock against Racism', legislation by governments, education, etc.]

CASE STUDY

IT7

Ethnic cleansing in Bosnia–Hercegovina

The area covered by Yugoslavia in 1990 (**22.17**) has been disputed over many years. It includes areas which have been ruled over by the Roman Empire, the Holy Roman Empire, the Ottoman Empire and the Austro-Hungarian Empire. Each of these rulers left its mark on the territory. The result was that, by 1990, Yugoslavia was a mixture of peoples of different

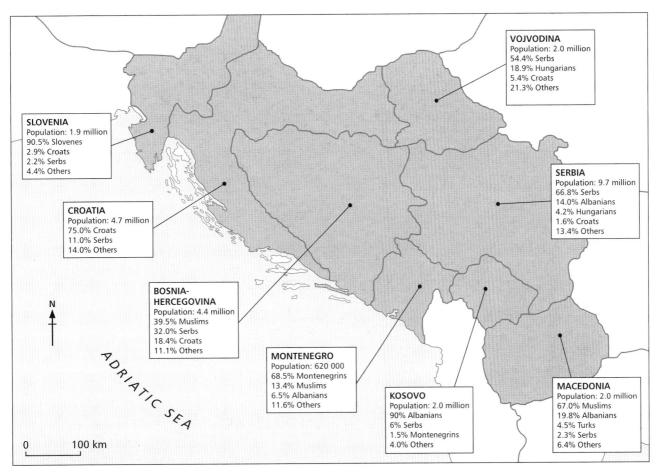

SLOVENIA
Population: 1.9 million
90.5% Slovenes
2.9% Croats
2.2% Serbs
4.4% Others

CROATIA
Population: 4.7 million
75.0% Croats
11.0% Serbs
14.0% Others

BOSNIA-
HERCEGOVINA
Population: 4.4 million
39.5% Muslims
32.0% Serbs
18.4% Croats
11.1% Others

MONTENEGRO
Population: 620 000
68.5% Montenegrins
13.4% Muslims
6.5% Albanians
11.6% Others

KOSOVO
Population: 2.0 million
90% Albanians
6% Serbs
1.5% Montenegrins
4.0% Others

MACEDONIA
Population: 2.0 million
67.0% Muslims
19.8% Albanians
4.5% Turks
2.3% Serbs
6.4% Others

SERBIA
Population: 9.7 million
66.8% Serbs
14.0% Albanians
4.2% Hungarians
1.6% Croats
13.4% Others

VOJVODINA
Population: 2.0 million
54.4% Serbs
18.9% Hungarians
5.4% Croats
21.3% Others

ADRIATIC SEA

N

0   100 km

■ **22.17** The Balkans – the ethnic composition of former Yugoslavia, 1990

ethnic origin. The most ethnically diverse of the constituent states was Bosnia–Hercegovina (**22.17**).

In 1989, Yugoslavia began to fall apart politically. The nation had been created at the end of the Second World War and was held together by a strong militaristic central government, under communist control until 1989. After this date, individual states began to declare their independence and to be recognised as new countries. For example, Croatia, Serbia and Slovenia took part in the 1992 Olympics, while in the same year Yugoslavia was omitted from the football European Nations Cup held in Sweden. This recognition put pressure on Bosnia because, when it declared independence, it knew that there would be problems from its large Serb and Croat populations. The trouble came, in 1992. Although denying their part in it, both the Serbian and Croatian governments attempted to gain territory from the former Bosnian state and, in so doing, to 'cleanse' the territory they took of unwanted ethnic groups –

which in fact meant Muslims. Huge numbers of Muslims were therefore expelled from Bosnia. Nearly one-tenth of the entire population of Yugoslavia had become refugees by August 1992 (**22.18**). By 1994, 18 per cent of Croatia's population were refugees.

The international community put some pressure on Serbia in particular to stop its policy of **ethnic cleansing** and to allow Bosnia–Hercegovina the right to sort out its own future. The United Nations imposed sanctions, which meant that Serbia was denied food supplies, oil and especially arms. A peace conference was called to try to stop the bloody fighting. The problem was that, with so many local pockets of inter-community fighting, the central government had in effect lost control. The war continued with huge loss of life.

The result of the ethnic cleansing policy was that the map of Bosnia–Hercegovina was totally re-drawn. The communities that had lived peacefully together had been set against one another and the result was large gains in 'pure' territory for both Serbia and

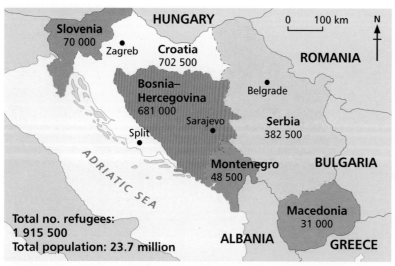

■ **22.18** The number of refugees in the former Yugoslavia in August 1992

■ **22.19** The result of 'ethnic cleansing' by August 1992

Croatia. The Muslims were driven out in huge numbers and the territory left to them was minimal (**22.19**). Ethnic cleansing was said to entail enforced removal from homes, abuse which led to people fleeing and the detention of Muslims in particular in 'concentration camps'. All sorts of horror stories abounded during the conflict, some of them entirely fictitious, but all illustrating the way in which inter-ethnic conflict is stirred up.

The *de facto* change in the ethnic composition of Bosnia–Hercegovina was recognised by the peace-makers. Under the auspices of the United Nations, a plan was put forward to recognise the intractable problems of ethnic conflict by suggesting the division of the state into semi-autonomous regions along the lines of the cantons which comprise Switzerland. When this idea fell through following continued fighting, the solution which came to the fore was for three largely independent states based on ethnic lines. It seems that institutionalised racism had won, but it left an impoverished and devastated land. How much better it would have been to recognise the advantages to the country of ethnic and religious diversity, as is the case in Switzerland, one of the world's richest countries.

11 a Define what is meant by the term 'ethnic cleansing'.

b 'Cleansing' is a positive word which implies that something dirty is being eradicated. In your view, is this a good use for the word? If not, suggest an alternative.

c A larger, stronger Serbian state created by conquering and 'cleansing' territory previously belonging to Bosnia–Hercegovina may in the long run be weaker economically and politically. How might the policy of ethnic cleansing lead to this impoverishment?

12 Collect information from a daily newspaper about the 'problems' of inter-community friction in one area. What do you think should be done about these problems?

13 *Essay title:* 'The mature country is one that allows itself to benefit from different cultural and racial inputs rather than attempting to exclude them.' Discuss, with reference to actual examples.

IT7

Population change in the British countryside

More than 80 per cent of Britain is rural, but only 20 per cent of the population lives and works in the countryside. Villages and hamlets all over the country, in the Fenlands of East Anglia, the hills of mid-Wales and the Downs of Sussex, for example, are losing their 'local' inhabitants as 'outsiders' move in. The agriculturally-based work opportunities are declining as farms become even larger and more mechanised. Local housing becomes too expensive for local people and is bought up by commuters or by people using it for weekend accommodation (i.e. second homes). The demand for local services, such as the shop and the post office, declines and they close down. People have to travel many miles to shop, and living in the countryside becomes more and more expensive as a result.

The results of the 1991 census showed considerable locational changes for the population as a whole. **22.20** is a map of the districts of England and Wales showing the change in population in the period of 1981–91. In general, it shows large increases in some of the more 'rural' areas as people relocate from the cities, but it also highlights some rural areas that are losing population heavily.

Some of the reasons for moving into rural areas are the following:

■ *Retirement.* People who have served all their working days in the rush and bustle of urban surroundings move to the quiet of rural areas, often in coastal areas or where they had previous family links.

■ *To find a better 'quality of life'.* Some people move to smallholdings or to run rural businesses well before retirement age because it offers them a more relaxed, more rewarding way of life.

■ *To run their business from a remote location.* With the availability of efficient fax, telephone and computer links, there is little to keep urban commuters from carrying out many of their tasks from a rural location. This is called 'teleworking' or 'telecommuting'.

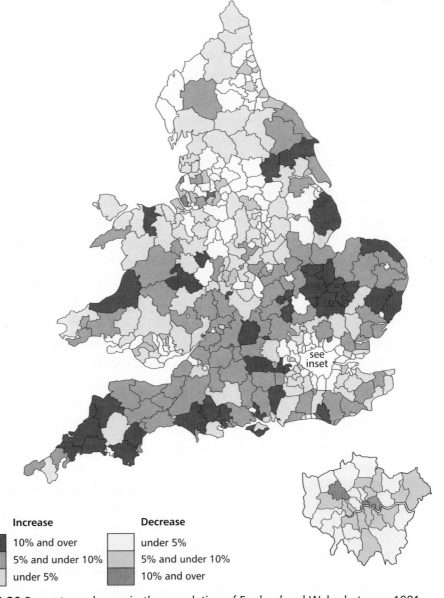

Increase

▓	10% and over
▒	5% and under 10%
░	under 5%

Decrease

□	under 5%
▨	5% and under 10%
▩	10% and over

■ **22.20** Percentage change in the population of England and Wales between 1981 and 1991

■ *Relocation of businesses.* Apart from individuals moving to rural locations, whole businesses are doing the same. Some have relocated to such areas as mid-Wales and the southern Lake District, to areas which are not only much more scenically acceptable to the workforce, but which also offer financial incentives for moves (such as heavy subsidies for industrial units).

Tips End is a settlement in the Norfolk fenland close to Welney. It has seen considerable changes in the period since 1960. For one thing, in 1994 it could no longer really be called a village, since it had lost its filling station, its post office and its pub. The sweet shop had closed and the local Zion Baptist Chapel was up for sale. The undertaker had moved out, the grocery van no longer called and the last remaining independent farm of 160 ha had recently been sold. Most of the surrounding land was owned by insurance companies. A builder had relocated his business and some 30 per cent of the property was for sale. Most of those properties that are sold go to wealthy 'incomers' who use them as weekend cottages or as an investment. The young local people cannot afford them. Tips End is a typical example of a settlement that is changing rapidly in an area of the country that is gaining population fast.

14 With reference to **22.20**:
   a Describe the pattern of areas in England and Wales that gained population at the fastest rate between 1981 and 1991.
   b Name five areas that gained population at the fastest rate and which could be called rural. [You may need to refer to atlas maps of economic activity to help you.]
   c Name four rural areas that lost population at a rate of up to 5 per cent during this time.

15 Make a list of push and pull factors (see page 284) to explain the movement of population in the British countryside.

16 The severe problems of loss of employment possibilities and affordability of housing in rural areas have led to a high degree of rural poverty. Some of the answers suggested or tried to combat this are:
   ■ teleworking (described above)
   ■ cooperative local ownership of shops
   ■ cheap housing for local people (either newly built or subsidised by rural housing trusts)
   ■ community transport scheme so that poorer workers can reach the services now concentrated in market towns.

   Assess the relative merits of each of these different 'solutions'.

17 Should the British rural population be assisted in some way? Should it be allowed to change as it does now, or should government take measures to control the changes? Write your answer to cover about one side of A4, including examples wherever possible to support your argument.

Population Structure

23.1 Definition: the population pyramid

The previous chapter looked at the movement of people, whilst Chapter 21 was concerned with the natural components of population change. Together, these two explain why the population of an area might be changing. This chapter shows how such changes can be described, predicted, managed and planned for.

The population structure of an area can be described by means of the **population pyramid**. This is a particularly poor name. Although it does show population, it is a two-dimensional figure rather than a three-dimensional one as a true pyramid would be. Neither is it always widest at the base as we expect of a pyramid. A good example of the lack of literal accuracy of the term is shown by the population pyramids for Kenya and Japan (**23.1**). Nevertheless, 'pyramid' is the term that is used.

The pyramid for Kenya is typical of those for the developing world. It has a wide base, showing a high birth rate and in this case an increasing population; a steep decline from one age group to the next, showing a relatively high death rate; and few people in the older age

groups, illustrating a low average age expectancy. On the other hand, the pyramid for Japan shows a low and declining birth rate, a relatively low death rate (as shown by the similarity in length between one bar and the next) and a high age expectancy. These features are typical of the developed world.

Population pyramids can be drawn for any administrative area with a large enough population. On a national or major area basis, they may be classified into four main types. These are shown in **23.2**. A pyramid is constructed from a series of bars stacked to represent the number or percentage of males and females in each age group. Three common ways of plotting the relative numbers in each group are used. These are absolute numbers in each age and sex group, percentage of the total population in that group, or percentage of the male or female population in that group. When using population pyramids, the x axis should be studied carefully to see which is being used in that particular case. It is usual to draw the bars for males to the

IPI

■ **23.1** Population pyramids for Kenya (1981) and Japan (1990)

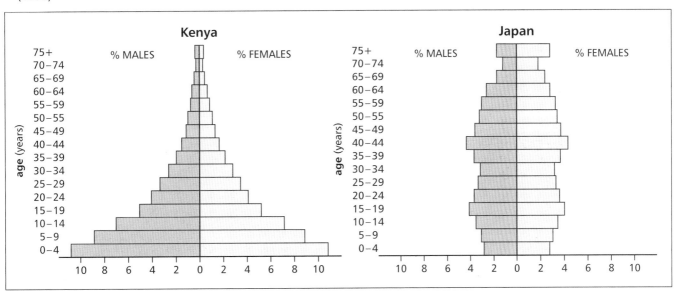

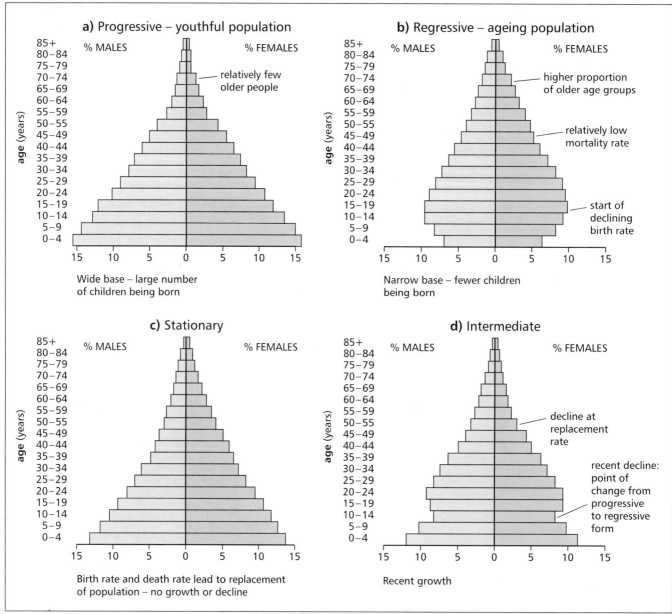

a) **Progressive – youthful population**

% MALES   % FEMALES

relatively few
older people

Wide base – large number
of children being born

b) **Regressive – ageing population**

% MALES   % FEMALES

higher proportion
of older age groups

relatively low
mortality rate

start of
declining
birth rate

Narrow base – fewer children
being born

c) **Stationary**

% MALES   % FEMALES

Birth rate and death rate lead to replacement
of population – no growth or decline

d) **Intermediate**

% MALES   % FEMALES

decline at
replacement
rate

recent decline:
point of
change from
progressive
to regressive
form

Recent growth

■ **23.2** Four main types of
population pyramid

left of the centre line and females to the
right. The size of the age group employed
depends on the statistics available and
the purpose for which the diagram is
being used. For example, if the pyramid
is being used to highlight the dependent
population (those too young to work and
those over retirement age–see next section), age groups of five-year intervals
might be used. If it is being used for planning school provision for a local authority, single year groups might be more
useful.

The population pyramid can be used
as a descriptive diagram or as a predictive one. Three major features that can
be described are highlighted in **23.5**.

1 a 23.3 is a population pyramid
for Great Britain in 1981. Use
the statistics in **23.4** to draw
another pyramid so that you
can compare it with the one
for 1981. [You might like to
construct it on a piece of
tracing paper placed over
23.3 so that comparisons are
made easier for the following
question.]

b What were the major changes
in age and sex structure
between 1981 and 1991?

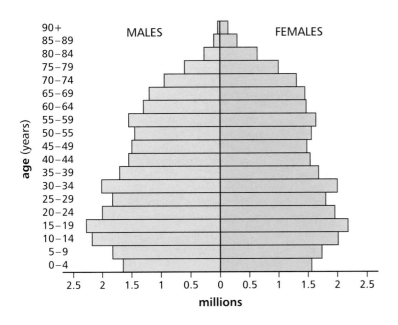

■ **23.3** Population pyramid for Great Britain, 1981

Age group	Males 1991	Females 1991
0–4	1858584	1774878
5–9	1762094	1678178
10–14	1692079	1607396
15–19	1804850	1732741
20–24	2028942	2076946
25–29	2148158	2215389
30–34	1984017	2013899
35–39	1812664	1833454
40–44	2001564	2017319
45–49	1684301	1686759
50–54	1497223	1503512
55–59	1405445	1433468
60–64	1359362	1464395
65–69	1264364	1473043
70–74	950060	1257827
75–79	709876	1109505
80–84	407166	808711
85–89	160253	437585
90 +	43955	188885

■ **23.4** Total population in Great Britain, 1991

2 Draw generalised population pyramids for each of the following scenarios. Make sure each is drawn to the same scale and carefully label what they show.

■ a developed country which has recently suffered internal conflict in which many were killed, but especially the young males (e.g. Bosnia)

■ a developing area which has gained population through immigration from a nearby rural area (e.g. Calcutta from nearby areas of West Bengal) – note that it is usually the young males who migrate first, followed at a later date by their families if their move has been successful

■ an island in the Outer Hebrides which has suffered major depopulation in the last 30 years.

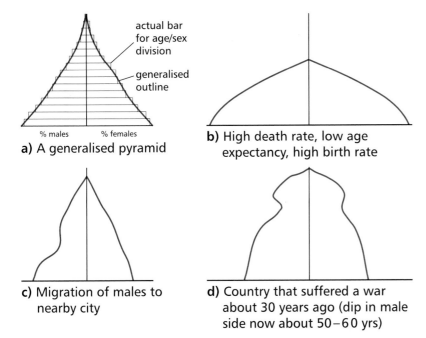

a) A generalised pyramid

b) High death rate, low age expectancy, high birth rate

c) Migration of males to nearby city

d) Country that suffered a war about 30 years ago (dip in male side now about 50–60 yrs)

■ **23.5** Generalised population pyramids

Of course, population pyramids are seldom as simple as those you have drawn in activity 2. They usually reflect a large number of influences on the structure. **23.6** is one such example. The complex pyramid is like the one you have already constructed from the 1991 UK census figures (activity 1a). It is a descriptive tool, showing the structure of the population at a particular time, but it is also a predictive one. From it can be identified the numbers of people who are going to be demanding particular services in the future. For example, the 1981 pyramid (**23.3**) shows that there is a bulge in the 30–34 year-old age group of people who will be drawing pensions and placing increasing demands on hospital and social services in roughly 30 years' time. The population pyramid drawn for 1991 shows the progress of this age group in the 10 years between 1981 and 1991. There was also a net addition to the 40–44 year-old age group through immigration.

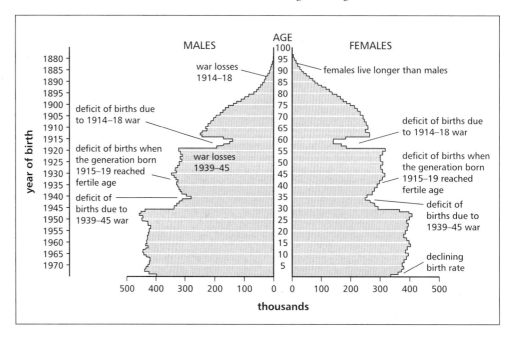

23.6 Population pyramid for France, 1975

23.2 **Dependent population**

The proportion of the population that is supported by the active part is called the **dependent population**. For many countries, children under 15 are not in active employment. Similarly, people over 65 are usually retired. There are variations in these ages depending on the economic status of the country and the statutory age of retirement, but the **dependency ratio** can be expressed as:

$$D = 100 \ (x+y)/P$$

where x = population over 15 (or 20 in some cases)

y = population of 65 and over
P = population between 15 (or 20) and 64.

This gives a ratio which approximately describes how many dependents must be supported by every 100 people in the economically active group. It can only be approximate as some people younger than 15 may be in full-time employment. On the other hand, some people over 15 may be staying on in full-time education. This is one of the most important measurements of a population structure, for the revenue derived from the active population has to support this non-active sector for such things as schooling, pensions, health care and housing provision, as well as food, clothing and shelter. Many of these have to be provided by government and are the subject of planning. Population pyramids, and projections made from them, are the main source of information to enable this planning to take place. Some of the aspects of old-age dependency are investigated in the next chapter. **23.7** shows dependency ratios by continent.

		Dependency ratio	
	Total	**Young** < 15 yrs	**Elderly** > 64 yrs
Africa	94	88	6
Asia	65	57	8
Europe	50	31	19
Latin America	70	65	5
North America	50	33	17
Oceania	56	43	13
USSR	52	38	14
World	65	55	10

23.7 Dependency ratios by continent, 1985

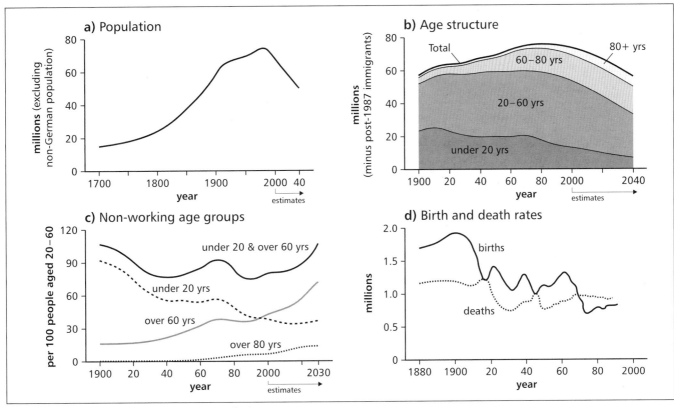

a) Population

millions (excluding non-German population)

b) Age structure

millions (minus post-1987 immigrants)

Total
60–80 yrs
80+ yrs
20–60 yrs
under 20 yrs

c) Non-working age groups

per 100 people aged 20–60

under 20 & over 60 yrs
under 20 yrs
over 60 yrs
over 80 yrs

d) Birth and death rates

millions

births
deaths

■ **23.8** Some aspects of the German population structure

3 a 23.7 shows that the world average for dependency (total) is 65. What does this mean?

b Compared with the world average, which areas have higher dependency ratios and which have lower dependency ratios?

c Apart from differences in the overall dependency ratios, what is the difference in the way the total dependency ratios are composed for Latin America and Europe?

d The population of which of the continents would best be illustrated by pyramid (a) in **23.2**?

4 23.8 illustrates some aspects of the German population and how it is predicted to develop after the year 2000.

a To what extent is the statement by Gunter Grass, that 'the Germans are dying out', borne out by the data?

b If you were to advise the German government on where the major increases in expenditure will come in the next 20 years, what advice would you give, and why?

23.3 **Sex ratios**

It might be expected that, for large populations, the number of males and females in those populations would be roughly equal. This is not the case, however. On a continental basis, the number of males to every 100 females ranges from 95 in North America and Europe to 105 in Asia. On a country basis, the number of males to 100 females is 94 in Italy and 107 in Bangladesh, for exam-

ple. As the figures in **23.9** show, there is also a regional variation in the UK (**23.9**). Not all of the reasons for these differences are understood.

One of the main reasons for female: male imbalance is the tendency for females to live longer. **23.10** shows the population of the regions of the UK by sex and age in 1991. If there are greater numbers of older women in the total

	Total	Males	Females	Males			Females		
				45–64	65–79	80+	45–59	60–74	80+
United Kingdom	57649.3	28131.8	29517.5	6129.5	3001.0	649.4	4776.4	5438.1	1496.1
North	3084.2	1501.1	1583.1	337.3	166.7	31.2	259.8	306.2	75.2
Yorkshire & Humberside	4954.2	2419.5	2534.7	525.9	263.1	54.5	409.3	474.3	128.9
East Midlands	4025.7	1984.5	2041.2	440.1	217.8	45.6	335.3	373.9	98.2
East Anglia	2091.2	1033.9	1057.3	224.6	119.6	28.3	170.6	202.1	56.3
South East	17557.6	8567.5	8990.1	1818.9	862.8	205.5	1427.7	1564.1	465.1
Greater London	6803.1	3289.7	3513.4	660.6	308.9	72.3	524.5	568.6	168.8
Rest of South East	10754.5	5277.8	5476.7	1158.3	553.9	133.2	903.2	995.5	296.3
South West	4723.3	2300.7	2422.6	514.6	285.2	70.2	398.3	501.2	151.5
West Midlands	5254.8	2586.5	2668.3	582.6	274.9	53.3	442.6	490.9	122.2
North West	6377.4	3093.5	3283.9	681.0	326.7	66.4	528.6	611.8	166.9
England	48068.5	23487.3	24581.2	5124.9	2516.6	555.0	3972.1	4524.5	1264.3
Wales	2886.4	1404.3	1482.1	316.9	166.5	32.9	244.5	296.9	78.4
Scotland	5100.0	2462.5	2637.5	538.7	250.3	48.7	437.3	487.7	123.3
Northern Ireland	1594.4	777.7	816.7	149.0	67.6	12.7	122.4	129.1	30.1

■ **23.9** UK population statistics for 1991, by age and sex

population, the sex ratio will be tilted in that direction.

Another reason is differences in infant mortality rates. In some countries, such as India, special circumstances operate which affect the female infancy death rate upwards and the male rate downwards (see case study on pages 275–78). In such areas, the female infancy death rate may be considerably higher than its male counterpart. In the UK, however, the reverse is true. **23.10** shows the deaths per 1000 population for specific groups. Comparison between the age groups under four years show a clear tendency for there to be a higher death rate among young male children than among females.

A third possible reason for imbalance is mobility. In the early stages of migration (see section 22.3), it is often the economically active males who move first. Not only does this result in a surplus of males at the place to which they are migrating, but also a deficit at the place from which they came. Although this situation is often rectified over time as the male returns (for example, when a job contract terminates) or as the rest of the family moves to join him, it can be a major component in sex imbalance (**23.11**).

There is also the tendency for male births to exceed female births. This has not been successfully explained as yet, but it is a biological fact. There is some evidence that the 'surplus' is adjusted by stillbirths and an increased death rate amongst young males (**23.10**). In the future, however, this tendency may be exaggerated in some areas. It has been shown (see case study on pages 275–78) that it is more desirable in some countries to give birth to a male than a female child. There are now several medical advances which help in this respect. There is a growing tendency in India for women who know they are carrying a male child to undergo Caesarian birth, taking away some of the risk. They know it is a male either through ultrasound checks or by

■ **23.11** Turkish population pyramid, Germany 1987

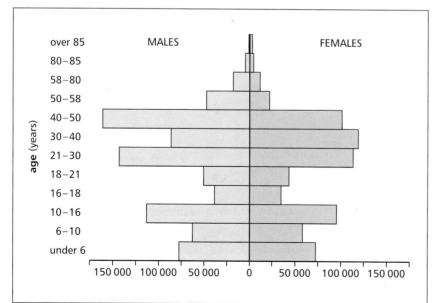

	Deaths /1000 population for specific age groups											SMR*
	Under 1	0–4	5–14	15–24	25–34	35–44	45–54	55–64	65–74	75–84	85 & over	(UK = 100)
Males												
United Kingdom	8.3	2.0	0.2	0.8	0.9	1.8	4.7	14.2	38.9	93.7	189.8	100
North	8.9	2.2	0.2	0.7	0.9	1.8	5.7	16.2	44.2	104.4	199.8	111
Yorkshire & Humberside	9.3	2.2	0.2	0.8	0.9	1.7	4.6	14.7	40.6	96.2	194.1	103
East Midlands	9.0	2.1	0.2	1.0	0.8	1.6	4.4	13.4	37.8	93.0	189.7	98
East Anglia	6.8	1.7	0.2	0.7	0.8	1.4	3.6	11.8	32.5	86.7	190.8	89
South East	7.5	1.8	0.2	0.7	1.0	1.8	4.3	12.6	35.0	89.5	180.5	93
Greater London	8.3	2.1	0.2	0.7	1.1	2.3	5.2	14.1	37.7	92.6	179.2	99
Rest of South East	6.9	1.6	0.2	0.7	0.8	1.5	3.8	11.7	33.6	87.7	181.2	89
South West	7.3	1.7	0.2	0.9	0.9	1.5	3.6	11.7	33.2	84.6	184.4	89
West Midlands	9.6	2.3	0.2	0.7	0.8	1.6	4.5	14.1	40.1	97.2	194.6	102
North West	8.4	2.1	0.2	0.9	1.0	2.0	5.3	16.5	43.0	99.7	192.4	109
England	8.2	2.0	0.2	0.8	0.9	1.7	4.5	13.7	37.8	92.7	187.4	98
Wales	7.5	1.9	0.2	0.8	0.8	1.7	4.5	14.5	40.2	94.8	179.9	100
Scotland	9.2	2.1	0.2	0.9	1.1	2.2	6.2	17.3	46.4	100.7	214.0	115
Northern Ireland	8.4	1.9	0.2	1.0	1.2	2.0	5.4	15.6	43.8	99.5	243.7	112
Females												
United Kingdom	6.3	1.6	0.2	0.3	0.5	1.1	2.9	8.4	22.2	59.4	161.0	100
North	8.4	2.0	0.2	0.3	0.4	1.1	3.4	10.0	26.4	66.0	169.2	112
Yorkshire & Humberside	7.7	1.9	0.2	0.3	0.4	1.1	2.9	8.7	23.9	60.9	160.5	103
East Midlands	6.4	1.5	0.1	0.4	0.4	1.1	2.9	8.4	21.2	59.5	159.7	99
East Anglia	5.0	1.3	0.1	0.3	0.3	0.9	2.6	6.8	18.9	54.4	160.6	92
South East	5.6	1.4	0.1	0.3	0.4	1.0	2.7	7.3	19.9	56.6	155.9	94
Greater London	5.7	1.6	0.2	0.3	0.4	1.0	3.0	7.9	21.5	56.9	152.7	96
Rest of South East	5.6	1.3	0.1	0.3	0.4	1.0	2.5	7.0	19.0	56.4	157.6	93
South West	5.3	1.2	0.2	0.3	0.4	1.0	2.5	7.0	18.6	54.0	154.6	91
West Midlands	7.8	1.9	0.1	0.3	0.5	1.1	2.9	8.5	22.6	59.3	159.6	100
North West	6.5	1.6	0.1	0.3	0.5	1.1	3.3	9.3	24.9	64.4	166.5	108
England	6.4	1.6	0.1	0.3	0.4	1.0	2.8	8.1	21.7	58.8	159.2	98
Wales	5.0	1.3	0.2	0.3	0.5	1.1	2.9	8.1	22.5	58.6	157.7	99
Scotland	5.6	1.4	0.2	0.3	0.6	1.3	3.6	10.5	26.5	65.2	175.0	113
Northern Ireland	6.4	1.5	0.2	0.3	0.4	1.3	3.1	9.2	23.4	60.9	193.7	109

* The standardised mortality ratio (SMR) compares overall mortality in a region with that for the UK. The ratio expresses the number of deaths in a region as a percentage of the hypothetical number that would have occurred if the region's population had experienced the sex/age-specific rates of the UK in that year.

■ **23.10** Age-specific death rates: by sex, 1991

chemical diagnosis (amniocentesis). This is not solely a phenomenon of the developing world, however. Clinics in the United States, the UK and France, for example, are advising on ways to conceive male or female children. Techniques range from eating specific diets to selection in the test tube (**23.12**). One extension of the argument for allowing social or medical reasons to influence conception is that abortion may be sought on the same grounds. If it is possible to determine the sex of a child early enough (and some claim to do it after only 11 weeks), then it would also be possible to abort the foetus without damage to the woman's chance of conceiving again. The moral question increases as the medical techniques advance.

Doctors back right to choose sex of child

Couples should be given a legal right to choose the sex of their children, doctors' leaders will recommend to colleagues this week.

The ethics committee of the British Medical Association has concluded that gender selection for medical or social reasons is a morally acceptable form of family planning.

Although at least one private clinic in London is already offering services to help couples choose whether they conceive a boy or a girl, the BMA said techniques were not yet scientifically validated. But Dr Fleur Fisher, head of the Association's ethics and science division, said yesterday: 'Gender selection is on the horizon and we believe it should be made available provided there are adequate safeguards.'

Services should be restricted to couples in stable relationships who already have at least one child, Dr Fisher and her colleagues say. Moreover, gender selection should only be used before conception.

The issue is expected to generate heated debate tomorrow among the 600 doctors at the BMA annual conference in Torquay. The motion emphasises that no doctor should terminate a pregnancy on grounds of foetal gender alone, unless a sex-related disease is present.

A BMA working party on ethics, headed by Dr Fisher, is this week launching a book, *Medical Ethics Today: its practice and philosophy*, which acknowledges that gender selection is potentially a moral minefield.

'Some believe that gender selection should be approved on utilitarian grounds since it would make more families happy. Thus, allowing couples to choose would increase the number of happy children and diminish the abuse or neglect of unwanted children,' the authors state. 'But the ability to plan the sex composition of one's family may give rise to trivial or misleading attitudes.'

Selection techniques include sperm sorting and the timing of insemination. It is possible to select after the egg has been fertilised or the embryo has implanted in the womb, but the law does not permit abortion on the grounds of foetal gender alone. Termination is permitted where the woman's mental or physical health would be impaired by continuation of pregnancy. 'In some cases the pressure brought to bear on a woman to produce a child of the desired gender may affect her health,' the BMA book points out.

■ **23.12** Extract from *The Independent*, 28 June 1993

---

5 a Work out the sex ratios for the regions of the UK in 1991. To do this, refer to the total numbers columns in **23.9**. For the United Kingdom the ratio is:

$$\frac{\text{number of males} \times 100}{\text{number of females}} = \frac{28131.8 \times 100}{29517.5}$$
$$= 95.3$$

b Plot the figures on a suitable map of the UK Standard Regions. Do the figures reveal any pattern?

6 One of the reasons for differences in sex ratios is life expectancy.

a Draw a population pyramid of the male and female populations over 45 for the UK. What does this reveal?

b If this pattern continues as the numbers of older people in the UK increase, what would this mean for firms providing personal products or services?

7 Differences in deaths per 1000 population between males and females by age group are shown in **23.10**.

a Devise a method to show graphically differences in deaths per 1000 population in the UK for
  i males and females under 4
  ii males and females aged 5–14
  iii males and females aged 65 and over.

b What does your technique reveal about male and female death rates?

c Is the pattern similar in all the regions of the UK? (The Standardised Mortality Rate will help here.) Suggest some of the factors that could affect differences in death rates in different areas.

8 *Essay title:* 'Population sex structure is a natural phenomenon and should not be manipulated'. Discuss, with reference to actual examples.

CASE STUDY

IT5,6

The retirement town

One of the features of relocation in the UK has been the movement of the older sections of the population at or about the age of retirement. Usually, this is either to the place of their origin or to a perceived ideal location. One of the places chosen on this basis is the coastal resort, and one such example in the UK is Bournemouth.

Background

Bournemouth is in the county of Dorset and in the South West Standard Region.

1 **23.9** shows population, by region. What is the percentage of people over 60 (females) and 65 (males) living in the South West Region? How does this compare with the other regions?

2 With reference to atlas maps of Dorset and the Bournemouth area, attempt to explain some of

the attractions of the area for retirement.

3 The influx of older residents has several effects on the population structure (**23.13**). These can be isolated if the structure is compared with the average structure. Copy the population pyramid for Bournemouth (**23.13**), then use the figures for the age–sex breakdown of the South West Region (**23.14**) to superimpose the 'average' population structure for the surrounding region.

4 What differences are there between the structure for the whole of the South West Region and for Bournemouth? Label them on your pyramid.

Planning

5 What particular planning problems would the structure of Bournemouth's population present to the local authorities?

6 If you were advising on developments in the Bournemouth area, what comments would you make about each of the following:
   a) a company intending to build 200 sheltered housing units

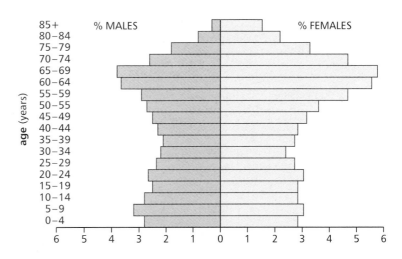

■ **23.13** Recent population pyramid for Bournemouth

b) a national furniture removal firm intending to set up an office in Bournemouth
c) a leisure firm intending to build a second ice rink in the town?

7 Imagine that you have to use **23.15** in producing a leaflet designed to promote Bournemouth. Write a suitable descriptive paragraph to go with the photograph.

■ **23.15** Bournemouth could be said to have all the benefits of a modern British holiday resort as well as a larger retirement sector than many

Age group	Total population	Males	Females
All	4 609 424	2 225 411	2 384 013
0–4	284 215	145 618	135 597
5–9	269 941	138 534	131 407
10–14	264 566	135 650	128 916
15–19	289 234	148 099	141 135
20–24	318 962	160 747	158 217
25–29	332 189	166 061	166 128
30–34	311 956	155 692	156 264
35–39	296 680	146 492	150 188
40–44	340 380	168 814	171 574
45–49	292 531	146 419	146 112
50–54	250 262	124 739	125 523
55–59	204 809	118 371	122 438
60–64	250 697	119 436	131 262
65–69	256 716	117 677	139 039
70–74	213 778	93 048	120 964
75–79	181 736	72 971	108 792
80–84	125 121	43 429	81 692
85–89	63 286	18 148	45 138
90 +	26 330	5 432	20 898

■ **23.14** Population data for the South West Standard Region, 1991

23.4 **Ethnic composition**

	White	Black Caribbean	Black African	Black other	Indian	Paki-stani	Bangla-deshi	Chinese	Other groups	Total (=100%) thousands
					%					
Great Britain	94.5	0.9	0.4	0.3	1.5	0.9	0.3	0.3	0.9	54889
North	98.7	–	–	0.1	0.3	0.3	0.1	0.2	0.3	3027
Yorkshire & Humberside	95.6	0.4	0.1	0.2	0.8	2.0	0.2	0.2	0.6	4837
East Midlands	95.2	0.6	0.1	0.3	2.5	0.4	0.1	0.2	0.6	3953
East Anglia	97.9	0.2	0.1	0.4	0.3	0.3	0.1	0.2	0.6	2027
South East	90.1	1.9	1.0	0.6	2.6	0.8	0.6	0.5	1.8	17208
Greater London	79.8	4.4	2.4	1.2	5.2	1.3	1.3	0.8	3.5	6680
Rest of South East	96.7	0.4	0.1	0.2	0.9	0.5	0.2	0.3	0.7	10529
South West	98.6	0.3	0.1	0.1	0.2	0.1	0.1	0.1	0.4	4609
West Midlands	91.8	1.5	0.1	0.4	3.1	1.9	0.4	0.2	0.7	5150
North West	96.1	0.3	0.1	0.3	0.9	1.2	0.2	0.3	0.5	6244
England	93.8	1.1	0.4	0.4	1.8	1.0	0.3	0.3	1.0	47055
Wales	98.5	0.1	0.1	0.1	0.2	0.2	0.1	0.2	0.4	2835
Scotland	98.7	–	0.1	0.1	0.2	0.4	–	0.2	0.3	4999

■ **23.16** Resident population by ethnic group in the UK, 1991 ('Black other' includes people who are Black, but who categorise themselves as 'Black British'.)

This is one of the most emotive topics in population geography (see case study on pages 292–94), and it is easy to fall into the trap of taking a firm stance on questions of race and culture without reference to sufficient data. For example, in 1993, several political speeches were made in the UK referring to the threat of inter-community violence due to the large and growing numbers of immigrants in some areas of the country. **23.16** shows the percentages of certain ethnic groups in the country as determined by the 1991 census. It would seem from these figures that such alarms were not at all well founded.

The figures are, however, overall figures and they say little about actual distribution. It has already been demonstrated (see the case study on pages 259–61) that concentrations can be hidden by such figures and this is certainly the case in any discussion of racial minorities. **23.17** is a map of the distribution of ethnic minorities in Britain. As can be seen, only a very few areas have concentrations over 25 per cent. Most have levels below 0.9 per cent.

The creation of successful multicultural societies is the aim of many nations in the world at the approach of the new millennium. Unfortunately, some of the examples which had been seen to function successfully (e.g. Bosnia–Hercegovina – see the case study on pages 292–94) have been ripped apart by inter-community strife. The following case study serves to highlight the factors which underlie the potential of racial mixture in a society and how it can benefit society as a whole.

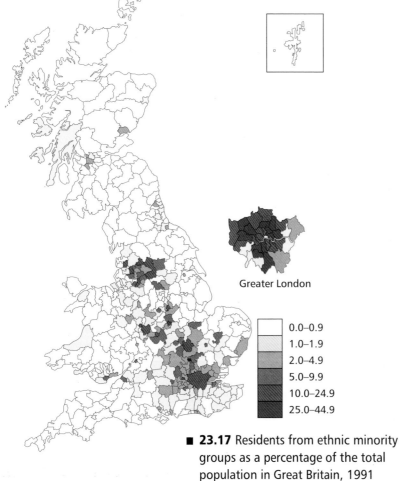

Greater London

0.0–0.9
1.0–1.9
2.0–4.9
5.0–9.9
10.0–24.9
25.0–44.9

■ **23.17** Residents from ethnic minority groups as a percentage of the total population in Great Britain, 1991

IT7

The Chinese minority in New Zealand – from 'undesirable immigrants' to 'a model minority'

Chinese immigration into New Zealand cannot be said to have started auspiciously. The first arrivals were those seeking success as gold prospectors in the mid-19th century. While there was no great competition for jobs all was well, but when the recession of the 1880s struck, hatred and intolerance flared up. This was especially so after the mining industry declined and the Chinese, amongst others, moved to the towns to find work. By 1857, an anti-Chinese Committee had been set up in Nelson. There was direction on the matter from the top. Sir George Grey, the Governor of New Zealand, warned his fellow countrymen against letting in 'people of inferior degree of civilisation'. He argued that once such races were allowed to grow in numbers, the Anglo-Saxon roots of the colonies in the whole of Australasia would be under threat. He therefore suggested that there should be government regulations to control the admission of the Chinese. In 1867, a by-law was passed in one of the major gold-mining towns in Central Otago to keep the Chinese outside the town boundary and thus ensure the maintenance of a relatively high standard of living. Worse than that, the Chinese were classified as 'undesirable immigrants' by the Immigration Act passed in 1881. Unofficially seen as 'the yellow peril', the Chinese were said by the Prime Minister, R. J. Seddon, to 'bring evils … worse than the bubonic plague'. With condemnation like this, the Chinese kept a low profile. They were not allowed to take up New Zealand citizenship until 1952, when many of them did so as a result of political unrest in their home country. The Chinese had come from many different countries, such as Malaya, Singapore, Vietnam and Laos, all of which were then in political and economic turmoil.

This long history of official discrimination served only to reinforce the Chinese philosophy of life and attitude to education. Confucian teaching values success, ambition and obligation of individuals both to family and to other members of the community. The cultural stress on hard work, detemination, ambition and success closely matches the Protestant code, especially the work ethic, inherited by the European settlers of New Zealand. So despite official condemnation, the individual and community behaviour of the Chinese matched very closely that of their 'hosts'. In addition to their high ambition, the Chinese traits of deference, conformity and compromise made them less conspicuous and have given them a greatly improved standing. Indeed, they are now seen as the 'model minority' in the country.

It does not appear to be anything the Chinese have done to change that has made the difference. On the contrary, sticking to their traditional values and strengths has simply changed their hosts' perceptions of them. Their educational achievements may have helped. In New Zealand, the Chinese have the highest percentage of students over 15 years of age in tertiary education establishments (15.7 per cent of females as opposed to 6.2 per cent overall and 19.3 per cent of males as opposed to 6.4 per cent overall). This has fed through to the job market and 23.3 per cent of Chinese males and 13.7 per cent of females are classified as 'employers'. Whilst having the lowest percentage of all racial backgrounds unemployed, they have well over the national average at 17.9 per cent who are in the professional, technical and associated areas. The dominant professions occupied by the Chinese community are architecture/engineering, medical/dental/veterinary science, and accountancy. As such, the Chinese occupy very well-respected niches in society and are seen to be valuable members of it. This is reinforced by the traditional Chinese respect for authority, which results in low levels of juvenile delinquency and crime in general. Spatially, New Zealand cities do not have the 'Chinatowns' which are common in other areas around the Pacific Rim. It is difficult, therefore, to identify any 'threat' to the traditional notions of New Zealand society.

9 What factors seem to have caused a complete turnaround in the official perception in New Zealand of the Chinese minority?

10 *Essay title:* 'Describe how population pyramids may be used for planning purposes.' Illustrate your essay with examples wherever possible.

Population Issues

It could be argued that population is the basic theme underlying political and economic debate in the late-20th century. It is difficult to open a newspaper or listen to any news bulletin without coming across some reference to 'the population problem'. This chapter investigates two different issues related to population, and offers pointers towards a third.

---

1 Look back at activity 5 in section 20.1. Remind yourself of the importance of population issues – look at the main TV news, or listen to the news on the radio. What percentage of news broadcasts deals with population-related topics?

ISSUE ONE: The global population : resource equation

Overpopulation is a term in very common usage. It is used by some people to explain famines, wars and economic decline. It would be useful, therefore, to define exactly what is meant by the term.

24.1 **Personal space**

IT4

In fact, many people who use the term 'overpopulation' do so without reference to measurement. Instead they refer to their perception. Throughout history, there are many examples of countries perceiving themselves to be overcrowded and thus 'needing more room'. Some duly started wars to acquire this territory. The Second World War started when Germany invaded neighbouring states in order to gain **lebensraum** (living space). By any rational measurement, Germany was not really overpopulated at the time, but the concept was used as a powerful justification for political ends.

The national perception of overpopulation may be derived from the sum of individual experiences. Human beings are animals and their behaviour is based on the same sort of interactions that occur in the rest of the animal kingdom. In particular, people have territories. These are subdivided into zones which are perceived by individuals in relation to the prevailing circumstances. **24.1** shows the extent of the zones as they apply to suburban Europeans. The zones vary according to experience – for example, someone from the outback of Australia would feel threatened by the approach of a stranger long before the person whose territory is illustrated in **24.1**. It would appear that if the 'intimate zone' is invaded often enough without invitation (such as would be the case on the London Underground, for example), in queues or in crowded shops, the subconscious message received by the person whose space is being violated would be that the area is overcrowded (**24.2**). Some people might react by moving to the countryside, some could become aggressive in their behaviour, and others would aim for a compromise, perhaps by commuting from a less

IT4

crowded area. In some extreme cases, part of the population may turn on another, as happened to the Jews in Germany in the Second World War and the Muslims in Bosnia–Hercegovina in the early 1990s (see case study on pages 292–94), though obviously many other factors also played a part in these situations.

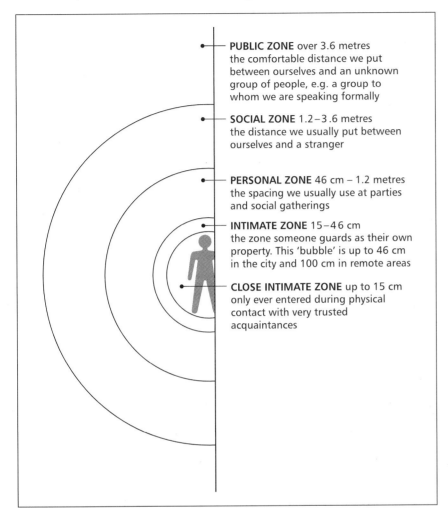

PUBLIC ZONE over 3.6 metres
the comfortable distance we put between ourselves and an unknown group of people, e.g. a group to whom we are speaking formally

SOCIAL ZONE 1.2–3.6 metres
the distance we usually put between ourselves and a stranger

PERSONAL ZONE 46 cm – 1.2 metres
the spacing we usually use at parties and social gatherings

INTIMATE ZONE 15–46 cm
the zone someone guards as their own property. This 'bubble' is up to 46 cm in the city and 100 cm in remote areas

CLOSE INTIMATE ZONE up to 15 cm
only ever entered during physical contact with very trusted acquaintances

■ **24.1** Personal space

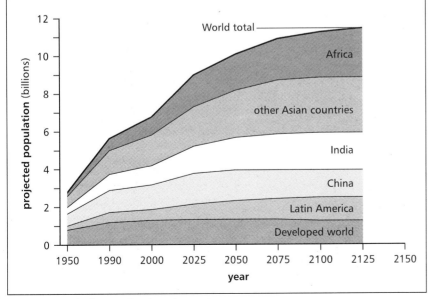

■ **24.3** Population projections by region

■ **24.2** Crowded Nevskii Prospekt, St Petersburg

24.2 **Towards a better definition of 'overpopulation'**

Analysis of world population growth (**24.3**) suggests that the planet may be approaching a crisis point. On closer inspection, the pattern is clearly regional rather than global, however (**24.4**). Some areas and countries are at a later stage of the demographic transition than others (see Chapter 21). Also, such statistics by themselves can be very misleading. A frame of reference is needed within which to judge the extent of the 'threat' posed by world population growth.

Many attempts have been made to measure population levels. The most meaningful definitions have related population to resources. A resource is defined in the dictionary as 'that on which one depends for support or

2 With reference to **24.3** and **24.4**:

  a Describe the change in total world population over the period 1950 to 2150. You should include in your answer:
- the population total for 1950
- the total expected for 2025
- the total for 2150.

  b By how many times is the population in 2150 expected to exceed the population in 1950?

  c Is world population heading towards stability or not?

  d Which continent is expected to show a steadily rising growth rate over this period?

  e What pattern of demographic change is exhibited by **i** Europe and Latin America and **ii** Asia and East Asia?

  f What is the underlying difference between the developed world and the developing world in terms of population change between now and 2150?

  g Which continent's rate of population growth is particularly high?

	1955–60	1965–70	1975–80	1985–90
World	1.86	2.06	1.74	1.73
Africa	2.35	2.63	2.95	3.00
Europe	0.80	0.67	0.45	0.22
Latin America	2.76	2.60	2.28	2.09
Asia	1.95	2.44	1.86	1.85
East Asia	1.53	2.42	1.41	1.31

■ **24.4** Estimated percentage population growth for selected regions `IT4`

■ **24.5** The Dust Bowl near Dallas in 1936

supply; skill in improvising'. Thus it means not only materials such as food, building materials and raw materials, but also human abilities. The geographer classifies resources into two main types. One category is **non-renewable (or stock) resources**, which include metal ores and fossil fuels that are constantly depleted by use. **Renewable resources** include food crops and animals, timber and fish, as well as human resources.

In the past, many resources were taken for granted and used as though they were infinite. This misuse led to the devastation of some areas, for example the timber resources of the Mediterranean basin and the soils of the Midwest 'Dust Bowl' States of the USA (**24.5**). Unfortunately, few of the lessons of the past have been learned and the constant depletion of non-renewable resources is now of major global concern. The prime example is the destruction of the rainforest (see Chapter 14), but such activities are now being viewed as a threat to continued industrial production and from the point of view of pollution of the planet. **Conservation** (careful use and protection of resources) has therefore become more important as a result. Conservation urges recognition from the world community that renewable resources should only be used at a rate that allows them to be reproduced for further harvesting, and stock resources should be used with the greatest of care. If the rate of use exceeds an optimum level (a **sustainable** level) then the balance of nature is upset and catastrophe could follow.

Visiting St Vincent in the West Indies on 27 October 1985, Her Majesty Queen Elizabeth II said:

> One must remember that the island's resources are finite and cannot accommodate infinite population growth. Families have to plan their lives just as the government has to plan the nation's development.

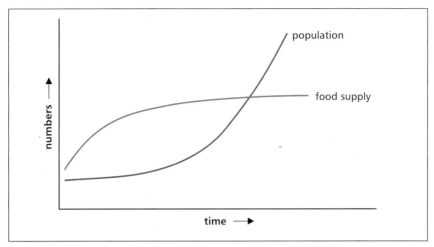

IT4

■ **24.6** Malthus: the differential increase in population and food supply over time

IT4

■ **24.7** The J-shaped curve

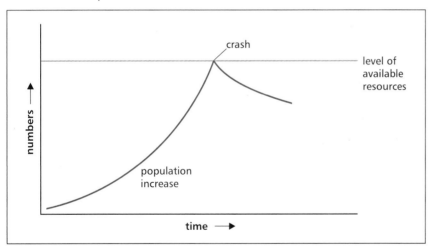

The Queen was emphasising the fact that there is a close link between population and resources, a fact that had been recognised many years earlier by the Reverend Thomas Malthus. In 1797, Malthus, working in England at a time of rapid population growth, had written his 'Essay on Population'. He suggested that human population has a tendency to increase at a geometric rate, with a doubling of the population every successive generation. Food supplies only increase at best in an arithmetical progression, however, giving uniform increments over time. With time, there would be a growing disparity between food supplies and population (**24.6**), and restrictions to population growth would come into play as a result, controlling population numbers. According to Malthus, these restrictions would consist of moral restraint (which he said would be unlikely), 'vice' (abortion, infanticide and the employment of contraception) and positive checks (starvation, disease and war).

Although Malthus' ideas only take into account the relationship between two variables – population and food resources – they clearly illustrate the concept of interrelationship. Malthus said that if imbalance were to occur, his 'positive checks' would come into operation and the result would be as illustrated in **24.7**, a population crash, represented by the 'J-shaped curve'. This situation has certainly developed in parts of Africa where droughts have cut food production, leaving the population to survive on fewer resources and leading to many deaths (**24.8**).

The situation predicted by Malthus has not yet arrived on a global scale, and later workers have pointed out that the curve illustrated in **24.9** is a

IT4

■ **24.8** Famine in Somalia

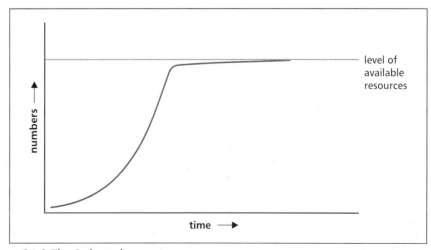

■ **24.9** The S-shaped curve

truer interpretation in many areas that have reached the limit of their available resources. If the population total is gradually adjusted to the resource level available, then the S-shaped curve is more likely to apply.

Another way of looking at the relationship between population and resources is to consider the **carrying capacity** of the area in question. This is the total population that can be supported by the resources of that area. A desert area has a lower carrying capacity than a humid temperate area, simply because of the amount of food that can be grown there. It is not as simple as this, however. Saudi Arabia has huge oil reserves which in turn give it financial resources and the power to obtain food from elsewhere by trade. The population of an area is related to its resources in the widest sense. If there are too few people in an area to use the resources efficiently, it could be termed **underpopulated**. If there are so many people in an area that the available resources cannot support them at a given standard of living, then it is **overpopulated**. Countries strive to achieve the level known as the **optimum population**. This is a population level which allows resources of all kinds to be used efficiently, giving a good standard of living to all of the people. Petersen (1975) defined optimum population as 'the number of people that, in a given natural, cultural and social environment,

produces the maximum economic returns'. This definition does not take into account the abilities and education of the people, their health or age structure, all of which determine the value of the workforce. Nor does it include the effect of those people on the environment. In 1972, Southward said that the optimum population was 'the maximum that could be maintained indefinitely without detriment to the health of the individuals from pollution or from social or nutritional stress'. This idea has been taken further by the **physical quality of life index (PQLI)**, which takes into account three factors: child mortality, literacy and life expectancy. Each factor is given equal weight in the compilation of the index. Areas of high income do not necessarily have high PQLIs, but there is an inverse relationship between birth rate and PQLI, with areas of high birth rate having low PQLIs (**24.10**).

Other ways of measuring the relationship between population and resources include **gross domestic product (GDP) per capita** and various measures of the standard of living. GDP is the total amount of revenue generated in an area. When divided by the number of people living in that area, it gives a measure of the amount of capital available to each person, but obviously wealth is not distributed that way. Commonly, a few people have a large share of the wealth and many others live at a much lower level. Standard of living indices are calculated by using various measurable factors, such as literacy, intake of calories per head, average income, average consumption of energy, and so on. Again these vary widely and a better comparative index of well-being is probably the **purchasing power parity (PPP)**, which takes into account the relationship between local income and what it buys, but gives a figure which means that the standard of living in New York can be compared with that in Upper Volta, for example.

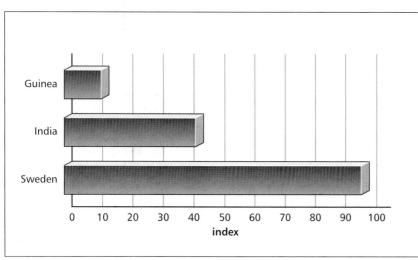

■ **24.10** PQLI for three countries

24.3 Predictions of future relationships between population and resources

IT3,4 The future relationship between population and resources on a world scale is a growing source of global concern. It is a subject of great debate. Various predictions have been made and most are pessimistic, insisting that unless drastic measures are taken on the human population side of the equation, the finite resources of the Earth will be under severe strain in the not-too-distant future. Such predictions were made by a group of scientists, industrialists and administrators known as 'The Club of Rome' working in the period from 1970 to 1972. They were sponsored by the Massachusetts Institute of Technology (MIT). Their resulting work, 'The Limits to Growth', showed that if consumption were maintained without new resource discoveries or changes in industrial policy, the world system would collapse (**24.11**). IT3,4

They used computer models to suggest that with a doubling of known resources, disaster would come even earlier than that, through vastly increased pollution. The Club suggested that the only way out would be an overall attack on the items used in their computer analysis in order to reach a 'state of equilibrium'. This would involve the achievement of equal birth and death rates, the recycling of resources, the stabilisation of industrial output and emphasis on food production and conservation. The Club said that these policies should be instituted by 1975 or it might be too late! Sad to report, very few of the suggestions have been taken up by the world's nations. The constant cry for industrial development brings with it a challenge to the future of the planet, and the achievement of an equilibrium between population and resources represents one of the most important challenges facing the world today.

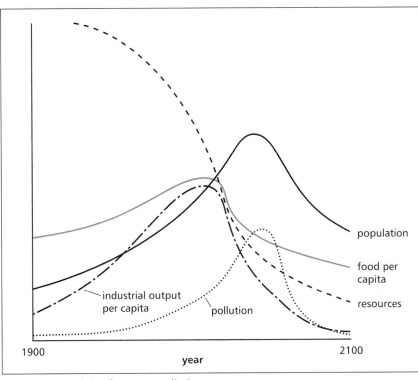

■ **24.11** The Club of Rome predictions

---

3 a Make notes on at least four different definitions of 'overpopulation'.
  b Which of the definitions do you think is best, and why?

4 Did The Club of Rome's predictions agree with those made by Malthus? Explain your answer.

5 Collect evidence from newspapers or magazines to show how the population of a country and its resources are linked. You might look for disputes over resources, migrations, political unrest due to inter-community disputes or the growth of towns in locations which are being exploited for particular reasons (climate, minerals, water supply, etc.). For each cutting you collect, write a short note to show how it illustrates the links between population and resources.

6 *Essay title:* 'World population growth – threat or potential?'

ISSUE TWO: Health

IT5

Can you remember the last time you had a really bad cold? What effects did it have on you? All or some of the items shown in **24.12** probably affected you or those immediately around you. Something as simple as a cold can be shown to have a major knock-on effect on relationships with other people, work performance, attendance and financial outlay. You can probably think of other effects on you personally.

In terms of the population at large, health issues are the sum of what happens to individuals. The main effects remain the same. Societies pay dearly for epidemics such as influenza (often involving the hospitalisation of the elderly) or for environmentally-induced disease such as lung cancer. Workforces may be savaged by certain diseases and economic costs ensue. The following examples show just how great and far-reaching the effects can be. Before moving on to them, however, it should be emphasised that the geographical study of health and disease has a very serious point to it. By plotting the incidence of, for example, cases of food poisoning on a map of a local area, it may be possible to track down the shop where the suspect item was purchased, or the restaurant which caused the outbreak. Looking at trends in disease and the location of sufferers could indicate environmental causes and thereby also the cure.

IT5

■ **24.12** The effects of a bad cold

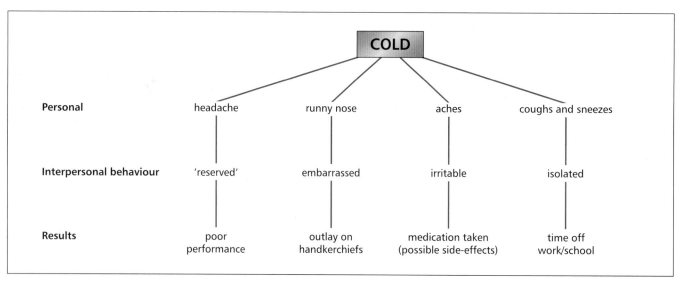

Personal	headache	runny nose	aches	coughs and sneezes
Interpersonal behaviour	'reserved'	embarrassed	irritable	isolated
Results	poor performance	outlay on handkerchiefs	medication taken (possible side-effects)	time off work/school

24.4 **A hopeful story**

IT5

In the 1950s, poliomyelitis was a killer disease. It was also widespread. Even in the USA there were 76 000 cases in 1955, many of them resulting in permanent paralysis or death. In 1954, however, a vaccine was introduced. Known as the inactivated poliovirus vaccine (IPV), this had an immediate effect and took the incidence of the disease down to around 0.5 per 100 000 (a total of 2500 paralysed patients) in 1961. In the same year, a new and more powerful vaccine, the attenuated oral poliovaccine (OPV) was introduced. Now, the wild virus is virtually extinct in the USA and the only new cases tend to be 'imported', by people arriving from places where poliomyelitis is still endemic. There is hardly any infection of third parties. The disease has, to all intents and purposes, been eradicated from the USA.

This is not the case, however, in other countries. **24.13** shows the incidence as reported by the World Health

IT5

■ **24.13** Incidence of poliomyelitis, 1985

Population	Average annual number of cases								
millions	1951–55	1966–70	1971–75	1976–80	1981	1982	1983	1984	1985
A 317	44391	470	221	34	9	79	39	9	10
B 332	2202	14453	10249	3837	1538	884	881	526	855

A: *Argentina, Canada, Cuba and the USA* **B**: *Brazil, Colombia, Mexico, Peru and 10 others*

■ **24.14** A comparison of poliomyelitis incidence in different parts of America

Rise in TB declared a global emergency

LIZ HUNT
Medical Correspondent

The World Health Organisation yesterday declared tuberculosis a global emergency which will claim 30 million lives within the next decade unless action is taken to halt its spread.

TB is the leading cause of death world-wide from a single infectious agent and three million people die from it each year, although drugs which cure it are readily available and cheap. Eight million people develop the disease annually.

Most cases are in developing countries but there has been an upsurge in the illness in industrialised countries, linked to the spread of AIDS, increasing homelessness, drug misuse and poverty. These factors are largely responsible for renewed interest in Europe and America in a disease which many thought had been dealt with by modern medicine. The appearance of strains of *Mycobacterium tuberculosis* which are resistant to several drugs is also causing concern.

In Britain, the decline stopped in the late 1980s – when incidence was about 6,000 cases a year. It is now running at 7,000 cases a year. There was a 12 per cent increase in the US between 1986 and 1991, a 28 per cent rise in Italy between 1988 and 1990, and a 33 per cent rise in Switzerland between 1986 and 1990. All three countries have a high proportion of HIV-infected individuals.

Professor Richard Feacham, Dean of the London School of Hygiene and Tropical Medicine, said TB killed far more people than AIDS, and equivalent money should be spent on research and prevention. He urged governments not to abandon school vaccination programmes.

Organisation in 1985. The pattern is clear. The developed countries have a very low incidence of the disease. The developing countries, on the other hand, are shown as having high incidence, equivalent to that in the USA in 1961. Far worse, however, is the fact that many of the countries are shown as having 'no data'. This is because medical facilities are poor and recording is bad or non-existent. **24.14** confirms the difference between the two groups of countries. Although there is the medical knowledge to eradicate the disease, it is still rampant in some parts of the world. Sadly, the story is the same for measles, leprosy and many other diseases.

IT5

■ **24.15** An extract from *The Independent*, 24 April 1993

7 Complete a diagram similar to that for **24.12** for an infectious disease such as measles, chickenpox or mumps.

8 Why is the death rate from infectious diseases often higher in urban areas than in the countryside, even in developing countries where most medical help is to be found in the towns and cities?

9 The history of tuberculosis is similar to, but perhaps even more dramatic than that of poliomyelitis. One major difference, however, is that it started to increase again in the 1980s. Do some research on tuberculosis, to find out:

- how the disease is spread
- what the situation was like in the early 1900s
- when control became effective
- what the situation was in the 1960s
- what was happening by the 1990s and why this was the case.

Bodies such as the World Health Organisation, Oxfam, Save the Children and the World Bank issue statistics and other information on this topic. **24.15** will help you.

24.5 **Tracking down the problem**

IT5

The importance of using geographical techniques to identify and therefore help to solve health problems has already been mentioned. One example where the use of these techniques has brought rewards is in Singapore.

In tropical developing countries in general, the incidence of typhoid fever is around 10 per 100 000 population. Regulation and careful screening in Singapore has led to a great improvement on this level, which it last suffered in the 1950s. Typhoid fever is mainly spread by the intake of water contaminated with *Salmonella typhi*. The availability of a safe water supply is therefore essential in stopping the spread of the disease. Environmental regulations, especially on food handling, also play a very important part in control (**24.16**).

IT5

In Singapore, typhoid fever has been greatly restricted since 1950. The continued decline since 1980 is illustrated in **24.17**. This has been achieved by:

- the mandatory notification of typhoid fever cases
- legislation against engaging in the food trade without a licence
- the wide provision of modern sanitation and a safe water supply
- the prohibition of food handlers who are known to be typhoid carriers from handling food indefinitely
- the provision of modern indoor facilities for the large number of hawkers who formerly sold food on the streets.

The death rate from typhoid fever in Singapore is now around 1.2 per 100 000 people. Compared with the rest of the developing world, this is a commendable figure, but is still much higher than in the USA (0.2 per 100 000) and Japan (0.1 per 100 000). In view of the very strict measures taken, therefore, why is this the case and what can be done about it?

■ **24.16** Food seller, Singapore

Year	Total deaths	Local cases	Imported cases
1980	210 (2)	142	68
1981	189 (2)	133	56
1982	164 (2)	91	73
1983	126 (1)	54	72
1984	97	39	58
1985	123 (2)	65	58
1986	150 (1)	62	88
1987	114	37	77
1988	163	45	118
1989	116 (1)	33	83
TOTAL	1452 (11)	701	751

■ **24.17** Incidence of typhoid fever in Singapore, 1980–89   **IT5**

There are several types (or phages) of typhoid. If these are analysed, it is possible to tell whether the source of infection was local or whether it was an external source. **24.17** gives data on these sources for Singapore.

10 a Plot a graph from the data in **24.17** using three-year moving means to reveal the trend in both local and imported cases of typhoid.

b Comment on the pattern shown by your graph.

c Which of the trends is more worrying and would benefit from further measures to control it?

24.18 is a graph showing the death rate in local cases of typhoid and the overall proportion of imported cases. It should be obvious from your answers to activity 10 and the data in **24.17** that it is the imported cases which need most attention.   **IT5**

Where are these cases to be found? The Singapore government's wise measure to require the notification of all cases of typhoid enables them to locate cases on a map, revealing potential links between them. In this way, they were able to track down 'outbreaks' (two or more cases believed to have originated from the same source). Over the 1980–89 period, 33 outbreaks were detected in this way, involving 199 cases. Seven of these were major outbreaks involving 11–33 cases. By locating them, the outbreaks were quickly isolated. Public food handlers were implicated in 12 of the clusters, and 10 were traced to 'carriers' (people whose gut contained *Salmonella typhi* but who showed no signs of developing typhoid themselves). In none of these cases was the phage of *Salmonella typhi* found to be a local one. The actual causes of the outbreaks were traced to iced drinks, cut fruits, salads and undercooked chicken. The monthly incidence of cases of typhoid was also plotted (**24.19**).

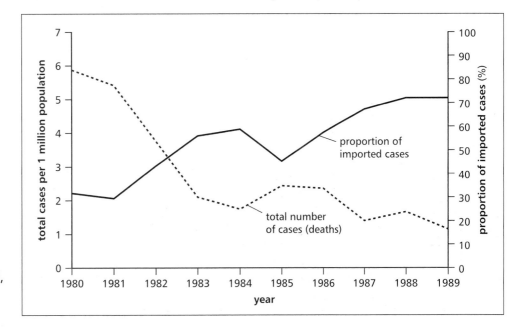

■ **24.18** Total death rates through indigenous typhoid, and proportion of imported cases, Singapore, 1980–89

■ **24.19** Monthly distribution of indigenous and imported typhoid cases, Singapore, 1980–89

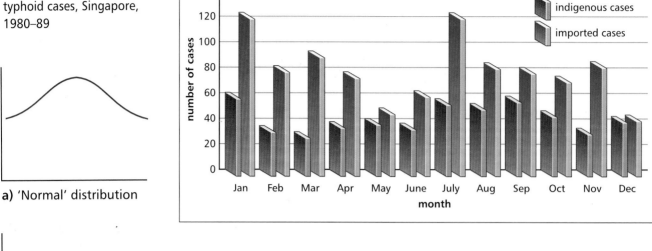

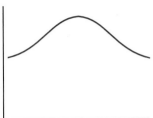

a) 'Normal' distribution

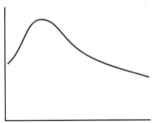

b) 'Even' distribution

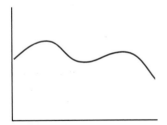

c) Unimodal distribution (positively skewed)

d) Bimodal distribution (two peaks)

■ **24.20** Different types of distribution

11 a Different patterns for local and imported cases of typhoid are revealed in **24.19**. Referring to the graphs in **24.20**, state which most closely relates to **i** local cases and **ii** imported cases.
 b The school holidays in Singapore end in January and July. To which of the distributions does this appear to offer a positive correlation?
 c Singapore is a multicultural society. Singaporeans visit relatives or travel, especially during school holidays. How might this explain one of the distributions shown in **24.19**?

12 You should by now have reached the conclusion that the Singapore government needs to address one particular source of typhoid infection if it is to make further inroads into the disease. This is the imported source, as isolated from the geographical analysis of the data. Some of the sources of imported cases are easier to control than others. Singapore is a regional hub and as such attracts itinerant workers from a wide region, as well as its share of illegal immigrants.
 a What measures would you suggest to cut down the cases of typhoid in Singapore even more?
 b How would you suggest these measures are implemented in order to reduce the risk of imported cases? [For example, you might suggest giving out leaflets at airports.]

24.6 **A problem for the present and the future – AIDS**

It is not known for certain where or when the AIDS epidemic began, but from the early 1980s reports started to appear of a wasting disease which left sufferers open to attack by secondary infection, such as pneumonia, from which they died. The disease was first identified and its cause suggested in 1984. From that time on the inexorable progress of the disease has been tracked, not least by geographers, and its possible course fed into economic forecasts. The following information is provided for analysis. Consider it in the light of the data already analysed on poliomyelitis and typhoid. Once diseases are fully understood, not only in a clinical sense, but very often in a spatial sense, they can be attacked and beaten. Since the study of AIDS is at such an early stage, it can safely be assumed that major advances will be made in the next few years.

What is AIDS?

AIDS (acquired immuno-deficiency syndrome) describes the condition in which an infected person is at the mercy of secondary infections because the body's natural defences have been put out of order by the HIV virus (the human immuno-deficiency virus). This virus fools the blood cells which normally attack unwelcome invaders (other viruses, for example) into believing that they are harmless. Secondary infections therefore stand a good chance of killing their host. The disease has the following characteristics:

- It is 100 per cent lethal, though patients can be treated so that they continue to live a considerable time after the first infection.

- It is most commonly sexually transmitted, but can in rare cases be passed on from an infected person

through fights, operations and other situations where blood can be mixed.

- It can be transmitted by the re-use of infected needles, as occurs in the drug culture of some developed countries, and with the under-resourced medical facilities of developing countries.

- It can be passed from mother to child during pregnancy.

- It has a long incubation period, perhaps up to 10 years.

24.21 is a report on a major world conference on AIDS which was held in 1992. It describes the rapid spread of the disease, but also indicates that it is a 'time bomb' with major effects on the world economy waiting to happen. **24.22** shows how far the disease had become 'a worldwide epidemic' by 1989.

How may AIDS spread in the future?

A group of scientists at Imperial College, London, and Oxford University have studied data on AIDS, including geographical location and growth rates, and have derived a computer model of how it may develop in the future. This has led to the conclusion that in many countries, particularly in Africa and South-east Asia, conditions exist for

■ **24.21** A report from *The Independent*, 21 July 1992

Every 15 seconds someone, somewhere gets HIV

One new person is infected with the AIDS virus every 15 seconds, while 10–12 million adults – and 1 million children – already have HIV, according to the World Health Organisation. More than 2 million have developed AIDS, writes Liz Hunt.

The world was at the beginning of an 'AIDS era', Michael Merson, director of its global AIDS programme, told a conference in Amsterdam yesterday.

Small, discrete epidemics of HIV had 'coalesced' into a worldwide epidemic, he said.

Transmission rates in parts of south and south-east Asia, which had been relatively safe, were now as high as sub-Saharan Africa. In central and eastern Europe 'new found freedom' had fuelled the spread of HIV, Dr Merson said.

Women and children were at increasing risk as the gaps in transmission rates between the two sexes narrowed everywhere. By 2000, more than half of all newly infected adults will be women. In sub-Saharan Africa more than 20 million girls aged

10 to 14 would soon become sexually active, he said. In some cities more than a third of adults were HIV positive, so a single act of intercourse was a substantial risk.

In developing countries family structures and whole villages were being destroyed as thousands of children became 'AIDS orphans' left with elderly relatives. Up to 80 per cent of hospital beds in some African cities are occupied by AIDS patients, and the disease would soon be claiming half of some countries'

national expenditure on health.

Anke Erhardt, from Columbia University's School of Medicine, said efforts at prevention were 'too limited and misguided'.

The public health realist was hampered by 'moralisers' who believed abstinence rather than condom use should be taught in schools. The female condom was an important step. There was no evidence that youngsters who started having sex would stop, she said. 'Programmes of revirginisation won't work.'

countries not affected or
not tested for HIV

countries having less than an
estimated 10 000 HIV carriers

countries having an estimated
10 000–100 000 HIV carriers

countries having an
estimated 100 000–2 million
or more HIV carriers

■ **24.22** HIV infection –
a worldwide epidemic

the virus to kill far more people than are being born for some time in the future. These findings are based on the tracking of women aged 15–45. Once the infection rate reaches 30 per cent in women of this age, even the highest population growth rates can be eroded to nothing.

A degree of uncertainty exists in the predictions because some countries still do not report AIDS data, or under-report its incidence. Also, the model does not take into account the reaction of the population to the threat. In the UK, some headway has been made through educational programmes, especially through the promotion of the use of condoms during sexual intercourse, a practice which significantly decreases both the risk of pregnancy and that of contracting AIDS.

A myth which developed in the early days of knowledge about AIDS was that it was only homosexuals or prostitutes who were at risk from it. In fact, the research group found that there are usually two stages in the epidemic within a country.

The first is where there is rapid growth amongst the high-risk population, especially prostitutes and their clients, but that there is a later peak when men who have visited prostitutes infect their wives or girlfriends, who pass it on to their children during pregnancy. The first epidemic sows the seeds of the second, and there may be a considerable time lapse between the two peaks.

Cultural differences further confuse the pattern of spread, but on average, HIV infection doubles in prevalence within a particular population over a period of about three years. It therefore takes 30 years for HIV to spread from an incidence level of 1 per 100 000 to 1 per 100, a level which would be much more detectable. The disease can remain hidden in a community until this point, by which time it may have taken root. Having reached 10 per cent it only takes a further three years to reach 20 per cent. At this point, the epidemic explodes.

IT5

IT5

IT5

Cameroon: the economic impact of AIDS

Cameroon is a state in West Africa (**24.23**) which mirrors the effect of AIDS on many of its neighbours (see **24.22** and **24.24**). A study of the present development of the disease in that country and how its development may affect the economy should therefore be instructive for learning about the wider impact of AIDS.

As in other locations, it has been found that AIDS tends to affect the upper socio-economic classes. This group is vital to the economic success of a country, including as it does the teachers, administrators, traders and entrepreneurs who keep the economy vital. Up to now, they have been relatively immune from the major ravages of common diseases since they have better sanitation, water supply, diet and access to medical facilities than their less fortunate compatriots. AIDS is different; **24.25** shows how it discriminates in three African countries.

The economy of a country can be 'modelled' according to average performance over a particular period. This model can then be used to predict future performance under certain circumstances. **24.26** is a model of the Cameroon economy (1979–80). The effects of AIDS in an economy reflect our initial look at how a bad cold affects the individual (**24.12**). The immediate impact is to give a decline in the labour supply, especially of skilled labour. Under-supply of labour leads to substitution with more expensive alternatives (investment in mechanisation or imported skilled labour) which lead to wage increases. There are also changes in demand brought about by a changing population balance, and the effects are shown in **24.27**.

Country	Cities	Rural	High risk*
Angola	1.3	nd	14.2
Benin	0.1	6.7	4.5
Botswana	0.8	0.1	1.2
Burkina Faso	1.7	nd	18.5
Burundi	17.5	nd	18.5
Cameroon	1.1	0.4	8.6
Cape Verde	1.1	0.4	8.6
Central African Republic	7.4	3.7	20.6
Congo	3.9	1.0	34.3
Djibouti	0.3	0.0	2.7
Equatorial Guinea	0.3	0.3	nd
Ethiopia	2.0	0.0	18.2
Gabon	1.8	0.8	nd
Gambia	0.1	nd	1.7
Ghana	2.2	nd	25.2
Guinea	0.6	0.2	nd
Guinea Bissau	0.1	0.0	0.0
Ivory Coast	8.5	3.3	23.8
Kenya	7.8	1.0	59.2
Lesotho	0.1	nd	nd
Malawi	23.2	nd	55.9
Mali	0.4	nd	23.0
Mauritania	0.06	nd	0.0
Morocco	0.0	nd	7.1
Mozambique	1.1	0.8	2.6
Namibia	2.5	nd	nd
Niger	nd	nd	5.8
Nigeria	0.5	0.0	1.7
Rwanda	30.3	1.7	79.8
Senegal	0.02	0.0	2.3
Sierra Leone	3.6	nd	2.7
Somalia	0.0	nd	0.4
South Africa	0.1	nd	3.2
Sudan	0.0	nd	16.0
Tanzania	8.9	5.4	38.7
Tunisia	0.1	nd	1.9
Uganda	24.3	12.3	86.0
Zaire	6.0	3.6	37.8
Zambia	24.5	13.0	54.0
Zimbabwe	3.2	1.4	nd

nd = no data
* prostitutes

■ **24.24** Percentage estimates of HIV incidence in selected African states, 1990

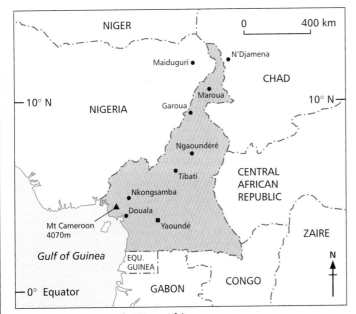

■ **24.23** Cameroon in West Africa

Country date	Type of sample size	Indicator of status	Percentage infection in socio-economic groups			
			Lower	Middle		Higher
Rwanda 1987	Urban adults in national sample 1255	Level of schooling	Primary or less 20.8%	More than primary 29.6%		
Zaire 1987	Employees of urban textile factory 5991	Category	Workers 2.8%	Foremen 4.6%		Executives 5.3%
Zambia 1985	Patients, blood donors and hospital personnel 1078	Years of schooling	0–4 yrs 8.0%	5–9 yrs 14.7%	10–14 yrs 24.1%	14+yrs 33.3%

■ **24.25** The relation between HIV infection and socio-economic status in three African countries

Sectors	1979–80 net trade billions of CFA francs	Export/ production ratio	Imports/ domestically produced supply ratio
Food crops	2.133	1.39	0.76
Cash crops	117.026	95.14	125.88
Forestry	22.314	75.71	0.32
Food processing	5.490	32.56	36.98
Consumer goods	−31.198	4.95	32.98
Intermediate goods	−37.241	35.63	75.70
Cement and base metals	−39.115	30.73	209.63
Capital goods	−130.881	37.27	209.63
Construction	0.000	0.00	0.00
Private services	7.187	13.26	13.94
Public services	0.000	0.00	0.00
Total		19.27	29.19

AIDS epidemic

↓

decline in labour force (esp. skilled)

↓

increase in wage bill

↓

influence on demand for goods

↓

change in allocation of scarce resources between competing sectors of the economy

■ **24.27** The effects of AIDS on an economy

■ **24.26** Model of the Cameroon economy, 1979–80

	Domestic prices	Output	Domestic exports	Imports
Food crops	+0.36	−0.11	−0.12	+1.05
Cash crops	+0.62	−0.70	−0.95	+0.06
Forestry	+2.03	−1.45	−1.52	nd
Food processing	+1.17	−1.37	−1.43	+0.93
Consumer goods	+1.55	−1.91	−1.94	+1.19
Intermediate goods	+0.80	−0.83	−0.80	−0.21
Cement/base metals	+1.39	−3.64	−3.73	−2.40
Capital goods	+1.77	−3.40	−3.43	−2.40
Construction	+2.24	−2.87	nd	nd
Private services	+2.35	−2.27	−2.35	−0.72
Public services	+6.06	−0.25	nd	nd

■ **24.28** Possible changes in the Cameroon economy as a result of declining labour supply, in terms of percentage change from base per year

nd = no data

If the model of the Cameroon economy (**24.26**) is investigated with the assumption that declining labour supply will affect it, the results might be as shown in **24.27**. It is assumed that the fall in skilled labour supply is accompanied by an overall decline in domestic production and in the demand for investment, an increase in domestic prices and real wages, lower exports, and a deterioration of public finances. The percentage changes from the original model (**24.26**) are shown in **24.28**.

13 Write summary background notes about AIDS, using the information in this section and any other material you may collect from magazines, your local surgery, newspaper articles, etc. In particular, your notes should include something under each of the following headings:
  a definition
  b the spread of AIDS
  c possible effects on the economy.
  In addition, keep track of the latest developments in the search for a cure. There are many hopeful lines of enquiry ranging from drugs to gene therapy.

14 a With reference to **24.23**, describe any differences you can identify between HIV infection in cities and rural areas in Africa. You may like to produce a graph (for example a scattergraph) to help you identify any differences.
  b Is the pattern a consistent one?
  c With reference to **24.24**, attempt to explain the differences you have found.

15 Using evidence from **24.22**, which countries would you expect to have a particularly high incidence of HIV infection in the general community within the next 30 years? Explain your answer.

16 Using **24.26**, describe the Cameroon economy using the following subheadings:
  ■ most important production in Cameroon
  ■ percentage of production entering export trade
  ■ largest imports
  ■ self-sufficient sectors
  ■ most important non-importing sectors
  ■ most important non-exporting sectors.

17 Using **24.28**, describe what changes would occur in the economy if wage rises followed a decline in the labour supply after AIDS took its toll.

18 *Essay title:* 'In what ways can geographical techniques help the identification and control of disease?' Use actual examples to illustrate your answer.

ISSUE THREE: An ageing population

IT5

Some of the previous items in this unit have referred to the growth of the older element in populations (**23.4**, **23.7**, **23.13**, for example). There are many other respects in which ageing is an important issue. Among these are:

■ provision of resources to cope with a large old-age dependency sector

■ a reduction in the workforce and a simultaneous growth in the percentage of the population over retirement age

■ rising divorce rates, with consequent problems for future care of the elderly

■ the possible need to re-design buildings and open spaces as the percentage of young people in our communities declines and the proportion of the elderly increases.

IT5

19 *Either:*

a Write a report entitled 'The ageing of the population'. It should use the resources in this unit, but should not be entirely confined to them. The data in **24.29** may be helpful. There are many bodies which issue information on this and related topics, amongst them Help the Aged, Population Concern and Age Concern. Your report, which should contain actual examples wherever possible and should be about 1500 words in length, illustrated with relevant figures, should follow the format:

Introduction – definition of the term 'ageing' in this context; an example of the historical development of the issue.

Examples – developing/developed world differences; regional variations.

Dependency ratios – what they are and how they are changing; what they mean from an economic point of view; how future funding may be affected by ageing.

Positive and negative aspects of the ageing of population – examples of how individual quality of life and the life of the nation may be affected; examples of measures being taken in various countries to meet the challenge of ageing.

Conclusion – meeting the reality of ageing is certainly a challenge. Is it likely to be advantageous or disadvantageous to society? Should it be seen as a problem or a benefit? What should communities be doing about it?

Or:

b Select one factor concerned with ageing and write detailed notes on possible changes in the next 50 years for one named area.

Mid-year figures estimates	UK	England	Wales	Scotland	N. Ireland
			thousands		
1961	52 807	43 561	2 635	5 184	1 427
1971	55 928	46 412	2 760	5 235	1 540
1976	56 216	46 660	2 799	5 233	1 524
1981	56 352	46 821	2 813	5 180	1 538
1986	56 850	47 342	2 820	5 121	1 567
1987	57 008	47 488	2 833	5 112	1 575
1988	57 159	47 633	2 854	5 094	1 578
1989	57 352	47 809	2 869	5 091	1 583
1990	57 561	47 992	2 878	5 102	1 589
1991	57 801	48 208	2 891	5 107	1 594
1992	57 998	48 378	2 899	5 111	1 610
of which percentages					
0–4	6.7	6.7	6.6	6.4	8.0
5–15	13.7	13.5	14.0	13.7	17.7
16–44	42.0	42.0	39.6	42.6	42.1
45–64M/59F	19.3	19.3	19.8	19.5	17.2
65M/60F–74	11.4	11.3	12.6	11.5	9.8
75 and over	7.0	7.0	7.4	6.4	5.2
Projections (based on mid-1992 population estimates)					
1996	58 784	49 067	2 930	5 146	1 642
2001	59 800	50 023	2 966	5 143	1 667
2006	60 610	50 814	2 993	5 115	1 687
2111	61 257	51 458	3 013	5 077	1 709
of which percentages					
0–4	5.7	5.8	5.6	5.5	6.7
5–15	13.5	13.5	12.9	13.6	15.3
16–44	37.4	37.5	35.9	36.2	39.7
45–64M/59F	23.6	23.6	23.2	24.5	21.2
65M/60F–74	12.0	11.9	13.4	12.4	10.7
75 and over	7.8	7.8	9.0	7.9	6.4

■ **24.29** The ageing of the UK population

■ **24.30** Sheltered housing for elderly residents may be in increasing demand in the future in some societies

Economic
Activity

25.1 Economic systems and sectors

IT1

Economic systems are geared towards satisfying societies' demands for goods and services. The **primary sector** involves the exploitation of natural resources from the land, air or water, as in agriculture, farming, fishing or mining. The **secondary sector** takes raw materials from the primary sector and manufactures them into useful products, for example wheat into flour or bauxite into aluminium products. In doing so, value is added to the end product. The **tertiary sector** is concerned with a huge range of services. Some, such as transport, retailing or finance, contribute to the commercial and trading functions of a country, whereas others supply basic human needs such as health and education. As a result of the increasingly sophisticated and complex nature of the tertiary sector in the more advanced economies of the world, a fourth sector, known as as the **quaternary sector**, has evolved. This encompasses services such as research and development (R & D), high-level decision-making, and all aspects of information processing. The services in both of these last two sectors can be vital earners for any economy, with tourism and financial services (known as **invisible exports**) making a very significant contribution to the balance of trade.

Traditionally the balance of the various sectors has been seen largely as a function of economic development. **25.1**, the sector model, shows how in a theoretical context the relative importance of the sectors changes as a country develops its economy. The simple explanation is that over time, people move from primary tasks into manufacturing to make a major contribution to a country's economy, as happened in the Industrial Revolution of the late-18th and 19th centuries in most of Europe and eastern North America. The goods thus produced can be exported or used to improve the quality of life within a country.

To support the growing industrial base and the growing aspirations of a more affluent population, many of whom live in urbanised areas, there is a need for a whole range of services including transport and utilities, consumer and financial services, leading to a relative expansion of tertiary activity (**25.1**). The decline of manufacturing is of major concern in many advanced economies. In some cases, as in the UK, Japan and the USA, the role of the tertiary sector has become so dominant that their economies are termed **post-industrial societies**. The various impacts of manufacturing decline, in a severe form termed **de-industrialisation**, are considered in Chapter 28, and the explosion in the service economy is evaluated in Chapter 29.

Chapter 30 explores issues of economic growth and development. Economic growth is a wider process than economic development as it involves the growing capacity of a country to increase industrial output and hence gross national product (GNP) per head. The

IT1

■ **25.1** The Clark–Fisher sector model

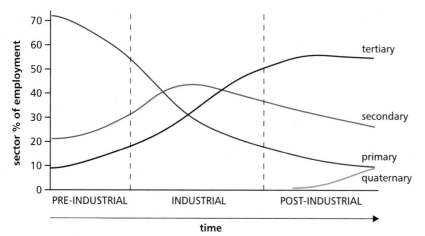

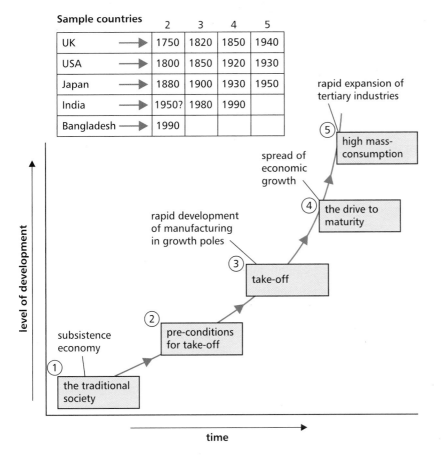

Sample countries		2	3	4	5
UK	→	1750	1820	1850	1940
USA	→	1800	1850	1920	1930
Japan	→	1880	1900	1930	1950
India	→	1950?	1980	1990	
Bangladesh	→	1990			

rapid expansion of tertiary industries

⑤ high mass-consumption

spread of economic growth

④ the drive to maturity

rapid development of manufacturing in growth poles

③ take-off

② pre-conditions for take-off

subsistence economy

① the traditional society

level of development

time

■ **25.2** Rostow's model of economic development

stages in economic growth are succinctly summarised by Rostow's model of economic growth (**25.2**), which because of its simplicity has provided a very widely-used framework. It has been discredited by some geographers because its sequence is based on Western capitalist economies, and may not be appropriate as an aid to analysis of many of the economies of the developing world. Also, the development process is in reality far more complex than Rostow would suggest. Issues arising from economic development are evaluated in Chapter 30.

The basic driving force of economic activity is the demand for goods and services created by the population. This can be satisfied by the producers, who use resources to make and supply goods and services. **25.3** shows how the economic system operates. Clearly the nature of the government (whether communist or capitalist, etc.) determines how the system operates.

1 Make a copy of **25.1** and describe (using precise numerical data) the trends shown.

2 Try to adapt **25.3**, which is essentially a capitalist market model, to show how a centrally planned economy might work. For example, the government will give strict commands to the producers on production quotas, etc.

■ **25.3** How a market economy works

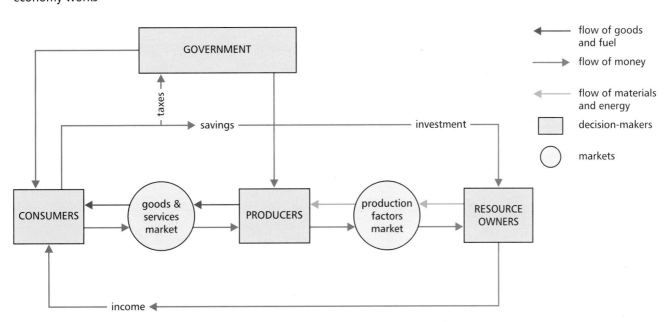

25.2 **Resources**

IT1

The inputs to the economic system comprise a range of resources – natural (e.g. raw materials), human (e.g. labour) and economic (e.g. capital). The owners of these resources have a critical role to play in the workings of the system. In the wider context of the environment, the economic system interfaces with natural systems. For this reason, the approaches adopted by producers and consumers, whether they are conservationist, sustainable or exploitive, will determine levels of pollution and environmental degradation.

IT4

Natural resources can be defined as 'the geographical features of the world, from the air, water and land, which enable societies to function'. **Reserves** are the economically usable portion of the total resources that can be exploited under prevailing technical and socio-economic conditions. For example, there are very large supplies of oil stored in tar sands and oil shales, but these are not usually considered reserves because under present economic and technical conditions their exploitation is not a viable proposition. **25.4** shows a standard classification system for resources. The essential division is based on their relationship with consumption. The **non-renewable** group (variously known as **finite**, **capital** or **stock resources**) will ultimately be depleted, but within the group there are major differences. For example, recycling rates for metallic resources can be as high as 60 per cent and because non-metallic resources such as sand and gravel are recoverable from a very wide range of geological deposits, they are ubiquitous and

very abundant. In contrast, consumable resources are totally destroyed by use and therefore depletion is totally dependent on consumption rates. In Chapter 27 you will have an opportunity to evaluate whether there is a genuine global energy crisis, as fossil fuels are depleted.

IT4

The other major category, **renewable resources** (usually known as **flow resources**), can be divided into two groups (**25.4**). One group, the **non-critical**, will be available for ever at a world scale because of their recurrent nature – examples are water, and solar energy – although the uneven distribution of the resource with respect to political boundaries may lead to international conflict. Geographers cite considerable evidence for potential water shortages generating wars in areas of deficit such as the Middle East in the 21st century. The other renewable group is termed **critical** or **sustainable resources**. If these resources, such as soil (see Chapter 26), fish (Chapter 17) and forestry (Chapter 14), are well managed, for example by manuring, by maintaining stocks, or by replanting, the supplies can be sustained. For each area there is a maximum sustainable yield, beyond which extraction rates will exceed renewal rates. Continued exploitation accelerates the decline of the resource until a critical threshold is reached, at which stage extinction becomes a major threat unless very extensive measures are taken, for example in the preservation of key species of flora or fauna such as the whale.

■ **25.4** A classification of natural resources

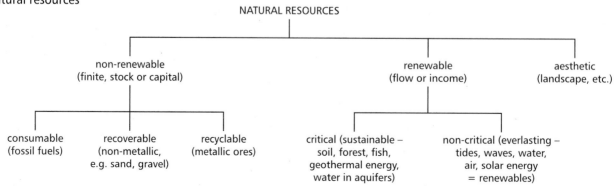

25.4 also shows a third category of natural resources which include landscapes and natural features, usually collectively called **aesthetic resources**. They are renewable, provided that they are managed, and protected from the excesses of mass tourism and other exploitation. The studies of Nepal (pages 362–63) and the Galapagos (pages

247–48) illustrate their vulnerability, and also the extreme difficulty of developing ecotourism.

There are further systems of resource classification, based on criteria such as mode of existence, availability, value and usage, but the one discussed above is most useful when considering global and national strategies of use.

The threat to wildlife

Unless action is taken, some 20% of the world's species will be extinct by the year 2000.

The threat to the forests

Every year, the world loses up to 15 million hectares of trees. At the present rate of destruction there will be a worldwide shortage of wood by the year 2000.

THE THROWAWAY SOCIETY

When something breaks, we throw it away and go out and buy a new one. Millions of tonnes of rubbish are dumped every year.

ENERGY CRISIS

Nuclear power – the answer to the energy crisis or a threat to all our futures?

Toxic Wastes

In the USA, 35 million tonnes of dangerous chemicals are produced each year. Only 10% are handled and stored safely.

WATER POLLUTION

Every day waste is poured into rivers from human sewage, factory wastes and farms.

Pollution of the sea

Every day, 450 million litres of human sewage and 800 million litres of industrial waste are poured into the North Sea. For too long the world's oceans have been regarded as sinks.

■ **25.5** The misuse of resources

25.3 **Sustainable development**

One key idea to emerge in recent years is **sustainable development**, which encompasses a number of features. For some people sustainable development implies maintaining an overall equilibrium between resource use and resource availability, either by lifestyle changes which reduce materials and energy consumption, or by making a given unit of resource produce more GNP by improved technological efficiency. The Brundtland Commission on Environment and Development (1987) defined sustainable development as 'development that meets the needs of the present, without compromising the ability of future generations to meet their own needs'. The concept of 'needs', in particular the essential needs of the world's poor, should be given overriding priority. The rationale for sustainable development is therefore to raise the standard of living of all, especially the least advantaged. The feasibility of sustainable development is

explored in all the following chapters with reference to energy, agriculture and industry. Obviously if exploitive, unsustainable strategies are practised, then future costs in the form of deteriorating environments and loss of valuable natural resources are to be expected.

The exploitation of resources is affected by their uneven world distribution, as geological or geographical features are rarely congruent with political boundaries. Theoretically, deficiencies can be overcome by **trade** – the movement of materials or goods from one country to another. The world economic system is characterised by a high degree of interdependence between countries, as shown in **25.6**. There are particular movements between certain groups, for example oil from OPEC countries is shipped and piped all over the world.

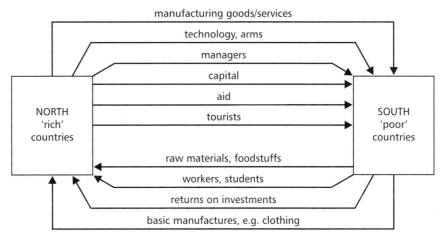

manufacturing goods/services
technology, arms
managers
capital
aid
tourists
raw materials, foodstuffs
workers, students
returns on investments
basic manufactures, e.g. clothing

NORTH 'rich' countries

SOUTH 'poor' countries

■ **25.6** North–South interdependence

3 Study **25.5** which shows some of the ways in which resources are being exploited. What ways would you suggest to avoid some of the worst uses of resources?

4 Study the following two views concerning resources:

- The Earth's natural resources are there for us to exploit. We must have food, water, air and energy, medicines, warmth, shelter and minerals to keep us alive and well fed, comfortable and healthy. If we use the resources carefully and sensibly they will last indefinitely.

- We must convince everyone of the need to conserve natural resources. At the moment we are

not allowing them to regenerate themselves. We will be short of fossil fuels, certain rare metals, and some food by the year 2010, as our resources are running out.

a What do you think is the present state of the world's resources?

b Which viewpoint do you agree with most? Support your answer with detailed evidence.

c Can the present state of the world's resources be considered a global problem?

5 Do you consider that **25.6** shows genuine interdependence? Justify your answer.

25.4 **Economic groupings**

IT5

■ **25.7** Economic groupings and the North–South Divide

In this book, especially in the remaining chapters of this unit, countries are placed into one of nine groups according to certain economic variables, such as GNP per capita, food and energy consumption. **25.7** shows the global distribution of the six groups. The North–South Divide is an imaginary line separating the wealthy countries of the world (the North) and the poorer countries (the South). The global North–South Divide was developed as a concept by the Brandt Report in the 1980s, which envisaged a more just form of interdependence

IT5

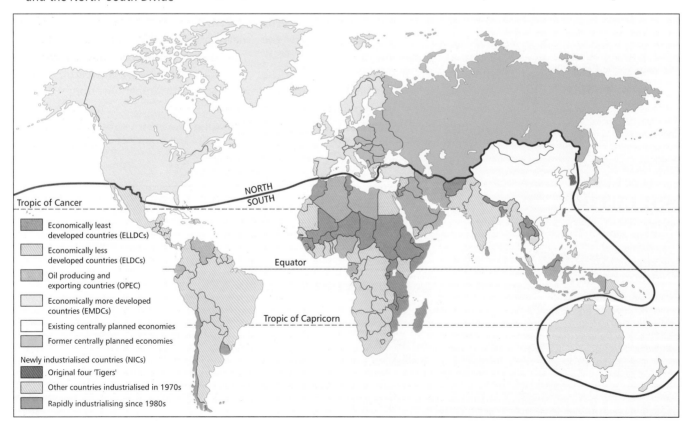

Tropic of Cancer

NORTH
SOUTH

Equator

Tropic of Capricorn

Economically least developed countries (ELLDCs)

Economically less developed countries (ELDCs)

Oil producing and exporting countries (OPEC)

Economically more developed countries (EMDCs)

Existing centrally planned economies

Former centrally planned economies

Newly industrialised countries (NICs)

Original four 'Tigers'

Other countries industrialised in 1970s

Rapidly industrialising since 1980s

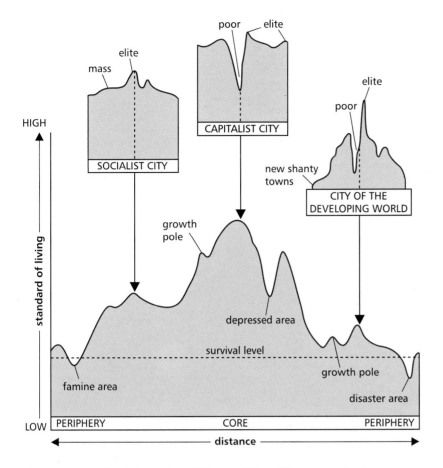

Labels on diagram:
mass — elite (SOCIALIST CITY)
poor — elite (CAPITALIST CITY)
poor — elite (CITY OF THE DEVELOPING WORLD)
new shanty towns
growth pole
depressed area
survival level
famine area
growth pole
disaster area
HIGH / LOW
standard of living
PERIPHERY — CORE — PERIPHERY
distance

■ **25.8** A generalised view of world inequalities of living standards

which would create a 'new world economic order' (see **30.6**).

25.8 tries to show how regional disparities within the countries fit in with the global disparities. The **core** refers to the rich countries of the North, and both socialist countries and the countries of the South are shown as poorer **peripheries**.

6 Analyse what the diagram **25.8** is attempting to convey in terms of disparity of living standards at a world scale. What does it suggest about standards in cities?

In subsequent chapters, the causes of both global and regional disparity are explained, with a detailed consideration of the issues of inequality within the world and within countries. Inevitably, there are plans to overcome disparity at a national scale. The issue of global disparity is investigated in Chapter 30, although solutions to it are retarded by national self-interest, as shown at the 1992 Earth Summit held in Rio de Janeiro. At this conference, national self-interest prevented the universal acceptance of many of the resolutions designed to promote strategies of sustainable and equitable development for all, such as those on global warming, biodiversity, and forest exploitation.

The provision of food for a rapidly expanding population is derived from both land and water. Chapter 17 gave some consideration to water, particularly the sea, as a source of food. The importance of fish in the human diet varies considerably across the globe, but in general it is the farming of land rather than of water that yields by far the greater part of human food supply. This chapter is therefore devoted to agriculture – the exploitation of the world's land-based food resources.

26.1 Introducing agricultural systems

The agricultural sector

Agriculture, in its broadest sense, can be defined as the cultivation and/or the production of crop plants or livestock products. With fishing, forestry and mining, farming forms part of the primary sector, which as shown in the sector model (**25.1**) has declined relative to the secondary sector initially, and ultimately relative to the tertiary sector. There is no doubt that globally the relative importance of agriculture has declined, because of the greater rate of growth of industry and services. The importance of agriculture can be measured in two main ways: as a percentage of total employment, and as the percentage contribution it makes to gross domestic product (GDP).

Historically, agriculture is shown to have employed between 70 and 80 per cent of the workforce and generated 40–60 per cent of the income of pre-industrial societies. As a result of industrialisation, the agricultural workforce fell below 50 per cent of the total in Britain in the 1780s, but nowhere else until the 1840s, and has still not fallen below 50 per cent in most of Africa and Asia. The falling contribution to GDP follows the same sequence, beginning first again in Western Europe and European-settled areas overseas, followed by Latin America and most recently the oil producers of the Middle East. Nevertheless in 1988, 43 countries defined by the World Bank as 'low-income countries'

had over 68 per cent of their population engaged in agriculture, and agriculture accounted for at least 30 per cent of the GDP. Typical of these countries is Bangladesh where, in 1991, 70 per cent of the total workforce were employed in agriculture and 36 per cent of GDP was derived from agriculture.

Agro-ecosystems

IT1

Agriculture systems are modified natural ecosystems (the term **agro-ecosystem** is appropriate). They differ from other 'wild' unmanaged climax ecosystems, in a similar physical environment, in being simpler, with less diversity of plant and animal species and with a less complex structure (i.e. spatial organisation of organic components). Not only are the number of species and associated lifeforms fewer, but because of genetic breeding crop plants tend to have less genetic diversity than their wild ancestors or near relatives. Cultivation, which deliberately aims to reduce competition by weeding, pest control, etc., channels a high proportion of the available light energy for photosynthesis into the crop plants to ensure maximum yield, and from there directly or indirectly (by way of domestic livestock) to humans. Thus, as can be seen in **26.1**, the food web is simple and the number of trophic levels reduced to two, or at most three.

■ **26.1** The agro-ecosystem – food chain and trophic levels

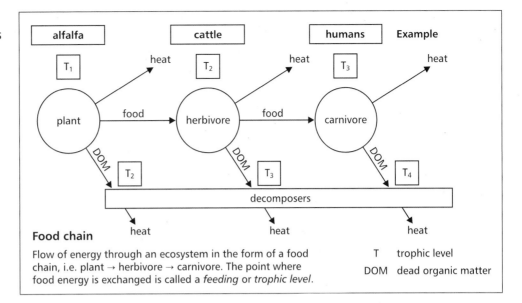

Food chain

Flow of energy through an ecosystem in the form of a food chain, i.e. plant → herbivore → carnivore. The point where food energy is exchanged is called a *feeding* or *trophic level*.

T   trophic level
DOM dead organic matter

IT1

The biomass of the large herbivores in the agro-ecosystem is considerably greater than that of animals normally supported by an unmanaged terrestrial ecosystem, mainly because they are sold by weight for their meat products. As a result, a much smaller proportion of the energy of the plant biomass is passed along the 'detrital' or decomposing route to the soil, with serious consequences for the health of the soil. Conversely, a higher proportion of plant biomass is consumed either by the domestic livestock or exported from the system directly as a crop product. Consequently, as the 'energy pool' in the form of dead or decaying organic matter and humus is in general less than that of unmanaged ecosystems, it has to be replenished by artificial means such as applied farmyard manure or fertilisers. The more highly concentrated energy flow is thus a key difference between agro-ecosystems and natural ecosystems (see section 13.3).

You will have noticed that in the agro-ecosystem there is a continual loss of nutrients from the system (sometimes slow, sometimes rapid) either in the crop or animal harvest or as a result of leaching losses, accelerated by soil tillage. Unless the nutrient loss through export is made good in the form of fertiliser application, the agro-ecosystem will inevitably tend to run down, the biomass will decrease, the soil will degrade and productivity will fall.

IT1

Agro-ecosystems also tend to be more 'open' systems with both a greater number and a larger volume of inputs and outputs. Various inputs 'subsidise' the input of solar energy. These inputs consist of the direct input of energy in traditional forms such as human and draught animal power, and that derived from fossil fuel which drives farm machinery. There are also indirect energy subsidies in the form of specially bred seeds, fertilisers, herbicides, machinery and irrigation water. All these inputs have the ability to 'buffer' production against environmental constraints, which may be physical (uncertain climate, indifferent soil) or human (primitive land tenure, capital shortages). Solar energy is used more efficiently because plants will not need to search for nutrients or 'fight off' pests if a ready supply of appropriate fertilisers and pesticides is used by the farmer.

1 Read through all the information in Chapter 13 and in this chapter, and devise a table which compares natural (unmanaged) ecosystems with agro-ecosystems in terms of their structure and functioning.

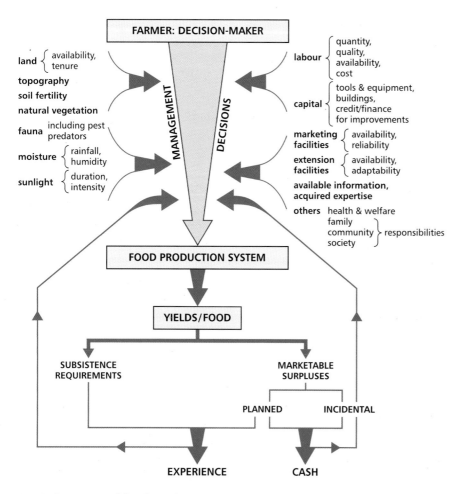

26.2 The nature of food production systems

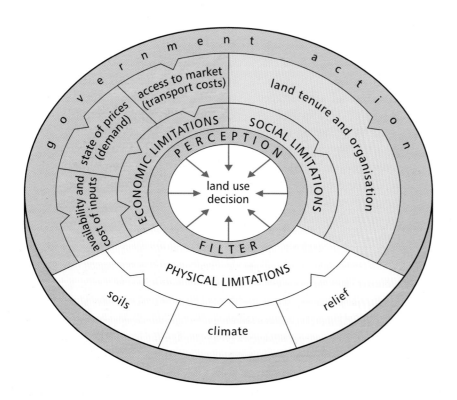

26.3 Factors influencing agricultural decision-making

The dynamics of food production systems

The production of food involves the farmer in regularly making a number of important decisions. These decision-makers should ideally have a good understanding of the environment in which they operate, as well as access to labour, capital and knowledge about possible markets for their produce. Food-producing systems are dynamic in that they are constantly changing as a result of the changing nature of environmental and socio-economic factors, some of which are beyond the direct control of the farmer.

26.2 shows how the farmer as a decision-maker manipulates a wide range of inputs, which in turn affect the character and level of productivity of the food production system. A distinction has to be made between **subsistence** systems where the prime aim is to provide food requirements for the family, and **commercial** or cash farming systems which are geared to market sales. As **26.2** suggests, over the years the farmer acquires experience in operating the system, and can turn this to advantage when deciding on the nature of future production systems.

Essentially therefore, as **26.3** shows, the farmers' land-use decisions are informed by physical, social, economic and political factors which are filtered through the decision-makers' perceptions prior to a decision being made. The personal values and goals of the decision-maker, whether it is a single family farmer or an agribusiness company, play a very significant part in the process.

26.2 Factors influencing agriculture

Environmental factors

The physical environment tends to operate as a constraint on agriculture, in that it is the land that provides all the basic essentials on which plant life, and consequently livestock, depends: heat, sunshine, water and soil. Different crops, and to a lesser extent animals too, vary in their specific environmental requirements.

Climate is generally regarded as the most significant control as it exerts both a considerable direct influence on the growth and survival of plants and animals, and an indirect influence as a result of its impact on soil formation and quality. Soils too can display a variety of characteristics, each of which can have an influence on plant growth. They can vary in terms of depth, degree of acidity, fertility, moisture-holding capacity, texture (workability) and liability to erosion. Crops particularly vary in terms of the soils in which they flourish. The relief of the land being farmed can affect agricultural activities in a number of ways, both directly and indirectly, through its effects on climate and soils. Aspect, altitude and slope are all significant here.

> 2 a Make a list of the ways in which climate, soils and relief affect agriculture.
>   b Think of an example that illustrates each of the impacts you have identified.
>
> 3 a Research ways in which the environmental constraints on agriculture may be overcome.
>   b How might the solutions in a country such as the USA differ from those in countries such as China or Bangladesh?

Farm size and tenure

As well as physical limitations, there are economic limitations placed on a farmer when making land use decisions. Farms vary in size from less than 1 ha (in market-gardening areas such as southern Holland or peasant farms in parts of Africa) to over 10 000 ha (cattle and sheep stations in Australia or state farms in the former Soviet Union). The size variation is largely a function of land quality and land availability, which are closely related to population density, how the area was settled, and inheritance laws. These factors determine whether the area is farmed by intensive or extensive means. Clearly if there is only a small area, this has to be farmed by intensive means to support a family, or alternatively if

the carrying capacity of the land is low, only a large farm would provide enough pasture to support sufficient animals to enable the farm to be viable. Farm size too can be a crucial determinant of the prosperity of farming, because large farms are able to benefit from economies of scale.

Land tenure is defined as the economic, political and legal aspects of the ownership and management of agricultural land. Globally, there is a wide variety of tenure systems and each can have far-reaching effects on agricultural practice, but the principal forms of tenure are the following:

1 **Owner occupation** is a common form of tenure in most advanced farming nations. The main advantage is that farmers have the freedom to exercise their entrepreneurial abilities to use the land as they wish, and can invest in the family farm for future generations.

2 **Tenancy** is a common arrangement; indeed many farmers own some land and rent other areas of their farms. Landlords vary from great estate owners (such as the Prince of Wales) with whom tenancy is secure and often handed from father to son, to pension funds or food-processing companies employing highly-trained farm managers. Generally, the landowner provides land and fixed equipment in exchange for an annual cash return, while the tenant provides working capital.

3 **Communal ownership** is extremely common in tribal Africa, but is also a feature of certain political systems such as the former collective farms of Eastern Europe and the Ukraine, the commune system of China, and the kibbutzim of Israel. There are advantages in terms of developing a unity of purpose, but frequently the communality leads to tortuous decision-making often by venerable, yet poorly qualified, leaders.

Economic factors

Capital usually refers to **fixed capital** (i.e. the fabric of the estate) and **working capital** (livestock, machinery, seeds, fertilisers, etc.). In most developed countries, agriculture tends to be capital intensive. Capital is generally used as an alternative to labour, or above all to modify the physical environment to achieve maximum yields. The major limiting factor is the availability of capital, which is largely raised through banks and other private institutions. The main problem is that it is the successful farmers who are regarded as the 'safest risk' and the whole system therefore operates against the small farmer who is seeking to expand. In less developed countries, raising capital for improvements is almost an impossibility for peasant farmers, who have to rely on the extortionate rates of village moneylenders. Co-operative systems have a vital role in providing start-up capital for small farmers at fair or low interest rates.

Both **transport** and **markets** were traditionally very important as limiting factors to the farmer's choice of crops. However, a whole series of technological developments, both in transport technology and food production technology, have diminished their control as factors. For example, vegetables from an agribusiness can be canned or frozen, or transported fresh by refrigerated lorry via motorways, or air-freighted. Increasingly, global markets are developing for fruit and vegetables, as international corporations set up subsidiaries to grow fruit and vegetables in economically less developed countries (ELDCs) for the high-value markets of the developed world. Vegetables come by air from countries such as Thailand, Senegal and Kenya, and flowers and fruit are flown in from all over the world.

Market prices, however, can have a major impact on the farmers' decision-making. The problem of price instability and exploitation is a major one for independent commercial farmers in agriculture-dependent ELDCs as they struggle to get a fair price for their commodities such as tea or bananas. Equally, fluctuating or falling market prices can be a major headache for farmers in the economically more developed countries (EMDCs). Increasingly, farmers there rely on government subsidies to influence their decisions as to which lines of agriculture to pursue.

Government intervention

Government (state) intervention has been identified as a major influence on contemporary agricultural systems, as it forms one of the supporting structures of the food supply system. A simplistic view suggests a considerable range in the scale and nature of government intervention, from more or less complete control over all aspects of agricultural production and marketing, to sporadic intervention with much less direct impact.

■ **26.4** Reasons for, and mechanisms of, state intervention

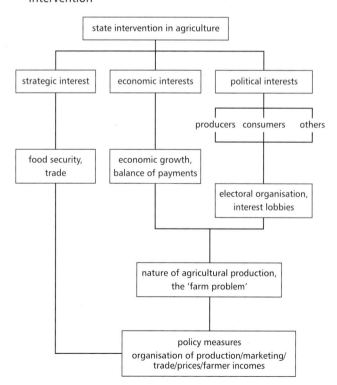

a) Reasons for state intervention in agriculture

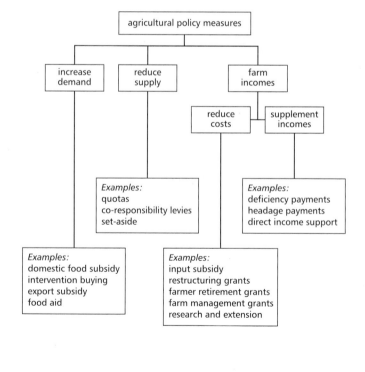

b) Mechanisms of government support to agriculture

■ **26.5** A summary of government agricultural policy in the UK

Many of the reasons for government intervention shown in **26.4** were especially pertinent in the depressed 1930s and in the period immediately following the Second World War, when it was vital to secure food supplies and to improve income and productivity in agriculture. By 1970, many of these factors had become less significant – food security in EMDCs had ceased to be an issue, with generally low world prices and abundant food stocks worldwide. Food imports too had become far less important as an element in the trade balance. These changing circumstances have led to a new sort of farm problem in the 1990s where the industrialisation of agriculture has led to a huge increase in yields. In developed countries, output from agriculture has risen at a faster rate than the demand for food, but farmers have not cut back their production to create equilibrium in the market, which has led to depressed farm prices and farm incomes, requiring further government intervention to support farmers at enormous cost. **26.5** summarises the history of government intervention in British agriculture; the nature and objectives of that intervention have so changed that it is possible to recognise three distinct phases.

Phase 1 1947–72	Measures
Aims • to promote a stable and efficient agricultural industry • to increase agricultural production • to promote self-sufficiency • to improve farm incomes • to provide adequate food at cheap prices	1 Price support by deficiency payments, guaranteed prices 2 Grants and subsidies – calf subsidy – ploughing grant – hill cow / hill sheep schemes
Phase 2 1973–83 (EC CAP policy)	
Aims • to increase productivity via technology • to ensure a fair standard of living for farmers • to stabilise markets • to guarantee food supplies • to ensure supplies at reasonable prices	1 Price support by intervention buying 2 Less Favoured Areas programme 3 Integrated development programme for rural areas
Phase 3 1984 onwards	
Aims • to control production • to reduce environmental damage	1 Production controls – guaranteed thresholds – quotas – set-aside – farm diversification schemes 2 Environmental initiatives – creation of ESAs 1986 – Nitrate Sensitive Areas 1990

26.3 **Classifying agricultural systems**

IT1

In order to study agricultural systems – by comparing their nature and analysing their distribution – it is necessary to try to classify them. **26.6** shows some of the criteria that might be used. The nature of the output is a clear means

IT1

■ **26.6** A classification of agricultural systems

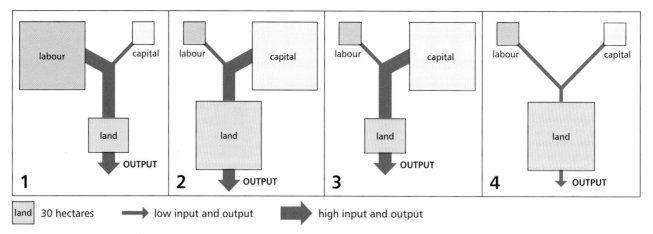

land ⬜ 30 hectares   → low input and output   ⟹ high input and output

■ **26.7** Four different farming systems

IT1

of distinction; so too is the nature of the physical environment in which the farming takes place.

A third criterion is the level of intensity. **Intensive farming** is defined by the ratio of labour, capital and other inputs to the available land area and usually gives a high yield per unit. At the other end of the scale, **extensive farming** occurs where land is sufficiently plentiful for the producer to think in terms of overall returns across the whole landholding and not primarily in terms of yield per unit area. Although only low to moderate yields per unit result, as inputs of labour especially are low, overall profits can be high, as in extensive prairie wheat farms, for example, where there is a high capital input of machinery and fertilisers.

4 In **26.7** four farming systems are shown.
  a Describe the farming systems, and classify them into intensive and extensive systems, giving your reasons.
  b Match the following four named farming types to the systems shown:
   i nomadic pastoralism in Kenya
   ii a spring wheat farm in Canada
   iii market gardening in south-west Lancashire
   iv a farm producing rice in Java, Indonesia.

■ **26.8** Subsistence and commercial farming systems

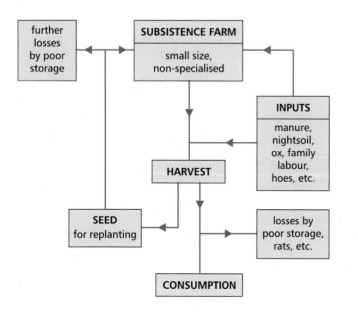

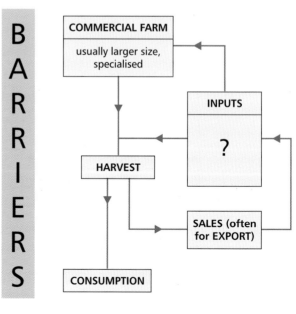

A further clear distinction can be made according to the differences between subsistence and commercial farms (**26.8**). These may include size, income, technology level, labour inputs and products, as well as a difference in market. Subsistence farming dominates much of Asia and Africa, where farmers are preoccupied with providing a range of crops for the survival of their families. Commercial agriculture dominates rural land use in the developed world, where its prime function is to make a profit – consequently inputs here are higher, to ensure higher levels of output. In reality, many subsistence farms do include elements of commercialism, for example in the growth of a few tree crops such as bananas or cocoa.

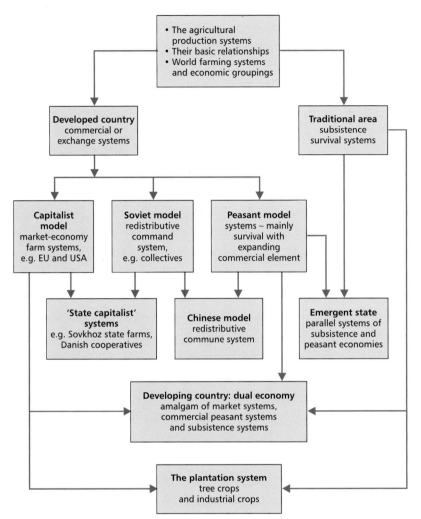

■ **26.9** World farming systems in their economic setting

5 With reference to **26.8**:
  a Identify some of the inputs which might raise levels of productivity in the commercial farming system.
  b What do you consider are the barriers inhibiting a move from subsistence to cash systems?

26.9 is a composite diagram of world farming systems in their economic setting. Farm systems are clearly linked to their historical development. For example, the plantation system, which still persists in the tropics, evolved from the colonial relationship between the 'First' and 'Third' worlds.

6 Farm investigations provide a possible topic for individual study. For example, using old maps you might record how a particular farm has changed over the last 20 years, and investigate the reasons for the changes. You should be able to produce comparative land use maps, systems diagrams and farm budgets, and look at all sorts of variables such as stocking rates, yields, field size and fertiliser inputs. Sometimes it is necessary to broaden out a study to compare two farms, one of which might practise conservation strategies, or to look at one aspect of farms in a parish, such as the impact of the milk quota, or hedgerow loss, or diversification strategies. The Ministry of Agriculture, Fisheries and Food publishes very full statistics for each parish, of farm size, crops, stock, employment, etc. and it is also possible to obtain from the Ministry or from a local resources library some historic farm parish statistics. You may wish to look at land use over a wider area rather than within a farm, and produce a transect across a suitable area of varied relief, geology and soils. If you consult standard texts on fieldwork techniques you will see how to present your results cartographically and graphically (using dispersion diagrams, etc.) and how to analyse them statistically, for example using chi-squared tests.

26.4 Agricultural change in the North (EMDCs)

Agricultural systems are essentially dynamic. They change, with varying frequency and to varying degrees, largely in response to altered 'external' conditions, such as a change in some aspect of the physical environment, increasing population or shifts in market demand. Broadly speaking, the nature and causes of agricultural change are different in the EMDCs and the ELDCs.

In the EMDCs of the North, such as the UK, the agricultural landscape which had gradually evolved over two centuries following the 18th-century Agricultural Revolution, largely based on mechanisation, has been transformed in less than 40 years by the 'High-tech Revolution'. All over Europe, farms have become much larger, more specialised in their production, and more technologically advanced; machines have replaced labour, and the number of farms, farmers and farm workers has declined.

Modernisation and industrialisation

Two main processes of agricultural change can be identified which together have had a major effect on the geography of British agriculture. Modernisation has led to:

- **intensification**, whereby output per hectare has increased spectacularly

- **specialisation**, where less profitable farm activities have been eliminated

- **concentration**, where output and resources have been concentrated in fewer farms, especially in East Anglia.

At the same time, industrialisation has led to the development of the **agribusiness**, such as the feedlots in Lincolnshire and the vegetable farms of the Fenlands. In an agribusiness, farming is organised around scientific and business principles, with the farm responsible for the growing, processing, storing and packaging of the products which are usually marketed to a major retailing chain. Spatially, much of this modernisation and industrialisation has been in the agricultural lowlands of eastern and southern England. The marginal hill lands (upland fringes) face a very uncertain future, especially as the farmers here are heavily supported by subsidies such as those for hill sheep and suckler cows.

The main agents of change have resulted from changing economic, social and political conditions. Three factors have been identified as significant catalysts, the most important of which is known as the **technological treadmill (26.10)**. The price–cost squeeze has forced farmers to try to maintain their income by raising levels of output, usually via high-tech intensification, by specialisation or by economies of scale from an enlarged farm. The technology is very expensive, so further increases in output are needed to pay for it, which will of course lead to ultimate overproduction and a fall in prices and farm incomes. The

■ **26.10** The technological treadmill

only way, therefore, for the individual farmer to keep up is to borrow more money to pay for the technology, or to buy more land (i.e. intensification and extensification). The smaller farmers are therefore stuck on a treadmill they cannot get off if they wish to survive in competition with large-scale factory farms or agribusinesses.

---

7 Why might each of the people sitting on the treadmill (**26.10**) want to turn it faster?

Changes in output

Overall, the amount of land devoted to agriculture has declined in many EMDCs during the second half of the 20th century, largely because of losses to urban growth, forestry and other non-agricultural uses. In the UK, arable land uses and permanent pasture have increased slightly at the expense of rough grazing. Within arable farming, temporary leys and fallow land have both become less important as intensification has increased and crops such as wheat, barley, oilseed rape and sugar beet (the four leading crops) have gained ground at the expense of oats, potatoes, fruit and vegetables.

Overall livestock numbers have increased in each of the main sectors (cattle, sheep, pigs, and poultry), but their distribution has polarised, with cattle and sheep concentrated in the north and west, and pigs and poultry increasingly associated with agribusinesses and cereal farming in eastern England. Issues of animal welfare are increasingly spotlighted on the factory farms that produce pigs, poultry, veal and eggs. In terms of overall farm output, arable farming is undoubtedly gaining at the expense of pastoral farming.

The high-tech revolution

The trend towards fewer and larger farms has been aided by major technological changes. Mechanisation has helped to transform agriculture in terms of increased yields and higher output per worker. The number of tractors in the UK increased fourfold between 1950 and 1987. Most buildings on modern high-tech farms contain a huge variety of equipment, such as automated seed drills or potato harvesters. There have been changes too in farm buildings, with computerised milking parlours, grain-driers, silage-makers and semi-automated feeding systems for intensive livestock units that provide almost totally artificial environments for pigs, poultry and calves.

As intensive systems of specialisation have largely replaced rotational mixed farming, it has been necessary to increase the use of nitrogenous fertilisers (rather than using manure from the livestock herd), and to use a combination of herbicides, pesticides and fungicides to control weeds, pests and diseases which are encouraged by continuous cropping. Their application is made easier by modern machinery and crop-spraying aircraft. There are clear environmental costs of the chemical revolution (these are investigated in the next section), as some crop pests have become immune, and yet weeds still grow.

Advances in plant and animal breeding – considered by some to herald the 'Third Agricultural Revolution', also known as the 'Gene Revolution' because of its biotechnological base – have possibly made the most significant contribution of all to agricultural intensification. New varieties of autumn-sown wheat are more productive than barley, and these combined with higher guaranteed prices (CAP) have led to an increase in wheat at the expense of barley in south-east England, although new short-stemmed varieties of barley have been very useful for barley/beef enterprises in the cooler and wetter north-west England. Artificial insemination has led to the 'cloning' of various livestock, so that better control of the breeding of sheep and cattle has been possible. A variety of moral issues have emerged as animals are treated with hormones to make them heavier and therefore more profitable at the abattoir.

Downstream changes

Since 1950 not only have 'upstream' activities developed (such as feedstock and fertilisers), but also the 'downstream' side of the food business – the processing and marketing of farm produce, for example, has become increasingly sophisticated, especially since the 1980s. In response to changing consumer tastes and new demands for ready-prepared food, there is now greater integration between production/processing and marketing, thus favouring the development of the agribusiness. Contract farming is growing (such as the farms producing peas for Birds Eye, Findus, Ross and Smedley in Lincolnshire), where the receiving companies lay down very strict standards of product.

As individual farmers find it more and more difficult to meet the marketing demands of major food retailers, they join together to form producer cooperatives. Cooperatives provide individual farmers with the opportunity to achieve economies of scale by bulk-buying, and with collective bargaining power to negotiate favourable contract prices with buyers such as the larger retailing companies.

Direct marketing has also grown as an outlet for smaller farmers, with the mushrooming of farm shops, roadside stalls, and Pick Your Own (PYO) farms. Direct marketing avoids the middle agent in the food chain (e.g. wholesalers and retailers) and should allow farmers to take more profit, yet at the same time allows customers to benefit from very fresh, competitively priced products. Direct marketing is common in all areas accessible to main roads, especially around large urban areas such as London or Birmingham, but there are notable concentrations of fruit-farming as in Kent, Hampshire or the Vale of Evesham, for example. Direct marketing is also an important vehicle for health foods such as free-range and organic products.

■ 26.11 Farm diversification

Tourism and recreation	Tourism	Bed and breakfast
		Cottages/chalets
		Caravans/camping
		Activity holidays
	Recreation enterprises	Farm museums
		Visitor centres
		Riding
		Game shooting
		Other shooting
		Fishing
		Farmhouse catering
Adding value to conventional farm products	Animal products	Meat (direct sales, etc.)
		Skins/hides/wool
		Dairy products (direct sales/ processing)
	Crop products	Milled cereals
		PYO and direct sales of vegetables
Unconventional agricultural enterprises	Animal products	Sheep milk
		Rarer breeds – wool
		Fish
		Deer and goats
	Crop products	Linseed
		Evening primrose
		Teasels
Use of ancillary buildings and resources	Woodland products	Fuelwood
		Craft timber products
	Redundant buildings	Industrial premises
		Accommodation
Public goods	Wildlife	ESA payments
	Landscape	Management agreements
	Historic sites	Heritage relief
	Access	Access agreements

Diversification

In spite of a high-tech revolution that favours the specialised agribusinesses of eastern England, many farmers in less favoured areas are practising farm diversification in the form of a wide range of activities (**26.11**) There are various reasons for farm diversification, the main one being to generate extra income, using available resources. Basically, additional income is needed in order to offset the slide in agricultural commodity prices brought about by overproduction and the removal of government price support mechanisms.

Diversification is also being encouraged in another way as the UK government, in line with revised EC farm policies, promotes three schemes to take land out of the agricultural system altogether – again, in order to reduce surplus production. **Set-aside** pays farmers to take arable land out of production, originally on a temporary, rotational basis; the **Farm Woodland Scheme** provides grants to plant broad-leaved woodland on previously arable land; and the **Farm Diversification Scheme** makes grants available to develop tourism, recreational and direct marketing facilities on all farms.

26.5 Agricultural change in the South (ELDCs)

Agriculture remains the main source of livelihood for the majority of people in developing countries, even though its relative importance as a contributor to the GDP has generally declined. Over the last 20 years, agricultural production has continued to expand, at a rate of around 3–4 per cent a year on average – almost three times the rate for the developed world. Per capita production, however, tells a very different story because, in spite of the encouraging increases in crop produc-

tivity, the continued high rate of population growth almost entirely erodes the effect. Over the period as a whole, increases in per capita production for all ELDCs averaged around 1 per cent a year, but this general figure masked very considerable regional and national variations. In Latin America, there were continued improvements in per capita productivity, whereas in Africa, in spite of significant expansions in productivity, per capita production fell on average at a rate of 1 per cent a year. Explanations for the declining per capita food production include adverse environmental conditions (such as drought or floods), overpopulation of tribal lands (as in Kenya), unsuitable agricultural practices, and neglect of the vital subsistence sector in favour of cash crops (as in north-east Brazil).

'Commodification'

The traditional agricultural systems have come under increasing pressure as they have been incorporated into the world economy, as a result of the 'commodification' of agricultural products, whereby the value of the product is determined by global market forces. The price levels of most tropical and subtropical crops, such as rubber, tea, coffee or cocoa, have always been determined by consumers in the developed world, but increasingly the agricultural policies of the developed world govern price levels globally.

It was during colonial rule that commercial production in agriculture first came to the South with the creation of plantations. This system was developed in order to produce cheap tropical and subtropical crops using slave labour. With the end of the colonial period in the 1960s, many plantations were taken out of the hands of foreign owners. Some were taken over by governments and others broken up into smallholdings. However, a significant number remain in the ownership of multinational agribusinesses, which continue to exploit the availability of cheap land and labour on a huge scale. For example, the trade in and production of bananas in the Caribbean and Latin America is largely controlled by three US agribusinesses – Standard Fruit, Del Monte, and United Brands Company (Fyffe and Chiquito). Together their operations employ over 120 000 full-time workers and 50 000 casuals; they provide much-needed export earnings for countries such as Panama and Costa Rica.

Land reform

'Land reform' is a blanket term for a wide range of measures introduced in a variety of circumstances to solve a range of problems. Some reform programmes seize and divide large estates, usually as part of a post-revolutionary strategy (as in Cuba). Others consolidate small or fragmented holdings (as in the Kikuyu region of Kenya), and others (as in Bangladesh) attempt to reform tenancy schemes.

A cost–benefit analysis of land reform produces different results depending on local circumstances. In Mexico, for example, there is little doubt that land reform improved the political, economic and social status of the peasantry. In 1923 large estates occupied 85 per cent of the total farming area, but by 1970 they occupied only 30 per cent, with agricultural production trebling between 1945 and 1975. In contrast, Bangladesh shows a history of abortive attempts to achieve land reform. What is very evident here is that land reform does not solve the problem of the landless labour force, which is generated by high population growth.

The Green Revolution   IT4

The term 'Green Revolution' is a widely used but ill-defined term. In its narrowest sense it refers to the breakthrough in plant breeding that produced high-yielding varieties (HYVs) of grain (**26.12**). In a wider sense, it includes a package of technology, including fertilisers, water control, pesticides and insecticides, and mechanised implements required to support HYVs. The term is now loosely used to describe the agricultural development strategies in which EMDC technology is applied to agriculture in ELDCs in order to increase food production.

Initial development of HYV strains took place in Mexico (suppliers of dwarf wheat) and at the International Rice Research Institute in the Philippines which produced IR8, the so-called 'miracle rice'. Subsequent work has been in a variety of locations such as Malaysia where a whole range of 'designer' seeds have been produced for individual farmers' needs. Although initial work was with wheat and rice, subsequent plant breeding has produced high-yielding maize, sorghum and potatoes.

The Green Revolution has generally accelerated the process of differentiation between rich and poor farmers and has disrupted the rural fabric, thereby accelerating rural–urban migration. It is also generally agreed that the level of yields of HYVs varies according to the amount of fertiliser used, the adequacy and availability of soil moisture (irrigation and flood control) and the quality of land preparation and crop tending. Water

control has been identified as the most important element in the establishment of HYVs of wheat and rice, so the new technology spread very rapidly in areas where irrigation and commercial production were either well established or developing rapidly, but not elsewhere. As many areas in the developing world experience serious annual or seasonal water shortages, only limited progress has been made in the development of irrigation and consequently of HYVs.

■ **26.12** The advantages and disadvantages of HYVs

Advantages	Disadvantages
They give up to four times the yield.	Some varieties have poor milling qualities and can taste inferior.
Some varieties are more responsive to fertilisers and give higher yields per unit of fertiliser.	They require heavy doses of chemical fertilisers
Many varieties are short and stalky and do not topple over when ripe.	They provide less straw for thatching and for use on the farm.
Many varieties are not sensitive to day length and can be grown in a wide variety of environments.	They are less adapted to drought and require more sophisticated water control from irrigation schemes.
They have a shorter growing period and this sometimes allows double or even triple cropping.	Many varieties are more susceptible to pests and diseases and require large applications of pesticides and fungicides.
	New seeds must be bought each year to ensure the purity of the strain.
	They need more careful weed control.

CASE STUDY

IP2, IT4

The Green Revolution in the Punjab

The Punjab in India is the area most closely identified with the success of the Green Revolution. During the 1960s and 1970s, agricultural change in many parts of the state was both rapid and spectacular (**26.13**).

Areas like Ludhiana, which was provided with research back-up from the University of Punjab to help farmers, were seen as the spearhead of the Indian agricultural revolution, which was needed to solve the famine problems. The mid-1960s was a period of crisis for Indian agriculture. Long-term growth in production appeared to be faltering, with Indian grain imports having risen steadily since 1960. With disastrous harvests in 1966 and 1967, grain imports reached 16 per cent of production, so Ludhiana's success was a milestone of achievement. However, in the early 1960s, Ludhiana was already one of the most advanced agricultural areas, even by Punjab

	1960	1970
Amount of land irrigated by tube wells %	35	70
Fertiliser application kg/ha	19.7	271.3
Area under HYVs ha	69	169 972
Wheat yields kg/ha	1552.3	3676.3
Tractors	500	2500–5000

■ **26.13** Agricultural change in the Punjab

standards. Farms were generally large because of widespread land reform in the 1950s, with 80 per cent of holdings over 4 ha, with only 4 per cent of farmers being sole tenants. Since the new seeds have been grown here, farm incomes have nearly tripled in Ludhiana, and doubled in the Punjab, but whereas the farms over 4 ha were generally much better off, those of less than 4 ha were often worse off.

26.14 explains the reasons for the differential success rates. As HYVs spread during the late 1960s, average yields fell, a reflection of the increasing number of small farmers involved in less favourable areas, without the fertile soils and well-established irrigation systems of the Punjab.

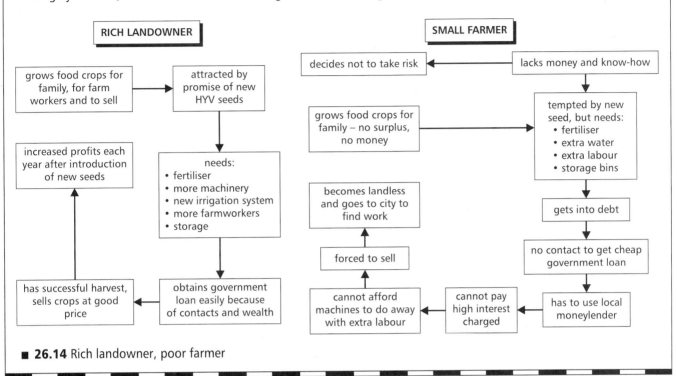

RICH LANDOWNER

grows food crops for family, for farm workers and to sell → attracted by promise of new HYV seeds ↓

needs:
• fertiliser
• more machinery
• new irrigation system
• more farmworkers
• storage
↓

obtains government loan easily because of contacts and wealth ←

has successful harvest, sells crops at good price ↑

increased profits each year after introduction of new seeds

SMALL FARMER

decides not to take risk ← lacks money and know-how ↓

tempted by new seed, but needs:
• fertiliser
• extra water
• extra labour
• storage bins
↓

grows food crops for family – no surplus, no money →

gets into debt ↓

no contact to get cheap government loan ↓

has to use local moneylender ←

cannot pay high interest charged ←

cannot afford machines to do away with extra labour ↑

forced to sell ↑

becomes landless and goes to city to find work

■ **26.14** Rich landowner, poor farmer

■ **26.15** 'Miracle Rice'

8 The cartoon **26.15** shows some of the doubts expressed by an Indian peasant farmer reluctant to change to 'Miracle Rice'. Identify the concerns that he has.

9 The item **26.16** attempts to produce a cost–benefit summary of the results of the Green Revolution. Use the following headings to evaluate the success of the Green Revolution: Environmental, Ecological, Social, Economic and political. Refer to other standard textbooks to help with your research.

Selective plant breeding has been going on since people first planted crops – they pick the best seeds for next year's sowing. But harvest yields have stayed much the same. Some 20 years ago, however, research found new varieties of high-yielding seeds – wheat, maize and rice – which could double harvests. By 1985 Green Revolution seeds were being sown on half the area devoted to rice and wheat in the developing world.

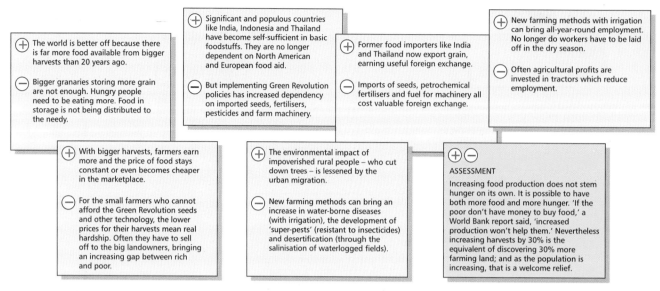

⊕ The world is better off because there is far more food available from bigger harvests than 20 years ago.

⊖ Bigger granaries storing more grain are not enough. Hungry people need to be eating more. Food in storage is not being distributed to the needy.

⊕ Significant and populous countries like India, Indonesia and Thailand have become self-sufficient in basic foodstuffs. They are no longer dependent on North American and European food aid.

⊖ But implementing Green Revolution policies has increased dependency on imported seeds, fertilisers, pesticides and farm machinery.

⊕ Former food importers like India and Thailand now export grain, earning useful foreign exchange.

⊖ Imports of seeds, petrochemical fertilisers and fuel for machinery all cost valuable foreign exchange.

⊕ New farming methods with irrigation can bring all-year-round employment. No longer do workers have to be laid off in the dry season.

⊖ Often agricultural profits are invested in tractors which reduce employment.

⊕ With bigger harvests, farmers earn more and the price of food stays constant or even becomes cheaper in the marketplace.

⊖ For the small farmers who cannot afford the Green Revolution seeds and other technology, the lower prices for their harvests mean real hardship. Often they have to sell off to the big landowners, bringing an increasing gap between rich and poor.

⊕ The environmental impact of impoverished rural people – who cut down trees – is lessened by the urban migration.

⊖ New farming methods can bring an increase in water-borne diseases (with irrigation), the development of 'super-pests' (resistant to insecticides) and desertification (through the salinisation of waterlogged fields).

⊕⊖ ASSESSMENT
Increasing food production does not stem hunger on its own. It is possible to have both more food and more hunger. 'If the poor don't have money to buy food,' a World Bank report said, 'increased production won't help them.' Nevertheless increasing harvests by 30% is the equivalent of discovering 30% more farming land; and as the population is increasing, that is a welcome relief.

■ **26.16** Benefits and costs of the Green Revolution

26.6 **Agriculture and the environment**

IT8

As we have already seen, no agro-ecosystem can exist and function as an isolated, self-contained, self-sustaining unit. Even in traditional subsistence agricultural systems, there has to be an input of energy in the form of human and/or animal labour, and some of the waste will be deposited outside the immediate cultivated area. Equally, there will be some disturbance of the equilibrium of the pre-existing natural ecosystems.

As the application of technical and scientific knowledge has risen since the 1950s, the relative intensity of agriculture in terms of the number and volume of inputs and outputs has increased very rapidly, with major repercussions for the environment. The intensification of livestock and crop production into an agribusiness has meant that these agribusinesses have acquired many of the characteristics of manufacturing industry, including a large output of waste by-products. Agricultural waste is now a significant source of air, water and soil pollution, and these negative factors impose high economic and social costs on other systems. The increasing

intensification also puts the natural landscapes and ecosystems under more stress.

IT8

Accelerated soil erosion

IT2

Probably the most damaging impact of all the impacts of agriculture on the environment is accelerated soil erosion. Soil erosion is a natural process but it is speeded up by the removal of a natural or semi-natural vegetation cover, causing the underlying soil to be exposed to the direct effects of wind and water. Cultivation, particularly ploughing, disturbs the soil and opens it up to the elements by turning it over, thus accelerating the decomposition of humus, and leading to a decline in the structural stability of the soil.

Soil erosion is undoubtedly a world problem, although it is often very difficult to obtain precise measurements at a global scale. Soil loss in the four major food-producing countries of the USA, the former Soviet Union, China and India (which together

IT2

account for half of the world's cropland) is calculated at 13.6 billion tonnes per year. Accelerated soil erosion is currently a major problem in tropical and subtropical areas of the world, as increasing demands for food from a rapidly growing population persuade people to indulge in environmental malpractices, such as deforestation and overgrazing.

IT8

Habitat change and modification

An inevitable consequence of the development and spread of agriculture has been the destruction of pre-existing wild or relatively unmanaged ecosystems. Habitat change or destruction can be greatly affected by land drainage, either designed to convert wetlands to agricultural use or to improve the soil–water balance on farmland. The loss of wetlands such as Halvergate Marsh (a 3000 ha area of semi-drained marshland which forms a triangle of land between the lower Bure and Yare rivers in eastern Norfolk) became a symbol for environmentalists of the need to reform agricultural and conservation policies. Wetlands often have special ecological value, and any drainage scheme will clearly have an impact beyond the immediate area (see Chapter 18).

Habitat reduction, damage or destruction is inevitably accompanied by the decline and/or disappearance of plant and animal species because of the modification of the food web. It has been

IT8

calculated that by 1981 Britain had suffered the following losses:

- 95 per cent of herb-rich grasslands
- 80 per cent of chalk/limestone grassland
- 60 per cent of lowland heaths
- 50 per cent of ancient woodland
- 50 per cent of fens and marshes (wetlands)
- 60 per cent of raised lowland bog
- 33 per cent of grass and heather.

There were parallel losses of animals whose existence was closely dependent on a particular habitat.

IT3

Fertilisers

The term **agrochemicals** has been adopted to cover all the chemical products which have been developed to increase yields either by adding nutrients, or combating losses caused by pests – that is, fertilisers and pesticides.

From 1939 to 1989, the amount of inorganic fertiliser used in the United Kingdom increased by over 600 per cent. Much of this increase was due to the dramatic fall in the price of nitrogen fertilisers, which made up three-quarters of all inorganic fertilisers. **26.17** clearly indicates that Britain has not been alone in 'doping' its cultivated land with nitrogen-based fertilisers.

Unfortunately, nitrates applied to fields are easily transferred, by runoff and leaching, to nearby lakes and reservoirs, rivers and streams. This can lead to eutrophication and the contamination of drinking water. They can also cause plant damage by 'burning' delicate roots, as well as lead to soil acidification.

In spite of all the disadvantages, there is no doubt that fertilisers have been of tremendous benefit in terms of raising agricultural productivity. There are also advantages in using them as opposed to organic alternatives such as green manure, farmyard manure and sewage sludge. Their concentrated nature makes them easy to store, and they can be applied

■ **26.17** Doping the Earth

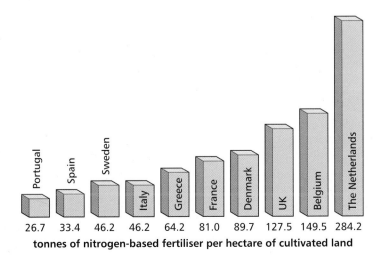

Portugal	Spain	Sweden	Italy	Greece	France	Denmark	UK	Belgium	The Netherlands
26.7	33.4	46.2	46.2	64.2	81.0	89.7	127.5	149.5	284.2

tonnes of nitrogen-based fertiliser per hectare of cultivated land

mechanically using only light equipment, which limits soil compaction. In addition, a known nutrient content is applied, and so supply can be equated with demand. The issue is therefore not to ban the use of nitrates, but to manage their use more effectively.

From a long-term point of view, many measures can be taken to ameliorate the nitrate problem. One option is to turn to organic farming. Organic manures are seen as more environmentally friendly but, as we have already noted, they can still be a distinct pollution risk. Fields fed regularly with farmyard manure may contain up to 100 kg more nitrate per hectare in the critical autumn months than chemically fertilised fields. Advocates of organic farming also extol the health bonus of crops that are guaranteed free from agrochemicals. Another frequently discussed option is to use less nitrogen fertiliser – research would suggest that halving the application of fertiliser would only cut the yield by 10 per cent, but that 10 per cent is of course the vital profit margin for the farmers.

Pests and pesticides

Any organism causing harm to crops is a pest. Agriculturally, an organism becomes an economic pest when the loss in crop yield exceeds certain proportions, usually 5–10 per cent of total yield. Clearly it makes no sense to control a pest unless the costs of control are less than the economic damage being done to the crop.

The aim of all pest control is to keep the size of the pest population below the economic injury level. This can be done in four ways:

- by increasing the death rate (e.g. spray with a pesticide)
- by decreasing the birth rate (e.g. releasing sterile males into a population)
- by increasing emigration of the pest (e.g. by using trap crops)
- by decreasing immigration (e.g. by removing favoured habitats).

There is a variety of ways of protecting crops from pests, such as crop rotation, weeding, liming and managing times of planting and harvest to avoid 'high pest' periods. Equally, crop sanitation (destroying all crop residues), physical barriers (e.g. sticky bands on fruit trees), mulching (to prevent weeds), stubble burning, intercropping and growing trap crops (planting worthless, highly favoured 'decoys' to lure pests off plants to be protected) are all physical means of controlling pests. The Chinese even use people to go out each day and manually collect all the particular pests they can find!

The main controversy in pest control is over the use of a battery of toxic chemicals to destroy weeds and control pest organisms. These include herbicides, fungicides and insecticides. Unfortunately, in solving or easing some of the farmer's immediate problems, not only are there often wider and long-term environmental repercussions, but human health is also threatened. Some of the toxic substances enter the food chain, while others have proved to be carcinogens. The sensible way ahead lies in **integrated pest management.**

Environmental impact on agro-ecosystems

Agro-ecosystems have themselves been increasingly subjected to inputs from the surrounding non-agricultural environment, such as the pollution of the air and soil. Perhaps the most spectacular example of this was the nuclear fallout resulting from the accident at Chernobyl (see the case study on page 364), which adversely affected farming in areas as far apart as Lapland and Wales. Increasingly, agricultural land is threatened by other uses, such as urbanisation, greenfield industrialisation and transport systems, and also by the demands of tourism and leisure. These particular pressures are very marked on the urban–rural fringes.

26.7 The global future for agriculture

IT5

We live in a confusing world. On the one hand we are bombarded by shocking images and headlines about starving people across the world – to such an extent that charities pleading for our funds feel that **disaster fatigue** has set in. On the other hand, the European Union and North America are producing too much food. A major current preoccupation of Northern governments is to devise strategies for producing less food. In the developed world, the health, fitness and diet industry is a multi-million-dollar business. A simple answer, of course, would be to improve the world distribution of food.

The reality is a highly complex problem which has developed from the badly managed distribution of available food because of government policies, the structure of international trade and inequalities in the access to technology.

The facts of the situation are these. Of the world's total population of some 5.5 billion people, perhaps as many as 2 billion (including many in impoverished areas of EMDCs), have a diet that is lacking in the proteins, vitamins and minerals that are needed for well-balanced nutrition. At least 500 million people cannot get enough food of any kind. Some people starve even in countries that have food surpluses, because the problem is not so much one of quantity of available food as its distribution and

price. For example, in the Bangladesh famines, those who have enough money can always get enough to eat, while those who do not have money may starve. Cereals are the most important food source for the majority of the world's population, yet in richer countries over half this cereal output is fed to animals to provide meat. In energy-efficiency terms this is a profligate waste of resources, and the universal adoption of US-style eating habits would pose an intolerable strain on global food resources.

IT5

> **10** The food production situation between 1981 and 1991 is reviewed in **26.18**. Briefly summarise and explain the trends shown.

IT5

Bearing in mind the trends shown in **26.18**, it is necessary to try to focus on the future. The report of the Panel on Food and Agriculture, published for the United Nations in 1992, succinctly states the issues thus:

> Over the next 20 years, food production will have to keep pace with the growth of world population from 5.5 billion to over 7 billion by the year 2010, an increase of 36 per

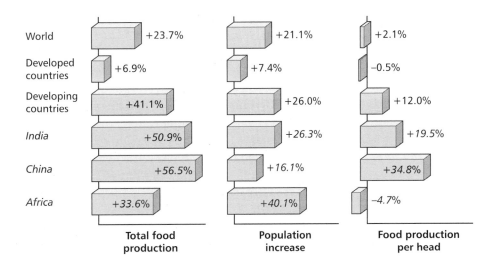

■ **26.18** Changes in world food production and population, 1981–91

cent, just to maintain the present situation. The great challenge for governments and the food, agriculture and fisheries sector is to ensure food and nutrition security and sustainable growth in a way that does not place undue pressure on the environment and leaves the world a healthy and safe place fit to live in.

One hundred years from now the Earth may have 10 billion inhabitants – about twice as many as it has now – although if demographic forecasts are correct, the human population will by then be approaching a stable level. Will the world be able to feed itself then? The short answer is *yes* – technology will provide. The long answer is not quite as simple – ultimately people can only survive if sustainable agricultural systems are developed. Not only must the food supply expand but it must expand in a way that does not destroy the natural environment or put an excessive strain on resources. The challenges of meeting these requirements and ensuring an element of food security are formidable, both environmentally and economically.

Sustainable agriculture

A consensus is emerging that new strategies are necessary if all societies are to obtain a more secure food environment based on the twin pillars of environmental conservation and social justice. The call for sustainable development in agriculture is based on the need to solve four issues:

1 Agricultural land is only a renewable resource if it is sustained. If it is abused it becomes a depletable resource-based activity. All over the world there are examples of declining soil fertility from land degradation, loss of and pollution of water resources, losses of biodiversity, and depletion of fossil fuels – all of which are manifestations of a declining resource base.

2 Agriculture will have to serve a larger and more affluent population in the developing world, especially in Asia.

There are already signs that affluence in parts of China is leading to a replication of meat-based Western diets, which clearly has major implications for food supplies.

3 Within agriculture there are enormous disparities in farm income, access to agricultural resources, nutritional levels and production per capita. The physical, biological, technological and socio-economic systems which influence agricultural production are interconnected by a whole series of complex linkages. Clearly, agricultural development cannot be separated from environmental conservation. 'Environmentally positive' agriculture maintains ecological systems, preserves biodiversity and ensures the sustainable use of both species and ecosystems, and is clearly one aspect of sustainable agriculture. Another is the need for a strategy that manages all assets, natural resources and human resources, for the increasing long-term wealth and well-being of all peoples. Thus the issue is one of equity as well as of conservation.

4 Sustainable development is about balancing the need for agricultural development against the limitations of the environment, and at the same time ensuring the nutritional and economic well-being of society now and in the future.

---

11 What are the prospects for achieving sustainable agricultural development, and what might sustainable systems look like in practice in the North and the South?

12 What changes need to be made to achieve sustainable agricultural development?

Ecological indicators

- Replenishment of soil nutrients removed by crops.
- Maintenance of the soil's physical structure.
- Constant or increasing levels of organic matter in the soil.
- No increase in soil activity or toxicities.
- Constant or increasing soil depth.
- Minimal off-farm environmental contamination.
- Maintenance of habitat for pollinators, biological pest control agents and wildlife (the latter with the proviso that there is minimal build-up of weeds, pests and diseases).
- Conservation of genetic resources of crop and animal species farmed; and farmers having equitable access to genetic material.
- A diversity of species farmed on a given site, and maximum useful nutrient and energy transfer between species.
- Continual cover of the soil by vegetation.
- High efficiency of water use, minimal evaporation from open water surfaces and sprays.
- The direction of technology change away from the use of non-renewable resources and subsidised energy, and towards the introduction of renewables, making more use of local resources and increasing photosynthetic efficiency.

Economic, policy and institutional indicators

- Prevailing prices, grants and subsidies encourage farmers to maximise long-term productivity and resource conservation, with security of supply as the main short-term goal – rather than to maximise short-term productivity.
- Extension, research, policies and procedures emphasise the farm system and not just individual commodities or enterprises; integrated advice is given to farmers.
- Policies, plans and targets do not emphasise solely output per unit area; farmers' net economic benefit and ecological sustainability are also goals.
- Regulations are in force to ensure that farming causes little off-farm environmental contamination.
- Land of the highest production potential is allocated to agriculture.
- Where agriculture produces regular surpluses, land is usefully retired to other productive uses, and marginal land is used for environmental conservation.
- Financial assistance to farmers is not linked to specific commodities in a manner that discourages the best use of a region's ecological suitabilities.
- Rather than the price of chemicals being subsidised, the opposite is the case: their price incorporates environmental costs; the 'polluter pays' principle is applied.

Social/cultural indicators

- The farmer plays the leading role in designing the farm system and choosing technologies; and these designs and technologies build carefully on the precise site characteristics and on traditional husbandry techniques.
- Farming and pastoral communities thrive, but not at the expense of other communities (especially the urban poor).
- Non-agricultural employment is also available in agricultural areas.

Output indicators

- Yields are reliably constant or increasing.
- Agriculture is profitable enough to secure adequate subsistence and income for the farmer's family.
- Farmers' targets are 'to optimise productivity on a long-term basis' rather than 'to maximise productivity now'.

■ **26.19** Indicators of sustainable agriculture

IT4 **26.19** provides a checklist of the indicators of sustainable agriculture. Sustainable development is a radical concept requiring dramatic changes to the existing social, economic, institutional and behavioural fabric of societies. It is the only long-term way ahead for agriculture, the environment and people. **IT4**

27.1 **Introducing the energy question**

Energy is probably our most useful and valuable resource. It is essential for heating, lighting and for driving machinery and transport. Today's cities, industries and transport networks could not function without regular supplies of energy. Fortunately, there are a large number of sources, including those from the Sun, the Moon, the atmosphere and the Earth, which can be converted to usable power – for example water into hydroelectricity. Using the resource classification introduced in section 25.2, energy resources can be classified into three main groups. Some energy resources, such as fossil fuels, are finite and therefore classified as **stock resources**. Other energy resources are renewable and therefore classified as **flow resources**. There is a fundamental division in the flow category as some are everlasting and therefore totally renewable, whereas many are only renewable in the sense that supplies can be sus-

tained if extraction rates do not exceed renewal rates.

> **1** Study **27.1** which shows all the sources of energy. Make a copy of the diagram and shade in the three classes of resource in different colours.

There are three aspects to the energy question. The first issue is the rapid overall increase in global consumption and its relationship to production. The second aspect is the nature of the energy mix and how it has changed over time. A third area for study is the difference in consumption in the various groups of countries in the world, in particular the increasing disparity of consumption between the more developed countries (EMDCs), and the economically less developed countries (ELDCs).

■ **27.1** Classification of energy resources

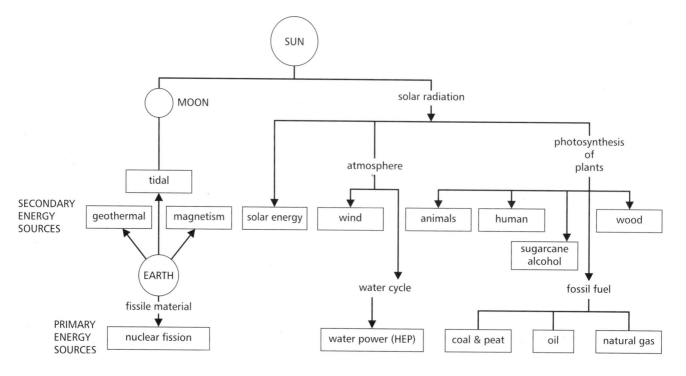

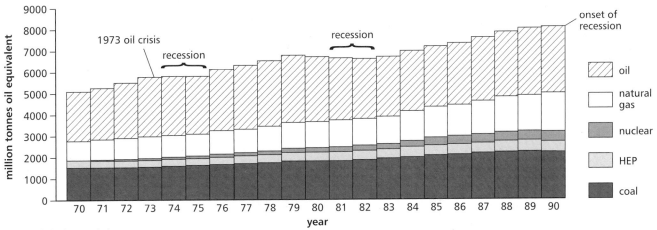

■ **27.2** Global trends in energy use

27.2 shows recent trends in world commercial energy use. Accurate figures for global energy use are not available, largely because of the lack of reliable detailed data on the consumption of fuelwood and other biomass, such as dung and crop wastes (see the case study of Nepal, pages 362–63) which are consumed locally and appear in no recognised market. Commercial energy use is increasing on average by around 2–3 per cent per year, although there are years, usually in times of recession, when there is very little increase.

As long as the population of the planet remained small and energy needs were restricted to cooking, heating and lighting, energy resources (even finite fossil fuels) could be exploited without significant depletion, or without serious damage to the air, water and land. Today, the escalation in the amounts of energy used, amplified by a growing global popu-

lation, has led to the development of the concept of the **energy gap**. The 'gap' is defined as the perceived shortfall between supply and demand for the world's non-renewable energy sources – the finite supplies of gas, oil and natural gas.

---

2 What factors can overcome the threat of an energy gap? Is a world energy crisis as big an issue in the 1990s as it was in the early 1970s?

The energy gap is largely the function of the profligate use of fuels by advanced industrialised countries (members of OECD, the Organisation for Economic Cooperation and Development) which in 1990 consumed nearly half of the world's energy, with the former communist countries consuming a further

■ **27.3** Energy consumption by region (million tonnes oil equivalent)

	Coal			Oil			Gas			Nuclear		
	1970	**1980**	**1990**	**1970**	**1980**	**1990**	**1970**	**1980**	**1990**	**1970**	**1980**	**1990**
OECD	718	748	883	1623	1818	1729	675	773	812	18	146	365
Former Soviet Union & E. Europe	531	564	548	317	562	540	192	381	640	1	21	61
Rest of the world	386	504	801	342	644	828	62	132	255	1	5	24
Total	1635	1816	2232	2282	3024	3097	929	1286	1707	20	172	450

	HEP			Total			Population millions		
	1970	**1980**	**1990**	**1970**	**1980**	**1990**	**1970**	**1980**	**1990**
OECD	222	226	263	3256	3751	4052	719	779	830
Former Soviet Union & E. Europe	35	60	73	1076	1588	1862	369	400	428
Rest of the world	48	106	191	839	1391	2099	2577	3203	3948
Total	305	432	527	5171	6730	8013	3665	4382	5206

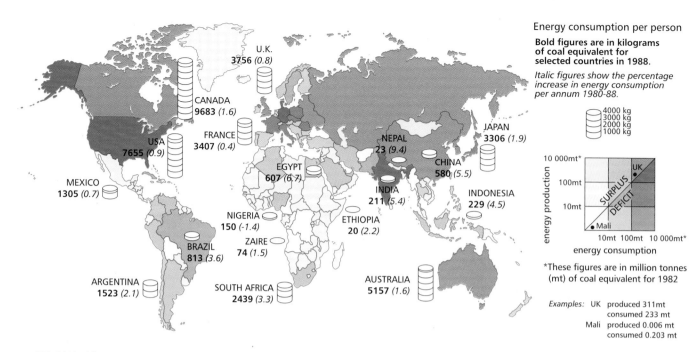

Energy consumption per person

Bold figures are in kilograms of coal equivalent for selected countries in 1988.

Italic figures show the percentage increase in energy consumption per annum 1980-88.

4000 kg
3000 kg
2000 kg
1000 kg

*These figures are in million tonnes (mt) of coal equivalent for 1982

Examples: UK produced 311mt
                   consumed 233 mt
            Mali produced 0.006 mt
                   consumed 0.203 mt

U.K. 3756 (0.8)
CANADA 9683 (1.6)
FRANCE 3407 (0.4)
USA 7655 (0.9)
MEXICO 1305 (0.7)
NEPAL 23 (9.4)
JAPAN 3306 (1.9)
CHINA 580 (5.5)
EGYPT 607 (6.7)
INDIA 211 (5.4)
INDONESIA 229 (4.5)
NIGERIA 150 (-1.4)
ETHIOPIA 20 (2.2)
ZAIRE 74 (1.5)
BRAZIL 813 (3.6)
ARGENTINA 1523 (2.1)
SOUTH AFRICA 2439 (3.3)
AUSTRALIA 5157 (1.6)

■ **27.4** World energy consumption and production

IT3,5

■ **27.5** Sustainable-world and consensus views of the future

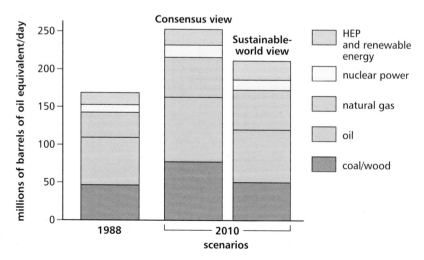

Consensus view

Sustainable-world view

millions of barrels of oil equivalent/day

HEP and renewable energy
nuclear power
natural gas
oil
coal/wood

1988   2010
scenarios

The consensus view assumes 'business as usual', with an overall growth in consumption. The sustainable-world view assumes radical improvements in efficiency, with demand stabilising after the year 2000.

quarter. Yet they contained together only around a quarter of the world's people. Thus people living in OECD countries consume approximately 10 times as much energy as those living in ELDCs – the rest of the world (**27.3**).

A further issue related to the increased global demand for commercial energy is that it has caused energy use to become a potentially destructive force. At a local scale, exploitation and use pollutes and contaminates the land, sea and air. Globally, energy emissions are considered to enhance the greenhouse effect (see section 12.6) and contribute to ozone layer damage. The dilemma is that, if properly used, energy technologies enhance the material well-being of people by improving their quality of life and wealth. At the same time, if current trends in exploitation and use continue, this could lead to a degraded, polluted environment and ultimately threaten human existence.

27.4 breaks down the situation to the national scale (individual countries). Countries are classified into nine categories of deficit and surplus on the basis of the ratio between energy production and energy consumption. Although many ELDCs, such as Mali, have a low consumption, unfortunately they have few resources for production either. The UK has a relatively high consumption, but its abundant resources of fossil fuels enable it to be just within the energy surplus category, in the same group as Canada, Australia, Russia and China. Although the USA has abundant resources, nevertheless it falls within the deficit zone because it has a very high consumption. The sound production base is shown by the position of OPEC countries such as Iran and Libya. The other dimension shown by **27.4** is the high disparity of consumption per capita between EMDCs, such as Canada and the USA, and ELDCs, such as Zaire and Ethiopia.

IT3,5

3 Refer to **27.3** and use the information in the tables to discuss the significance of the imbalance of reserves between the three groups of countries.

4 Two scenarios for the global energy mix in the year 2010 are shown in **27.5**. Briefly compare them, and then identify how the balance of each differs from the energy mix in 1990 (**27.2**).

27.2 **Fossil fuels**

Over the last two centuries the fossil hydrocarbon fuels – coal, oil and natural gas – have had a major impact on the developed economies. In the 19th century, great concentrations of heavy industries, based on coalfields, developed in areas as wide apart as Appalachia in the USA, the Ruhr in Germany, north-east England, the Donbas in Russia, and New South Wales, Australia. In the 20th century, the same process can be seen increasingly in ELDCs, as in the large coal-based industrial regions in the Damodar Valley, India, and Manchuria in China, and the oil-based industrial complexes of Kuwait and Saudi Arabia. There are good reasons why fossil fuels are so popular. First, they are accessible in one form or another in most, if not all, regions of the world. Secondly, people have learned to convert fossil fuels economically and safely into required forms of energy. They can be readily converted from one state to another, for example from solid to gas, or liquid to gas. The cleanliness of fossil fuels is variable, with gas considered to be far more environmentally friendly than coal or oil. Thirdly – and this applies to oil and gas in particular – they make excellent fuels for transport as they are easily portable. Finally, fossil fuels can be regarded as valuable feedstocks of raw materials for the chemical industry to make plastics, artificial fibres, fertilisers and pesticides, as well as pharmaceutical products. Indeed, some scientists argue that this role is so important that fossil fuels cannot be 'squandered' on other less important uses such as transport. **27.6** shows the estimated reserves for the three fossil fuels at 1990 production and consumption rates. It emphasises the disparity between the three fuels, as the world's reserves of coal will last twice as long as the combined reserves of oil and natural gas.

■ **27.6** Estimated reserves of the three fossil fuels

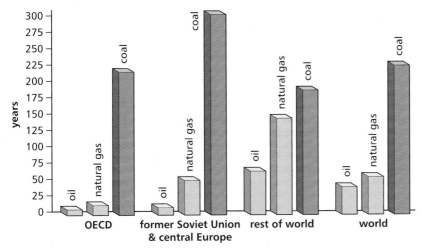

years

At today's production rates, the world's reserves of coal will last twice as long as the combined reserves of oil and gas.

27.3 **Coal**

World reserves of economically recoverable hard coal are currently estimated at 528 billion tonnes of coal equivalent. To this can be added an estimated 136 billion tonnes of coal equivalent of lignite or brown coal (largely found in Eastern Europe and almost exclusively used to produce electricity).

The production of coal has generally followed an upward trend, with minor fluctuations related to the world price of oil and changes in public and government attitudes towards nuclear fuel (**27.2**). This trend, however, masks two facts. First, the upward growth in coal production, in absolute terms, has been far less rapid than in other fuels, thus leading to a relative decrease in its importance at the expense of natural gas and nuclear fuels. Secondly, there have been quite radical changes in the importance of some of the main producing areas, and the pattern and direction of trade over the last 25 years. Compared with 1970, the three giant powers of the USA, the former Soviet Union and China are still the three leading producers, but there have been very significant increases in production in China (now the world's leading producer). Australia and South Africa, are also now two major exporters, where there are very favourable mining conditions permitting the mechanised production of high-quality coal. All this has been at the expense of a decline from OECD high-cost producers such as the UK, Germany, France, Belgium, Spain and Japan, where production has fallen by 32 per cent since 1980.

The future of coal is difficult to predict, as new ways of using it are constantly being researched, such as coal liquefaction and coal gasification. In spite of these developments, however, the future of coal is at present very closely linked to its success in retaining its two major markets, as coke for steel production and for electricity generation. The use of coking coal in blast furnaces is under threat from the development of other fuels such as oil and gas, and the demand for coking coal is forecast to fall. The use of coal in the electricity market is inextricably linked to the prices of oil and gas, and to the availability of reserves in these two fuels, as well as overall prospects globally for economic growth. The case study below of the British coal industry shows one view of the future of coal, and if this was replicated all over Europe it would have a major impact. On the other hand, the United Nations has estimated that the world coal demand in the year 2000 will be between 4.0 and 4.5 billion tonnes a year, of which about 500 million tonnes a year will enter international trade – a very bright future indeed. The one irrefutable fact is that the world has very large reserves of coal, spread very widely over the world. Can we afford not to use them?

CASE STUDY

IT7

Coal in Britain – 'the black future'

Since the Second World War, with the exception of the 1984/85 miners' strike, the British coal industry has shown the following trends:

- Output down from around 200 million tonnes to an estimated 30 million tonnes in 1995.

- Output per 'man' up from 250 tonnes per year to nearly 800 tonnes (1990).

- Rationalisation of collieries from over 950 to 30 (1993).

- Decline in the labour force from 700 000 to under 20 000 (**27.7**).

In many ways this can be regarded as a success story, with record outputs at many pits, and coal being produced increasingly economically – Britain's coal mines are undoubtedly some of the most efficient within the EU. Yet in 1993, there were only 30 pits operating, and by 1994 as few as 18, employing just under 20 000 men, with the agreed market for coal being targeted around 40 million tonnes.

What are the main reasons for this catastrophic decline? Since 1947, the market for British coal has changed radically. In 1947, only 20 per cent of production went to power stations (the rest went to domestic use, industrial uses such as coking coal for steel, for making gas and for driving steam trains). Yet in 1990, a staggering 80 per cent went to produce electricity, thus linking coal's future irrevocably with that of electricity.

In March 1990, under the government's privatisation programme, the Central Electricity Generating Board ceased to exist and its assets were taken over by four

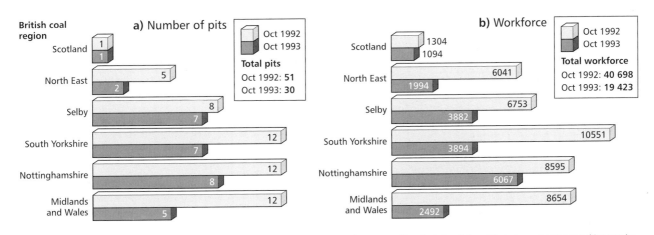

British coal region

a) Number of pits

- Scotland: Oct 1992: 1, Oct 1993: 1
- North East: Oct 1992: 5, Oct 1993: 2
- Selby: Oct 1992: 8, Oct 1993: 7
- South Yorkshire: Oct 1992: 12, Oct 1993: 7
- Nottinghamshire: Oct 1992: 12, Oct 1993: 8
- Midlands and Wales: Oct 1992: 12, Oct 1993: 5

Oct 1992 / Oct 1993
Total pits
Oct 1992: 51
Oct 1993: 30

b) Workforce

- Scotland: Oct 1992: 1304, Oct 1993: 1094
- North East: Oct 1992: 6041, Oct 1993: 1994
- Selby: Oct 1992: 6753, Oct 1993: 3882
- South Yorkshire: Oct 1992: 10551, Oct 1993: 3894
- Nottinghamshire: Oct 1992: 8595, Oct 1993: 6067
- Midlands and Wales: Oct 1992: 8654, Oct 1993: 2492

Oct 1992 / Oct 1993
Total workforce
Oct 1992: **40 698**
Oct 1993: **19 423**

Figures represent 'men on colliery tasks' and do not include contractors working at pits.

■ **27.7** Coal in decline in the 1990s

new companies: National Power, PowerGen, Nuclear Power and National Grid. The first two companies took over the nation's stock of coal-fired power stations. As privatised companies, clearly there is a duty to make maximum profits for shareholders, so electricity must be produced by the most efficient and economic means. The companies argued that with stockpiles of 34 million tonnes of coal, there was only a guaranteed market for around 30 million tonnes a year from British Coal after 1993, when existing contracts ran out.

By the year 2000, the power companies envisage a fuel mix as follows: 15 per cent nuclear, 25 per cent natural gas, 5–10 per cent oil and around 50 per cent coal. Neither of the two generating companies is building large new coal-fired power stations, and both have sought a reduction in the amount of coal they must take from the domestic industry. It is claimed that imported coal largely from Australia, the USA, South Africa and Colombia is up to 33 per cent cheaper than domestic coal. It is also claimed to have a lower sulphur content and therefore to be less environmentally damaging. The use of imported coal also gives the power generators an increasing security of supply (a lingering spectre from the 1984/85 miners' strike). To support coal imports a series of new coastal terminals has been built, for example at Immingham.

What are the main arguments for keeping a significant coalmining industry? First, there is the strategic issue of a secure and reliable supply of domestically-produced fuel (although the 1984/85

Miners' Strike had a very damaging effect on the government's belief in coal). Secondly, there is the argument of diversity of supply – keeping a balanced fuel mix to guard against sudden problems in supply or technology. Thirdly, there are economic arguments in favour, since home-produced coal is competitively priced compared with alternative fuels. The fourth argument is that although coal is environmentally damaging, the technology is in place to overcome much of the harm it inflicts. It is also deemed to be a safer fuel than some of its competitors. The fifth argument is a social one.

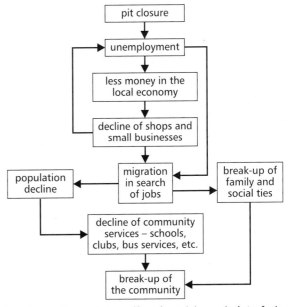

■ **27.8** The demultiplier effect (or 'vicious circle' of pit closures)

Mining communities are almost entirely dependent on coalmining for employment and evidence would suggest that the closure of coal mines leads to a **demultiplier effect (27.8)**. There is ample evidence to suggest that as clusters of mines have closed, longer local dole queues are testament to the fact that former miners have great difficulty in finding work outside the industry.

Thus there have been dramatic changes in the shape of the coalmining industry in Britain, largely as a result of government privatisation policies which have caused planned decline to become accelerated 'free-fall'. This will possibly leave the privatised coal industry with around 14 core deep mines, plus perhaps some outliers of privatisation from previous closures. Increasing shares of the diminished electricity demand for coal will come from opencast sources (for every pit that shuts, at least two opencast sites open) and from imported coal via new modern terminals.

5 Prepare cases for and against the closure of more pits down to a pre-privatisation target of 14 remaining pits. Think of environmental, social, political and economic arguments. Which do you think are the most important issues?

6 There are numerous individual studies you can undertake which look at the changing nature of coal in Britain. For example:

- Very successful studies on opencast issues explore landscape and ecological loss, and measure the potential impacts of dust, blasting, visual eyesores and traffic noise, as well as looking at economic issues such as loss of house price value and recreational amenity versus employment gains.

- You may be fortunate enough to attend one of the planning enquiries which are mandatory before the acceptance of a proposal.

- The closure of a local pit is another interesting topic, as you can use historical records to chart its original development, and see the impact of the production cycle (British Coal statistics) on employment structure, settlement and population.

- If you are planning to look at any environmental benefits, it is vital you gain access to an old project, so that you can have a baseline to compare your results against.

- The impact of subsidence is a very interesting issue to document, as there is so much evidence you can collect by first-hand observation, although because of controversial impending litigation some information from official sources may not be available.

27.4 Oil and natural gas

Oil

27.9 shows world oil demand in 1992, which has slowly edged up, with particularly strong demands from South-east Asia. Demand in the former Soviet Union continues to decline largely because of a fall in economic activity there. The pattern of the demand is very different between OECD and non-OECD countries. In OECD countries, demand is dominated by gas oil and petrol (together nearly 60 per cent of the total). In non-OECD countries, it is fuel oil and gas oil that dominate demand. Gas oil is used for commercial transport, and fuel oil is largely used for electricity production, in the absence of investment in costly nuclear installations or renewables. Prices in crude oil are highly volatile but since 1986 have fluctuated around $15–20 a barrel, a lower level than prices following the first oil crisis in 1973.

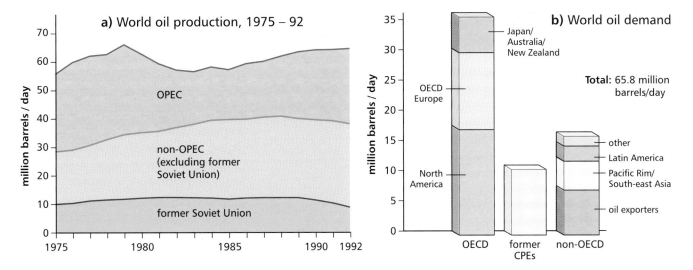

a) World oil production, 1975 – 92

million barrels / day

OPEC

non-OPEC
(excluding former
Soviet Union)

former Soviet Union

1975   1980   1985   1990 1992

b) World oil demand

million barrels / day

Japan/
Australia/
New Zealand

OECD
Europe

North
America

Total: 65.8 million
barrels/day

other
Latin America
Pacific Rim/
South-east Asia
oil exporters

OECD   former
CPEs   non-OECD

■ **27.9** World oil production
and demand

7 a What caused the oil crises of
1973 and 1979/80?
b Find out by how much the
cost of a barrel of crude oil
increased during the 1970s.

Oil has one advantage over other fuels. As a liquid resource, it can be easily transported by pipeline, and also by very large supertankers. A new generation of tankers, built to go round the Cape of Good Hope, have a capacity of 400 000 tonnes plus and dock at superports such as Europort near Rotterdam, Europe's largest oil-importing centre. World trade in oil exceeded 31 million barrels/day in 1992, with more than two-thirds of this exported from OPEC countries (**27.9**). Saudi Arabia alone exported over a quarter of this total. Of the non-OPEC total, the former Soviet Union, Norway and Mexico were the main exporters (some 15 per cent of the world total). The world's top oil importers are the USA, Japan, Germany, France and Italy, which together account for more than 60 per cent of total imports.

The nature of crude oil means that the exploration and development of petroleum resources does lead to environmental changes. At the production stage, although the well-heads are inconspicuous there is a need for storage and collection and processing facilities which are still visually intrusive in spite of careful landscaping There is always the risk of explosion from blow-outs and accidents, and the risk of spillage. This is especially a problem since the industry extended itself to offshore environments. Spillages at sea, such as the *Exxon Valdez* in 1989 and the *Braer* in 1992, are largely the result of human error – as is the case with most accidents. Oil spillages also occur on land, and with damaging consequences.

Spillages are a particular problem in environmentally-sensitive areas such as Prince William Sound, Alaska or the Shetlands. There is some controversy about how great these environmental or economic impacts are. Oil is readily dispersed in tropical, high-energy seas, but the impacts are clearly a major problem in environmentally vulnerable areas, such as salt marshes, mangrove swamps, coral reefs and areas containing rare fauna. Oil ingested by fish and crustaceans can easily enter the food chain, perhaps reaching humans. Research suggests that treatment involving chemicals may have more adverse effects than the initial spill. Preventive action such as double-hulled tankers, or controlled routeing, all increase costs. The question has to be asked whether the world can have both cheap fuel and a pristine environment. The oil-spills really hit the

IT3,8

IT3,8

headlines when economic activities are threatened, such as the salmon-fishing industries of Alaska and Shetland, or the beautiful beaches of Venezuela.

In general terms, although oil is perceived to be a cleaner fuel than coal in terms of particulate pollution, it can be a source of sulphur dioxide. It is by no means blameless in its contribution towards acid deposition and the greenhouse gases, and is a major contributor to urban pollution via the internal combustion engine (see Chapter 12). Lean-burn engines and catalytic convertors can only ameliorate these effects to an extent.

Oil production has very important direct and indirect impacts on the economic and social life of the local area, on the region and nationally, many of them very beneficial. The oil companies' operations bring wealth into the area by direct expenditure on local goods and services, and employment and training opportunities are greatly improved. One adverse effect of North Sea oil was a property boom in Aberdeen, which made northeast Scotland one of the most expensive places in the UK. Nationally, the contribution of North Sea oil to Britain's balance of payments cannot be overemphasised as for over a decade the country has been self-sufficient in terms of its total oil requirements – although this has only been achieved by exchanging light North Sea oil for heavy oils produced elsewhere.

Natural gas

Natural gas can be flared off as a waste product in oil production, but where there is a sufficiently large market it can become a very valuable product. The less volatile components, such as butane and propane, may be removed as LPG (liquefied petroleum gas), which is an invaluable fuel for rural areas, as in Spain or Portugal. The residue, which is chiefly methane, is cleaned, dried and piped to consumers as natural gas. In the southern North Sea, 'dry' natural gas is found without oil, which has led to a major North Sea gas industry in the Netherlands, Germany and England, where it is piped ashore to the east coast terminals of Easington, Theddlethorpe and Bacton.

Natural gas has many strengths as a fuel, as it has good 'green' credentials, contributing around half the carbon dioxide of other fossil fuels. It also has a very high calorific value, which makes it a very efficient fuel. The only problem is that of transport. Most movement is by pipeline, such as the transcontinental pipelines from the former Soviet Union to Europe, but movement by sea is expensive as the methane has to be converted to LPG and transported at very low temperatures by special refrigerated ships which dock at dedicated terminals.

27.10a shows the distribution of the proven reserves, which are concentrated in the former Soviet Union and the

■ **27.10** Reserves and production of natural gas

a) Proven natural gas reserves, 1992

Total: 131 500 000 million m³ @ 9500 kcal/m³

Former Soviet Union and Eastern Europe

Western Europe

Asia-Pacific

Africa

Western Hemisphere

Middle East

b) Natural gas net production

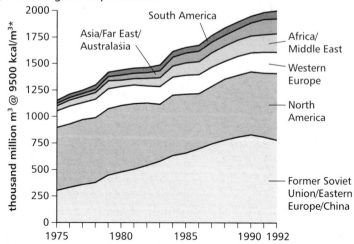

*excludes re-injected/flared gas and shrinkage due to the extraction of natural gas liquids

Middle East. Estimates of reserves have doubled every 10 years since 1960 due to increasingly sophisticated exploration techniques. Supply of reserves is presently around 75 years, but some scientists say this could be extended up to 200 years, provided the use is monitored. The other encouraging fact is that the number of countries with known gas reserves also increased from about 40 in 1960 to 85 in 1990. World production has increased steadily since 1975, with only the former Soviet Union – a driving force in the 1980s – showing a decline (**27.10b**).

The only question in this expansive situation is can the increased use of gas be justified? The arguments in both environmental and economic terms are very favourable compared with the other fossil fuels. Gas has always been used for domestic and industrial heating, but the recent 'dash for gas' also involves its use for electricity generation. Gas-fired power stations have lower capital costs, shorter construction times, lower space requirements, greater acceptability to local people, and running costs are lower than those of nuclear power – but it is a finite resouce.

27.5 The fuelwood crisis – the other people's energy gap

The fuelwood crisis is a reality to 2 billion people. Nearly half of the world depends on wood for heating, light and cooking, as fuelwood accounts for a large proportion of all energy consumption in many ELDCs. Although theoretically fuelwood is a sustainable resource, close to 1.3 billion people are consuming fuelwood resources at a faster rate than they are being replenished.

This problem has a major impact on the lives of the people and the environment they live in. It is made an even greater crisis because there are few alternatives available for these people. The countries in which they live have few viable alternative fuels, and where there are alternatives they cost too much. Fuelwood gathering for a family can take up to 250 days of labour each year, so it dominates daily life to the detriment of other rural or agricultural work. There are clear implications for health and nutrition too, as boiling water and producing hot, well-cooked food are unaffordable luxuries.

In urban areas, the main fuel is often charcoal made from fuelwood. Unfortunately, converting fuelwood to charcoal consumes more than half of the original energy, so each town dweller actually uses twice as much wood for a given amount of energy. Thus a 'ring of woodland destruction' encircles many large cities in the developing world. As the urban population continues to increase at a rate of over 8 per cent per year in some ELDCs, so too does the wasteful production of charcoal, which represents up to 75 per cent of all fuelwood consumption. Up to 40 per cent of family income is spent on the purchase of fuel in urban areas.

In several areas, the fuelwood crisis is beginning to hit agricultural productivity. Once fuelwood becomes so scarce that people have to burn alternatives like animal dung or crop residues to cook their meals, as in Bangladesh or Nepal, the soil is robbed of fertilisers, thus reducing food output by up to 15 per cent. Extra food is needed especially by women, the main fuel

gatherers, who often expend an extra 500 calories each day walking up to 20 km to collect 3–4 kg of wood.

Because trees are cut down faster than the timber stock can replenish itself – especially the younger trees which are more easily harvested – there is a loss of tree cover, a declining protective canopy and a lack of regenerative capability. The loss of tree cover inevitably leads to a loss of soil cover, and so there is a huge amount of soil erosion. This, in turn, leads to the silting up and flooding of rivers.

There are numerous plans to solve the crisis. In the short term the following are suggested:

- more careful fuel management
- adaptation of cooking patterns with communal village kitchens
- reducing the non-fuel uses of wood
- switching to other fuels such as kerosene or LPG, which obviously cost more
- employing men as well as women in fuelwood collection as agriculture is mechanised
- developing more fuel-efficient stoves such as the Lorena stove built in Guatemala which cuts fuel use by half
- improved fuelwood distribution networks
- the adoption of better charcoal-making techniques
- use of stoves using green charcoal.

In the long term, the main solution is to plant more trees for fuel – a fivefold increase in planting levels is needed to sustain supplies for the future. In 1990 the World Bank estimated that to meet the fuelwood crisis this will require planting 55 million ha with fast-growing trees at a rate of 2.7 million ha each year. The right species have to be selected for each particular environment, and they have to be planted in a place where they will be used, and by the people who have need of them.

IP2, IT4,8

The fuelwood crisis in Nepal

Nepal's energy budget reflects its status as an ELLDC. In 1992, there were low income levels of under $180 per head, and only 5 per cent of the workforce was employed in modern manufacturing. The consumption of commercial fuels at 25 kg per head is amongst the lowest in the world, yet energy imports of oil account for over 30 per cent of income earned from exports. To add to the problem, Nepal is a landlocked country sandwiched between the two giants, India and China. For over five years, India has shut its border with Nepal, thus denying access for supplies of kerosene (for cooking) – all because the Nepalese government allowed Chinese technicians to work on development projects in a perceived sensitive zone near the Indian border.

Central to Nepal's energy crisis is the state of the country's biomass fuel supply. As **27.11** shows, the absolute increase in demand has been almost exclusively provided for by increased demands on fuelwood, but the relative role of the fuelwood has decreased in comparison with dung and crop residues.

Although most of Nepal's biomass fuel still comes from natural forests, an increasing proportion (around 25 per cent in 1991) is supplied from farm woodlots, gardens and orchards, as well as from crop and animal residues. In two places – Kathmandu Valley, where over 80 per cent of rural households use dung, root stocks and chopped stalks, and in central and eastern Terai where crop residues, dried grass, dung and leaves are used as fuel for cooking – fuel supplies are just not available. In other areas too, such as the Siwalik Hills, it is possible to chart the retreat of the forest frontiers from mid-1950 onwards. The most accessible areas of forest have therefore been degraded, forcing farmers to switch to biomass fuels such as dung and crop residues. Many women are reduced to spending half a day collecting dead leaves in order to make one hot meal for their families.

	1979/80 % energy consumption	1989/90 % energy consumption
Fuelwood	93.2	76.0
Crop waste	1.6	10.9
Animal dung	0.6	8.5
Petroleum	3.5	3.6
Coal	0.7	0.5
Electricity	0.4	0.5
Total	100.0	100.0

■ **27.11** Energy consumption in Nepal, 1979/80 and 1989/90

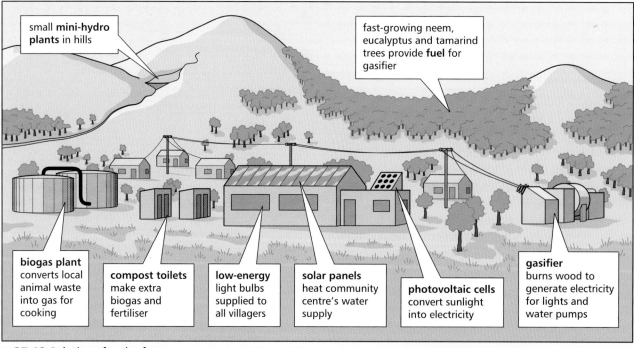

small **mini-hydro plants** in hills

fast-growing neem, eucalyptus and tamarind trees provide **fuel** for gasifier

biogas plant converts local animal waste into gas for cooking

compost toilets make extra biogas and fertiliser

low-energy light bulbs supplied to all villagers

solar panels heat community centre's water supply

photovoltaic cells convert sunlight into electricity

gasifier burns wood to generate electricity for lights and water pumps

■ **27.12** Solutions for the future

Nepal's biomass energy crisis is only part of a multi-faceted problem of environmental degradation involving forest loss, soil erosion, flooding and maintenance of farming systems in which land fertility is achieved largely through the feeding of forest fodder to livestock. Nepal's latest plan involves the planting of 2 million ha of forestry over the next 25 years to provide a reservoir of woodland for fuelwood and fodder. Other solutions have to be considered for the future, the most promising of which is the building of mini-hydro plants. Already there are 600 of these being built in Nepal. In an impoverished rural area, solutions must be through intermediate or low technology. **27.12** shows other possible solutions. It is clear, then, that any acceptable solution must be cheap to build, inexpensive and straightforward to maintain, and easy to use.

8 Analyse the data in **27.11**. What were the main changes in energy consumption, and why? Remember that 94 per cent of Nepal's final energy demand is in the domestic non-commercial sector, with commerce and transport consuming no more than 6 per cent.

9 Which of the suggestions in **27.12** do you think Nepalese village communities should favour?

27.6 **A nuclear future?**

IT2

■ **27.13** The rise and stagnation of nuclear power

Whether the world should develop nuclear power is the single most controversial topic in the field of energy studies. Nuclear power at one time was hailed as the solution to the world's energy problem, yet now it is condemned as the most dangerous and unfitting way to produce energy. People's views are markedly polarised. Some people, usually scientists, record the harnessing of

IT2

Year	Capacity MW	Year	Capacity MW
1954	5	1974	61 000
1955	5	1975	71 000
1956	50	1976	85 000
1957	100	1977	99 000
1958	190	1978	114 000
1959	380	1979	121 000
1960	830	1980	135 000
1961	850	1981	155 000
1962	1 800	1982	170 000
1963	2 100	1983	189 000
1964	3 100	1984	219 000
1965	4 800	1985	250 000
1966	6 200	1986	276 000
1967	8 300	1987	297 000
1968	9 200	1988	311 000
1969	13 000	1989	321 000
1970	16 000	1990	329 000
1971	24 000	1991	326 000
1972	32 000	1992	328 000
1973	45 000		

a) Installed electrical generating capacity of world nuclear power plants, 1954–92

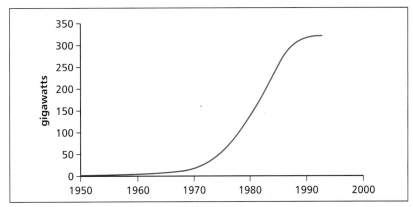

b) Generating capacity of world nuclear power plants, 1950–92

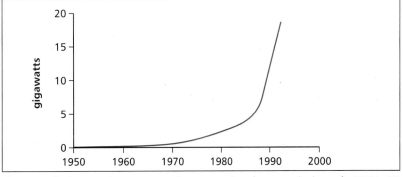

c) Cumulative nuclear generating capacity decommissioned, 1964–92

nuclear power as almost the greatest technological development of the modern age, because at a stroke the energy gap can be bridged by producing almost unlimited quantities of cheap energy from safe, non-polluting sources. Others, particularly those who fear the inextricable linkage between nuclear power and the development and use of nuclear weapons, protest against 'nukes' and the linked problem of nuclear waste disposal. At present, there is a stalemate in the global nuclear power programme, largely brought about by two mounting concerns – accidents, and the disposal of nuclear waste (**27.13**). The public's fears of the dangers of nuclear power have been raised by two notable accidents – Three Mile Island, Pennsylvania in 1979 and Chernobyl, Ukraine in 1986. Both accidents have become landmarks in the development of nuclear policy and political opposition to it.

In 1991 there were 418 nuclear reactors operating in the world and they contributed 17 per cent of the world's electricity (**27.14**).

The principal limitation is that nuclear power can only be used to generate electricity. Even then, it has to supply base load because it is not flexible enough to meet fluctuating peak

---

10 Using appropriate techniques, draw a map to show the world distribution of nuclear reactors (**27.14**). Why do you think that reactors are increasingly concentrated around particular sites? For example, some locations in Canada such as Lake Huron have eight reactors on one site.

CASE STUDY

IT2,3

The accidents at Three Mile Island and Chernobyl

Three Mile Island was in many ways 'the accident that might have been'. Mechanical failure compounded by human error caused a partial fuel meltdown, which released a comparatively small amount of radioactivity (around 20 curies) into the atmosphere.

The main impact was that the accident challenged the prevailing scientific view that it was impossible for an accident such as a meltdown to happen in a pressurised water reactor. It therefore accelerated the erosion of public confidence in nuclear technology. The ensuing overhaul of the American nuclear industry led to mandatory safety innovations and design changes which crippled the cost-effectiveness of the nuclear industry, and crystallised public opposition to 'nukes'. Locally, the legacy of Three Mile Island has been the growth of the residents' distrust of government and industry, and also many cases of psychological stress.

Chernobyl was a milestone in another way. It was the largest and most catastrophic nuclear power plant accident in the history of atomic power. More than 1500 km^2 of land and water were contaminated around the reactor. There was also radioactive fallout throughout Europe as the radioactive plume was spread around by the diverse prevailing wind pattern in the region, and deposited widely as a result of continuous rain. Dozens of people were killed immediately; more are languishing with thyroid cancer and other malignant tumours.

The severity of Chernobyl, the international nature of its impact and the reluctance of the Soviet Union to acknowledge and report the accident to the International Atomic Energy Agency (IAEA) led to a number of controls on the nuclear industry, including two international treaties. Politically, Chernobyl created great worldwide anxiety about the safety of nuclear power plants, especially in Russia, Eastern and Central Europe, where there are many reactors of identical design. Much EU money is spent on aid to countries such as the Czech Republic, Slovakia and Bulgaria to improve the safety of old reactors. Austria is in the forefront of the opposition to Russian-designed reactors in Eastern Europe, as the country lies immediately downwind from any fallout. Austria has even offered to compensate the Czech Republic for lost electrical power for four half-built reactors, in an effort to stop their completion and to supply technical support to replace the lost power.

demands; it is even less flexible than electricity from coal-fired power stations. Its biggest selling point is its cleanliness in terms of its greenhouse gases. Other issues such as cost are far more controversial. Cheap fuel and low running costs are offset by technology costs, such as research and development, reactor repairs, breakdowns and ultimately decommissioning, so total costs are high.

IT5

The technology of waste management is another issue, because of the health risks from the radioactive nature of waste materials. All workers at nuclear power plants are monitored for radioactivity but it is not the extreme dose which represents a problem. In spite of strict limits, there is persistent if conflicting evidence of cancer clusters around nuclear installations such as the one at Sellafield. There are three categories of nuclear waste: low-level, which presents few problems; intermediate, which has to be entombed in concrete; and the high-level waste of spent fuels, which has to be reprocessed either on site or at purpose-built plants.

	Number of sites	Number of reactors
Argentina	2	2
Belgium	2	7
Brazil	1	1
Bulgaria	1	5
Canada	5	19
CIS	15	42
Czechoslovakia	2	8
Finland	2	4
France	19	55
Germany	16	21
Hungary	1	4
India	4	7
Japan	17	41
Mexico	1	1
Netherlands	2	2
South Africa	1	2
South Korea	4	9
Spain	7	9
Sweden	4	12
Switzerland	4	5
UK	14	37
USA	70	119

■ **27.14** Global distribution of nuclear power stations, 1990

11 Argue the pros and cons of a nuclear power programme. In which direction do you think the arguments tip?

27.7 **Renewable sources of energy**

IT4

Concerns, previously explored, about acid rain, oilspills, urban smog, nuclear accidents and global warming, are prompting a thorough and urgent re-examination of alternatives to coal, oil and even nuclear power. Although the so-called **alternative energy** sources are not universally pollution free, nor indeed are they all renewable (for example, geothermal power and biomass are renewable only if they are used in a sustainable way), they do have two outstanding advantages. They certainly appear to be environmentally less damaging, and they are not linked to finite sources which at present rates of usage may last, in the case of oil, for as little as 40 years. The main problems to surmount are technological – can they be developed to produce energy in sufficiently large quantities, at economically viable prices, in the foreseeable future? It may be of course that economic viability is not the key factor, and that environmental considerations should be paramount.

IT4

Hydroelectricity (HEP)

Since the 1950s, HEP production has grown steadily; in 1991, it reached 644 000 MW, providing just over 20 per cent of the world's electricity. At present, just under a quarter of the world's HEP potential has been exploited, but it is unlikely that all of it ever will be, owing to environmental, economic and social constraints.

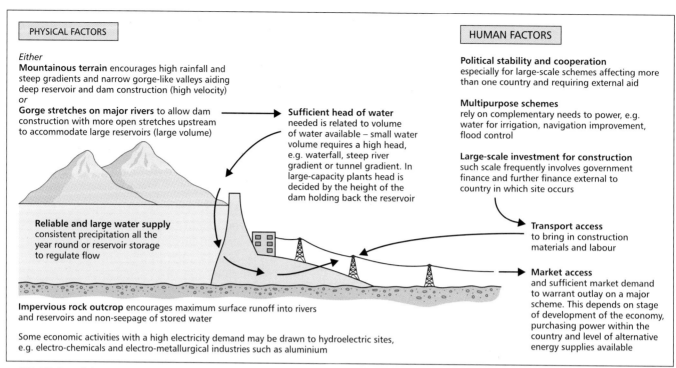

PHYSICAL FACTORS

Either
Mountainous terrain encourages high rainfall and steep gradients and narrow gorge-like valleys aiding deep reservoir and dam construction (high velocity)
or
Gorge stretches on major rivers to allow dam construction with more open stretches upstream to accommodate large reservoirs (large volume)

Sufficient head of water needed is related to volume of water available – small water volume requires a high head, e.g. waterfall, steep river gradient or tunnel gradient. In large-capacity plants head is decided by the height of the dam holding back the reservoir

Reliable and large water supply consistent precipitation all the year round or reservoir storage to regulate flow

Impervious rock outcrop encourages maximum surface runoff into rivers and reservoirs and non-seepage of stored water

Some economic activities with a high electricity demand may be drawn to hydroelectric sites, e.g. electro-chemicals and electro-metallurgical industries such as aluminium

HUMAN FACTORS

Political stability and cooperation especially for large-scale schemes affecting more than one country and requiring external aid

Multipurpose schemes rely on complementary needs to power, e.g. water for irrigation, navigation improvement, flood control

Large-scale investment for construction such scale frequently involves government finance and further finance external to country in which site occurs

Transport access to bring in construction materials and labour

Market access and sufficient market demand to warrant outlay on a major scheme. This depends on stage of development of the economy, purchasing power within the country and level of alternative energy supplies available

■ **27.15** Conditions necessary for HEP

IT4

In EMDCs, nearly half the potential has been realised, but in ELDCs it is significant that only 7 per cent of the potential has been harnessed, with Africa offering enormous prospects for the future.

However, HEP is not a universal panacea to each nation's energy crisis, as its potential tends to be constrained by physical conditions. Rain and snow deposited at higher elevations represent a vast storage of potential energy, but unfortunately such areas are often remote wilderness areas of pristine beauty and high biological diversity, and therefore highly prized environmentally. In ELDCs, although plentiful sites do exist in theory, it is not always clear how the large quantities of power drawn from those prestigious schemes could be utilised, or who, other than transnational corporations, would be beneficiaries. **27.15** summarises some of the key factors affecting the location and implementation of HEP schemes.

IT4

■ **27.16** Costs and benefits of large-scale HEP projects

Costs	Benefits
Problems of limited life of some dams (30–50 years) because of silting	Well established, proven technology; no real danger except accidental dam failure
Capital-intensive – dams expensive and transmission costs high	Low running-costs – free fuel constantly available and totally renewable
Causes river management problems downstream – reduced flows, reduced sediment directly interferes with life cycle of fish, clear-water erosion	Multipurpose – electricity generation, flood control, irrigation and reservoirs offer potential for aquaculture, recreation and tourism
High secondary environment costs – flooding of land, disruption of wildlife and lifestyles of indigenous people, loss of agricultural land	Pollution-free in terms of the production process; no contribution to global warming or acid rain
Promotion of water-borne diseases as a result of the formation of huge artifical lakes	Provides a vital source of electricity in areas where no other is available in large quantities

12 A cost–benefit analysis of HEP is presented in **27.16**. Which is the winner in your view – costs or benefits? Would you get the same result with mini-hydro plants?

Other sources

IT4

All the other sources of renewable energy are far less widespread than that for HEP, but advances are being made all the time. Electricity from wind is certainly likely to be cost-competitive in the mid-1990s, as is tidal power, which has analogous technolo-

Nature of renewable source	Exploitation	Potential	Strengths	Weaknesses
1 BIOMASS • from natural vegetation • from straw • from energy crops • from organic wastes • from refuse • from landfill gases	Direct use of fuelwood – charcoal by pyrolysis 12 000 small straw burners and 30 straw-fired district heating systems in Denmark Widespread use of sugarcane in Brazil to make gasohol Widespread use of dung and human manure in biogas convertors in India and other ELDCs The valuable energy content of waste products can be harnessed via refuse incineration. 350 energy-from-refuse incinerators, mainly in in Japan and Germany (one in Nottingham) Decomposing refuse generates gas – by 1990, 240 landfill gas projects, nearly 100 in USA	Wide-scale development of fields of quick-growing trees, e.g. willows, will provide cleaner biomass Use of fast-growing water plants, e.g water hyacinth Many new schemes being developed for local uses from an increasing variety of waste materials, e.g. coconut shells	• Very widely available • Provides a basis for rural development in ELDCs • If grown sustainably, creates no build-up of CO_2 • Recycling of waste products	• Some environmental degradation and health hazards • Can take land away from food production, e.g. displacement of Brazilian peasants by sugarcane plantations
2 SOLAR • from photothermal sources • concentration of large amounts of sunlight onto a small area to allow build-up of high temperatures • from photovoltaic cells converting sunlight directly into electricity	Development of passive and active collection of solar energy:– building designs to incorporate passive solar technology. Development of Trombe walls Use of thermal collectors and solar panels, 350 MW of solar thermal power plants in USA Solar power towers (in USA) Harnessing satellite technology of the 1950s	Development of solar technology in houses as they are built Solar thermal electrical technologies will improve to make 200 MW power plants Development of large photovoltaic cells in arrays which could produce base-load power	• World-wide potential – could be used for peak utility loads and for modular power plants in rural areas	• Variable availability; relatively low power density, for top-up power only • Limited market prevents mass production • Conversion efficiencies limited to 15–20% – costs have decreased, but the main barrier to development is cost • Huge expense, but costs will fall when mass production is possible
3 WIND • wind-generated turbines	17 800 wind turbines in Denmark and California during the past 10 years. Wind turbine technology is thoroughly tested and proven. Some wind farms and single wind generators in Great Britain	Increased size of units available (0.5 MW in 1995). Advances in wind turbine technologies, e.g. advanced materials for aerofoils. Costs could decrease with 'smart' blades and electronically controlled optimal orientation devices	• Potentially fully competitive with coal-fired stations – can be deployed at several scales	• Variability and unpredictability – some concern about environmental impacts, such as aesthetic, and risks to wildlife
4 OCEAN ENERGY SYSTEMS **a** WAVES • converting the mechanical energy of the waves to electricity	Systems still in infancy. Small nearshore and shoreline devices in place (e.g. Islay) but limited applicability and potential	Large, powerful offshore energy plants possible in future OTEC (ocean thermal energy conversion) is at prototype stage, in tropical locations only		• Only possible with government capital because very high capital costs • Only 25% efficiency because variable height of wave crests. Energy available in remote areas away from centres of consumption
b TIDES • tidal energy drives turbines similar to HEP	Proven and established technology operational at Rance in France. Some small-scale schemes in former Soviet Union, China and Canada	Modern tidal barrages equipped with a series of gated sluices, using flood, ebb or two-way generation	• Capable of large-scale generation capacity • Longevity of structures (about 120 years) • Environmental benefits – barrage protects coast	• Only practicable when tides are large and suitable sites for dams can be found (around 20 sites in world) • Extraordinarily high capital costs, intermittent operation • Problems with estuarine ecosystems
5 GEOTHERMAL • from radioactive batholiths • from hypothermal areas where natural hot water is used • from hot dry rock fields	Widely used in Japan, Hungary, former Soviet Union, Hungary, Iceland and New Zealand, largely as a source of direct hot water and heating. 9750 MW produced globally	Hot dry rocks are the geothermal sources of the future. Trials taking place in USA and UK (Cornwall) but difficulty lies with creating a commercially viable system. Water is injected through a separate borehole after being heated by the rock	• Very widespread if localised potential, e.g. in Colombia, Tanzania and Ethiopia. Can be used for base load	• Noxious gases, especially sulphur, a problem • Can be very costly to develop, for example in Japan as costly as nuclear power

■ **27.17** Renewable energies compared

gies to HEP, in the foreseeable future. Geothermal power has been used for several decades in localised areas such as Iceland and North Island, New Zealand. **27.17** summarises the present development and potential of these alternative sources and evaluates their strengths and weaknesses.

Cumulatively these other sources constitute a vast resource. The technology costs are high, but conversely operating costs are potentially low. Another bonus of renewable resources is their widespread availability. Most developments at present are low-intensity and small-scale,

and are especially useful for a dispersed deployment in rural areas to supply power to the immediate locality. In a sense, such developments run contrary to the normal developed world pattern of massive power stations enjoying the advantages of economies of scale, and linked to an efficient national grid. As there is such a variety of alternative sources, most countries have some potential for development, which is particularly encouraging for ELDCs lacking oil resources. Another consideration is the likelihood of widespread public acceptability.

CASE STUDY

Renewable energy sources in Great Britain

Renewable energy has always been seen in Britain as the poor relation of coal and especially of nuclear power. But the climate of opinion is beginning to change as the government and private organisations invest in R & D.

One of the main strands of Britain's renewable strategy has been biomass energy generation using a variety of fuels from wastes and crops. Locally, various energy plants prepare and use dry organic wastes in the form of refuse, agricultural wastes, straw and wood chippings. The main thrust recently has been to grow 'energy forests' by short rotational forestry, involving single-stem trees and coppicing techniques. Farmers have been keen to consider this new crop, if the price is right.

Land-based wind energy is undoubtedly a very promising renewable energy technology for the British Isles, both in the amount of energy it could produce (20 per cent by the year 2010 is an optimistic estimate) and at a cost that is competitive with fossil fuels and nuclear power. To provide 10 per cent of Britain's electricity would require over 1000 wind farms, which has clear implications for many of the most beautiful areas in Britain (**27.18**). Anxieties also persist about noise and interference with TV, although modern technology suggests that these fears are misplaced. Nevertheless, wind farms are spreading, as farmers see them as a profitable 'crop', largely in the hill areas of the Pennines, the

Lake District and North Wales. The examination of the impact of wind farms on the people and environment of the area is an excellent one for individual study.

Locally inshore, wave energy has been successfully developed on the island of Islay in the Inner Hebrides. In May 1991 the energy from this wave power was fed into the national grid for the first time from a prototype which uses an oscillating water column to turn the rotors in the Wells turbine. At present its applicability will probably be restricted to providing power to remote highland sites which would be very expensive to supply by other means.

Although large-scale HEP schemes have been producing power for many years (especially in the Scottish Highlands where 80 per cent are located), attention has turned to the possibility of developing small-scale, low-head schemes (less than 5 m). There is no doubt that new technology could make this development potentially valuable but as yet it is still in the experimental phase, and there are some concerns about the impact on rivers.

Over the last 10 years, tidal energy has been seen as the great hope for large-scale production of renewable energy. These tidal barrage schemes could certainly produce up to 20 per cent of Britain's electricity in the foreseeable future, using adaptations of HEP technology. Detailed plans and feasibility studies costing £20 million have been carried out for a Severn barrage, a Mersey barrage, and a Morecambe Bay scheme.

However, recent opinion suggests that these tidal barrages may be mere dreams in spite of their ability to generate large quantities of clean power. The main problem is that private-sector companies would not have the resources to build them at a cost of over £1 billion each. As the Channel Tunnel experience showed, it is very difficult for private companies to carry out such large projects without very substantial government support. They also have major environmental implications for Britain's estuarine ecosystems (see section 17.4).

Geothermal power has great potential for development in south-west England, the Lake District and in Weardale and could in theory produce up to 10 per cent of Britain's electricity in the foreseeable future. Geothermal energy can be tapped from aquifers – underground deposits of hot water in porous rocks and hot dry rocks. In Cornwall, at Rosemanowes, a scheme has been developed to exploit geothermal energy from the latter, but this is only at an experimental stage.

Solar energy supplies – other than those incorporated as a part of buildings which use the form and fabric of the building to capture solar radiation to reduce energy costs – are very limited. Although active solar heating has had considerable R & D attention, it is unlikely to be cost-effective except for special applications such as swimming pools. Photovoltaic cells as an export technology are well developed in the UK, but costs remain very high as energy from the sun is both very variable and frequently of low intensity in this country.

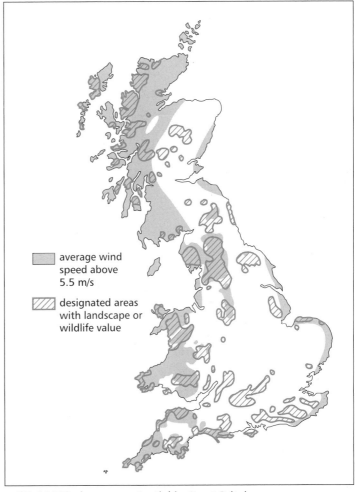

average wind speed above 5.5 m/s

designated areas with landscape or wildlife value

■ **27.18** Wind power potential in Great Britain

27.8 **Energy conservation – another option**

IT4

The search for and harnessing of alternative sources of renewable and environmentally friendly energy is one possible strategy for the future. Another is to cut back on and conserve our current non-renewable resources of energy by using that energy much more efficiently. There are many who believe that increased energy efficiency is the key to global sustainability in energy use.

Although the current debate on energy conservation and efficiency focuses mainly on the problem of CO_2 emissions, global warming and the prevention of acid deposition, the range of arguments is much greater than just the environmental ones. There are vital social and economic dimensions to be considered. The least radical reason for advocating energy efficiency – but likely to be the most widespread within governments – is as a means of saving money. Although government policies to promote energy efficiency cost

IT4

money, they are an investment. Private and corporate consumers of energy save money, the public sector as a consumer saves money, the general public saves money, and even the energy producers have to invest less in new plant, often in high-cost areas. Moreover, the national economy benefits with reduced manufacturing costs and improved balance of payments, with less money spent on imported energy supplies.

A second reason for advocating the promotion of energy efficiency is as a means of reducing energy dependence. Energy supplies may be running down (in the case of finite fossil fuels), or energy efficiency may obviate the need for an expansion of the nuclear power programme, or it may reduce dependence on imported fuels such as oil which largely comes from the volatile Middle East.

A third reason for increased energy efficiency is in part connected with the idea of shifting the world economy in total towards sustainability. Thus energy efficiency policies are seen as part of a general overall process of 'greening' the world economy and at the same time promoting international equity.

Ultimately, however, the most important argument for promoting energy efficiency is that based on the consideration of equity or fairness – both intergenerational equity (fairness between people in different generations), and international equity (fairness between all nations). Intergenerational equity hinges around the issue of the current generation destroying the global environment and using up the resources, so that there will not be any left for the use of future generations. The concept of international equity clearly challenges the current situation in which a little over 15 per cent of the world's people in OECD countries use over half of the world's energy.

Energy-efficiency strategies are very closely allied to the world's technological potential to support them. In industry good progress has been made, promoted or enforced by rising energy costs and rising interest rates which have forced companies to become industrially competitive. Industrial processes consume 40 per cent of the developed world's energy. Within the industrial sector, there are numerous improvements possible in the efficiency of manufacturing processes and machinery.

In transport too there is enormous potential for technological improvements. About half of the world's oil supply is consumed by a fleet of 500 million road vehicles, posing both economic and environmental issues. Fuel can be saved by better car design, the extensive development of public transport, by car pooling, by enforced lower speed limits and by improved urban design.

In buildings, both domestic and commercial, all sorts of design developments have led to savings of over 60 per cent from a variety of sources including improved heat efficiency through better insulating materials, heat pumps, improvements in air-conditioning efficiency, and windows which adjust opacity to maximise solar gain.

Unfortunately the technological benefits cannot, and will not, happen overnight, as it takes a long time and huge costs for the current stock of homes, cars and industrial machinery to be replaced. Nor will technological advances be put in place unless the price is right. There is little incentive if energy is very cheap.

Energy-saving strategies will need to be very different in the North and in the South. In the North, using existing technologies, strongly promoted by government incentives, we could by the year 2000 cut energy consumption by 25 per cent and fossil fuel consumption by 50 per cent, thus slowing environmental damage. The essential strategy is to separate economic growth from growth in energy use.

In the South, many countries have had to face up to the fuelwood crisis. In order to achieve sustainability, mass tree-planting programmes have had to be instituted with help from international aid agencies such as the World Bank. In the South, the biomass fuels (dung, wood and charcoal) will continue to play a far larger role than fossil fuels or electricity. Fossil fuels are rarely cheap enough for anything but the most essential uses, and the generation of electricity is small (see the case study on pages 362–63) and was until recently confined to urban areas. Plans to bring renewable schemes to villages, and energy-efficient measures such as new stoves and lights, represent exciting hopes for the future (see **27.12**).

13 Suggest ways in which you personally could cut down on your energy consumption.

Manufacturing can be defined as 'the production of goods by industrial processes'. It clearly has a key role to play in the economy as a provider of jobs, as a creator of wealth via the multiplier effect, and as a vital component in foreign trade. For these reasons it plays a major part in government and other policy-makers' development strategies. It also has a major impact on the environment and the lives of people. The significance of manufacturing to a country's economy is usually measured by the contributions it makes to a country's wealth (gross domestic product) and to employment. 28.1 shows how the relative importance of manufacturing varies from country to country. Many countries, developed and developing alike, refer to their **manufacturing base**. The use of the term is significant because it implies a belief in the crucial importance of manufacturing. It is seen as the foundation of an economy; the vital generator of economic development, wealth and prosperity. However, it is a perception that is increasingly being challenged.

When studying manufacturing, geographers are concerned with its distribution in space, and the processes which influence that distribution. They are also interested in the processes which cause the character and location of manufacturing to change over time and from place to place. This chapter aims to explore these two basic themes of distribution and change at a variety of spatial scales.

■ **28.1** The role of manufacturing in selected countries

	% GDP from industrial production		% employment in manufacturing	
	1965	1990	1965	1991
Bangladesh	5	15	5	10
Brazil	24	39	20	23
Japan	34	42	36	34
Kuwait	3	9	34	42
Niger	3	13	1	3
South Korea	18	45	15	34
UK	29	22	33	20
USA	28	27	32	26

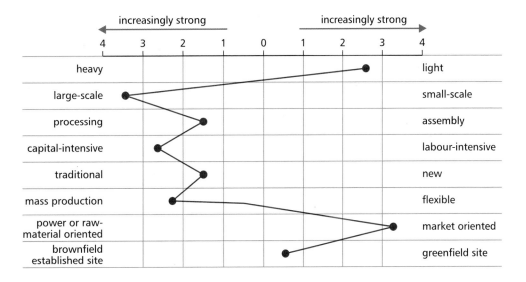

■ **28.2** Industrial profile of a tobacco factory

<table>
<tr><td></td></tr>
</table>

1 With reference to **28.1**:

   a Why do you think the importance of manufacturing varies from country to country?

   b What changes have there been since 1965?

   c What is the relationship between percentage employment and percentage contribution to the national economy?

2 a Try to create a profile similar to **28.2** for the brewing and aluminium-smelting industries.

   b Choose a local industrial plant known to you and create a profile for this industry.

28.1 **Input considerations in industrial location**

IT1

As suggested by **28.3**, manufacturing involves decisions about production inputs, such as land, labour, capital, raw materials and energy. The actual location of the individual factory is decided in relation to these inputs and also with regard to market opportunities for the products (or outputs). The decision may also be influenced by various forms of government intervention. The decision-maker may be an individual entrepreneur, or a large private or nationalised corporation, in which case linkages with other plants may be of paramount importance.

Raw materials

There are few industries, other than processing industries such as copper-smelting or oil-refining, that use a single (or totally dominant) raw material. Most modern industries (car production, for example) use a variety of raw materials. Generally speaking, as raw materials are manufactured they lose weight, for example as timber is processed into wooden planks or iron ore is converted into pig iron. This ratio between the weight of the localised materials and the weight of the finished product is known as the **material index**. If the material index is greater than 1, it is highly likely that raw materials will play a major part in locational decisions – that is, the industry will be oriented towards its most important raw materials. If the industry is weight-gaining on production, as for example when water is added to barley and hops to make beer, the industry will not be raw-material oriented.

Where raw materials are ubiquitous

■ **28.3** The manufacturing process system

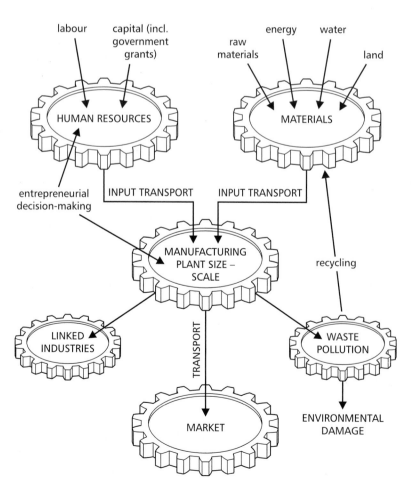

(i.e. found everywhere), their importance as a primary location factor will be of little significance. However, as few raw materials are ubiquitous, many countries with sophisticated manufacturing bases need to import raw materials. Tidewater locations therefore assume a similar role to raw-material locations. Large ports like Rotterdam's Europoort contain marked concentrations of industries such as oil-refining, metal-smelting, flour-milling and sugar-refining, as they are the point of import for oil, ore, wheat and sugarcane. Traditionally, industrialisation has taken place at the point of commodity import, but increasingly as economically less developed countries (ELDCs) industrialise, the point of export has also become a significant location. For example, most OPEC countries such as Saudi Arabia now refine oil before export. Tidewater locations represent **break-of-bulk** locations as commodities change transport mode. In this context and with the development of very large crude carriers (VLCCs), deepwater locations have become critical for industries such as the steel industry. The importance of Kimitsu and Oita as centres of the Japanese steel industry thus stems from the fact they can accommodate bulk carriers of up to 250 000 tonnes.

---

3 There are 12 sugarbeet factories in eastern England. Most of these are concentrated in arable East Anglia where most of the sugarbeet is grown. Explain why sugarbeet production is a raw-material oriented industry.

Energy

The same principles outlined for raw materials can in many cases be applied to energy as a factor of production. For example, in the Industrial Revolution, which was based on coal as a source of energy, the transport of the coal, a very bulky material, was extremely expensive, especially since much of its weight was burnt off as gas when generating steam power. Therefore nearly all the manufacturing industries became coalfield-based. The coalfields of Europe and North America spawned great centres of manufacturing, much of it of a heavy calibre. Even today, some coalfields, such as the Ruhr in Germany, remain important industrial regions, but many have struggled to adapt to 20th-century locational demands. A significant number have become 'problem regions' because they have disadvantages such as obsolescent infrastructure, unattractive derelict urban landscapes, and generally poor images for investors. However, because they have acquired advantages such as a pool of skilled labour, **industrial iner-**

tia is a powerful force, retaining some industries on the same sites, although many, if not all, of the original advantages have disappeared.

During the 20th century, as electricity and gas became the main sources of power, so energy became a ubiquitous resource. Because electricity and gas can be made from a variety of raw materials, and because they can be transmitted by grid or pipeline, the availability of energy has diminished in importance as a locational factor. However, its cost may be a very significant factor for industries that use vast quantities of electricity, namely the power-oriented industries such as aluminium smelting and the manufacturing of fertilisers. Southern Norway has in effect become an energy-oriented industrial region, with many plants powered by HEP located at the fjord heads.

Transport

The impact of transport on industrial location is complex. As **28.3** shows, it is required at both the input and output stages. Essentially, transport costs consist of **terminal costs** (docks, rail sidings, parking space, etc.) plus **line costs** (fuel, equipment, wages, etc.). The actual costs will depend on pricing policies of either the state or private transport enterprises. Frequently, individual contract quotations are made for a particular company based on the nature of the product, and the volume of business. For example, cars in a 'knocked-down' form (component parts) are easier to transport than the finished product, thereby encouraging final assembly as a market-oriented activity.

In general, transport is seldom a key factor in industrial location today, although it was often an important consideration in the past. In Stoke-on-Trent, all the 'pot banks' were located beside canals to ensure easy import of raw materials such as china clay and, more importantly, careful export of fragile end-products. As transport technology has improved, so transport costs have in general diminished as a percentage of total costs. However, for those industries that make heavy bulk products or require low-value bulky raw materials, the potential cost of transport can still be a significant secondary locational factor. Availability of transport can be a vital factor where perishable products such as flowers, fruit or fish are involved.

Land

Manufacturing industries vary enormously in terms of their space demands, and even within the individual industry those demands will differ according to plant size. Broadly speaking, the significance of site or land costs in the location equation increases commensurately with the size of the space demand. Large plants, such as car assembly works, will seek out locations where land is relatively cheap; small factories making high-value goods may be able to afford more expensive sites.

Labour

In **cost** terms, labour accounts for between 20 and 30 per cent of total costs. Differentials in global wage and salary rates can be a powerful locational influence, particularly for TNCs. Those companies involved in the manufacture of sports shoes or in electronics assembly, for example, shift their mass production from country to country (known as **transfer pricing**) to secure the greatest profits. Because of rising wage levels, Nike sports goods, for example, have moved most of their mass-production of shoes from South Korea and Taiwan, leaving these countries to concentrate on designer shoes. The mass-production manufacture has been transferred to Indonesia and China where labour is cheaper. Indeed, global differentials in wage levels are a key factor in the 'global shift' of manufacturing from EMDCs to ELDCs (see pages 383–88).

Labour quality is also very important. It can be very significant in the knowledge-based, innovative industries such as software development. Many firms find it advantageous to locate in university towns, like Cambridge (see

case study on pages 382–83). They do so because of the supply of graduates there, and because science and technology parks are now part of the business ventures of many universities.

Labour relations can also be very significant. Centres of trade union activity are regarded by some employers as potential centres of militancy and therefore perceived as a negative location factor. Labour availability can be influential; for example, when setting up their branch plant in Washington, north-east England, Nissan had the pick of a reservoir of unemployed young men, many trained in transferable engineering skills. Some assembly plants even locate in mining districts such as South Wales, as they perceive the area to have a surplus of nimble-fingered females for production work.

Labour is often quoted as being a mobile asset. However, although it may be an asset in the case of highly-qualified workers, paid to move within a multi-plant company, for most workers there are many frictional forces. Many knowledge-based industries which require a high quality of labour find it advantageous to locate in places which are perceived as excellent to live in. One such place in the USA is Denver, Colorado which, because of its beautiful surroundings, is rated as one of the most desirable locations in the whole of the country.

CASE STUDY

Search for a Toyota site

When Toyota, a Japanese company, made the decision to build a large car plant in the UK, numerous local authorities intimated they were interested. Toyota's initial specification was for a greenfield site of 100 ha or more located outside the expensive South East. A total of 28 possible sites were shortlisted, and each was sent a 25-page questionnaire which was designed to produce a dossier of comprehensive information on the site: its general ambience, its location, the skills of the local workforce, the quality of schools and colleges,

details of other employers in the area, and so on.

Burnaston (a site on an old airfield) near Derby was the winner because of its skilled workforce (1.5 million people live within 45 minutes' commuting time) and because, following recent job losses at Brell and Rolls-Royce Aero, a reservoir of highly-trained labour was available. Other significant factors included the relatively good access to the West Midlands car component industry via a new motorway link, and the cooperation and total support of Derbyshire County Council, which was prepared to invest £20 million in the site and offer every facility required.

4 You have to prepare a submission to a large transnational electronics company which is planning to establish a new factory employing 1000 workers to make printers and computers. Prepare a bid in which you outline all the advantages of your area, and suggest a possible site. Ideally your finished product should be desktop-published to give it professional presentation.

5 Read the newspaper cutting describing the selection process for the production workers at the new Toyota plant at Burnaston (**28.4**).

a Why is personnel selection so important for factories such as Toyota?
b What qualities do you think the selection tests are designed to find?

6 a Think of your own family situation and identify some of the factors which might prevent you or your parents moving for work.
b Think of all the places where you would like to work in Britain and in the world, and all the places where you would hate to live and work. What factors influenced your choices?

TOYOTA GEARS UP

The first Carina E family saloon yesterday rolled off the production line at Toyota's Burnaston factory, Derbyshire, which the company chairman described as 'a truly EC or British plant'.

To the workers – or rather 'team members' – who had produced the car, some decidedly un-British recruitment practices had brought them together.

Employees have typically spent six or seven months in the extensive recruitment process, undergoing assessment for a total of 16 hours.

Toyota's 'total production system' bases its management philosophy on mutual trust and respect which allows sharing of responsibility. This makes it a difficult club to join: out of more than 20 000 applicants, only about 400 have jobs on the production line initially.

'We didn't want the traditional 20-minute interview, and the you-go-to-the-same-football-match-as-me-so-you

-must-be-okay line,' Bryan Jackson, director of human resources, explained yesterday. 'We want people who can work as a team and who have ideas for improvements and can demonstrate an ability to learn.'

The detailed five-page application form – 'designed to test commitment' – includes detailed questions about personal values and achievements.

Those whose forms were acceptable then entered a process of mental and physical testing that would make the Japanese game show Endurance look tame. First there was a three-hour 'testing and orientation phase'. A series of tests measured their numerical skills, attitude and ability to learn.

A Video-Interactive Test of Learning asks candidates how they would respond to a series of situations.

Next comes the 'targeted behavioural interview', 75 minutes of

questions. Candidates were asked to talk about real situations they had faced and to analyse their decisions. 'It's well known that past behaviour is a good predictor of future behaviour,' Mr Jackson explained.

Then came the crunch. The biggest test – six hours at a simulated production line.

Candidates had to build fuel filters or wheel trims under real pressures.

Those who reached the final interview – another hour – submitted two references and underwent a medical.

Geoff Armstrong, Director-General of the Institute of Personnel Management and a former personnel director of British Leyland, said last night that such systematic recruitment techniques were likely to spread across industry. 'This process has been commonplace for graduate recruitment for some time, but it is unusual at shop-floor level.'

■ **28.4** A report in *The Guardian*, 17 December 1993

IT1

Capital

As a locational factor, capital can be thought of in two major ways: in purely financial terms, and as **fixed capital** (i.e. investment in plant and machinery) which is clearly immobile when compared with pure finance. Capital can be raised via government grants, through bank loans or by share issues. A major concern when investing in manufacturing is to minimise risk and maximise profit. South Africa, for example, has traditionally been regarded as a very favourable investment location, but as the country moved towards democratic elections (1994) to establish a multiracial state, many investors became concerned about potential instability and the loss of profits. It is understandable that private investors tend to invest in prosperous growth regions unless government strategies make it more profitable for them to do otherwise. Capital is also a particularly vital factor for those industries operating close to the frontiers of research and new technology. The aerospace industry is one such example – the sums of money required are dauntingly immense and the risks high.

28.2 External considerations in industrial location

Three considerations need to be singled out for discussion. The first, the market, relates to the output side of the manufacturing system. The other two, agglomeration economies and government intervention, are important in a contextual sense; the former is particularly significant in those branches of manufacturing with complex linkages, whilst the latter can profoundly influence the evaluation of factors on both the input and output sides of manufacturing.

Market

'Market-oriented industry' is a very common term. Essentially markets are the places where manufacturing goods are sold. Industries are concerned with the potential size of a market for widely-used consumer products such as toilet rolls or soft drinks, but increasingly marketing personnel conduct sophisticated analyses of the make-up of the market, for example by age, sex, ethnicity and social class, to predict potential spending on the product.

Market areas vary in size according to the product. They may be very localised, regional, national or even international. Obvious examples of industries that would benefit from a market-based location include those where the product is perishable, fragile or gains weight during production, such as beer or soft drinks. However, an analysis of the alcoholic and soft drinks industry would show that as transport, packaging and processing technology developed, the market area expanded to the national level. Forty years ago, because of problems with transport, the industry was very small-scale and localised, and unable to take advantage of the external and internal economies associated with large plants. Cars are a good example of a modern market-oriented industry: the assembled final product is more difficult and expensive to move than the various components.

Agglomeration economies

Agglomeration economies are sometimes termed **external economies of scale** and are probably the most important single factor in promoting industrial concentrations. **28.5** shows the car production process as a system, emphasising that there are three major processes prior to the final assembly: the manufacture of engines and transmission, the making of bodies, and the component industry. Many modern car plants have adopted the highly successful Japanese methods of production, including the concept of 'just in time', whereby components for final assembly are delivered precisely at the appropriate moment, thus obviating the need for huge storage areas. Thus large car factories such as Nissan UK in Washington have developed **backward linkages** with a whole series of reliable parts suppliers to supply tyres, exhausts, seats, etc. Clearly, close association with the parts suppliers cuts down on transport costs and improves reliability of supply. It is therefore usual for both car and engine plants to attract a clustering of linked firms making parts.

Traditionally, agglomeration economies are most evident in urban areas, because this is where services, such as banking and marketing, are most concentrated and where the levels of infrastructure (especially in an ELDC context) are more comprehensive. However, as information links begin to lessen the need for physical agglomeration, many companies are taking up the advantage presented by greenfield sites in non-urban locations, where land or rent costs are lower, traffic congestion is less and there is a more congenial working and living environment for employees.

Government policies and intervention

The role government plays in industrial location can be considered as a spectrum from planned command economies, such as those presently found in Cuba and China, through to market economies dominated by private investment and enterprise, as in the USA and the UK. Even in the latter situation, the government has a major role to play as a stimulator, facilitator and controller of industrial development. Government policies and intervention can operate at a variety of scales from a trade bloc or continental level through national, state and county levels right down to the level of the local authority.

The first role of government is to stimulate the development of industry. **28.6a** outlines and illustrates some of the ways by which this can be done. A second function is as a regulator or controller of industrial activity. **28.6b** lists some of the policies govern-

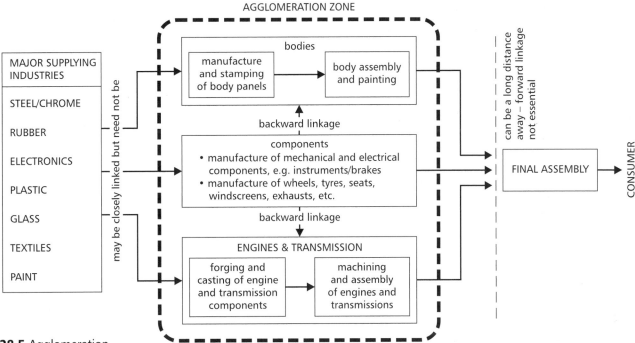

■ 28.5 Agglomeration and linkage in the car industry

ments might employ to regulate industries. In general, the policies outlined in **28.6** are applied selectively to certain sectors of industry (such as key strategic industries which need preserving) or certain types of firm (for example, to attract Japanese companies), or to certain geographical areas as part of regional policy. Inevitably, these policies cost money, and in the new era of accountability and the need to provide value for money, governments must undertake the complex task of evaluating the success of their investment or intervention.

7 Think of examples of each of the items listed in **28.6a** and **b** and organise them under the headings 'Industrial promotion' and 'Industrial control'.

8 Find out if government policies have had any impact on manufacturing in your local area.

■ 28.6 The role of government in industrial location

a) Policies aimed at stimulating industrial activity

	Examples
Investment incentives – capital-related – tax-related	● Investment grants, advances for factories ● Tax concessions as in Enterprise Zones, e.g. a tax holiday for specified start-up period
Labour policies – subsidies – training	● Direct subsidies, e.g. Regional Employment Premiums ● Grants for training
State procurement policies	● Government contracts, e.g. in the defence industry
Technology policies	● Initiatives to stimulate R & D in key industries
Small firm policies	● Support for small firms, e.g. Business Enterprise Schemes
Policies to encourage industrial restructuring	● Rationalisation of nationalised industries such as British Steel
Policies to promote investment	● Building of new motorways and other infrastructural developments such as the creation of a 'teleport'

b) Policies aimed at regulating industrial activity

- State ownership of production assets
- Merger and competition policies
- Company legislation
- Taxation policies
- Labour regulation
  – labour union legislation
  – immigration policies
- National technical and production standards
- Environmental regulations
- Health & safety regulations

28.3 Internal factors affecting location

The location of manufacturing is also influenced by a series of factors which are, in a sense, 'internal' to the firm or plant rather than directly to do with inputs and outputs.

Plant size

There is a clear link between plant size and unit costs. In general, the larger the plant the greater the savings on production within a plant, as large plants can make bulk purchases of raw material, save on plant facilities such as catering, save on R & D costs, and retain greater potential for matching product to market needs. These savings are generally termed **economies of scale**. Nevertheless, although there is a minimum size for efficient working, there is equally a maximum size of operation for efficient working, beyond which **diminishing returns** operate. It has been calculated that 6 million tonnes of steel output a year is the minimum economic size for a modern steel plant, but there is a danger that with the need for continuous operation of furnaces, a very large unit producing 12 million tonnes may be too large and too inflexible to cope with short-term fluctuations in demand.

Clearly, the size of a plant will have a direct bearing on its input requirements such as land, raw materials, labour and capital, and their relative weighting in the decision-making process. Ultimately, therefore, plant size will have an influence on location.

The decision-makers

Often it is the personal viewpoint of an individual or the collective assessment of a board of directors which makes the final locational decision concerning where to set up a new factory or a new branch. That decision may not always be made for economic reasons, as not all firms carry out such thorough research as Toyota did when establishing the Burnaston plant (see the case study on pages 374–75). Many entrepreneurs have a less than perfect knowledge of the strengths and weaknesses of a particular location, and allow emotion to take over. Some decision-makers may not wish to optimise profits, but may be **satisfiers** who are more influenced by their personal values or emotions and make a decision on a location which feels 'comfortable' to them. Personal preferences are especially significant for small business owners who may prefer to stay in their home town or choose an environmentally attractive location with beautiful beaches or golf courses.

Behavioural studies have looked at decision-making processes. Pred, for example, has devised a behavioural matrix to show the likelihood of an entrepreneur reaching a sound economic decision. Some of the small entrepreneurs who chose their home town have had a major impact on industrial location, as their initial enterprises have developed into major names of worldwide repute. Wedgwood of Stoke, Christiansen of Billund in Denmark, Ford of Dearborn and Boot of Nottingham are cases in point.

When decisions are taken by larger concerns such as Toyota, controls are inevitably much tighter because TNCs have to think globally and first choose the correct country to locate in before looking at the local scale.

CASE STUDY

Japanese manufacturing in the UK

Japanese investment in UK manufacturing began in 1972 with the establishment of the YKK plant in Runcorn, Cheshire. You may think you have not heard of YKK but look at any zip in an anorak or jacket and almost certainly it is made by YKK.

The reasons for Japanese investment in the UK and elsewhere in Europe are many, but the main driving force has been the fear of protectionist measures being imposed by the EU against Japanese imports such as cars and electronic goods. By setting up a branch plant, the Japanese manufacturer is able to penetrate inside any trade barriers that might be erected. Also, the last 20 years have been a period of strengthening Japanese currency (the yen), making imported Japanese products extremely expensive. The EU has a consumer potential of 350 million purchasers, many of whom are relatively affluent. As soon as the first Japanese firms had made their investments in Europe, a snowball effect developed, as no major firm could afford not to invest there if it wished to compete effectively with its rivals.

Within Europe, the UK has been the most favoured location for Japanese companies for the following reasons:

- highly-publicised encouragement from successive Conservative governments
- the availability of all sorts of incentives offered both by the Government and the EC/EU in the context of regional aid
- improving industrial relations
- the presence of a work-hungry labour force

- the advantage of English as an almost universal second language for Japanese businessmen.

The decisions to locate in Great Britain can be seen as a multi-stage process, with different factors operating at different scales to influence the final decisions (**28.7a**). **28.7b** shows the take-off in the Japanese industrial presence during the 1980s. **28.7c** analyses that presence in regional terms.

a) Factors influencing location

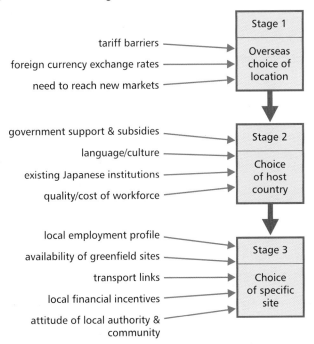

b) Japanese manufacturing companies in the UK, 1972–91

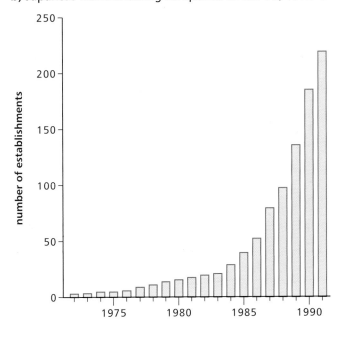

c) Japanese manufacturing companies in the UK by region, January 1992

| Region | Number of companies | | | | Associated employment | | | | Total no. of employees in manufacturing | Employment in Japanese firms as % of total manufacturing employment |
	Acquired	Joint	Wholly-owned subsidiaries	Total	Acquired	Joint	Wholly-owned subsidiaries	Total		
South East	15	2	15	32	4606	350	1424	6380	1417778	0.45
East Anglia	1	1	2	4	100	600	223	923	184600	0.50
South West	1	0	7	8	533	0	1969	2502	390936	0.64
East Midlands	5	1	12	18	473	20	2555	3048	507999	0.60
West Midlands	2	6	19	27	1950	1866	4737	8553	641578	1.33
Yorkshire/ Humberside	0	1	8	9	0	100	2920	3020	487006	0.62
North West	5	3	7	15	850	218	930	1998	665999	0.30
North	2	7	20	29	731	1074	7654	9369	289167	3.24
Wales	1	6	36	43	100	958	14705	15763	248384	6.31
Scotland	2	1	26	29	215	30	5502	5747	428880	1.34
Northern Ireland	2	0	3	5	1066	0	1175	2241	101863	2.20
UK	36	28	155	219	10624	5216	43704	59544	5364190	1.11

■ **28.7** Japanese manufacturing in the UK

28.4 Techniques: The location quotient

One useful statistical technique you could use is the location quotient. This measures the degree of concentration of a specific industrial group within a particular area – in this case, Japanese manufacturing industry within the UK.

The location quotient (LQ) is expressed by:

$$(a \, / \, A) \, / \, (b \, / \, B)$$

where

a = number of people employed in industry X in area A

A = number of people employed in all manufacturing industries in area A

b = number of people employed in industry X nationally

B = number of people employed in all manufacturing industries nationally.

The national average always has an LQ of 1.00. The higher the index, the greater the degree of concentration within that area. Certain industries such as steel, textiles and cars tend to be very concentrated within certain areas, such as cotton textiles in Lancashire, whereas other industries such as brewing historically were found in most areas and tended to show less than average concentrations. A superficial glance at 28.7c would suggest that Japanese industries are possibly concentrated in regions such as Wales.

The location quotient for Wales works out as follows:

a = number of people employed in Japanese industry in Wales = 15 763

A = number of people employed in all manufacturing in Wales = 248 384

b = number of people employed in Japanese industry in UK = 59 544

B = number of people employed in manufacturing in UK = 5 364 324

LQ = (15 763/248 348) / (59 544/5 364 324)
= 0.0635/0.0111 = 5.72

This means that Wales has a concentration of Japanese industry over five times greater than the national average.

---

9 Now apply this measure to some of the other regions listed in **28.7c**, including your own, and see what results you obtain. You could do this activity in groups, each group taking one region.

28.5 Changing manufacturing

Since the 1960s, all EMDCs have experienced major changes in the scale, the nature, the organisation and consequently the location of their manufacturing industries. One of the most significant of these changes has been the shift in the nature of manufacturing, basically from heavy to high-tech industries and the production of consumer goods. No less noteworthy has been the decline in the percentage of the working population engaged in manufacturing. There has been a massive drift of labour in all EMDCs towards the tertiary and quaternary sectors (see **25.1**). In the UK, manufacturing's share of the labour market contracted by over 20 per cent during the period 1979 to 1986 (**28.8**). However, declining employment has not necessarily meant reduced output. Gains in the efficiency of production have led in many countries to an increased productivity per worker. After average productivity increases of 0.7 per cent in the 1970s, Britain recorded productivity rises averaging 4.7 per cent in the 1980s, a feat surpassed only by Japan, albeit from a low base.

In some EMDCs, the shake-out from, and slimming down of the manufacturing sector have been on such a scale that the sector no longer plays a major role in the economy. France and the UK are two such countries, and because of the slim-

a) UK employment by economic sector, 1972–92 (m)

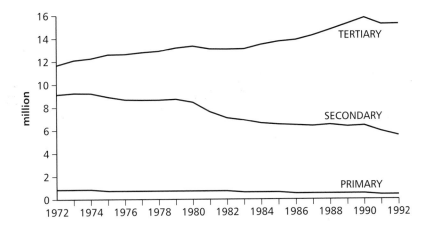

b) Percentage change in employment by economic sector, 1972–92

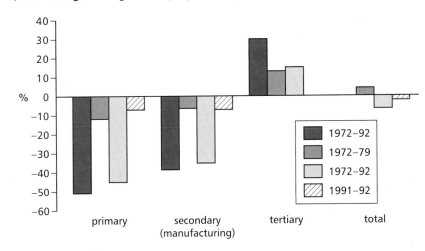

Legend:
- 1972–92
- 1972–79
- 1972–92
- 1991–92

c) The manufacturing sector

	Change in output 1981–91 % p.a.	Change in employment 1981–91 %
Metals	1.4	–17.3
Other mineral products	1.0	–49.1
Chemicals	3.3	–24.8
Synthetic fibres	1.0	–24.8
Metal goods	0.5	–13.8
Mechanical engineering	0.3	–14.3
Electrical and instruments	4.0	–37.8
Motor vehicles and parts	1.5	–36.3
Other transport equipment	0.2	–41.4
Food	1.0	–19.2
Alcohol and tobacco	0.4	–19.2
Textiles	–0.8	–50.1
Clothing	0.1	–23.2
Paper, printing and publishing	2.8	–3.7
Total manufacturing	1.9	–22.5
Total services	2.4	+16.9

■ **28.8** Some aspects of de-industrialisation in the UK

down they are beginning to experience what is referred to as **de-industrialisation**, and the dawn of the so-called **post-industrial society**. De-industrialisation is characterised by a number of features:

- an absolute decline in the numbers of people employed in manufacturing
- a decline in manufacturing's share of total employment (relative decline)
- a failure of the country to achieve a surplus of manufacturing exports relative to manufacturing imports
- a fall in the index of production in many key sectors (falling output)
- a contraction of output so severe that it leads to balance of payment problems; the country struggles to pay for necessary imports
- an economy which shows the impact of marked import penetration within a wide range of sectors, suggesting a loss of international competitiveness.

High-tech industry

Despite the onset of deindustrialisation, countries like France, the UK and the USA contain prosperous agglomerations of high-tech industry as on the Côte d'Azur in France, around Cambridge in the UK, and in Silicon Valley, California (see case study on pages 382–83).

However, high-tech industries are also showing evidence of a global shift in production. Many transnational companies have moved much of the assembly work such as microchip assembly, wafer fabrication and circuit design to areas where labour is cheaper, such as Thailand, Malaysia and the Philippines. R & D work is gradually being undertaken in Hong Kong, Singapore and South Korea, moving away from some of the core areas such as Japan, the USA and Europe.

10 Write an analysis of the changes shown in **28.8**.

IT7

High-tech industry in the UK

For the purposes of this case study, high-tech industry is defined as an activity which is undergoing rapid technological change combined with high inputs of scientific research and development. It produces new, innovative and technologically-advanced products. Typical products would be lasers, computers, scanners, semi-conductors and missiles as well as services such as software and telecommunications.

High-tech industry is characterised by the following features:

- rapid technological change which leads to a very short product life cycle, as for example in microchips
- rapid growth in market demand, for example in home computers
- the vital importance of 'brain power' which 'fuels' the R & D units – key staff, especially the innovators, are a very significant locational factor and explain the growth of locations such as Cambridge.

In 1990, the industries which made up the high-tech sector collectively employed over 1 million people and provided a quarter of Britain's manufacturing employment (**28.9a**). Historically, high-tech industry was located in London and south-east England (nearly half of the total), where the greatest number of innovations were patented, but over the last decade new developments have led to locational dispersal (**28.9b**).

Key locational factors, in ranked order, are as follows:

1 a pleasant working environment

2 access to a 'good' (high-quality) workforce

3 available greenfield sites

a) High-technology employment, 1981

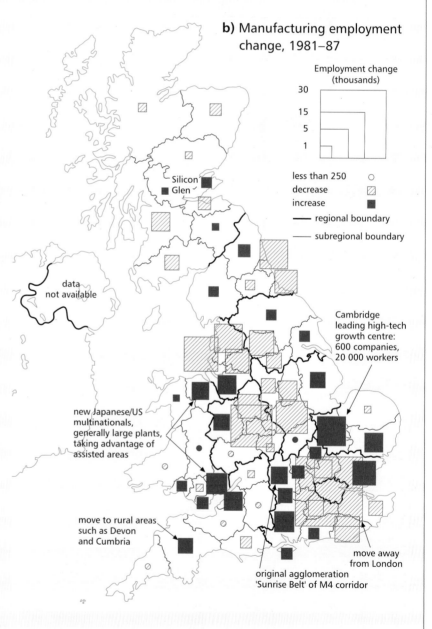

b) Manufacturing employment change, 1981–87

Employment change (thousands)
30
15
5
1

less than 250 ○
decrease ▨
increase ■

—— regional boundary
—— subregional boundary

Silicon Glen

data not available

Employees (thousands)
100
50
20
5
1
<1

Cambridge leading high-tech growth centre: 600 companies, 20 000 workers

new Japanese/US multinationals, generally large plants, taking advantage of assisted areas

move to rural areas such as Devon and Cumbria

original agglomeration 'Sunrise Belt' of M4 corridor

move away from London

■ **28.9** Changing manufacturing in the UK

4 proximity to other high-tech firms (the agglomeration factor)

5 support from local authorities or development agencies

6 university research institute links (30 science parks have now been developed by UK universities.

Biotechnology firms show an even more dispersed location to environmentally attractive locations; for example, Microplants, which breeds plants using hydroponic methods, is located at Longnor in the Peak District.

The **Cambridge phenomenon** is a term that was used by a group of economic development consultants to describe the rapid growth of high-tech industries in Cambridge. The 'spawning' of new independent companies is symbolised by the Cambridge Science Park which was set up in 1972 on a 33ha site on the northern edge of the City. At present, it contains 68 companies employing 1500 workers, and a further 10ha expansion is planned. Recent arrivals at the Science Park include IBM (with a listening post), R & D units for a US pharmaceuticals

company, and an oil industry research unit. Around 30 new companies start up each year and there are now 600 companies in Cambridge employing 20000 workers. Nearly one-third of the founders have come from the University and its research units. The University is a major generator of research ideas and scientific innovations; it also provides a supply of highly-qualified graduates both as employees and further entrepreneurs. A sort of 'snowball effect' of cumulative causation gradually takes place as there is marked interaction and linkage between different firms and entrepreneurs, research institutions and business service organisations. This interaction, in turn, adds to the general dynamism and leads to agglomeration economies. The cumulative process is known as **synergy**. Other locational advantages include the ambience of the historic city, the high quality of local residential environments and the efficient transport links to London's airports by motorway and electrified rail link. Cambridge is also an appropriate location for trade with the EU via Felixstowe.

28.6 The global shift

One of the recent features of manufacturing industries and to a certain extent service industries has been the increasing globalisation of activities. Industries such as the manufacture of textiles and clothing, motor vehicles and electronics, and the financial and banking services and tourism, are all examples of economic activities which are experiencing **globalisation**. Globalisation of manufacturing is evident in the wider production of goods and the resultant pattern of trade flows, and in the explosion in the volume of transnational investment.

The NICs

28.10 shows how the pattern of manufacturing has changed between three groups of nations. Such broad groupings mask major variations in manufacturing importance between individual countries. **28.11** is a global map of manufacturing output. Wide variations are evident between members of all three groups. It can also be seen that three-quarters of world manufacturing produc-

■ **28.10** The global shift in manufacturing

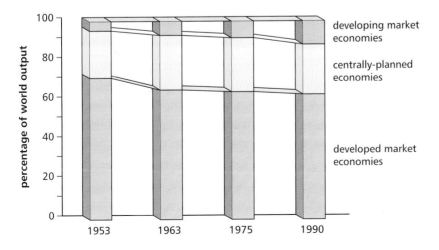

developing market economies

centrally-planned economies

developed market economies

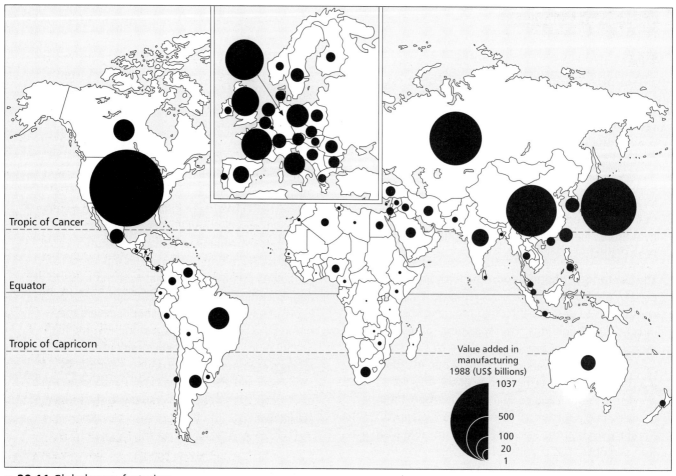

■ **28.11** Global manufacturing production

tion is located in the USA, Western Europe and Japan, although five developing market economies are included in the top 20. Of these, three (China, India and Brazil) can be numbered amongst the largest countries in the world with significant internal markets, but two more (Taiwan and South Korea) are not. These two countries, along with Hong Kong and Singapore, are called the 'Four Tigers' or 'Four Dragons' and are the first of the so-called **newly-industrialised countries (NICs)**. Their development owes much to the Japanese model.

Together the Four Tigers have had a dramatic impact on the established world order. Not only have they experienced phenomenal growth rates (on average 10 per cent per annum) over the last 30 years, but because so much of their production is for export, they have had a dramatic impact on trade patterns. About 75 per cent of South-east Asian exports go to the USA and Western Europe. Moreover, this export-led growth

model is one which many economically less developed countries would wish to emulate. They see industrialisation as providing the key route to economic development (they believe in the power of the manufacturing base). Thus a second generation of industrialising nations, casually called **recently-industrialising countries (RICs)** is growing up, hoping to follow in the footsteps of the Four Tigers.

Various new trends are becoming apparent in the NICs, namely an increasing diversity of manufacturing and a shift away from low-technology traditional manufactures such as textiles and wood manufactures towards high-tech industries such as data-processing equipment. Import penetration has become so overwhelming in certain sectors that it has become a very controversial issue in recent GATT negotiations. In OECD countries there is concern about the impact on home-based manufacturing industries and on trade balances.

IT7

The Four Tigers – the first of the NICs

The rise of the Four Tigers has been remarkable. In 1960, 40 per cent of South Korea's employment was in agriculture, and agricultural goods constituted 70 per cent of total exports. Similarly, in Taiwan in 1962, 32 per cent of the population were employed in agriculture and 70 per cent of exports were food-processed goods such as rice and sugar. In both countries, by 1982 agricultural exports had dropped to under 10 per cent. The other two countries, Hong Kong and Singapore, have always been rather different, in that they are very small, densely-populated countries where wealth has traditionally come from trade and where there is very little spare land for agriculture (**28.12**). The common factor to all four countries was that before 1960 manufacturing accounted only for around 12 per cent of GDP. Yet by 1980 their manufacturing exports per capita were among the highest in the world.

The question has to be asked: How has this economic miracle been achieved? There are several common denominators, some of which are local in origin, some of which are global, but the particular mix is unique to each state and the end-product slightly different. The differences in style of achievement are also a function of different political systems.

In many ways, the 1960s were an appropriate time for the Four Tigers to expand as there was a huge consumer boom for manufactured goods in the OECD countries. At the same time, TNCs began to invest in ELDCs to meet this market, a particularly crucial factor in the case of Singapore as it had very limited supplies of indigenous capital. In the 1970s, all four governments invested heavily in education, training and infrastructure, which in turn encouraged greater productivity and a potential to diversify into high-tech industries. All Four Tigers had relatively low wage-levels, in some cases using imported labour, as for example Chinese refugees in Hong Kong. The 1980s proved more difficult, and the Tigers reacted in various ways to several new threats.

First, wage rates were rising in relation to those in the even newer RICs such as Mexico and Thailand, which led TNCs to reconsider the location of their mass production of low-technology, labour-intensive goods within the Four Tigers. Secondly, a world

	South Korea	Taiwan	Hong Kong	Singapore
Natural resources	Limited supplies of coal, tungsten, zinc; most resources lost to North Korea after the Korean War	Limited supplies of copper, oil and gas but insufficient for domestic demand	None	None
	Limited agricultural land because both are quite mountainous		Limited land for agricultural developments; no agricultural exports	
Size	Modest	Modest	Around 100 km² only	
Colonial status	Japanese domination during early 20th century; establishment of industrial base and improved infrastructure		Formerly part of the British Empire. Superb geographical trade positions. International port status because of magnificent natural harbours	
	All devastated during the Second World War			
Political crisis	Korean War debilitated the country	Huge influx of refugees from Communist China	Influx of refugees from Communist China	Cession from Malaysian Federation
Population	All highly populated with motivated, well-educated workforces which in South Korea and Taiwan could provide a sizeable local market			
Government	All have strong stable governments, which are largely autocratic in their planning			
Foreign investment	All benefit from large-scale Japanese and US investment			

■ **28.12** The Four Tigers

recession diminished the markets for goods in the EMDCs, on which the Four Tigers were so dependent. Furthermore, all four countries had very strong currencies which raised the price of their export products, although they were able to buy raw materials relatively cheaply.

Of the four countries, Singapore has been affected the most, mainly because of its dependence on regional markets and because of rapidly rising wages. South Korea has also become one of the largest debtor nations of the world in order to finance its growth, which has led to repayment problems. Hong Kong, and to some extent South Korea, have also suffered from political uncertainties. The countries have responded to the crisis in different ways.

All four countries are now investing their resources elsewhere in Asia, and although their industrial development is seen as a model for other countries that wish to industrialise, the reality is that there is no common Pacific Asian model. All that can be said is that there are some parallel strands, in that the early growth was export-led and stimulated by foreign investment.

The TNCs

The single most important force in creating the global shift is the growth of the transnational corporation (TNC), which may be defined as 'a company that has economic activities in more than one country'. When evaluating the role of TNCs, opinions are extremely polarised between those who see them as a great force for international well-being and expansion of local economies, and those who see them as exploitive and bringing about the destruction of local economies.

Transnational companies can be classified according to size, by major sector of operation, or by country of origin. Historically, TNCs have often been concerned with minerals or plantation crops – a legacy of a past colonial era – with marked vertical integration of product growth, processing and marketing. Companies emerging in the 1960s were largely concerned with the manufacture of motor vehicles, electrical and electronic goods. A significant number of these companies developed as a result of mergers. Others, such as Lonrho, were conglomerates that sought to diversify their product base by providing both manufactures and services. Initially, many of these companies were European or American, but latterly Japanese and even NIC-based enterprises have become huge global operators.

28.13 summarises the effects that TNCs have on their host economies. Clearly, those effects depend on the nature of the firm and its operational purpose, and also on the level of economic development of the host country. Earlier in this chapter, the favourable impact of Japanese TNCs on revitalising some regions in the UK was emphasised. In this case, the cultural discordance between TNC and host country is manageable. In ELDCs, however, the arrival of a large TNC may generate shock-waves, as the host country has very different socio-cultural characteristics from those of the company's home country. A whole series of questions has to be asked:

- To what extent do TNCs manipulate the government of the host country?
- Do they really transfer technology?
- If they do, is it appropriate technology?
- Do they generate local multiplier effects?
- How do they contribute to the host country's trade balance?
- Do they treat their workers fairly, or are they exploited?

11 Attempt to answer each of the questions above. You should obtain further information, for example from company reports, to support your answers.

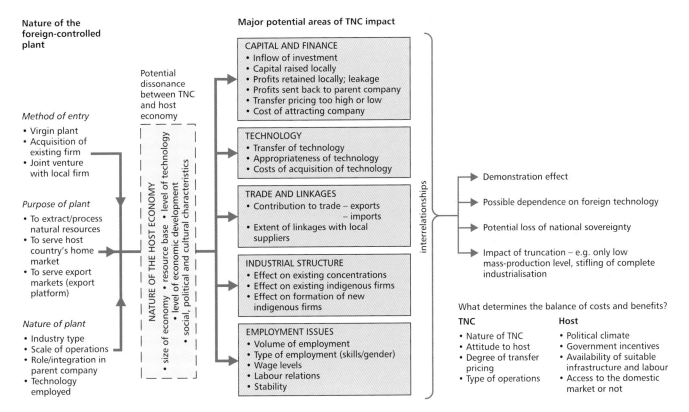

Nature of the foreign-controlled plant

Method of entry
- Virgin plant
- Acquisition of existing firm
- Joint venture with local firm

Purpose of plant
- To extract/process natural resources
- To serve host country's home market
- To serve export markets (export platform)

Nature of plant
- Industry type
- Scale of operations
- Role/integration in parent company
- Technology employed

Potential dissonance between TNC and host economy

NATURE OF THE HOST ECONOMY
- size of economy • resource base • level of technology • level of economic development • social, political and cultural characteristics

Major potential areas of TNC impact

CAPITAL AND FINANCE
- Inflow of investment
- Capital raised locally
- Profits retained locally; leakage
- Profits sent back to parent company
- Transfer pricing too high or low
- Cost of attracting company

TECHNOLOGY
- Transfer of technology
- Appropriateness of technology
- Costs of acquisition of technology

TRADE AND LINKAGES
- Contribution to trade – exports
  – imports
- Extent of linkages with local suppliers

INDUSTRIAL STRUCTURE
- Effect on existing concentrations
- Effect on existing indigenous firms
- Effect on formation of new indigenous firms

EMPLOYMENT ISSUES
- Volume of employment
- Type of employment (skills/gender)
- Wage levels
- Labour relations
- Stability

interrelationships

→ Demonstration effect

→ Possible dependence on foreign technology

→ Potential loss of national sovereignty

→ Impact of truncation – e.g. only low mass-production level, stifling of complete industrialisation

What determines the balance of costs and benefits?

TNC	Host
• Nature of TNC	• Political climate
• Attitude to host	• Government incentives
• Degree of transfer pricing	• Availability of suitable infrastructure and labour
• Type of operations	• Access to the domestic market or not

■ **28.13** Summary of the impact of TNCs on host economies

Industrialisation and the developing world

Historically, it was taken for granted by most ELDCs that economic development will entail industrialisation, especially since many of them have been victims of price fluctuations in primary commodities such as cocoa and tin. Industrialisation is thus seen both as an alternative and as a support for agricultural economies, as processing can add value to agricultural exports and agricultural efficiency can be improved by fertiliser or machinery production. Manufacturing is clearly an additional source of employment for their rapidly growing urban populations. Many ELDCs also pursue industrialisation as they see it improving their trade balance. 'Home-grown' products for which an increasingly wealthy society will have a need (beer, cigarettes, bicycles, shoes, etc.) can be substituted for imports, thus saving valuable foreign exchange. Manufacturing industry is also seen as prestigious in countries such as India, and capable of military benefits too.

When taking an overview of industrialisation in the developing world, it is a fallacy to assume that it is spatially restricted to a small number of countries. There is a variety of industrial development types, as suggested by the following classification:

■ ELDCs whose manufacturing growth has been strongly influenced by export-led growth, e.g. the Four Tigers

■ ELDCs whose manufacturing growth has been primarily linked to their home market, e.g. Brazil, China, India and Bangladesh

■ ELDCs whose manufacturing growth has been linked to their oil revenues, as they have been able to invest the surplus from their oil export revenues, e.g. the Gulf States

■ ELDCs without large home markets, without oil, and whose manufacturing exports constitute less than 0.5 per cent of manufacturing exports from all ELDCs, e.g. Ethiopia, Peru, Papua-New Guinea.

Industry	Raw material used	Air	Water resources		Solid wastes and soil	Risks of accidents	Others
			Quantity	Quality			
Textiles	Wool, synthetic fibres, chemicals for treating	Particulates, odours, SO_2, HC	Process water	Biological oxygen demand (BOD), solids, salts, toxic metals, sulphates	Sludges from effluent treatment	Industrial injuries	Noise from machines, inhalation of dust
Leather	Hides, chemicals for treating and tanning	Odour	Process water	BOD, suspended solids, sulphates, chromium	Chromium sludges	Industrial injuries	
Iron and steel	Iron ore, limestone, recyled scrap	Major polluters: SO_2, particulates, NO_x HC, CO, hydrogen sulphide, acid mists	Process water, scrubber effluent	BOD, suspended solids, oils, metals, acids, phenol sulphides, sulphates, ammonia, cyanides, effluents from wetgas scrubbers	Slag, wastes from finishing operations, sludges from effluent treatment	Risk of explosions and fires	Accidents, exposure to toxic substances and dust, noise
Oil refineries	Inorganic chemicals	Major polluters: SO_2, HC, NO_x CO, particulates, odours	Cooling water, process water scrubber effluent	BOD, chemical oxygen demand (COD), oil, phenols, chromium, effluent from gas scrubbers	Sludges from effluent treatment, spent catalysts, tars	Risk of explosions and fires	Risk of accidents, noise, visual impact
Chemicals	Inorganic and organic chemicals	Major polluters: organic chemicals (benzene, toluene), odours, CFCs		Organic chemicals, heavy metals, suspended solids, COD, cyanide	Major polluter: sludges from air and water pollution treatment, chemical process wastes	Risk of explosions, fires and spills	Exposure to toxic substances, potentially hazardous products
Non-ferrous metals (e.g. aluminium)	Bauxite	Major local polluters: fluoride, CO, SO_2, particulates	Scrubber effluents	Gas scrubber effluents containing fluorine, solids and hydrocarbons	Sludges from effluent treatment, spent coatings from electrolysis cells (containing carbon and fluoride)		
Micro-electronics	Chemicals (e.g. solvents, acids)	Toxic gases		Contaminations of soils and groundwater by toxic chemicals (e.g. chlorinated solvents); accidental spillage of toxic material	Sludges		Risk of exposure to toxic substances due to spills, leaks
Biotechnologies			Process water	Used effluent treatment, modified organic species	Used for clean-up of contaminated land		Fears of hazards from the release of micro-organisms into the environment

■ 28.14 Major sources of industrial pollution

28.7 The impacts of manufacturing

IT3,5

Manufacturing industries generate both costs and benefits, which have a major impact on the environment and the lives of working people. These side-effects are usually termed **externalities**. Some, such as the creation of wealth, prosperity and employment, are clearly **positive**, whereas other, such as the environmental impacts, are frequently **negative** unless they are carefully managed.

On the environment

The precise nature of the environmental impact of manufacturing industry varies considerably with place and time. As can be seen from **28.14**, large-scale processing industries such as chemicals, iron and steel and non-ferrous metals tend to be major polluters of the environment, but it is a fallacy that high-tech industries such as micro-electronics and biotechnology are completely free of pollution. Micro-electronics industries are heavy users of complex new materials that produce toxic gases, water pollutants and hazardous wastes, and the environmental impacts of some of the new biotechnologies are yet to be defined comprehensively. The impacts of heavy industries are particularly serious where they are agglomerated into an industrial region such as the industrial complexes of the Ruhr (Germany) or São Paulo State (Brazil). Even with so-called 'clean' industries, journeys to work generate lead pollution from vehicle exhausts; there is also the inevitable dust from the movement of heavy vehicles, as well as rush-hour noise. Local climatic and physical conditions can promote air pollution, for example in the highland basin of Mexico City and the lowland bowl of Los Angeles.

IT3,5

Another major issue is the fact that pollution travels. Air pollution is carried by winds, water pollution by rivers and currents into the lakes and the sea, and land pollution percolates underground. Pollution has in effect become a global problem, especially in the world's atmosphere and oceans. Global problems that rely on co-operation between nations to produce possible solutions are therefore very complex.

Even the clean-up of the North Sea, which is only continental in scale, is proving beyond the powers of the EU, largely because chemical companies have been legally permitted to discharge agreed quantities of effluent containing heavy metals. As the flow diagram of Minamata disease shows, toxic chemicals are concentrated in food chains over many years (**28.15**). Minamata disease, characterised by serious damage to the human motor system, is organic mercury poisoning, originally caused by industrial waste from Chisso Corporation's chemical factory in Minamata, and contracted from the ingestation of poisoned fish such as tuna. People are still dying from an event that took place more than 30 years ago.

IP1

■ **28.15** Minamata disease

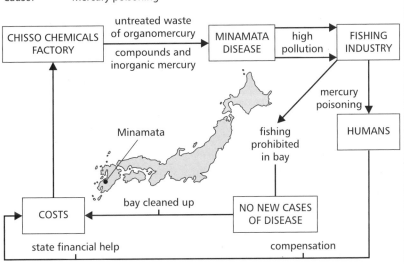

Location :	Minamata, Kyushu	
Casualties:	By 1980	By 1988
	305 dead	1079 dead
	1243 official patients	2893 official patients
	6009 files for compensation	4402 applied for registration
Symptoms:	Numbness, loss of vision and hearing, clumsiness of movement, tremor, mental retardation of children, degeneration of nerve cells	
Victims:	Chiefly fishermen and their families	
Cause:	Mercury poisoning	

It is estimated that industrial operations are collectively responsible for about 20 per cent of total air pollution, but to this must be added the secondary pollution from electricity generation. Levels of air pollution vary according to the levels of economic development. In most Western industrialised countries, there has been a marked decline over the last 20 years of most air pollutants, with the possible exception of lead and volatile organic compounds. However, in Eastern Europe, the former Soviet Union and China, and in spite of growing concern and some remedial action, industrial air pollution has reached seriously high levels with well-documented problems at Krakow in Poland, Ostrava in the Czech Republic and Benxi and Shenyang in China. All these areas are centres of heavy industry and the industrial activities also contribute to environmental damage caused by acid deposition of sulphates and nitrates. In ELDCs, such as Thailand which has begun to industrialise and has growth rates of 10 per cent per annum, and in NICs such as Taiwan, economic growth has sometimes been at the expense of environmental protection, and there are major problems of air pollution in cities such as Bangkok and Taipei.

Adding to the incidence of environmental pollution are industrial accidents, such as those at Seveso in northern Italy (1976) and Bhopal in India (1988), which also resulted in death and injury.

Social and economic consequences

Industrialisation can also have an impact on the social environment. For example, industrialisation fuels urbanisation, leading in many instances to unattractive social environments, such as Glasgow's 19th-century tenements and Rio de Janeiro's 20th-century shanty towns. Manufacturing also has a major impact on human health and well-being. Adverse effects on health include exposure to heat, radiation, pressure, noise, vibration and noxious or toxic substances. It is a sad fact that as the older industrial diseases of the last century have declined, as a result of new technologies and new materials being used, diseases that were unknown a century ago have now emerged as a new challenge for the medical profession, such as the cancers caused by asbestos and pesticides, and repetitive strain injury. Occupational health, which promotes the physical, mental and social well-being of workers, is now seen as a major sector of the economy, because so many lost working days could be saved.

Another negative externality of manufacturing industry arises in times of recession, and when there is industrial restructuring. This is **unemployment**. Unemployment is defined as 'the deficit between employment opportunities available

■ **28.16** The geography of UK unemployment

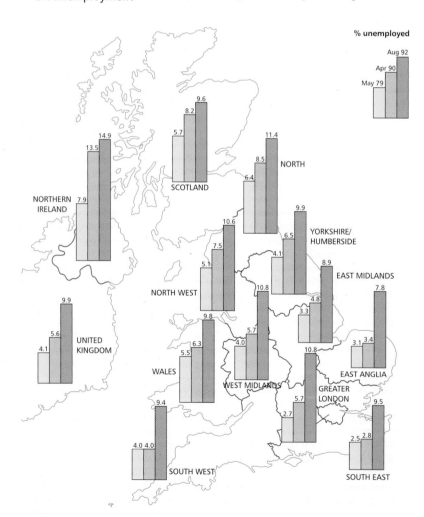

(labour demand) and the number of workers wishing to be employed (labour supply)'. The existence of high unemployment is economically inefficient, since national output is less than it would be if the labour force was fully employed (**28.16**). It is also inefficient and a great drain on resources, because government expenditure is required to provide social benefits and income support to those unable to find jobs. Additionally, geographical variations in unemployment raise important questions of social justice. The persistent lack of job opportunities is socially inequitable, because a higher incidence of unemployment increases problems of poverty, thus generating family stress, problems of housing (many families find themselves unable to pay mortgages), inadequate skills, poor health and other problems of deprivation. In particular, the problem of unemployment associated with manufacturing seems especially resistant to solution. It is easy to say that government should create new

manufacturing jobs, but at what cost, and is it really feasible at times of global recession? **28.17** portrays some aspects of the vicious circle launched by manufacturing decline, and gives a clear warning of what happens if there is no intervention.

12 A summary of the regional geography of unemployment in the UK is given in **28.16**. Write a short analysis describing how the distribution of unemployment in the UK has varied over time. In general, recession leads to rising unemployment, and a wider geographical distribution of joblessness, with marked contrasts between regions and local areas, and between inner and outer parts of cities. Do your findings support this?

The issue of a shrinking manufacturing base poses all sorts of questions for governments. Besides weighing the capital costs of intervention against the political and socio-economic costs of doing nothing, vital decisions have to be taken on whether to stay with manufacturing or to diversify into other sectors. Might the chances of job creation be rather better in, say, services? But would such alternative jobs promise the same level of wealth generation as has been delivered in the past by manufacturing? What would be the most effective form of intervention, and at what spatial level might it best be made? Should it be applied nationally, or targeted at specific regions or even at individual cities?

■ **28.17** The vicious circle of manufacturing decline

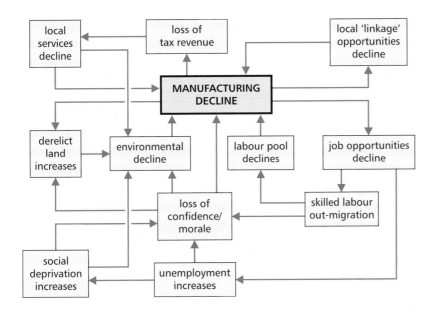

29.1 Emergence of the service sector

The growth of the service sector must be seen as parallel to the concept of de-industrialisation, which was explored in section 28.5. Simple explanations such as the Clark–Fisher sector model (**25.1**) suggest how the economy passes through a series of stages. Initially, primary employment is the most significant, then the secondary sector dominates during the industrial stage, and finally the tertiary sector during the post-industrial stage. There is a tendency to link these stages neatly to the process of economic development as countries at various stages show particular characteristics. For example, most economically more developed countries (EMDCs) have around 60 per cent of their population employed in services.

The key processes which supposedly drive these sectoral changes are increases in productivity per employee and elasticities of demand for goods and services. For example, productivity in agriculture, brought about by mechanisation, releases people for manufacturing. Then increases in manufacturing productivity release people for the service sector, where productivity is supposedly more difficult to improve, as in many cases the personal touch is the key to a quality service. Equally, as people's income increases, they supposedly demand proportionately less agricultural goods but more manufactured goods, and then in turn fewer manufactured goods than services.

The picture in reality is much more complex, both in terms of what happens in each sector and the underlying processes. There are significant changes within the service sector going on at this time. In the 19th century, the railway companies and domestic service were huge employers with an estimated one-eighth of the workforce providing services in those areas. During much of the 20th century, banking, financial and public services expanded, but in the late 1990s the most marked trend is for full-time male jobs to be replaced by part-time female jobs. Although new categories of service employment are emerging (can you think of some?), for the first time doubts are being expressed about the future prospects of the service sector. There is also a fundamental concern as to whether or not the service sector can generate economic growth and wealth to the same degree as manufacturing has in the past.

29.2 The nature of the service sector

So far we have described the growth of the service sector and touched on a simplistic explanation of that growth, without defining exactly what it contains. Indeed, the issue has been raised that the service sector is not necessarily the same as 'service industries', as many service industries are found in the manufacturing sector supporting the new lean, efficient production. The service industries are sometimes very difficult to identify, and in some government classifications, they are a residual category: 'activities which are neither dug out of the ground, nor manufactured'.

One problem associated with defining the service sector lies in its overlap with the industrial sector. Service activities take place in mining and manufacturing (for example, marketing and transport). In the post-industrial society, professionalisation of the workforce has led to more

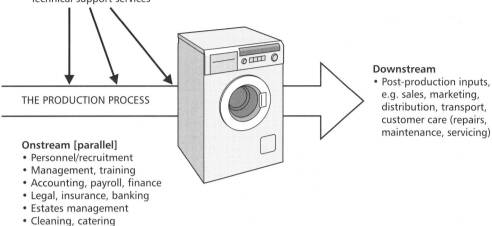

Onstream [production]
- Quality control – production information systems (PIS)
- Production planning and management
- Repair, maintenance of production machinery
- Technical support services

Upstream
Service inputs prior to production
- Research & Development
- Design prototype testing
- Market research
- Raising venture capital
- Some software design

THE PRODUCTION PROCESS

Onstream [parallel]
- Personnel/recruitment
- Management, training
- Accounting, payroll, finance
- Legal, insurance, banking
- Estates management
- Cleaning, catering
- Security
- Management information
- Systems, software, etc.

Downstream
- Post-production inputs, e.g. sales, marketing, distribution, transport, customer care (repairs, maintenance, servicing)

■ **29.1** How services contribute to the production process

administrative, professional and technical workers within the manufacturing sector. Within the secondary sector today, there is a whole range of producer services (**29.1**). In some cases, services such as auditing, market research, sales and promotion are provided 'in-house'; in others they are contracted out. In the former instance, it may well be that workers employed in those services will be counted as part of the industrial rather than the service workforce.

29.2 shows the main categories of service activities as defined by GATT, and

emphasises the diversity of the sector. The activities shown range from the highly sophisticated knowledge and information-intensive activities to very basic services such as simple cleaning or basic maintenance, in both public and private organisations.

A common distinction is made between **tertiary services**, which include construction, transportation, business and trade services, **quaternary services**, which include finance and insurance, and **quinary services**, including education, government, health and research. However, although 'quaternary' is a widely-used term, and usually attached to the sophisticated services which transmit, receive and process information (including research and development), 'quinary' is rarely used.

A more useful distinction commonly adopted is to divide services into **consumer** and **producer** (or business) services. This classification is clearly based on what is seen to be the final output, or who is the customer for the particular service. A further subdivision is based on the durability of the outcome, whereby consumer services can be perishable, semi-durable or durable. Thus a visit to a launderette, a Pizza House or a football match can be considered perishable, dental treatment is

> **1** If you have an opportunity to study a local manufacturing company, see if you can devise a similar diagram to the one in **29.1** to show how the various service jobs relate to production. How do the numbers directly employed in production relate to the numbers employed in these services? How does the human resources profile compare in terms of age, sex, qualifications, etc. between the manufacturing (production staff) and producer services?

CONSTRUCTION SERVICES	BUSINESS SERVICES	INSURANCE SERVICES
Site preparation New constructions Installation and assembly work Building completion Maintenance and repair of fixed structures	Rental/leasing of equipment Real estate services Installation and assembly work Professional services (incl. legal services, accountancy, management services, advertising, market research, design services, computer services) Other business services (incl. cleaning, packaging, waste disposal)	Insurance on freight Non-freight insurance (incl. life insurance, pensions, property, liability) Services auxilliary to insurance (incl. brokerage, consultancy, actuarial) Reinsurance

TRANSPORTATION SERVICES
Freight services
Passenger transport services
Charter services
Services auxilliary to transport
(incl. cargo handling, storage)
Travel agency and tour operator services
Vehicle rental

TRADE SERVICES; HOTEL AND RESTAURANT SERVICES
Wholesale trade services
Retail trade
Agents' fee/commissions related to distribution
Hotel and similar accommodation services
Food and beverage serving services

EDUCATION SERVICES

HEALTH-RELATED SERVICES
Human health services
(incl. hospital services, medical and dental services)
Veterinary services

RECREATIONAL AND CULTURAL SERVICES

FINANCIAL SERVICES
Banking services (commercial and retail)
Other credit services (incl. credit cards)
Services related to administration of financial markets
Services related to securities markets
(incl. brokerage, portfolio management)
Other financial services
(incl. foreign exchange, financial consultancy)

COMMUNICATION SERVICES
Postal services
Courier services
Telecommunications services
(telephone, telegraph, data transmission, telemetrics, radio, TV, etc.)
Film distribution and related services
Other communications services
(incl. news and press agency, library and archive services)

PERSONAL SERVICES
(not included elsewhere)
e.g. house cleaning/maintenance;
day-care services, hairdressing

PUBLIC ADMINISTRATION
Local government
Civil service
Defence
Police, fire, etc.

■ **29.2** The range of the service sector

usually semi-durable, while a mortgage is classified as durable because it usually lasts for 25 years. Producer services can be treated in a similar way.

> **2** The following is a list of producer services. See whether you can classify them with reference to durability: computer consultancy, advertising copy for a promotion, waste disposal for an industrial estate, publishing a textbook, a delivery service such as Federal Express, factory cleaning, architect consultancy.

It is now possible to summarise some of the essential characteristics of the service sector.

■ As a result of its extreme diversity, it includes a wide spectrum of pay and conditions. These range from high salaries and generous fringe benefits for business executives to the poor and insecure working conditions of low-paid casual and semi-casual workers in catering and cleaning.

■ Employed in this sector are large numbers of female workers (who earn only 68 per cent of average male earnings overall), large numbers of part-time workers (who generally do not benefit from sick pay and pension schemes), and in certain non-skilled sectors, large numbers of recent immigrants, many of whom have great difficulty in obtaining employment in more favourable environments, in spite of having qualifications.

■ The sector contains an increasing number of people who are classified as self-employed. The contribution of the small business to manufacturing is significant, but in the service sector it is even greater. By 1990, some 12 per cent of the British service sector workforce was classified as self-employed.

■ The nature of jobs within the service sector is changing rapidly.

- As services are essentially market-oriented, directly to consumers or indirectly to other producers, they tend to be concentrated in urban areas. The urban areas contain large numbers of densely concentrated potential consumers, and many agglomerations of producer (business) services are also found within urban areas.

- As in manufacturing, there is marked localisation of particular types of service activity in some areas. For example, UK business and financial services are concentrated in London and south-east England.

- There appears to be a close correlation between the relative importance of the service sector in a country's economy and its degree of urbanisation and level of development (**29.3**).

- Although services are overwhelmingly concentrated in urban areas, new technology has enhanced their footloose status, and there has been some decentralisation, including the growth of 'teleworking'.

■ **29.3** Three development variables for selected countries, 1990

	% employed in services	% urban	GNP per capita $
Bangladesh	34	16	210
Brazil	47	75	2 680
Hungary	43	61	6 116
India	27	27	360
Japan	59	77	17 616
Kenya	12	24	370
Kuwait	70	96	14 630
Libya	53	70	9 100
Niger	12	20	310
Poland	35	62	4 237
Sweden	69	84	17 014
Thailand	19	84	1 420

3 a Use graphical or statistical techniques to assess the degree of correlation between levels of urbanisation and percentage employed in services (**29.3**).
   b Suggest reasons for your results.

29.3 Service-sector location factors

It is difficult to apply general locational principles to such a diverse sector. Some services can be footloose, others are very closely tied to a particular location (usually the very specialist services), some are office-based and others are warehouse-based. **29.4** shows, for example, how offices, factory-based business services, warehouses and retail outlets rank locational factors in a completely different order.

4 a Try to give reasons for some of the differences in **29.4**.
   b Make a composite ranking to show the overall picture for all services.

■ **29.4** Ranking of locational factors

Scale of 1 to 8:
1 = most important
8 = least important

Factor ranking	Office	Factory-based business service	Warehouse	Retail
Labour supply	1	1	5	4
Proximity to markets	3	2	2	1
Access to transport networks	5	6	1	2
Site location	2	4	3	2
Quality of life	4	3	8	4
Proximity to suppliers	7	5	4	6
Availability of grants	6	7	6	6
Other miscellaneous factors	8	8	6 (location of competitors)	8

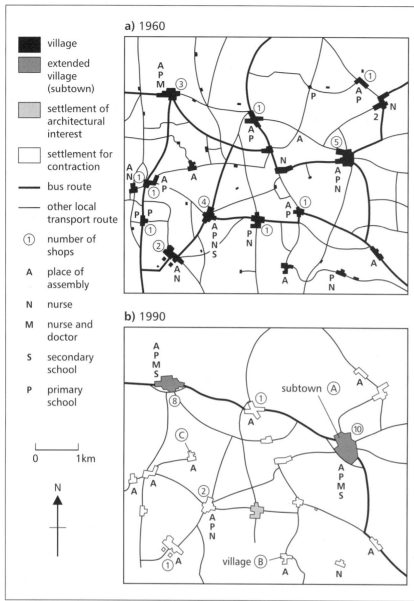

a) 1960

b) 1990

village
extended village (subtown)
settlement of architectural interest
settlement for contraction
bus route
other local transport route
① number of shops
A place of assembly
N nurse
M nurse and doctor
S secondary school
P primary school

0   1km

N

■ **29.5** Changing service provision in a rural area of eastern England

5 Changing service provision in a rural area of eastern England is shown in **29.5**.
a Briefly describe how the provision has changed.
b Evaluate the advantages and disadvantages of the new provision for the following:
   i a family living in A, both parents working, own a car, children aged 14, 12 and 8
   ii a pensioner living in B, aged 70+
   iii a single-parent family living in C, children aged 3 and 7.

For each individual service, there has to be a market, which is expressed by means of supply, demand and price. Obviously, private-sector services have to be economically viable or they fail. Access to individuals or designated firms, whether physical (via transport) or non-physical (via information links), is vital. Access can be considered in terms of cost, reliability and convenience. The need for quality access tends to favour richer 'core' areas for service location at the expense of poorer, more remote 'peripheral' areas; this is one of the many factors that promote regional disparity. The supplying of efficient, cost-effective services to remote, sparsely-populated rural areas represents a challenge for all entrepreneurs and governments. With declining finance, various rationalisation strategies have to be adopted, which inevitably cause hardships for some.

The principles of Christaller's central-place theory, which aimed to explain the size and spacing within settlement hierarchies, can be applied very effectively to the location of consumer service industries. Different services all have market areas of various sizes and each service will have a minimum number of individual customers or firms it must serve in order to be viable – this is known as a **threshold**. Services that are required infrequently tend to have a high threshold. For example, hypermarkets or large department stores often require a potential catchment of 100 000 people and operate with a long **range** – that is, the maximum distance people are prepared to travel to obtain the service. Some of the largest shopping malls in the UK, such as MetroCentre, Merrywood, Thurrock and Meadowhall, draw people for day outings from a distance of up to 150 km, and have a catchment area of well over half a million people. These centres are therefore located far apart. Equally, services with a high frequency of demand have a low threshold of viability and are widely distributed in many towns. Thus a hierarchy of services can be established in shopping, in services such as post offices, and in health and education.

Factors such as the distribution and density of the population, the purchasing power (a measure of income levels), need (for example, old people need medical services) and patterns of access, all have a major impact. In Christaller's model, **isotropic** (uniform) **surfaces** were assumed with equal accessibility, to develop the theoretical arrangement; inevitably, the actual hierarchies are less clear-cut because of differences in demand and access.

Producer services do not really follow Christaller's market area principles as they rely on links with other industries, not the final consumer. Agglomeration with other like or linked services is often a key requirement for many producer services of a managerial or professional character. Hence the clustering of professional and business services in parts of the CBD, the clustering of quaternary services in purpose-built science or business parks, or the development of specifically designed business nodes as in Tokyo (see case studies on pages 461–62 and 491–93). However, analysis of changing office locations shows how difficult it is to establish general principles even with producer (business) services. Decisions often rest with the personal preferences of various entrepreneurs, based on the information available. Pred used the information diffusion theory to explain how existing areas of producer services are likely to generate more new start-ups, not because of any intrinsic advantages but because the information available is biased towards these areas; they represent lower risks to incipient entrepreneurs. This behavioural explanation again reinforces agglomeration.

Services like manufacturing have to consider inputs such as labour and capital, and available sites and accessibility to transport. The labour requirements of service industries are often very specific – hence the high ratings in **29.4**. These requirements range from specialist skills, such as in R & D, to the need for low-cost labour in labour-intensive operations such as hotels and restaurants. Cost is only one aspect, as the retention of the right kind of labour is often the key to successful, quality services. The nature of the labour requirements is closely linked to transport issues, as low-paid workers may rely on public transport, which is always more comprehensive in a central or inner urban area. Suburban locations often offer greater ease of access and parking spaces for the cars of more highly-paid employees.

Many service industries occupy specialised buildings. Office buildings, for example, are frequently specifically designed by property companies for rent or leasing. These companies are heavily dependent on raising risk capital from financial institutions. Therefore the locational decisions are tied to the degree of availability of appropriate premises. In some areas, landowners, property-owners, development companies and local authorities have refurbished or redeveloped redundant warehouses or factories to make new offices for businesses. Refurbished premises are most appropriate for small offices, as large companies experience difficulties in installing complex information technology into multi-floor premises.

Locational decisions by business enterprises are also influenced by the institutional environment. Planning controls by local government, reinforced by central government legislation, such as the need for development permits in overcrowded city centres, will determine the volume and type of development that is permitted at any one location. Curtailment of new building can lead to astronomic rises in rents. Although the character of the organisation – whether a large-scale TNC employing thousands or a small business employing 20 people – inevitably plays a part in the locational decision-making process, similar factors operate but not necessarily to the same degree. The type of service is more important than the scale of operation in influencing locational decisions.

29.4 **Changing services – offices**

London	Sydney	Toronto	Manchester
1 Contact with external organisations 2 Tradition 3 Communications within UK 4 Prestige 5 Contact with government 6 Contact with associates 7 Central location 8 Supply of staff 9 Central to operating area	1 Availability of premises 2 Customer/client accessibility 3 Proximity to public transport 4 Rent and rate costs 5 Prestige 6 Possibility for expansion 7 Staff availability 8 Ease of access to executive parking 9 Access to associated businesses	1 Concentration of clients 2 Prestige 3 CBD amenities 4 Access to public transport 5 Staff availability 6 Availability of associated businesses 7 Proximity to government institutions	1 Easy access for clients 2 Close proximity to clients 3 Availability of premises 4 Prestige 5 Ability to obtain staff 6 Rent and rate costs 7 Proximity to CBD services

■ **29.6** Factors influencing the location of office-based businesses in four cities

■ **29.7** A model of the evolution of office-based services

Traditionally, both offices and retailing have been located in city centres, often concentrated in the wealthy core regions of EMDCs, with the large metropolitan areas such as London and Paris having the greatest concentrations of all (**29.6**).

Recent locational trends have tended to lead a downward filtering away from the largest metropolitan centres, especially of producer services, and also a decentralisation of both shops and offices away from city centres into retail and business parks in the suburbs. In some cases the functions are combined as part of a new development, as for example at Festival Park in Stoke-on-Trent which contains retail, office and leisure activities.

29.7 is a model of the evolution of office location within metropolitan regions. It shows four phases. Prior to 1960, the locations were highly centralised in the CBD. The 1960s saw the beginnings of dispersion, with random locations being chosen by individual companies. In contrast, in the 1970s clusters of offices began to develop in the suburbs, usually at favourable locations

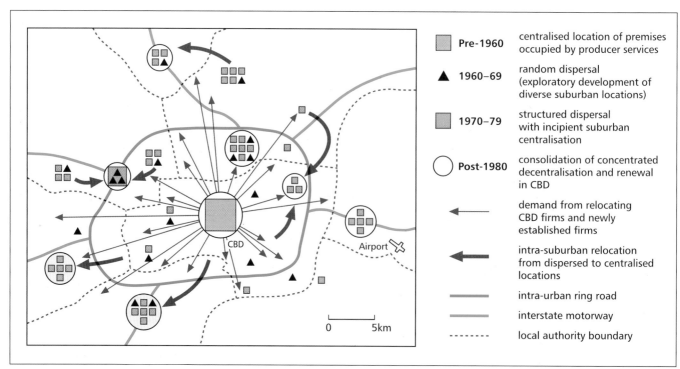

such as intersections of major highways where radial roads meet ring roads, or at public transport interchanges. Such locations were favoured because of their high degree of accessibility. By the 1980s, some of these concentrations evolved into major suburban agglomerations, which replicated the idea of a CBD, but in the suburbs. In the 1990s, the trend has been to decentralise still further out into many semi-rural locations. What do you think will be the implications of this trend for the people and the environment?

IP1

As with any model, the actual developments vary considerably. However, some cities – Tokyo, for example – do conform to the model at least in part. Within Tokyo's downtown area there is marked zoning, with Marunouchi containing the traditional focus of banking financial services and Kasumigaseki noted for its concentration of government offices. In the post-war period, suburban business centres were created to relieve the acute downtown congestion. These five satellite business centres including Shinjuku, Ikebukuro, Shibuya and Ueno, are highly accessible locations adjacent to major terminals of the suburban rail network. They contain a whole range of services including major business areas (see case studies on pages 461–62 and 491–93).

The planning of the 1990s favours even further decentralisation with the establishment of 'Self-sustained Urban Areas' (see Chapter 35). Currently, five are planned including Tama, Chiba and Kanagawa. In many ways they are analagous to British New Towns as they will provide a high level of employment, services and housing, and hopefully attract people from Tokyo to live there. The only difference between the model and Tokyo is that Tokyo's planning regulations limited the evolution of the intermediate stages.

IP1

However, the model (**29.7**) oversimplifies what have been very complex changes of location. For every force encouraging decentralisation, other circumstances promote and reinforce centralisation. Overall, there has been a growth of demand for services which has encouraged downward filtering to areas such as suburbs and market towns. With increased demand, thresholds can now be reached by locating at lower levels in the urban hierarchy. Conversely, the trend towards increased externalisation of services is favouring the continued centralisation of large companies in major metropolitan areas. Yet even here, whereas computer services are provided centrally, other lower-level services such as cleaning and security are provided locally for branch plants. A further complicating factor is that demand has changed because of the decentralisation of population as a result of counter-urbanisation.

Land costs are one of the main push factors encouraging decentralisation (**29.8**). However, high space costs *per se* do not deter the concentration of offices in CBDs if they are compensated by savings in other costs. Patterns of labour availability may reinforce or may counteract the impact of land and rent costs. Universities, for example, are key pools of highly-skilled technical and managerial labour, and their residential preferences for leafy suburbs and market towns as areas of perceived high quality of life favour non-central locations. Certain locations are reservoirs of particular sorts of labour. For instance, many office functions are performed by predominantly female staff, who are often poorly paid. It follows, therefore, that certain demographic profiles will yield this supply. Many staff have developed an anti-commuting mentality, and

■ **29.8** Factors encouraging decentralisation

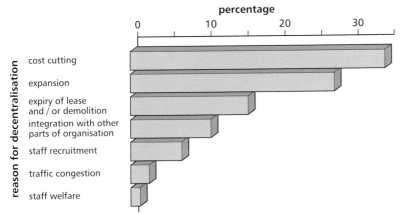

favour suburban locations with less congested journeys and access to purpose-built car parking areas.

Technological factors also play their part in the complex locational jigsaw. New technology makes distance home-working possible in companies such as ICL or Rank-Xerox, yet the same technology also leads to excessive centralisation at a huge computer headquarters. Government (both central and local) can develop strategies to promote decentralisation, and at the same time can favour centralisation by other policies. Decentralisation forces are frequently balanced by strong centripetal tendencies which encourage a city centre (centralised) location.

As a result of the complex factors of evaluation, offices are found in a variety of locations, as shown in **29.9**. The variety of locations and the sequence they were built in suggests a more diverse model than that developed in **29.7**. The locations shown range from city centre to semi-rural market town.

■ **29.9** Emerging patterns of office location

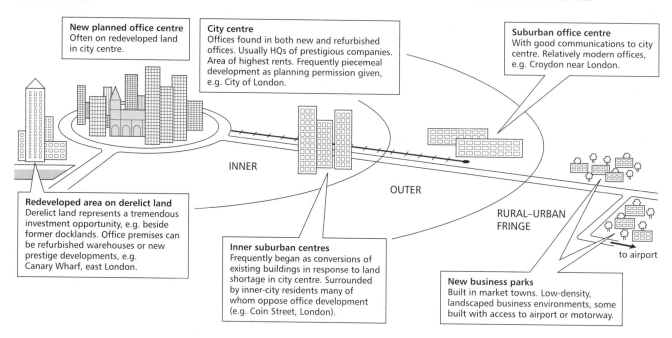

New planned office centre
Often on redeveloped land in city centre.

City centre
Offices found in both new and refurbished offices. Usually HQs of prestigious companies. Area of highest rents. Frequently piecemeal development as planning permission given, e.g. City of London.

Suburban office centre
With good communications to city centre. Relatively modern offices, e.g. Croydon near London.

INNER

OUTER

RURAL–URBAN FRINGE

to airport

Redeveloped area on derelict land
Derelict land represents a tremendous investment opportunity, e.g. beside former docklands. Office premises can be refurbished warehouses or new prestige developments, e.g. Canary Wharf, east London.

Inner suburban centres
Frequently began as conversions of existing buildings in response to land shortage in city centre. Surrounded by inner-city residents many of whom oppose office development (e.g. Coin Street, London).

New business parks
Built in market towns. Low-density, landscaped business environments, some built with access to airport or motorway.

29.5 **Changing services – retailing**

An important function of any city is the retailing of goods and services. Retailing, like business services, includes all manner of outlets, from local corner shops through department stores to hypermarkets. The main trend as in offices has been decentralisation, a trend which first appeared in North America in the 1950s and is now firmly established in nearly all countries of Europe. As well as locational changes, there are parallel organisational changes, such as the decline in the independent small trader at the expense of the company-owned store. Internationalisation has also come to retailing, with companies such as Carrefour hypermarkets operating in Europe and in the Americas, and Marks and Spencer opening key 'prestige' stores in Paris and Brussels. Over the last 20 years there have been many changes in the methods of selling, largely facilitated by new technology. These range from discount warehouse 'clubs' to teleshopping, plus numerous variants of the self-service revolution of the 1970s. Thus retailing has been going through a revolution in terms of its organisation, methods of selling, use of technology, and location.

One of the most visible impacts of the revolution has been the development of a whole series of planned shopping centres (malls) or retail parks. Shopping has now overtaken fishing as the number one pastime in the UK, and in the USA the average visit to such a centre lasts four hours – it is perceived as a truly recreational activity.

Planned shopping centres in their present form originated in the 1950s in North America and the concept spread to Europe in the early 1960s. Up to 1991, the West Edmonton Mall in Alberta was the largest in the world.

The first shopping centre to open in Britain was at Billingham, but up to the late 1960s most of them were of modest size, and located in town centres as part of pedestrianisation schemes. During the 1970s some larger (60 000 m²) schemes opened, largely in New Towns such as Milton Keynes and Telford. Only Brent Cross could be considered a truly regional out-of-town centre at this time, as other large contemporary schemes, like Arndale Manchester, were in city centres. The North American 'multi-purpose mega-mall' concept did not come to Britain until the building of MetroCentre at Gateshead in 1986. With 160 000 m² of space, it was at the time the largest shopping centre in Western Europe and contained Marks and Spencer's first excursion outside the city centre. Other similar centres have followed at Meadowhall, Merryhill, Dudley and Lakeside at Thurrock.

Although many of these shopping centres are now built out of town, and all the mega-malls occupy this type of site, there are many large and successful high-quality shopping centres in towns. Newcastle-upon-Tyne has an extremely successful example, Eldon Square, which competes effectively with MetroCentre. Equally, the Potteries Shopping Centre in Hanley, Stoke-on-Trent, is more than capable of competing with Festival Park and other out-of-town areas in Stoke-on-Trent.

The degree of decentralisation varies from country to country. The trend is most marked in North American and Australian cities, where the CBD is no longer the most important city shopping centre. In Britain, CBD decline has been as a result of three waves of decentralisation, the latest of which is threatening to completely kill off many high streets because it has happened during a period of serious recession. The first wave, which was generated in the 1960s and reached its zenith in the late 1970s, was centred on the food-based superstores. A second wave began in the 1970s and involved retail warehouses selling DIY, carpets, electrical goods ('white' goods) and flat-pack furniture. The third and most recent wave is the opening of regional shopping centres selling traditional high-street goods, such as jewellery, clothes and shoes – as shown by the names of all the chain stores and department retailers to be found there. These regional shopping centres do everything the high street can do – and some would say they do it better! However, in 1994 there were signs of a rethink on the policy of decentralisation.

Why decentralise?

The reasons for the decentralisation can be summarised as follows:

- **Demand** The primary factor responsible for the growth of suburban retail activity is the decentralisation of demand caused by the shift in population to the suburbs, and more recently counterurbanisation to rural areas. The movement is largely of the higher-salaried, young, more mobile elements of society whose lifestyle favours the use of retail parks and superstores. Increased car ownership, leading to better personal mobility, combined with more female employment, has encouraged the growth of evening and family weekend shopping outings to retail parks with guaranteed car parking. The concept of one-stop superstore shopping appeals to those who have more money than time. Other technological developments such as freezers for the storage of food have merely reinforced this trend towards the 'one-stop big shop'.

- **Organisation** Changes in the organisation of retailing have blurred the distinction between wholesaling and retailing, with the development of discount stores and cash-and-carry wholesalers. This has promoted the growth of large retailing organisations, known as **multiples** or **chains**, which enjoy economies of scale from bulk-purchasing. The spread of the self-service concept has also promoted the need for space-consuming superstores, whilst the difficulty of providing a satisfactory layout in old market towns, where land is often in long narrow plots, has also encouraged the move to less central locations.

- **Land costs** As with offices, one of the major factors encouraging decentralisation has been the high cost of city-centre land, which has made it very expensive for space-consuming activities, and the large sites required by large stores. Developers of shopping centres undoubtedly offer inducements to the major prestigious high-street names to come to their new centres to become anchor tenants, for example by providing purpose-built stores at 'peppercorn' rents.

- **Labour** Access to labour also encourages decentralisation as the suburbanisation of the population has not only moved the demand centre but also the focus of the labour supply. Retailing has become increasingly dependent on a part-time female labour force, which can be recruited from suburban areas.

- **Technological changes** This too has sometimes reinforced these other factors, not least by the increased availability of motor cars for the affluent groups within society. Lower-income groups, dependent on public transport, are forced to rely on local or central shops, which are declining in number, quality and range. Information technology makes a major contribution to store efficiency and also ultimately could lead to the widespread use of 'teleshopping', which could slow down the rate of decentralisation.

At present, in many countries including Britain there is a great debate over decentralisation of retailing and its impacts. This has evolved around environmental and ecological issues, as well as social and economic considerations. **29.10** summarises the principal 'pros' and 'cons'.

IT7 **Does the high street have a future?**

29.11 shows four graphs which record shopping trends. The high street still accounts for just over half of retail spending, although the percentage has declined slowly since 1980s, by 2 per cent. When considering the future of the high street, it is worth remembering that one-third of households in Britain still have no car, and therefore still need shopping centres that are accessible by public transport or provide a full range of shops within easy walking distance of one another.

6 Changing retail provision is an excellent topic for individual studies, because you can carry out land use surveys for the present and the past. The ideal resource for your surveys is a GOAD plan, obtainable from the company in Old Hatfield, Hertfordshire. These plans, plus accompanying shopping-centre profile reports on shop counts and floor space, can be obtained for both the present day and the past for most town centres. Reports are also available on shopping centres, and directories are published of out-of-town shops. You can support your direct fieldwork by questionnaire surveys of shoppers and shopkeepers, as well as car parking and other environmental impact surveys such as traffic flows. It is obviously best to focus on a well-defined topic, such as what have been the environmental and socio-economic effects of retail park X on the surrounding area? Or what impact have the retail parks had on town centre X or the villages Y and Z?

Pros	Cons
• Relieves town-centre traffic congestion • Low land rents on edge of town keep prices low • Provides abundant on-site car parking • Town centres cannot accommodate 2000 extra cars • One-stop all-hours shopping for working families • Allows customer to choose goods from a huge range of choice at bulk-buying prices • Out-of-town makes shopping fun; a day out in a retail park • Clean functional building • Forms new focus for suburban, peripheral developments • Hypermarkets encourage people to do more shopping – in addition to town centre shopping	• Loss of countryside and agricultural land • Causes serious localised traffic congestion • Companies control prices • Up to 25% of population have no access to a car • Town centres have special short-stay parking • The stores are difficult for aged, infirm, disabled, disadvantaged people to reach • Traditional service is lacking • No heritage; vast barn-like structures blight the landscape • Blights CBD, where streets function as social–cultural focus • We have more than enough shops already, with so many vacant premises in town-centre precincts

■ **29.10** The pros and cons of out-of-town shopping

a) High street shops still account for most of our spending

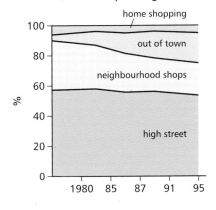

b) More new shops are being opened in town centres

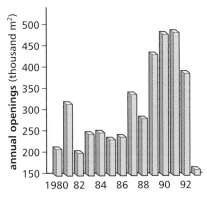

c) Fewer out-of-town shopping centres are being built

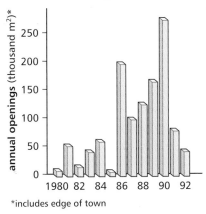

*includes edge of town

d) Fewer retail warehouses are being constructed

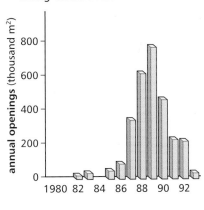

■ **29.11** Shopping trends in the UK `IT7`

More importantly, people with a high income seem to enjoy shopping in town centres, provided they can park their cars easily and economically. Nevertheless, there have been large withdrawals by multiple retailers from the high street. For example, in 1987 Next had 1860 outlets and now has only 316 shops; Curry's have shut 43 town-centre shops and opened 14 new superstores out of town. Even Marks and Spencer, the bastion of the traditional high street, has 12 out-of-town/edge-of-town outlets, when in 1987 it had none. So the question is, how is the high street to survive in the future?

The recipe for survival is to provide a highly concentrated shopping area focused around a mall, and a quality high street. The mall shopping area is vital as it affords warm, dry shopping in winter, and an air-conditioned environment in summer, with fountains, sculptures, security and resting places for weary shoppers. The historic environment provided by the existing urban fabric provides a wonderful backdrop for modern quality retailing – it is the quality that increases the revenue. Specialist precincts containing old-fashioned shops selling luxury goods can be concentrated in the historic back-streets. Castle Mall Centre in Norwich is an example of a recently refurbished, modern in-town mall.

The revival of the neighbourhood store

Another potential casualty of decentralisation and the growth of the large shopping centres, retail parks and superstores is the corner shop, and by implication also the retail cluster, or neighbourhood shopping unit, consisting of a small group of low-order convenience stores. Tens of thousands of small corner shops have been closed down in recent years. Particularly vulnerable are some of the inner-city parades which do not provide car-parking, and thus cannot easily capture passing trade from car customers, and which have been affected by marked local population decline. Even the centres in residential areas which were purpose-built in the 1970s are under threat because they cannot compete with the range of choice and price offered by the new superstores. In the 1980s, suburban district centres were often actually built around a superstore and have proved to be very successful.

In spite of all these changes, there has been a recent interest in developing new types of corner shop with two client groups in mind: local people, most of whom walk to the store for their basic needs; and those who 'top-up' their superstore shopping with things they have forgotten! Already there are a number of these chains which are owned by cor-porations – 7-Eleven, K Mart and Kwik-Mart are just three brand names. Franchising forms a significant element of the organisation, and stores are frequently built around petrol stations so that they can sustain long opening hours, and develop trade.

These new-style stores retain many of the advantages of the traditional corner shop – personal service, open all hours, a wide range of basic goods – but take the concept a stage further with a modern self-service layout, and an even wider range of goods and services. The product range is geared towards the two client groups described above, and usually includes confectionery, newspapers and books, toiletries, cigarettes, wine and spirits, food of various types, as well as services such as photographic printing, dry cleaning and video hire, all geared around the carefully market-researched concepts of emergency and impulse buying. The locations of these stores are critical for success, and must ideally include the crossing of busy pedestrian flows, with car-parking for passing trade from busy roads.

29.6 **The globalisation of services**

There is no doubt that emergence and expansion of the service sector is a phenomenon experienced in all countries except the poorest. The service sector not only accounts for the largest slice of the GDP, but increasingly it is the largest source of employment. The development of the service sector is seen as a key strand in the economic growth strategies of ELDCs, for example through the encouragement of tourism or financial and business services.

There are two ways in which services have been 'internationalised': through international trade, and by some sort of 'presence' in a particular overseas market or location. **29.12** shows the McDonalds restaurant in Moscow, which represented a 'cultural sensation' when it first opened in 1989, and was regarded as the arrival of the American Dream by young Muscovites. This presence can be achieved via direct foreign investment, via production of a licensed product such as Coca-Cola, via a joint venture or via sub-contracting, with increasingly flexible arrangements being developed in response to local conditions. Globalisation takes internationalisation a stage further, as it implies an organised linkage between functionally dispersed activities.

The globalisation of services, as in the case of manufacturing, owes much to the activities of transnational corporations (TNCs). All TNCs have highly developed 'producer' services which are 'traded' internally within the company. As manufacturing TNCs proliferated globally, so too did services which are very much part of the support sector for the business executive abroad. Thus began the internationalisation of major banks, advertising and property companies, travel and hotel chains, car rental, credit, and enterprises to ensure comfort and security. **Cumulative causation** operates to generate a complex web of both producer and consumer services (see **30.7**). Although many service companies are successful in supplying a specific service function to many different countries, others form conglomerates which supply services that are strongly complementary to each other, such as airlines and hotels, management consultancy and accountancy, or advertising and public relations. This is taken a stage further by companies such as Mitsubishi (one of the giant Japanese trading companies), which handles tens of thousands of different products not only in the service sector, but also in the primary and secondary sectors via thousands of linked companies across the globe. In 1990, it was estimated that these giant Japanese conglomerates were responsible for over 12 per cent of world trade, much of it within the Pacific Rim region.

There are four key factors which have encouraged internationalisation to evolve into globalisation: the increasing 'tradability' of services, advances in telecommunications and IT, high-quality design and marketing of services (customisation), and government deregulation which allows foreign access to home markets.

■ **29.12** McDonalds in Moscow

29.7 Tourism – a global industry?

IT6

Definition

Tourism is an example of an international service industry. Indeed, it may even be regarded as global in that there are few countries which do not experience its effects. It can also be considered globalised because TNCs, which are often based around airlines such as BA, United or JAL, have developed worldwide holdings and business interests to profit from tourism. Tourism is part of the spectrum of leisure activities. A basic distinction between tourism and other forms of leisure is the travel component. As the following definition by the English Tourist Board suggests, a technical definition of tourism includes at least a one-night stay away from the place of residence.

> Tourism is all activities undertaken by people staying away from home for 24 hours or more, on holiday, visiting friends or relatives, at business or other conferences, or for any purpose other than, for example, semi-permanent employment as a construction worker. It does not include day trippers from a home address either outside the country or within it.

This definition is obviously very convenient for statistical purposes as it efficiently categorises trippers, but it does somewhat anomalously exclude all cross-Channel shoppers who spend a day purchasing jumpers in Marks and Spencer at Dover or Folkestone, or stocking up with a month's supply of beer or wine from Calais hypermarkets.

IT6

The interrelationships between tourism, recreation and leisure are shown in **29.13**. There is an obvious overlap, for example, between tourism and recreation as they may share many of the same facilities at a resort or national park.

Growth

According to the World Tourist Organisation (WTO), in 1990 tourism accounted for 13 per cent of the world's gross national product. Already, it is claimed, tourism has created 100 million jobs, which means that in 1990 globally it employed more people than any other single industry, with one in five of the world's workforce employed in tourism-related activities. With a growth rate of 1600 per cent over the last 40 years, the development of tourism can be described as a 'phenomenal explosion'. **29.14** shows how tourist arrivals and expenditure are projected to increase up to the year 2000. This projected trend is exponential, but tourism is a very volatile industry and a whole range of factors could change, which might well cause the projections to be either over-optimistic or under-optimistic.

■ **29.13** The relationships between leisure, recreation and tourism

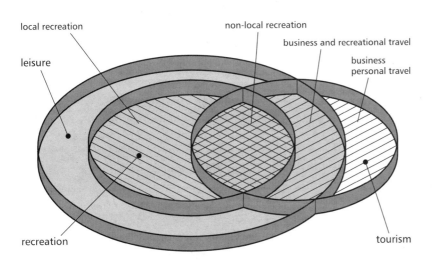

local recreation

non-local recreation

business and recreational travel

business personal travel

leisure

recreation

tourism

---

7 Using the headings 'Environmental', 'Cultural', 'Social', 'Political' and 'Economic', identify factors that may cause the tourist trade to fluctuate. As an example, 1989 was a very poor year for foreign tourists (especially Americans) visiting the UK, but 1993 was a bumper year for tourist arrivals. What factors might account for this difference?

As can be seen from **29.14**, tourism remains very much a phenomenon of the developed world, with 90 per cent of the world's travel market living in EMDCs. The USA (22 per cent) is the largest single market. Although two-thirds of international arrivals are concentrated in just 20 highly industrialised countries, ELDCs are increasingly seeing tourism as a major agent of economic development. These developing areas now capture up to a quarter of the global arrivals and receipts from the 'long-haul market', a phrase used by the travel trade to describe tourists who spend many hours in an aeroplane.

8 Can you think of any disadvantages of ELDCs as tourist destinations?

There are number of reasons for the explosion of tourism as a global industry. On the demand side, the main driving forces are the amount of disposable income and the availability of time. As a general trend, both of these have grown at record rates in EMDCs during the last 25 years. Another vital factor, especially for international travel, has been the technological advances in the field of transport, such as fuel-efficient, wide-bodied jets. Within continents, the astronomical rise in car ownership in EMDCs has also enhanced family mobility.

■ **29.14** Growth in international tourism

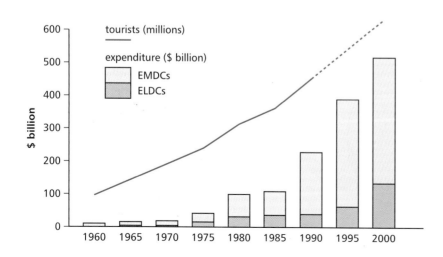

Psychologically, attitudes to travel and tourism have also changed, with holidays seen as 'prestigious', 'relaxing', 'fulfilling' and 'fun'. Such attitudes are reinforced by travel companies, many of which are very large TNCs that own retail, transport and accommodation businesses and therefore have the capability to promote and market tourism both effectively and efficiently. The ultimate in package deals is well typified by some of the major Japanese companies. Japan Airlines, for example, has a tourist division called 'Jalpak' which looks after the total interests of their clients in areas such as Hawaii, the Queensland Coast and Tahiti.

Simple single-cause theories are inadequate in explaining why people take holidays – the industry is subject to wild fluctuations in the volume and patterns of flow. In 1991, for example, heavy media exposure of some long airport delays, with powerful visuals of Gatwick and Luton airports as squatter villages, combined with the vagaries of the English weather – a fine, hot, semitropical early summer – led to a temporary change in the balance between domestic and international flows in the United Kingdom.

Costs and benefits

Tourism is seen as bringing many economic benefits. It can provide much-needed foreign exchange, especially of so-called 'hard' currency if the local currency is subject to frequent devaluation. Tourism is also seen as one way to boost the GNP as a result of the multiplier effect – defined as 'the way in which tourist spending filters through the economy, stimulating other sectors as it does so'. When calculating the possible multiplier effect, it is most important to consider the concept of 'leakage' from all compartments of the system. For example, hotels catering for the needs of their clients have to import luxury goods such as Scotch whisky and bathroom cosmetics. The tourist industry can

IT6,7 also be a direct revenue earner for the government via such devices as tourist taxes, which can constitute up to 20 per cent of expenditure (for example in the Turks and Caicos Islands). Tourism can be a generator of many new jobs, although the majority of these may be low-paid, part-time or seasonal, supporting the theory that the economic impacts of tourism are most valuable in the early phases of development and will diminish as industrialisation takes off.

9 Study the factors shown in **29.15** and suggest how they might influence the money-earning potential of tourism in an area.

10 State what advice you would offer the Ministry of Tourism in an ELDC on how to develop tourism to ensure that the maximum economic advantages are gained from tourist schemes.

type of tourist affecting volume and intensity of expenditure

accessibility and attractiveness of tourist areas and facilities

level of economic development of destination area

success of promotion and publicity campaigns

size of economic base of destination area, e.g. capacity for local crafts, etc.

MAGNITUDE & SUCCESS OF TOURISM'S ECONOMIC IMPACT

how well the destination manages seasonality of demand

role of government (local and national) in providing infrastructure incentives

degree of foreign ownership of facilities such as hotels

% employment of foreigners in key managerial posts

how far tourist expenditure is recirculated in the local economy

■ **29.15** Factors controlling tourism's economic impact

IT6,7 How great the impact of tourism will be economically depends on a number of factors (**29.15**).

As well as economic benefits, there can be economic disadvantages. Frequently, tourism can lead to increased inflation, rising land values which affect local housing, and increased pressure to import. There are also very heavy infrastructural costs at start-up (for example, an international-standard airport) and there is a danger of having much of the labour force tied up in a service industry which may have poor productivity prospects. An overdependence on one sector, or one product within it, is always a high-risk strategy; recent research in Kenya and Tanzania suggests that in many cases the economic benefits have been inflated and need close scrutiny. Moreover, economic benefits have to be set against serious environmental and socio-cultural costs.

IT6,8 Environmental damage caused by tourism manifests itself in a variety of ways. Examples are the destruction of forests in the Alps for ski-pistes, the pollution of inland lakes such as Lake Balaton in Hungary (now officially biologically dead), the health hazards of the Mediterranean Sea (high in levels of untreated sewage), the erosion of outstanding archaeological sites such as the Pyramids and the Sphinx near Cairo in Egypt – the list is endless and well documented.

IT4,6 It is clear that in the long-term interests of both the rich industrialised EMDCs (the main suppliers of tourists) and the economically poor, largely agrarian EDLCs (the long-haul destinations of the future), conservation of the environment has to be a key aim. Environmental damage ruins the lives of the indigenous people and detracts from the pleasure of the tourists. Indeed, sensible tourism planning involves the investment of some of the revenues gained from tourism in conservation, restoration and improved management strategies. There are now numerous examples of good practice, established in response to widespread concern, collectively known as 'green tourism', 'eco-tourism' or 'new tourism'. The main aim is the sustainable development of the resource. The essential watchwords of eco-tourism are 'carrying capacity', 'conservation', 'congruence with the environment', 'sustainability'. Plans can be developed at both the macro scale and the micro scale to manage the diametrically opposed forces of recreation and conservation.

■ **29.16** Tourist activities and ecological damage to different habitats

- – little or no sensitivity
- ❀ slightly sensitive
- ❀ ❀ moderately sensitive
- ❀ ❀ ❀ highly sensitive
- ✳ effect due to disturbance
- ✚ recorded damage within heritage coasts

11 There are numerous examples of the negative externalities of tourism.
  a Study the matrix shown in **29.16** and assess how tourist activities have a damaging effect on the coast.
  b Which do you consider to be the most damaging activities?

12 A very popular individual study involves the investigation of the impact of tourism on a site of environmental or ecological value. Many different types of survey can be carried out, provided that correct sampling techniques are used, without the need to question tourists. Once activity surveys (by age, sex, activity) have been carried out to measure the distribution of tourists, specific investigations can be made, for example into litter, footpath use and erosion, car-parking, ecology (e.g. to show trampling), or pollution (in streams, noise, etc.).

	Cliff tops	Quarries	Rocky shores	Shingle	Sand dune	Salt marshes	Mud	Reed beds	Woodland
Off-road vehicles	❀❀ ✚	– ✚	–	❀❀❀	❀❀❀ ✚	❀	❀	❀	❀❀ ✚
Camping, caravans	❀❀❀ ✚	– ✚	–	❀❀ ✚	❀❀❀ ✚	❀	❀	❀	❀❀❀ ✚
Trampling	❀❀	❀	–	❀❀	❀❀❀	❀	–	–	–
Path erosion	❀❀❀ ✚	❀	❀	❀❀ ✚	❀❀❀ ✚	❀ ✚	–	–	– ✚
Horseriding	❀ ✚	❀ ✚	–	❀❀	❀❀❀ ✚	–	–	–	❀ ✚
Diving	–	–	❀❀ ✚	–	–	–	–	–	–
Canoeing	–	–	–	–	❀	❀	❀ ✳	❀ ✳	–
Powerboating	–	–	–	–	❀	❀	❀ ✳	❀ ✳	–
Sailing	–	–	–	❀	❀	❀	❀ ✳	❀ ✳	–
Windsurfing	–	–	–	–	–	❀ ✳	❀❀ ✳	❀❀ ✳ ✚	–
Rockclimbing	❀ ✚	❀	–	–	–	–	–	–	–
Wildfowling	–	–	–	–	–	❀❀ ✳	❀❀ ✳	–	–
Fishing and bait digging	–	–	–	–	–	❀❀	❀❀ ✚	–	–
Natural history interest	–	❀	❀ ✚	❀ ✳ ✚	❀ ✚	❀ ✚	–	❀ ✳ ✚	

On the macro scale, various strategies operate nationally or regionally to disperse mass tourism away from environmentally sensitive, high-value areas. Certain areas are designated 'honey-pot' sites and are managed as mass tourism areas. New honey-pots in low-value areas, or near urban areas, are developed to take pressure off the more remote countryside. In Britain, both urban parks and country parks have been created to

relieve the increasingly accessible national parks. In high-value areas, strategies to control access by means of wilderness permits and limited access points have been developed. This results in zoning, which is particularly well developed in the national parks of the USA, such as Yosemite and Grand Canyon. These policies are all supported by strong education programmes which outline codes of conduct such as that developed for trekkers using the Himalayan area (**29.17**).

At the micro scale, most high-quality sites such as SSSIs, National Nature Reserves and English Heritage sites operate management plans which deal with matters such as way-marking, interpretative boards, signposting, footpath routeing and design, car-parking and site access, waste disposal and providing appropriate facilities.

■ **29.17** The Himalayan Code

THE HIMALAYAN TOURIST GUIDE

By following these simple guidelines, you can help preserve the unique environment and ancient cultures of the Himalayas.

Protect the natural environment

◆ **Limit deforestation – make no open fires** and discourage others from doing so on your behalf. Where water is heated by scarce firewood, use as little as possible. When possible choose accommodation that uses kerosene or fuel-efficient wood stoves.
◆ **Remove litter, burn or bury paper** and carry out all non-degradable litter. Graffiti are permanent examples of environmental pollution.
◆ **Keep local water clean and avoid using pollutants** such as detergents in streams or springs. If no toilet facilities are available, make sure you are at least 30 metres away from water sources, and bury or cover wastes.
◆ **Plants should be left to flourish in their natural environment** – taking cuttings, seeds and roots is illegal in many parts of the Himalaya.
◆ **Help your guides and porters to follow conservation measures.**

The Himalayas may change you – please do not change them

As a guest, respect local traditions, protect local cultures, maintain local pride.

◆ **When taking photographs, respect privacy** – ask permission and use restraint.
◆ **Respect holy places** – preserve what you have come to see, never touch or remove religious objects. Shoes should be removed when visiting temples.
◆ **Giving to children encourages begging.** A donation to a project, health centre or school is a more constructive way to help.
◆ **You will be accepted and welcomed if you follow local customs.** Use only your right hand for eating and greeting. Do not share cutlery or cups, etc. It is polite to use both hands when giving or receiving gifts.
◆ **Respect for local etiquette earns you respect** – loose, lightweight clothes are preferable to revealing shorts, skimpy tops and tight-fitting action wear. Hand-holding or kissing in public are disliked by local people.
◆ **Observe standard food and bed charges** but do not condone overcharging. Remember when you're shopping that the bargains you buy may only be possible because of low income to others.
◆ **Visitors who value local traditions encourage local pride and maintain local cultures.** Please help local people gain a realistic view of life in Western countries.

Be patient, friendly and sensitive
Remember – you are a guest

Tourism Concern, Froebel College, Roehampton Lane, London SW15 5PU Tel: 081-878-9053

Tourism Concern is a network of tourists and tourism professionals which aims to promote greater understanding of the impact of tourism on host communities and their environments.

13 Visit a local tourist site and work through the following tasks:
  a Obtain a summary of the management plan (operational or proposed).
  b Summarise with maps and diagrams the objectives of the plan.
  c Outline any potential management problems.
  d Suggest any possible improvements to the plan, or any solutions to the problems you have identified.
  e Evaluate the success of strategies such as interpretative boards and litter-bin provision.

The social and cultural impacts of tourism are perhaps more complex to analyse and possibly more difficult to overcome by management plans. Few writers argue convincingly the case for mass tourism as a cultural exchange, or as an improver of international understanding. Major concerns are more frequently documented. They include the strains of hospitality, the dehumanising nature of much of the employment, the debasement of local cultural expression, and the adverse impact on community life. The social impact of tourism will vary according to the degree of difference in lifestyle between hosts and tourists, whether in terms of numbers, ethnicity, culture or social outlook. According to UNESCO reports, tourist–host encounters are invariably transitory and usually compressed by space/time constraints. Most encounters are, moreover, preplanned as part of tour schedules, managed to be a pleasant tourist experience (for example, a rainforest walk) yet with a spirit of controlled adventure. A typical tourist experience would be a visit to a native Indian village in outback Venezuela, with a demonstration of tribal dancing, followed by poisoned dart-throwing, wood-carving and a ride in a dugout canoe. They usually involve a financial transaction; for example, in some inland Sierra Leone villages the tribal chief invests the money gained from tourism in village projects like schools and health centres. An extreme example of the negative social and cultural impacts of tourism is provided by the sex-tourism industry of Thailand, where half a million young women work as prostitutes or hostesses in the sex industry. The health risks are considerable.

Tourism has been described as 'a double-edged sword'. There are numerous examples of poorly-managed tourism, and this section has tried to explore some of the costs and benefits.

The *World Travel Gazette* writes quite optimistically on 'tourism in the future':

There will be rapid expansion, but the tourist of the future will have rising expectations in terms of quality and in general will be much more conscious about environment and heritage. There is likely to be less demand for mass sun, sea, sex and sand holidays as worries concerning AIDS and skin cancer accelerate, with a consequent movement away from the massive concrete resorts of the 1970s to exclusive low-rise attractive villages. Long-haul destinations, especially in Asia, will increase, as will specialist cultural and education tours for a growing number of 'Yuppies' who will demand world tourism.

14 a Is the above quotation a true vision of the future? Visit a travel agent to discuss how tourist habits are changing.
   b Question a cross-section of people (by age, class and sex) to find out their opinions on the vision of the future. How have their holiday habits changed over the years?

You will almost certainly find that organised tourism and transport activities are run by large leisure groups which combine the various segments such as sales (travel shop), tours (tour company), airline and hotel. Many of these companies are international and run a genuinely globalised operation. Some ELDCs resist the power of these TNCs as they feel that too much income goes abroad. Instead they have developed their own state-run tourist agencies, as has happened in Nepal and the Seychelles.

29.8 The future scenario in services

Recently there has been a slow-down in the expansion of service employment, and in business and financial services there has been spectacular job-shedding (for example, in 1992–93, major banks shed 4000 jobs in the UK), largely attributed to technological factors such as the widespread adoption of computer technology. The question is posed that, if this is part of a far stronger downward trend which affects all service industries, what will happen to the fundamental assumption of the right for all to have full employment?

Any assessment of the future prospects for the service sector may therefore have to begin by assuming new attitudes towards employment, involving part-time employment via job-sharing, or involving shorter working hours. Can advanced economies function as economic systems without the prospect of full employment, or by paying workers very high wages for short hours? These economic changes will have major social impacts, as for many people to be without work has a social stigma. The workplace also provides an important social function in people's lives. The effect of new technology may be expected to have a major impact on the future of services, as almost all services involve data-handling or financial transactions. The pace of change is exponential and is largely related to developments in one product – silicon chips!

30.1 **Defining development**

'Development' is a word or concept that is often so taken for granted that people do not really consider how the meaning of it has changed over time. Development is frequently considered to be synonymous with growth – but is it? In the colonial era of the 19th century, Western powers talked about the 'underdevelopment' of the indigenous peoples in the colonies – some countries were deemed to be less developed than the developed colonial powers because of certain environmental and ethnic traits within their boundaries.

In the 20th century, it became commonplace to divide the globe into three 'worlds': the First and Second Worlds referred to the developed or advanced nations predominantly located in the North, whereas the Third World included all of the developing nations, often referred to by their location as 'the South'. The difference between the First and Second Worlds was in the way they had developed. The First World developed as a capitalist system, whereas the Second World developed within a command economy, with the government replacing the market. Initially, the idea behind the terms was that they represented contrasting paths to development: the capitalist way and the socialist way. By implication Third World nations could choose between the first and second way, or invent a third path. Over time, it was held that the Third World would modernise and so catch up with the other two. This was what was considered, therefore, to be development – achieving modernity via rapid economic growth (see **25.2**).

Since the 1970s, differentiation has occurred within the Third World to the extent that it is now possible to distinguish between different groups of countries:

- least developed countries such as Myanmar (Burma), Bangladesh, Nepal, and many African countries
- standard less developed countries which still have a low income but lack the extreme poverty of least developed countries
- middle-income countries, which have either followed the path of industrialisation (see the case study on NICs, pages 385–86) or have been fortunate to have the advantage of oil to export (OPEC countries such as Saudi Arabia).

To add to this economic differentiation, there are seven critical components which explain why the Third World economies have become so diverse:

- size (geographic area and population)
- historical and colonial background
- the degree of endowment of physical and human resources
- the nature of the employment structure
- the relative importance of the public and private sectors in the economy
- the degree of dependence on external economic and political forces
- the institutional and political structures within the nation.

> **1** With reference to examples you have studied, suggest how these seven components can lead to diversity within the Third World. Take two contrasting countries and research their differences.

In the First World, there has been substantial restructuring with a decline in the economic and political fortunes of some countries, such as France and Britain, and a relative rise of others, especially the new united Germany, and Japan. It is now much more realistic to think of the First World as consisting of three parts: Western Europe, North America, and the most developed economies in the Asian sector of the Pacific Rim.

It is argued by some that the final demise of the 'three worlds model' was not provided by these very significant changes in the First or Third Worlds, but by the collapse of the Second World, including so far the break-up of the former Soviet Union, the changes in Eastern Europe and the reunification of Germany, East and West. It is hardly possible to have a three worlds model when one of the worlds has in effect almost completely disappeared. Since the model was fundamentally a geopolitical product of the Cold War era, it is clearly an inappropriate way of looking at global development in the mid-1990s.

IT5

In recent years, a new pluralism in development studies has begun to emerge and so redefine the process of development. The two significant changes are the adoption of the **populist approach** (which looks at development in terms of basic needs) and the 'greening' of development theory (which rests upon the question of sustainability). The old view of economic development saw the process in terms of the planned alteration of the structures of production and development to produce rapid gains in overall and per capita GNP. In contrast, the new view defines development in terms of the reduction or elimination of poverty, inequality and unemployment within the context of a growing economy.

In 1991 the World Bank identified the challenge of development as 'the need to improve the quality of life' – but it involves more. It encompasses, as ends in themselves, the rights to better education, higher standards of health and nutrition, less poverty, a cleaner environment with safe water, more equality of opportunity, greater individual freedom,

and a richer cultural life. The new style of development, therefore, is a multi-dimensional process involving changes in social structures, popular attitudes and national institutions, as well as the acceleration of economic growth, the reduction of inequality, and the eradication of poverty.

IT5

Three core values of modern development are sustenance, self-esteem and the freedom to choose. **Sustenance** involves the ability to meet basic needs of food, shelter, health, etc. **Self-esteem** involves the right of peoples and societies to dignity, respect and recognition of indigenous, as opposed to imported, cultural values. **Freedom to choose** involves having the wealth to choose between options in environmental management, and also political freedom.

Thus the objectives of the new populist approach are:

- to increase the availability and widen the distribution of those things that satisfy basic human needs (food, shelter and health)

- to raise levels of living standards, including job provision, better education, etc. as well as higher incomes

- to expand the range of environmental, economic and social choices.

The other strand to a modern redefinition of development includes the 'greening' of development. Within the last decade, a rising tide of concern about the environment and development in economically less developed countries (ELDCs) has become a central feature not only of the rhetoric, but also in the planning of development projects and in the thinking in development studies. To environmentalists, the loss of natural habitats and breakdown in indigenous and subsistence ways of life caused by development projects has been a powerful focus for the extension of pressure-group politics. Typical of these campaigns is Sting's campaign to save the traditional way of life of the

IT4

indigenous peoples of the Amazon, the opposition to rainforest destruction, and the protests against the building of mega-dams. These issues follow on logically from concerns about pollution, whales and the countryside. These campaigns to save environments in the developing world reflect the growing integration of the 'global village'. The term **sustainable development** has been universally adopted as the watchword of green development strategies and has become part of the jargon of the development business.

Sustainable development in agriculture and energy resource use has been investigated in previous chapters. The

concept is incorporated in all the development plans of international agencies such as the World Bank and the United Nations. The widespread use of the rhetoric reflects the success of environmentalist pressure on aid donors, which is supported by effective media coverage and was evident in the renewed concern at the Environmental Summit held in Rio de Janeiro in 1992. The question remains – and you will have the chance to explore this when considering development projects – as to how this rhetoric is to be converted into reality.

30.2 **Measuring development**

Traditional definitions of development have emphasised economic growth and the acquisition of wealth. Thus initial measurement was based on economic measures such as GDP or GNP per capita. **GDP per capita** is calculated by dividing the money value of all the goods and services produced in a country by its total population. When figures for 'invisible' trade are included, the term **gross national product (GNP) per capita** is used. In general, European countries use GDP per capita as an economic indicator, and the UN and USA use GNP per capita.

> **2** In what order would you rank the following countries on the basis of their GNP per capita: Algeria, Bangladesh, Bolivia, Ethiopia, France, Germany, Hong Kong, Japan, Kenya, Korea, Saudi Arabia, Tanzania, United Kingdom, USA and Zimbabwe? Now check your answer by referring to **30.1** and using other sources.

You may have thought the USA was the highest – after all, America symbolises wealth – but in fact some of the others show higher GNP figures. Equally,

you may have perceived Ethiopia as the poorest on the list in terms of GNP as a result of extensive media coverage of its recurrent famines, but in fact several countries record lower figures. Although GDP and GNP figures are easier to measure and to obtain than some other development indicators, such as social factors, there are limitations to their use and validity. The figures are much more accurate in countries that have well-documented economies with many economic transactions and where trade in goods, labour and services can be measured as they pass through a market-place. Where markets are less well developed and trading is done informally through bartering, and most of the goods are made in the home for personal subsistence, GDP and GNP figures are very unreliable measures. Centrally-planned economies again operate a largely non-market economy, play a relatively small role in international trade and include far fewer services, so their GDP figures are difficult to calculate and interpret.

> **3** Briefly analyse the distribution shown in **30.1**. How, in your view, could the map have been made even more useful?

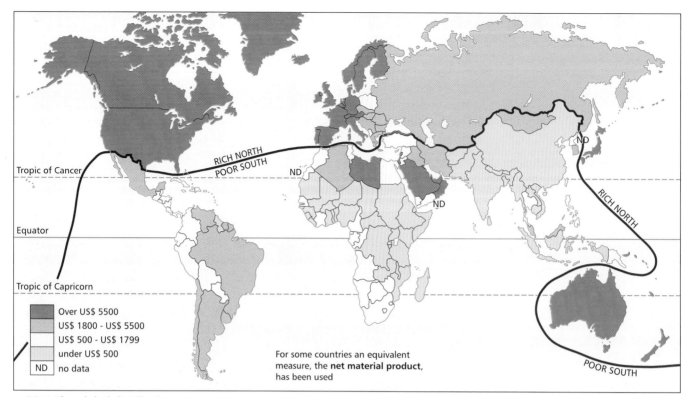

■ **30.1** The global distribution of per capita GNP

Map legend:
- Over US$ 5500
- US$ 1800 – US$ 5500
- US$ 500 – US$ 1799
- under US$ 500
- ND no data

For some countries an equivalent measure, the **net material product**, has been used

If we are to move towards a new definition of development which emphasises the satisfaction of basic needs, it is very apparent that measurement of development must be broadened to reflect this. Clearly, multivariate analysis may be more reliable, as few countries perform uniformly across the whole spectrum of development. For example, some countries have high levels of social development (high literacy and health standards), but comparatively low GNP per capita. The creation of development profiles, as shown in **30.2a**, is an effective way of assessing the relative level of development across several indicators. The chosen indicators have to be selected to provide a balance.

■ **30.2** Measures of development

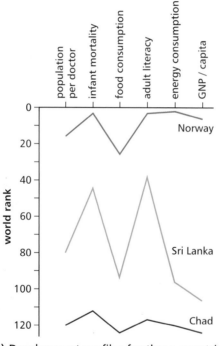

a) Development profiles for three countries

	Norway	Saudi Arabia	Hungary	Portugal	Bolivia	Indonesia	Sri Lanka	Chad
GNP per capita	7	12	32	41	80	88	105	122
Energy consumption	2	38	27	44	71	85	94	120
Adult literacy	4	115	11	53	59	62	39	116
Food consumption	26	55	8	32	114	76	92	124
Infant mortality	4	89	31	41	101	73	45	111
Population per doctor	16	53	5	27	57	96	82	120

b) World development rankings of eight selected countries

4 Study the table in **30.2b** and explain how the chosen indicators could be used to study levels of development. Can you think of five more indicators you might use?

5 Use the figures in **30.2b** to complete the development profiles. What do you notice about the patterns of the development profiles when comparing the countries? Why is it that some countries such as Sri Lanka have such an uneven profile?

IT5

The idea of combining several indicators into a multiple or composite index of development was first explored by Berry in 1960. Since then, two composite indexes have been devised and are now widely used – the **Physical Quality of Life Index (PQLI)** and more recently the **Human Development Index (HDI)**.

The PQLI is the average of three characteristics: literacy, life expectancy and infant mortality. Each is scaled from 0 to 100. For example, literacy rates of zero and 100 per cent would be scaled as 0 to 100 respectively, exactly as in the raw data. The life expectancy figures are scaled similarly; for example, in 1990 Sierra Leone had the world's shortest life expectancy and was scaled to 0, whereas Norway, with the world's highest life expectancy of 77 years, was given an index of 100. The same process operates for the raw figures of infant mortality, with Cambodia (260 per 1000) – the highest in the world – having an index of 0, and so on.

IT5

30.3 shows the world distribution of PQLI values, whilst **30.4** gives the per capita GNP values for a ranking of countries based on the PQLI.

■ **30.3** The global distribution of PQLI values

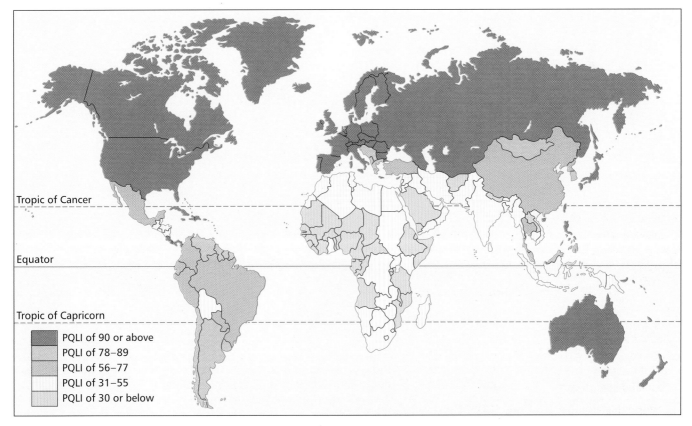

Tropic of Cancer

Equator

Tropic of Capricorn

	PQLI of 90 or above
	PQLI of 78–89
	PQLI of 56–77
	PQLI of 31–55
	PQLI of 30 or below

IT5

6 Compare
  a the distribution patterns of
  30.3 and **30.1**
  b the two sets of data in **30.4**.
To what extent do they coincide?

Country	Per capita GNP $	PQLI
Gambia	348	20
Angola	790	21
Sudan	380	34
Pakistan	349	40
Saudi Arabia	12720	40
India	253	42
Iraq	3020	48
Qatar	27790	56
Tanzania	299	58
Zimbabwe	815	63
Brazil	2214	72
China	304	75
Sri Lanka	302	82
Singapore	5220	86
Taiwan	2503	87
Costa Rica	1476	89

■ **30.4** Comparison of per capita GNP and PQLI values

IT5

■ **30.5** The global distribution of HDI values

In response to the new definition of development, in 1990 the UN devised a measure, the **Human Development Index (HDI)**. Like the PQLI, it takes three variables, which are given equal weight – adjusted income per capita, educational attainment, and life expectancy at birth. The UN index takes the highest and lowest levels observed for each variable among the world's countries. The interval between them is given a value of 1 and then the value for each country is scored on a scale of 0 to 1, with 1 being the best for each of the three variables. The HDI is the average score of the three variables, expressed as a value between 0 and 1 (**30.5**).

How useful is the HDI? In 1994 there were still many problems with it, especially in obtaining appropriate data. Quantity measures (e.g. a literate population of over 90 per cent) tell us nothing about quality, i.e. what standards of literacy have been achieved. Although the HDI does give a broad perspective on progress, its creation was partly a political strategy designed to focus people's attention on the need to spend money on health and education. Another limitation arises from its use of rankings: the index is a measure of relative rather than absolute development.

IT5

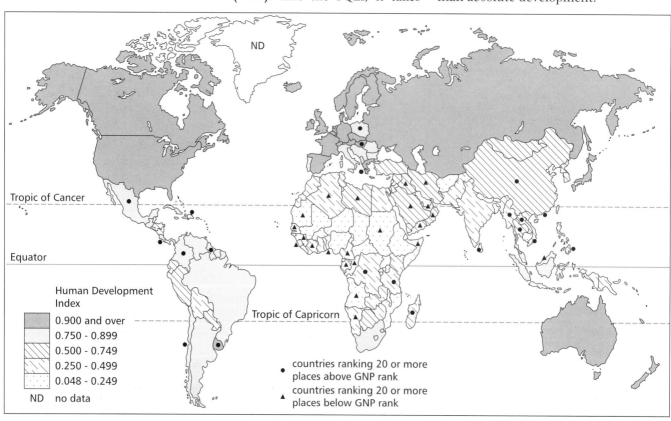

30.3 Disparity – a global and a national problem

IT5,7

30.6 forcefully summarises the disparity between the North and the South. Frank has suggested that the **developmental gap** between them has largely been created by the economically more developed countries of the North. He argues that the ELDCs of the South were not originally poor, but have become so as a result of colonialism and exploitation of their resources.

---

7 Try to devise a series of graphs which show the essential features of the unequal world.

■ **30.6** The North–South Divide – the facts

North–South is a very simple way of showing how the world divides into rich and poor countries (see **25.7**).

Countries in the rich **North** are those in North America, Europe, the former Soviet Union, Japan, Australia and New Zealand.

Countries of the poorer **South** are mostly in Asia, Africa, and Latin America. Countries of the **South** are sometimes called 'Third World' or 'developing' countries because they are generally poorer.

NORTH

- 25% of the world's people
- 80% of the world's income
- a person can expect to live on average more than 70 years
- most people have enough to eat
- most people are educated at least through secondary school
- over 90% of the world's manufacturing industry
- about 95% of world's spending on research and development; nearly all the world's registered patents
- dominates most of the global economic system and institutions of trade, money and finance

SOUTH

- 75% of the world's people
- 20% of the world's income
- a person can expect to live, on average, to about 50 years (in the poorest countries 25% of children die before the age of 5)
- 20% or more of the people suffer from hunger and malnutrition
- half of the people still have little chance of formal education

---

According to the Brandt Report, about 800 million people (40% of the South) are barely surviving. Most of these live in the poorest countries of sub-Saharan Africa and South Asia. About two-thirds of the world's very poorest people live in Bangladesh, India, Indonesia, and Pakistan.

IT5,7

But inequalities also exist at spatial scales other than the global one. Those readers living in the UK should be very familiar with the national phenomenon of the North–South Divide, although it should be added that the persistent recession of the 1990s may well have reduced rather than enlarged the gap between the two halves of the nation. A similar division is also to be found within Italy, where the Mezzogiorno (the name given to the southern part of Italy) is relatively less economically developed compared with the prosperous northern regions of the country, to the extent that it has living standards which could be associated with ELDCs.

As ELDCs develop, inevitably there are favoured regions where development is concentrated, usually known as **core regions**, and these contrast markedly with many of the **peripheral** or **outback regions** where conditions of extreme poverty exist. Venezuela and Brazil are frequently quoted as examples of ELDCs with marked regional disparities, but the more growth takes place in ELDCs the more widespread the phenomenon of regional disparity becomes. It is also very much a feature of modern China, with the phenomenal growth of special economic zones such as Shenzhen, or in Mexico in the 'Maquilas' which were introduced as part of a Border Industrialisation Programme, in cities such as Tijuana.

Regional planning is perceived as the solution to spatial disparities within a nation. Leading the field has been the UK. Various strategies have been used in Britain since 1934 to counteract regional disparities. Most notable has been the designation of development and assisted areas.

There are several theoretical perspectives which can be used to demonstrate how and why regional imbalances in development occur, and models have been devised (notably

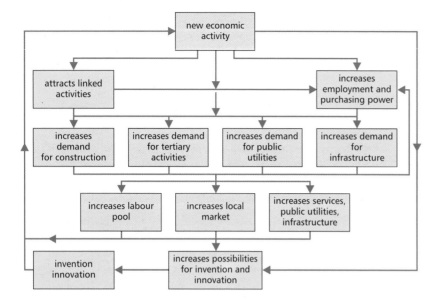

The boxes in the diagram:

new economic activity

attracts linked activities

increases employment and purchasing power

increases demand for construction

increases demand for tertiary activities

increases demand for public utilities

increases demand for infrastructure

increases labour pool

increases local market

increases services, public utilities, infrastructure

invention innovation

increases possibilities for invention and innovation

■ **30.7** The process of cumulative causation

The diagram in **30.7** shows how the multiplier effect operates, the process of growth in a given area being fuelled by flows of workers (migrants), capital and would-be entrepreneurs from the less advanced surrounding areas. The process of spatial concentration of economic activity into a core is variously known as **backwash** (Myrdal's terminology) or **polarisation**. It generates **upward spirals** or **virtuous circles** in the core and sets off **downward spirals** or **vicious circles** in the periphery. Again, the result is an accentuation of regional disparity.

In this situation, therefore, how do the peripheral areas ever develop? Growth is supposed to **spread** (Myrdal) or **trickle down** from the core, as expansion of core activity requires extra food and resources from the periphery, and the core supplies the periphery with innovative goods and services as income levels rise. As land costs and congestion increase in the core, many branch plants decentralise into the periphery, thus providing a further stimulus to growth. Government regional policies may emphasise this as a result of spending on infrastructure. Whether the gap between the core and the periphery widens depends on the relative rates of **backwash** and **spread**, as is shown in **30.8**.

All these concepts are assembled together in Friedmann's model of spatial development, which is derived from the development histories of Venezuela and Brazil (**30.9**). Four types of area can be designated within a country according to the model: a **core** (usually the capital city or a former colonial trade port); **upward transitional areas** which benefit from their close proximity to the core; **downward transitional** or **declining areas** distant from the core and found in the periphery; and **resource frontiers**, areas of the periphery being exploited for their primary products. Resource frontiers and upward transitional areas have the potential to develop into secondary cores.

Friedmann's) to show how eventually the regions of a nation become spatially integrated over time.

Classical economic theory states that any regional imbalance in real wages or job opportunities is resolved by migration of firms to poorer areas where they can benefit from lower production costs, thus relieving pressure in the richer areas where there is competition for labour and land. The reality is that a reverse flow of selective migration takes place from rural to urban areas of young, active, better-qualified labour, thus reducing this theoretical incentive for firms to migrate to peripheral low-cost areas.

More recent theories recognise the inevitability of regional imbalance. The process of **cumulative causation** means that successful, growing areas attract even more economic activity over time, thereby accentuating regional disparity.

■ **30.8** Backwash or spread?

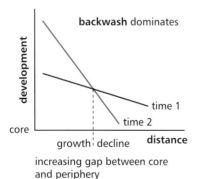

increasing gap between core and periphery

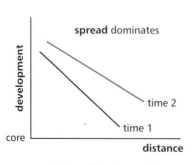

equalising of development over time – all areas developing

IT5,7

Stage 1 Relatively independent local centres; no hierarchy. Typical pre-industrial structure; each city lies at the centre of a small regional enclave.

Stage 2 A single strong core. Typical of period of incipient industrialisation; a periphery emerges; potential entrepreneurs and labour move to the core, national economy is virtually reduced to a single metropolitan region.

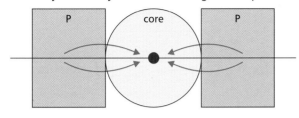

Stage 3 A single national core, strong peripheral subcores. During the period of industrial maturity, secondary cores form, thereby reducing the periphery on a national scale to smaller intermetropolitan peripheries.

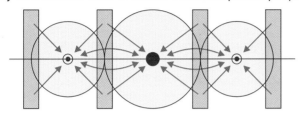

Stage 4 A functional interdependent system of cities. Organised complexity characterised by national integration, efficiency in location, maximum growth potential.

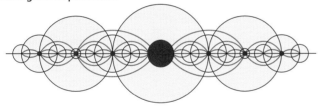

■ **30.9** Friedmann's model of spatial development

Brazil is one country whose development is said to follow Friedmann's model. Modern economic growth became concentrated in the South East region, in the industrial heartland of São Paulo. The planned aim was for this wealth to trickle down into the less developed provinces. Unfortunately, both the Amazon region and the North East became problem regions, and a key strat-egy of the Brazilian government was to develop them. As a first prerequisite, a nationwide transport network was built, including the Trans-Amazon Highway. This has encouraged a range of new economic activities, such as mining, to develop in the Amazon region. In the North East region, there has been heavy investment in new industries using power from the São Francisco river. To spearhead the development of the periphery, the capital-city function was moved from Rio de Janeiro to the new city of Brasilia. Such developments have been typical of the so-called 'top-down' approach to regional development, wherein central government intervenes to overcome the disparity between the richest and poorest regions.

Typical of the 'bottom-up' approach to regional development are the rural development strategies of East African countries. Tanzania has followed a radical development strategy aimed at achieving uniform levels of development as part of a self-reliant, socialist society. The keystone of this policy lies in the programme of rural development and cooperative production known as 'Ujamaa'. Tanzania's predominantly rural population was reorganised into cooperative settlements with all basic services, to raise living standards in the countryside and to improve agricultural production. However, Ujamaa was never a truly bottom-up development as the whole system was devised by the central, socialist government. It is only bottom-up in the sense that it was applied at a local or village level. More genuine bottom-up development, as opposed to rural development, can be found in Indonesia and Zimbabwe.

30.4 **Issues of finance**

30.10 shows the economic system of an ELDC. Clearly, as there are limited supplies of local money to invest, finance for development has to be obtained via a range of loans, foreign investment and aid from a variety of sources, and from exports. This section aims to evaluate the strengths and weaknesses of all three.

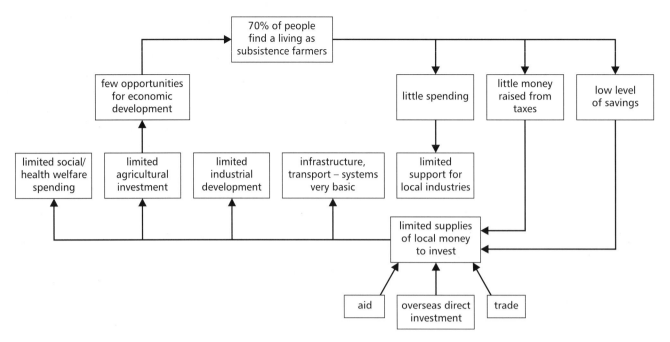

■ **30.10** The economic system in the developing world

The growth of foreign or **overseas direct investment (ODI)** from private firms in EMDCs rose very rapidly between 1960 and 1980, when it levelled off at around $17 billion. However, in 1989, 71 per cent of ODI went to just 10 countries: Brazil (12 per cent), Singapore (12 per cent), Mexico (11 per cent), China (10 per cent), Hong Kong (7 per cent), Malaysia (6 per cent), Argentina (4 per cent), Thailand, Egypt and Colombia (3 per cent each).

8 a What do you notice about the nature of the leading recipients of ODI?
b Why do you think they fare so well?
c What sorts of country fail to attract ODI?

■ **30.11** Seven key issues concerning the role and impact of TNCs

Key issues	Sources of dispute
■ International capital movements (income flows and balance of payments)	◆ Do they bring in much capital (savings)? ◆ Do they improve the balance of payments? ◆ Do they remit 'excessive' profits? ◆ Do they employ transfer pricing and disguise capital outflows? ◆ Do they establish any linkages to the local economy? ◆ Do they generate significant tax revenues?
■ Displacement of indigenous production	◆ Do they buy out existing import-competing industries? ◆ Do they use their competitive advantages to drive local competitors out of business?
■ Extent of technology transfer	◆ Do they keep all R&D in home countries? ◆ Do they retain monopoly power over their technology?
■ Appropriateness of technology transfer	◆ Do they use only capital-intensive technologies? ◆ Do they adapt technology to local factor endowments or leave it unchanged?
■ Patterns of consumption	◆ Do they encourage inappropriate patterns of consumption through elite orientation, advertising, and superior marketing techniques? ◆ Do they increase consumption of their products at the expense of other (perhaps more needed) goods?
■ Social structure and stratification	◆ Do they develop allied local groups through higher wage payments, hiring (displacing) the best of the local entrepreneurs and fostering elite loyalty and socialisation through pressures for conformity? ◆ Do they foster alien values, images and lifestyles incompatible with local customs and beliefs?
■ Income distribution and dualistic development	◆ Do they contribute to the widening gap between rich and poor? ◆ Do they exacerbate urban bias and widen urban–rural differences?

Almost all ODI comes from transnational companies, which invest money when establishing a new local factory, and also bring to the country new technologies and a new style of living. In Chapters 27, 28 and 29 we considered the role of TNCs in energy exploitation, manufacturing and service provision, and emphasised their enormous economic and political power. Clearly, there are advantages and disadvantages of ODI from the TNCs. The main advantage is that their investment makes up the shortfall in funding for the ELDCs, but many ELDCs have grave reservations about the power of TNCs. **30.11** summarises the seven key issues that arise.

Where there is congruence of interest between the TNC and the host country, undoubtedly ODI can be an important stimulus to economic and social development, as in Firestone's investment in Liberia, but TNCs see their role in terms of global output, efficiency and profit maximisation. Individually the host countries may be manipulated by the TNCs as the TNCs inevitably look for the most profitable investment opportunities, engage in transfer pricing and repatriate profits back to their home countries.

30.5 **Issues of aid**

IT5

An alternative source of finance is of course foreign aid. As the *Human Development Report 1992* states, 'foreign aid has critical weaknesses – in quantity, equity, predictability and distribution'. **Aid** is defined as any flow of capital to ELDCs which meets two criteria:

1 Its objective is non-commercial from the point of view of the donor (an issue raised in the Pergau dam controversy of 1994).

2 It is characterised by concessional terms, i.e. the interest rate and

repayment period for any borrowed capital should be 'softer' than commercial rates.

IT5

However, aid can consist of an enormous variety of 'give-and-take' measures other than the strictly financial one (**30.12**). However, as the cartoon **30.13** shows, there is frequently a very thin line dividing purely developmental grants and loans from those offered for security (e.g. in return for a military base) or commercial interests.

■ **30.12** The 'give-and-take' of international aid

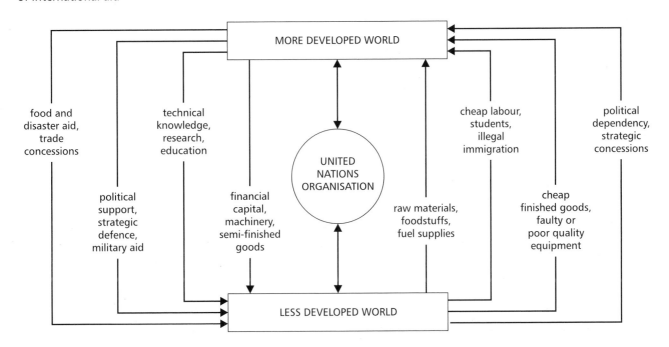

■ 30.13 Different views of aid

In analyses of aid, a distinction is usually made between:

- official development assistance (ODA), which includes bilateral grants, loans and technical assistance as agreed on a one-to-one basis between a donor and a receiver country,

- multilateral aid, whereby a country provides aid through a third party such as the UN, and

- voluntary aid, which is given by individuals rather than governments to national and international charities like the Red Cross and Oxfam.

It would seem from the statistics that the allocation of foreign aid is rarely determined by the needs of developing countries (**30.14**). Of key importance in understanding this discrepancy is the consideration of why donors give aid. Donor countries (**30.15**) give aid primarily for three reasons, which are often interconnected – political, strategic, and for reasons of economic self-interest. Some development assistance given by governments is undoubtedly altruistic in its motivation (e.g. emergency disaster aid or food relief) but in general, donor nations assist others in the expectation of receiving corresponding benefits on a quid pro quo basis.

9 What conclusions do you draw from the information in **30.14**?

■ 30.14 Foreign aid allocations and the poor

Ten developing countries with greatest number of poor	Number of poor millions	Poor as a percentage of total world poor	Official development assistance (ODA) per capita $	ODA as a percentage of total world ODA
India	410	34.2	1.8	3.5
China	120	9.9	1.8	4.7
Bangladesh	99	8.3	18.0	4.7
Indonesia	70	5.8	9.3	3.9
Pakistan	37	3.1	8.8	2.5
Philippines	36	3.0	20.3	2.9
Brazil	33	2.8	1.1	0.4
Ethiopia	30	2.5	17.7	2.0
Myanmar	17	1.4	4.7	0.4
Thailand	17	1.4	14.1	1.8
Total	869	72.4	4.2	26.8

Donor country	1985		1990	
	Billions of dollars	**Percentage of GNP**	**Billions of dollars**	**Percentage of GNP**
Canada	1.6	0.49	2.5	0.44
France	4.0	0.78	9.4	0.79
Germany	2.9	0.47	6.3	0.42
Italy	1.1	0.26	3.4	0.32
Japan	3.8	0.29	9.1	0.31
Netherlands	1.1	0.91	2.6	0.94
United Kingdom	1.5	0.33	2.6	0.28
USA	9.4	0.24	11.4	0.21
Others	4.0	0.35	7.1	0.51
Total	29.4	0.35	54.4	0.35

IT5

Aid can be accepted for political reasons, for example by corrupt dictators wishing to make their position more secure, by silencing the opposition and keeping the people happy. Sometimes aid goes to provide internal security systems and military equipment to support a regime whose political opinions are congruent with the donor. Equally, it is possible to see the distribution of US aid today in terms of its need to find strategic friends in various places; for example, in 1993 Egypt and Turkey were perceived as good friends as a result of their support of US policy in the Gulf War.

There are undoubted economic motivations which cause donors to direct their aid in a particular way. Increasingly aid is given in the form of loans as opposed to outright grants. Frequently, aid is tied to trade, whereby the receiver agrees to take a whole series of exports from the donor, purchased with the aid money. In such arrangements, aid can involve providing the ELDC with the opportunity to purchase goods and services from the donor, often at relatively expensive prices.

The basic question must therefore be asked: Why do ELDC recipients accept aid, if the terms are so unfavourable? The major reason is clearly economic. Success stories from Taiwan and South Korea confirm the proposition that aid is a crucial and essential ingredient in the development process, which will in time lead to self-sustained growth (see **25.2**). Thus ELDCs have to rely on the donor

IT5

perception of what poor countries require to promote their economic development. The quality of aid is therefore of paramount importance. Quality features include untied aid, which allows countries to direct aid finance to any projects they wish and to allocate aid more by need and with less regard for politics and strategy. More time should be allowed for the repayment of loans, in more flexible forms, especially when more aid is directed towards the ELDCs. At present, many ELDCs are demanding more aid in the form of grants and low-cost, long-term loans, with the minimum of strings attached.

IT4,5

At the Rio Summit in 1992, ELDCs pressed for very substantial increases in foreign aid not only for development purposes but also for environmentally sustainable projects which would cause less pollution. The implication was that the rich countries would have to pay a price if they wished to stop ELDCs from taking the similar rapid, destructive path to growth, as sustainability costs more.

So far this discussion has concentrated on government aid, but increasingly charities are taking the lead in the forefront of new-style aid projects. Many of these aid charities, such as Christian Aid, Oxfam and Save the Children, are so well known that they have become household words. Although they differ in their emphasis of approach, administration and

Develop appropriately

The problem

Western aid is frequently tied to the construction of unwieldy and useless projects designed by foreign 'experts' who don't understand the African predicament or environment. These people are imported at great cost to do jobs they are often ill-qualified to do at home. They rarely speak the local language or ask local people what they want. And they design projects with more regard to how they appear on paper than to whether they meet local needs or capitalise on local knowledge. The result is frequently irrelevant to local requirements, relying on costly Western technology and great technological expertise. African elites have copied this style of Western development, taking out huge loans to build show projects, and imposing vast state farms on Africa's peasants, thereby destroying traditional ways.

The way forward

Development projects must involve the full participation and approval of local people, and be designed to meet local needs. They should build on 'common' knowledge about the environment and social requirements. And they should be small-scale and sustainable in terms of resources available. Good projects are often modest in their expenditure and fit naturally into local ways of doing things. In general the voluntary agencies are much better at doing this than government departments. Foreign aid is usually best spent funding local people to solve their own problems, rather than employing foreigners who have little understanding of the African situation.

■ **30.16** Aid to Africa: the problem and the way forward

target groups, many are now responsible for enormous budgets. Major controversies include how much of your charity donation is spent on administration rather than on the poor or needy, and how political their campaigns should be.

New views of foreign aid are slowly beginning to prevail, particularly as regards what are deemed to be its most appropriate forms (**30.16**). Gradually more emphasis is being given to the real development needs of recipients, who are also being allowed more freedom of action. Grandiose prestige projects are now giving way to schemes aimed more at the basic wants of people. Programmes of medical aid designed to reduce mortality rates are now being promoted in tandem with schemes to raise local food production using appropriate technology, and campaigns to curb the fertility rate.

30.6 **Issues of trade**

Many observers argue that the creation of better opportunities for profitable trade between EMDCs and ELDCs and other groups is of much more vital importance to economic growth in the developing world than purely quantitative increases in development assistance. The Brandt Report (1980), for example, argued for real development-oriented trade, which would enable the development process to be financed in ELDCs. Eliminating poverty, minimising inequality, promoting environmentally sustainable development and improving the quality of life of the mass of people living in ELDCs might turn out to be of more fundamental self-interest for EMDCs too.

Before evaluating the role of trade in development, a brief examination is necessary of the major features of world trade. **International trade** can be defined as the exchange of goods and commodities (**visible trade**) and services (**invisible trade**) between countries (**30.17**). As with any budget, countries have great difficulty in balancing the books, i.e. selling enough by the way of exports of com-

modities and services to pay for all the imports which they especially need during times of economic growth. Many ELDCs have trade balances that are dominated by the export of often a single commodity. One area of growing concern is that the prices of raw materials and cash crops have not risen enough to keep pace with the rise in the prices of oil, manufactured goods and services since the late 1960s. This fact almost automatically ensures that most ELDCs have debt problems in their balance of payments, a fact which has led to a world banking crisis. Adding to the predicament of ELDCs is the volatile nature of global commodity prices; they are constantly rising and falling and generate much economic uncertainty.

The current world trade pattern is a very complex one. As can be seen from **30.18**, world trade is dominated by the OECD countries (the EMDCs of North America and Europe, plus Japan). With high levels of GNP, and sophisticated specialised economies, OECD countries rely on international

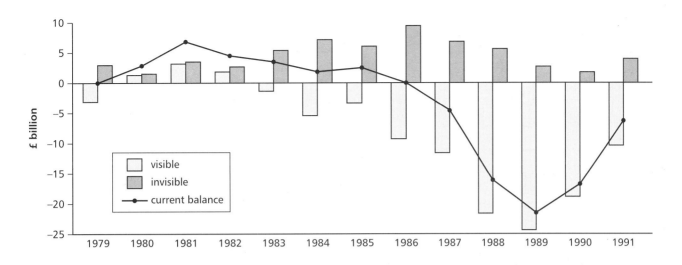

■ **30.17** UK balance of payments, 1979–91

IT7

trade and have very large volumes of both imports and exports. If you look at **30.18**, you can see that the vast majority of OECD trade is between the member countries, largely in manufactured goods. The global car industry typifies this type of trade pattern. Of great concern to many OECD members is Japan's very favourable trade balance, with far more exports than imports – a source of friction between the USA and Japan in the mid-1990s. Three other 'players' in the global trade pattern need to be identified: the centrally planned economies, the oil-producing countries,

and the ELDCs, particularly the NICs.

IT7

As far as trade between EMDC and ELDC countries is concerned, the traditional pattern is the exchange of manufactured goods produced in EMDCs for foodstuffs and raw materials from ELDCs. In spite of independence from colonial links and the embarkation of many ELDCs on industrialisation, this pattern of exchange is still very prominent, largely because of the power of the TNCs. At present, there is very little evidence of much trade between ELDCs, although this will certainly develop in the future as

■ **30.18** Patterns of international trade

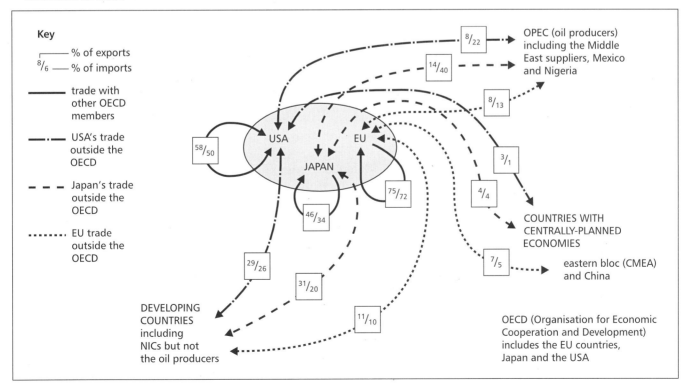

trading blocs form such as LAFTA (Latin American Free Trade Association) and ASEAN (Association of South East Asian Nations).

In 1993 the countries of the world signed a new agreement (GATT4), aimed at encouraging more free trade between all groups of nations as a means of generating further economic growth. There are many arguments in favour of trade liberalisation. Free trade promotes competition and thus lowers production costs, and generates pressures for increased efficiencies, product design improvement and technical change. Free trade allows ELDCs to export many more products to markets previously protected by tariff barriers. At the same time, it makes indigenous industries more vulnerable to floods of foreign products as they are no longer protected.

In contrast, trade pessimists favour greater protectionism, more inward-looking strategies and greater import substitution by indigenous products. They argue that trade will actually hinder aid to the developing world. They support their arguments cogently, saying that export-led growth will lead to a violent balance of payments problem. A whole range of prohibitionist measures exist to

control trade flows; these include tariffs, incentives and quotas.

The key question that needs to be raised now is this: 'Can trade lead to development?' The answer has to be a qualified 'Yes'. It can certainly lead to growth, as shown by the example of the Four Tigers (case study, pages 385–86)), but as shown by the recent take-off in China, quite commonly the wealth ends up in the bank accounts of a small minority (in this case often led by very able Taiwanese expatriates). Trade too emphasises and enhances disparity, as shown again by the regional management problems of the new China. ELDCs will only have the necessary control to secure a fairer style of trade if they form regional trading blocs and operate a policy of collective self-reliance. Such collectives would give the countries of the South more 'clout'.

10 Organise a debate entitled: 'This house believes that more aid and fairer trade is the answer to the development gap'.

30.7 Towards global interdependence

'Global interdependence' is a somewhat idealistic term, but it is nevertheless a very real one. For many ELDCs, dependence on rich nations is, and to an extent always has been, a stark fact of economic life. Equally, the EMDCs now realise that in an age of increasingly scarce natural resources, global environmental threats, burgeoning Third World debt and accelerating refugee and migration problems, they are heavily reliant on how ELDCs manage their affairs. The rich OECD nations increasingly need the market of the populous developing world for their products.

The Earth Summit held in Rio de Janeiro in June 1992 brought together

118 nations, hundreds of environmental organisations and over 10000 concerned individuals to find ways of coping with the permanent environmental damage that has accompanied recent economic developments. Specifically, this meant devising strategies for coping with the effects of the build-up of greenhouse gases, the accelerating loss of biodiversity, and concerns over the environmental consequences of rapid population and industrial growth in the ELDCs.

The Rio Summit produced Agenda 21, a blueprint aimed at cleaning up the global environment and encouraging environmentally sound development in the 21st century. Six very promising fields of international activity were proposed:

- Allocating development assistance to programmes focusing on poverty alleviation, environmental health and meeting basic needs.

- Investing in research and agricultural extension services to reduce soil erosion and permit more environmentally sensitive agricultural strategies.

- Allocating more resources to family planning and to expanding educational and job opportunities for women, so that population growth can be reduced.

- Supporting ELDC governments in their attempts to curtail or modify projects that are known to harm the environment.

- Providing funds to protect natural habitats and biodiversity.

- Investing in R & D on non-carbon energy alternatives to reduce greenhouse gases and curtail climatic change.

As the focus shifts towards sustainable development and EMDCs express concern at some of the environmental impacts of Third World developments, a new form of global interdependence has emerged. In this new scenario, ELDCs can actually apply leverage to international economic and political decision-makers, and obtain money from EMDCs on the grounds of providing a cleaner and more viable world for all. Of all the ELDCs, those of sub-Saharan Africa present the greatest problems (**30.19**). A recent report for the World Resources Institute states:

Sub-Saharan Africa poses the greatest challenge to world development. Recurrent famine there is only the symptom of much deeper ills. Africa is the only major region in the world where PQLI, food production and industrial production have declined over an extended period – the only developing region where development appears to be in reverse. Conventional development efforts by donors and governments have largely failed to halt the spiral, and indeed in some cases they have aggravated it.

Whatever criterion you consider – employment, health, social welfare – Africa lags behind the rest of the world, with 325 million people below the poverty line, 150 million malnourished, 60 million unemployed or underemployed. To this report of human tragedy must be added the enormous potential impact of AIDs: in 1991 the World Health Organisation estimated that 6 million Africans were infected with HIV.

What are the causes of the tragedy, and what can be done? Some causes, such as drought, are beyond control; others – depressed commodity prices, foreign capital withdrawals and diminished aid combined with mounting debt – are rapidly moving beyond control; still others may be ascribed to poor government policies, as for example waging war or neglecting the country's agriculture.

Of equal importance, and a problem exercising more interest and action than the woes of sub-Saharan Africa, is how to help the former republics of the Soviet Union and the countries of Eastern Europe as they make the transition from the constraints of their command economies to some form of capitalism. Initially, chaos and uncertainty have led to economic contraction, with declines in GDP and employment, accelerating inflation and widening trade gaps. The concern is that restructuring and regeneration of these economies will

	1980	1990	% change
Income per capita $	582	335	−42
Consumption per capita $	465	279	−40
Investment % GDP	20.2	14.2	−30
Exports $ billion	48.7	31.9	−35
Food production $ per capita	107	94	−12
Total foreign debt $ billion	56	147	+163
Population below poverty line %	50	62	+24
Share of global trade %	2.8	1.0	−64

■ **30.19** Changes in sub-Saharan Africa

require huge amounts of international finance, and that these funds could be diverted from the developing world (especially from the sub-Saharan region), a situation known as a **crowding-out phenomenon**. Once the economies are realigned, they could themselves have a major impact on world aid, trade and finance within 10 years.

The globalisation of financial services could provide the enabling mechanism for low-income economies to be drawn into the economic mainstream. However, for most ELDCs the global markets for money are very restricted and the mechanisms are loaded against what are seen as bad risks. If ELDCs are to share more fully in the fruits of global progress, reforms of the global system of finance

will be necessary. Reforms could include a reduction in the debt-service burdens, an increase in flows of resources and technology, official development assistance to more ELDCs, and an opportunity for ELDCs to increase their share of world trade. The reforms of the IMF (International Monetary Fund) and the World Bank are also necessary, to revolutionise lending strategies.

The key to solving these challenges lies in the promotion of the 'One World' concept, in which nations and peoples are forged together by a common environmental and economic destiny, and guided by the humane principles of peace, friendship and mutual respect. This is both idealistic, and realistic.

Settlement

31.1 **Settlements – a response to processes**

The large house in Kumasi (**31.1**) is one of several built in various towns by a rich Ghanaian cocoa farmer in the 1940s and '50s. He wished to provide for his children, all of whom he saw through secondary education. Kwesi, one of his 18 children who is now a qualified pharmacist with two chemist shops in Kumasi, still lives in this house.

However, with smaller families now the norm, many of the rooms have been let out and the building is really a tenement block. The **process** (a rich farmer investing in future generations in towns) that led to the building of this **structure** (the house) has changed, and so has the **function** of the building.

The nature of settlements reflects the interaction of process and structure. Although these two elements cannot exist separately, it is their combination that really provides the key to understanding settlements. Processes change all the time, and structures created during one process either change or become obsolete as new processes develop. The case study opposite describes some developments that are typical of English settlements. In order to understand the geography of a settlement, or of a pattern of settlements, anywhere in the world, it is necessary to look at past processes and functions as well as those operating today, and to be especially aware of this constant interaction between process and structure.

■ **31.1** A large house in Kumasi – Kumasi is the capital of the old Ghanaian kingdom of Asante and the traditional centre of cocoa farming in Ghana

■ **31.2** A village in southern England, showing affluent housing, and a council-built estate in the left distance

■ **31.3** A canal warehouse in Birmingham, now a craft centre

1 What evidence is there from the photographs **31.1**, **31.2** and **31.3** of change in the settlements shown?

2 In a group, discuss the following questions with reference to your own immediate locality:
  a What are the most important activities (processes) in the locality?
  b How does the structure (buildings, pattern of roads and paths, etc.) reflect these?

c Have the buildings been modified or have they changed their functions?

d How have these changes accommodated new activities and new processes?

3 Choose an older building and trace its history. Relate the changes in its use and in its structure to what was happening locally and further afield.

CASE STUDY

IT8

Changing process and structure in English settlements

In England there are many examples of changing processes and structures of settlements.

Villages originally built for farm workers are now the home of long-distance commuters and retired people (**31.2**). The cottages have been modified and the life in these affluent homes is very different from that of the original large peasant families.

In many large towns, terraced villas built at the beginning of the 20th century for the aspiring new middle classes of service workers are now the houses of first-time buyers and ethnic minority communities. Again, the lives are different and the structures have been adapted to new needs.

In some industrial cities, canal-side warehouses built in the early 19th century to store bulk goods have been demolished and replaced, but in others they have changed their functions several times, now providing facilities for craft workshops, markets or exhibitions (**31.3**).

31.2 The 'what' and 'where' of settlements

- **Site:** local physical features
- **Location:** position in relation to other settlements, transport links, etc.
- **Size:** area and population
- **Form:** a general term for *structure* and *morphology*
- **Structure:** the layout of the settlement including transport networks and land use zones
- **Morphology:** similar to *structure* but with more detailed attention to type, age, construction and quality of buildings
- **Function:**
  (a) of whole settlement – major activities and functions in the region/nation/world, e.g. mining, manufacturing, retailing, banking, etc.
  (b) the use made of buildings or zones, the processes taking place.

- **Quality of environment:** housing, amenities, density of population, etc.
- **Households:** socio-economic, ethnic, religious characteristics and distribution
- **People:** age, education, employment, income, etc. and distribution
- **Interaction:**
  (a) within settlements – shopping, schooling, employment, leisure activities
  (b) with the surrounding area – journeys to work, retail needs, distribution of goods, spheres of influence of newspapers, local government, etc.
  (c) with the wider world – migration in and out, capital investment, economic, cultural and political links.

■ **31.4** Elements of settlement study

The introduction to process and structure in the section above rather begs the question, 'What is a settlement?' The niceties of a definition are for your discussion (e.g. Is a highland HEP station with accommodation for a caretaker a settlement?), but it can be agreed that usually anything from an isolated farmstead, through a group of buildings with people living there, to a giant conurbation, is a settlement. All these settlements can be studied in a variety of ways, particularly in terms of their form and function (**31.4**).

It has been conventional in geographical studies to classify all settlements as either **rural** or **urban**. Generally speaking, a rural settlement is small, surrounded by countryside, and its people are involved in work on the surrounding land or in the settlement. An urban settlement is large – various population or size thresholds have been suggested to qualify a settlement as a 'town' – but function is a better guide. An urban settlement is likely to have more industrial and large-scale commercial functions. **31.5** suggests some working definitions.

In industrialised nations, this division between urban and rural settlement is now less realistic, as smaller settlements in rural areas are often closely linked to urban centres rather than to the surrounding countryside. Rural areas and their settlements have been increasingly 'invaded' and 'captured' by growing towns and cities. In most countries elsewhere, however, small settlements still have a rural function (see Chapter 32). But no matter where they are located, whether large or small, settlements are a dominant feature of many landscapes, and can be clearly identified on aerial photographs and false-colour satellite images. The activities below suggest ways of exploring them for information.

■ **31.5** Some settlement definitions

RURAL
- **Dispersed settlement:** scattered individual homesteads
- **Hamlet:** very small, a few houses
- **Village:** small settlement surrounded by countryside (but used colloquially in cities for local centres that were once villages)

URBAN
- **Town:** threshold population varies, usually 1500 to 5000, but even up to 50 000 in some countries; other criteria may be used to define 'urban' population, so comparisons between censuses or countries can be very difficult
- **City:** in this text, just a large town – other specialist definitions are used in different parts of the world
- **Metropolis:** largest town or urban agglomeration in a region or country
- **Conurbation:** continuous built-up area formed by expansion and coalescence of previously separate towns
- **Megalopolis:** very large urban spread, containing some open land, formed when conurbations or metropolises link up
- **World city:** large city with major international function

4 Study **31.6** for evidence of the form, function and other characteristics of the part of Kano shown on the photograph.

5 Make a drawing or tracing of part of **31.6** and annotate it to describe the housing in this area.

6 In groups, 'brainstorm' to compile a list of what other information you would need about Kano, about its locality and Nigeria, in order to complete a general study of the city.

7 a See **31.9** on page 434. Trace the outline of Japan and mark on the 12 largest settlements. Use an atlas to name these.
   b Using the evidence of the satellite image, describe the location and spread of large cities in Japan in relation to the relief, land use and vegetation zones of the country.

[Save the results of all these activities for later work.]

■ **31.6** Kano, Nigeria

31.3 Urbanisation and urban growth

Urban settlements can 'grow' in both population and area. Usually towns grow in both ways at once, often swallowing up surrounding small towns and villages. Sometimes a town can grow in numbers without increasing its area, in-filling and high-rise, high-density housing permitting the increase in population on the same land area. On the other hand, in parts of Europe and North America towns are still expanding their areas whilst their populations can even be shrinking.

The classic process of **urbanisation** is taking place when the proportion of people living in towns and cities increases, so that the proportion of people living in small settlements correspondingly decreases. The process took place in England in the 19th century, so that England was highly urbanised even by 1900 with nearly 80 per cent of the population living in towns. **31.7** shows how urbanisation is taking place in a sample of countries around the world. The big difference between the process in

the 19th and early 20th centuries and now is that in countries like Bangladesh and Peru the actual number of people living in rural settlements is still increasing, even though their proportion of the total population is decreasing! **31.8** shows recent changes that have taken place in Latin America and Peru.

It is important to understand, however, that urbanisation is not simply a matter of an increasing percentage of people living in towns and cities. It is a multidimensional process involving physical, economic, social and demographic changes. The more important of these are summarised in urban model A (**31.10**). This is one of a series of models to be found in this unit to explain links between process, function and form. During urbanisation, the various aspects of the process focus activity into core areas which, because they already have some advantages, consolidate their economic and political position at the expense of

■ **31.7** Percentage urbanisation in selected countries around the world

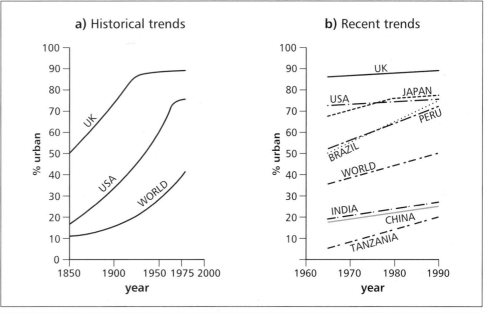

■ **31.8** Urbanisation in Latin America and Peru between 1950 and 1989

millions	Latin America		Peru	
	1950	**1975**	**1980**	**1989**
Population	160.1	319.2	17.3	21.8
Urban	65.4 (41%)	193.0 (60%)	11.1 (64%)	15.1 (69%)
Rural	94.7	126.2	6.2	6.7

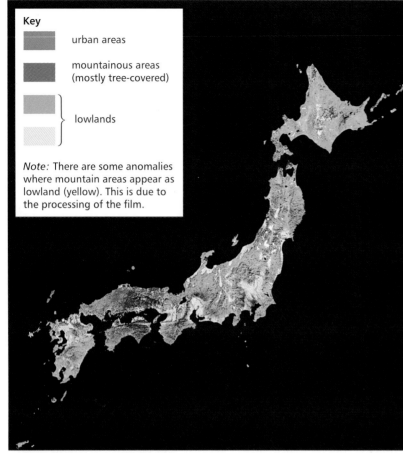

Key

- urban areas
- mountainous areas (mostly tree-covered)
- } lowlands

Note: There are some anomalies where mountain areas appear as lowland (yellow). This is due to the processing of the film.

■ **31.9** Satellite image of Japan

peripheral areas around them. Spatial core–periphery patterns can be seen at different scales, from the global to the local (see section 30.3). For example, at a global scale the European Union, the USA and the north-west part of the Pacific Rim are core areas to the peripheral rest of the world. At a national scale, south-east Brazil is a core area with the rest of the country being peripheral. At a regional scale, Kumasi in Ghana is core to the state of Asante.

A recent feature of urban growth has been the development of many giant cities (**31.11**). Not only have individual cities expanded at a great pace, but they have tended to coalesce. Urbanisation in the 19th and early 20th centuries involved mainly the growth of individual towns. In more densely populated areas, particularly of the developed world, they have since spread to join together into **conurbations**, and these, in turn, have become merged into mammoth **megalopolises**, as along the eastern seaboard of the USA and the Pacific coastlands of Japan, and between London and Manchester in the UK.

■ **31.10** Urban model A: Processes and features of urbanisation

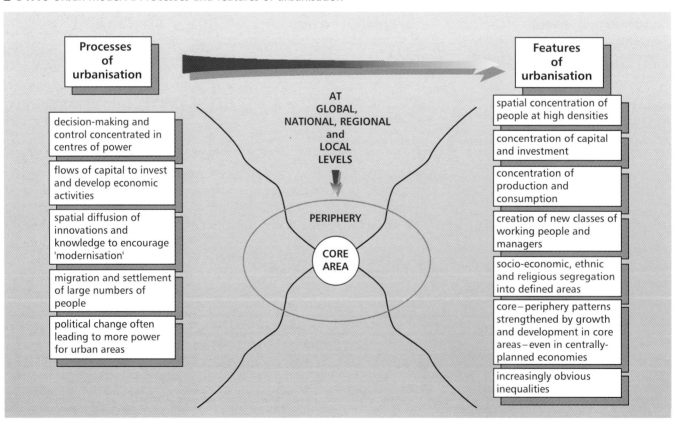

Processes of urbanisation

- decision-making and control concentrated in centres of power
- flows of capital to invest and develop economic activities
- spatial diffusion of innovations and knowledge to encourage 'modernisation'
- migration and settlement of large numbers of people
- political change often leading to more power for urban areas

AT GLOBAL, NATIONAL, REGIONAL and LOCAL LEVELS

PERIPHERY

CORE AREA

Features of urbanisation

- spatial concentration of people at high densities
- concentration of capital and investment
- concentration of production and consumption
- creation of new classes of working people and managers
- socio-economic, ethnic and religious segregation into defined areas
- core–periphery patterns strengthened by growth and development in core areas – even in centrally-planned economies
- increasingly obvious inequalities

- ⊙ >14 000 000
- ● 10–14 000 000
- ○ 5–9 000 000

■ **31.11** The world's giant cities `IT8`

`IT8` Today, urbanisation in Latin America and Asia and, to a lesser extent, in Africa is different, with huge urban agglomerations expanding very quickly and creating their own subcentres for shopping and services as they expand. There seems no limit to the size of these urban areas like Mexico City, São Paulo or Calcutta. This reflects a changing process. In earlier times, only a few cities, perhaps one in each wealthy nation, could draw in resources from far afield and expand into giant cities. But in the late 20th century, with the internationalisation of production, distribution, business and commerce, cities all over the world no longer rely only on the region around them for resources, nor even only on their nation. They are international cities in the sense that they rely on resources from all over the world. Most of them deserve the title **world city**.

Most recently, in nations that have become highly urbanised, with 80 per cent or more of the population living in urban areas, a drift back to rural areas has begun; the process of **counter-urbanisation** has set in. This is a form of population dispersal and economic decentralisation, as opposed to the concentration and centralisation which are the main thrusts of urbanisation. Disenchantment with **urbanism** – the

urban way life – is one cause of this `IT8` trend. The image of large cities as centres of poverty, crime and drugs, promoted by the mass media in North America and Europe alike, encourages this trend. But other factors make it possible. Fast, reliable passenger transport now enables people to live in rural areas and work in towns; the relocation of factories and offices on or just beyond the urban fringe provides work opportunities that are accessible from rural areas, whilst an ageing population, with a greater proportion retired, is free to choose to live in the countryside.

Although this slight drift from towns and cities during the 1980s and early 1990s has been confirmed in many parts of Europe and North America, it may be that the whole concept of separate 'town' and 'country' is misleading and increasingly out of touch with reality. With modern transport and technology, it is more useful to think of urban and rural areas as a **continuum** merging into each other, bound together by a complex web of linkages and interactions. This whole idea is explored further in Chapter 32.

- Centralisation of power to control large areas for food and resources
- Availability of energy (fuelwood, gas, electricity, etc.)
- Organisation of large supplies of water to one place
- Power to collect taxes to pay for public building – roads, drains, sewers, buildings, etc.
- Need for secondary industries to be near to each other to exchange goods and information
- The need for face-to-face contact between business people
- Development of transport technology to move people and goods greater distances more quickly
- Development of rapid personal communication – post, telephone, radio, computer links, fax
- Accumulation of capital, by making profits, which can be invested in building
- Development in the scale and technology of secondary industry, needing many workers in one place
- Development of large business organisations that control widespread activities from one centre and need many office workers

- The attraction of 'bright lights' and entertainments
- The opportunity to meet more people and live an active social life
- More opportunities for employment
- Chance of a better standard of living
- Better health facilities – clinics, hospitals, etc.
- Wider choice of housing including low-cost dwellings
- Better water supply, sanitation and energy supply
- Better public transport
- New technologies in agriculture requiring fewer workers
- Low wages in agricultural and rural work
- Fast growth of population with better health, etc. in urban areas
- 'Snowball' effect of hearing success stories from urban relatives and friends
- Investment by world financial institutions in urban construction
- Image of towns as 'modern' and 'go-ahead'

■ **31.12** Urbanisation cards

8 On a copy of **31.7b**, add to the horizontal axis of the graph and extend the urbanisation curves until each country reaches a highly urbanised state at about the 80 per cent mark. When do you expect each country to reach this state?

9 Represent the data in **31.8** by a graph or diagram.

10 With reference to **31.10**:
  a identify the different processes and explain how each plays a part in urbanisation
  b examine the features of urbanisation which are shown and suggest an example of each
  c explain how each process may be linked to these features.

11 Use an atlas to name the cities shown on **31.11**.

12 Make a copy of the urbanisation cards in **31.12**, and cut them up.
  a Discuss each statement with a partner or group and classify each one as **i** necessary for urbanisation, **ii** a cause of rapid urbanisation, or **iii** a reason for continued urban growth.
[You may feel that some can be in more than one class – overlaps are possible.]
  b Take each group and arrange the cards in a triangular pattern with the most important at the top, the least important at the bottom.
  c Add any other factors you think are important.
  d Display your conclusions on a large piece of paper for class discussion.
  e Link your conclusions to the urbanisation processes listed in **31.10**.

Rank	Population thousands
1	4770
2	1840
3	860
4	500
5	430
6	225
7	167
8	159
9	156
10	149
11	128
12	126
13	101

■ **31.14** Bangladesh's largest towns

31.4 **Settlement systems – continuum or hierarchy?**

A glance at any map shows that there is some kind of organisation to the size and spacing of settlements. Large towns are located further apart than small ones, transport routes from smaller ones feed in branching patterns to larger ones, large towns are linked by major through-routes, and so on. One aspect of this organisation is the relationship between the numbers of settlements of each size. These patterns can be studied by listing the settlements found in an area in population rank order, and then making a graph like that in **31.13**.

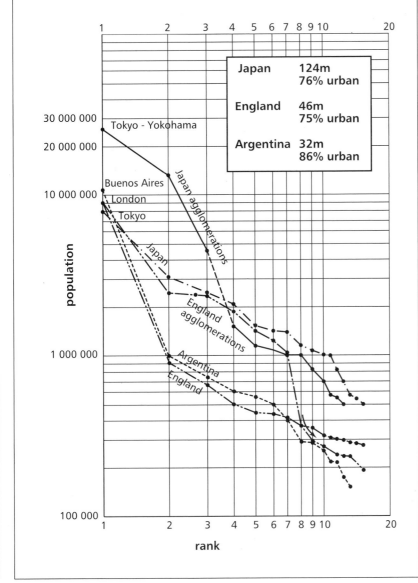

Japan	124m 76% urban
England	46m 75% urban
Argentina	32m 86% urban

■ **31.13** Rank–size graphs for Japan, England and Argentina

How big is a town?

There are problems in defining settlement sizes. Words like village, town and city do not have precise meanings in everyday usage. So when a place is said to have a certain population, it is important to know how the place has been defined. Often administrative boundaries are used – so, for example, the City of Birmingham would include the suburb of Sutton Coldfield but exclude Solihull. Sometimes the edge of the built-up area may be used to define the limits of the town – so the population of the West Midlands conurbation could be used for the 'geographic' town. How did you define the settlements in Japan in activity 7?

The ideas of rank–size rule and central place are based on assumptions of discrete urban settlements, rather than giant sprawls of conurbations.

The rank–size rule: a continuum

One argument suggests that a logical pattern of settlement size would be a consistent 'growth' relationship. Put another way, it means that the second largest town or city would be half the size of the first, the third would be a third, the fourth a quarter, and so on. The populations in **31.13** are plotted on a logarithmic scale, so that if the pattern does conform to this rank–size rule, it will appear as a straight line. Such a pattern is sometimes described as being **lognormal** and that of a **continuum**.

A hierarchy

Another argument suggests that settlements are more likely to develop in a **hierarchy** or vertical class system, with a few very large towns and cities, each serving and being served by several medium-sized towns, each of which, in turn, have a number of small towns located within their tributary area. Due to the clustering of settlements into different size classes, the plot on the rank–size graph would be a broken one rather than a smooth straight line.

Neither of these concepts – the continuum and the hierarchy – is easy to visualise and comprehend. It is suggested that you work through the following activities and then re-read this section.

13 With reference to **31.13**, describe the rank–size relationships of settlements in England, Japan and Argentina. What difference does the use of 'agglomerations' instead of administratively defined towns make?

14 a Draw a rank–size graph for Bangladesh using **31.14** (the towns are marked on **31.17**). Trace the axes from **31.13**, but renumber the population axis.

b Would you say the plotted relationship for Bangladesh is closer to the rank–size rule or to a hierarchy, or is it a mixture, or something else?

31.5 **Central places**

■ **31.15** Possible measures of central-place function and status

Urban population	Measure
< 50 000 50–200 000 > 200 000	Number of different retail functions Number of different wholesale functions Regional or national functions – newspapers, government, health, leisure, labour catchment, etc.

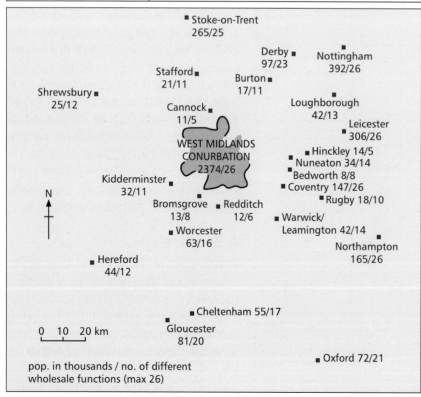

■ **31.16** The distribution of wholesale activities in the West Midlands

Rank–size relationships begin to make more sense when the distribution of the settlements is studied. In Argentina, for example, Buenos Aires dominates the most productive area and is the historical core of the whole nation. It has grown into a **primate city**, being far larger than you would expect from the sizes of other Argentinian towns. This is a reflection of its function. Its sphere of influence and market area are the whole of Argentina. Just across the Rio de la Plata from Buenos Aires is Montevideo. It is another primate city in its own country. One reason why these two large cities were able to grow up close to each other was that each was the capital of a nation, and their ports served different hinterlands.

The spacing of settlements is fundamentally a reflection of their functions as **central places** – as centres of collection, processing, distribution, marketing, financing, and of political, economic and social activities. Each settlement will interact with the area around it, the size of its sphere of influence or tributary area reflecting the importance of its central-place functions.

One simple way to assess the central-place status of a town is to assume that the larger its population the greater its central-place function. This is a good rule of thumb, but not very sophisticated. For example, an important central-place function is retailing; almost every town of over 50 000 population in England provides a full range of retailing functions. So measurement by this specific central-place activity is likely to indicate less of a difference between large towns than might be suggested by the differences in their populations. **31.15** suggests measures you might use in England and Wales to assess the central-place functions and status of towns in order to be able to put them in rank order, or identify a hierarchy if there is one.

15 The rank–size graph for Bangladesh (see activity 14) suggests a gap between the first five or six towns and the rest. How does physical geography help to explain the growth and probable market areas of these largest towns?

[Narayanganj is an industrial port linked commercially to Dhaka, and can be included with Dhaka for this work.]

16 a Draw a rank–size graph for the West Midlands, using information on **31.16**. Use the number of different wholesale functions to rank the towns for the x axis, and the measure of size for the y axis.

  b Define a three-level central-place hierarchy for towns in the West Midlands.

  c Draw a map for each level of your hierarchy showing the probable market area of each town. Start with the highest level, and remember to include the largest towns at each of the lower levels.

  d How do you think the hierarchy will have changed since 1970? Give reasons to support your answer.

[Save your results for later activities.]

31.6 **Spacing of settlements**

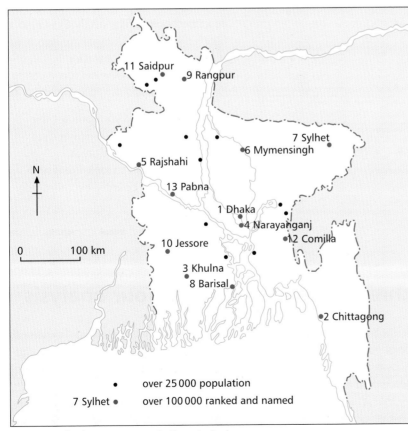

■ 31.17 The largest towns in Bangladesh

- over 25 000 population
- 7 Sylhet ● over 100 000 ranked and named

The spacing of settlements reflects the area needed by each to provide its resources and a market for its goods and services. Obviously, larger settlements tend to be spaced further from each other than smaller settlements. The main factors influencing the spacing of settlements can be summarised under two headings:

1 In a given area the *distance* between settlements will partly depend on:
  - the density of population
  - the means of transport available
  - the size of the settlements being studied
  - the productivity of the area.

2 In a given area the *spacing* of settlements (even, random, clustered, linear) will reflect:
  - transport routes
  - variations in the landscape
  - variations in the productivity of the landscape
  - the availability of water
  - the need for defence.

IP2

■ **31.18** England's largest towns

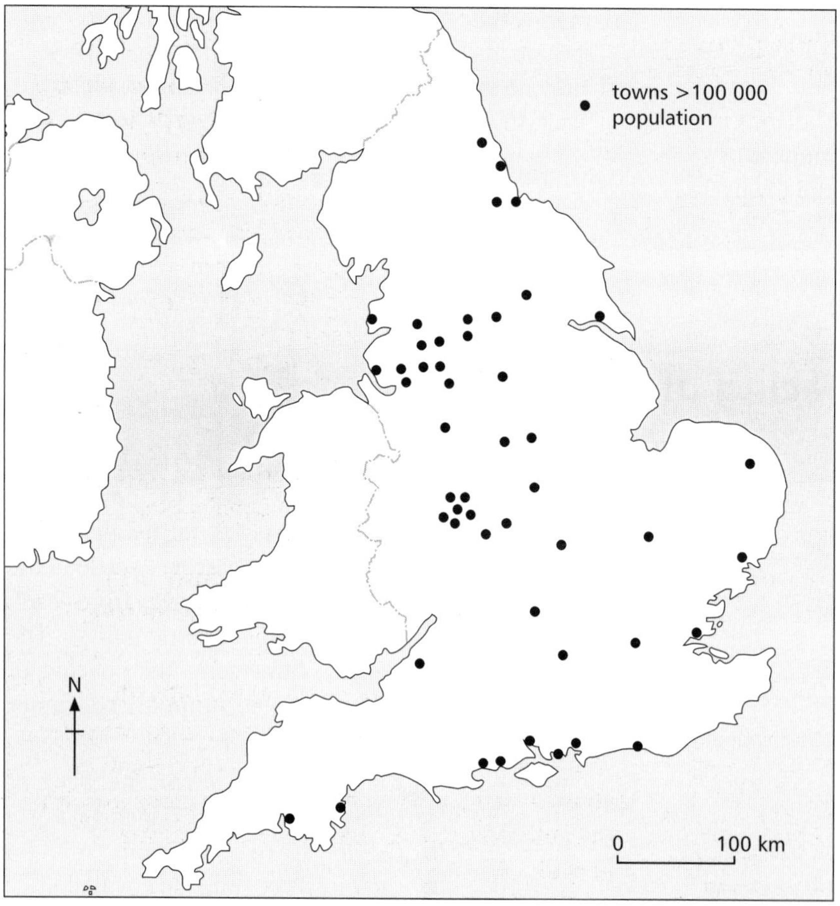

Bangladesh and England are countries with approximately the same area (England 130000 km² and Bangladesh 144000 km²), but Bangladesh has more than twice the population. At the same time Bangladesh is about 22 per cent urbanised, whilst England is over 80 per cent urbanised. In England, Greater London accounts for over 20 per cent of the population; at present Greater Dhaka, estimated variously at 6 to 7 million, accounts for about 5 per cent of Bangladesh's population.

IP2

By eye, the largest towns in Bangladesh seem quite evenly spaced (**31.17**), particularly when compared with the distribution pattern in England (**31.18**). It is possible to measure spacing using the distance from each settlement to its nearest neighbour. The technique, known as **nearest-neighbour analysis**, is described below. The analysis is also a very good way of comparing one area or distribution with another.

towns >100 000 population

N

0   100 km

20 What would you forecast the spatial pattern of towns over 100 000 population in Bangladesh to look like if and when the country becomes fully urbanised?

31.7 **Techniques: Nearest-neighbour analysis**

IP2

Using a simple formula based on probability, nearest-neighbour analysis gives an index which shows how far the measured pattern of settlement is from being a 'random' one – that is, a pattern generated by chance. Greater or lesser index values indicate that the pattern has a tendency to

be either evenly spaced, or clustered. The index value runs from 0 (highly clustered) to 2.15 (evenly spaced); randomness occurs around a value of 1.0 on the scale. [The results for an analysis of towns over 100 000 in Bangladesh are given below at each stage.]

IP2

1 Decide on the boundary of your study area. Calculate the area in km². [Bangladesh: 144 000 km²]

2 Decide on the size of settlement to be studied. [Towns over 100 000]

3 Measure and tabulate the distance in kilometres from each place to its 'nearest neighbour'. Remember that some may be 'reciprocal pairs' – each other's nearest neighbour – and the distance must be counted each way. [Table of 13 measurements]

4 Calculate the mean distance to nearest neighbour. [71 km]

5 Compare this with the random distance by using the formula to calculate the index R:

$$R = 2D\sqrt{(N/A)}$$

where D = the mean distance
N = the number of places
A = the area
[$R = 2 \times 71\sqrt{(13/144\,000)} = 1.35$]

6 Look up your value for R on the probability graph (**31.19**) to assess the significance of the result.

[1.35 for 13 points – just significantly 'evenly spaced' at the 95% probability level; this even pattern would have occurred less than five times in a hundred by chance.]

■ **31.19** Nearest-neighbour graph

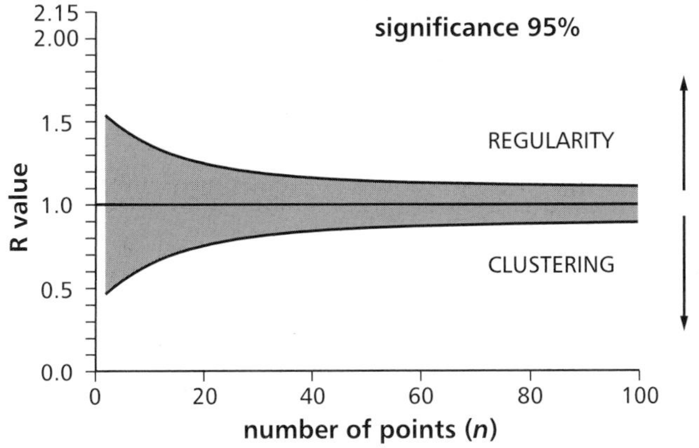

21 Using **31.18**, calculate the nearest-neighbour statistic for towns in England with populations over 100 000. Compare your result with that for Bangladesh. What conclusions do you draw from the comparison?

22 What difference would it make to your findings in activity 21 if 'continuous built-up area' is used to define separate 'towns' in England?

23 Look back at your work on Japan (activity 7). Use an atlas and reference book to find the size of the towns you identified, and the population density of Japan. Measure the nearest-neighbour distances of the towns. Compare your results with those for Bangladesh and England. What similarities and differences emerge?

24 Calculate the nearest-neighbour statistic for towns with population over 25 000 in Bangladesh.
  a Are the towns evenly spaced?
  b Are there areas where towns are closer than expected, or where towns seem to be 'missing'?
  c Can you explain these variations?

25 Look back at your work on the West Midlands (activity 16). Measure the average distance between wholesale centres in the first and second levels of your hierarchy. How does this pattern compare with the national patterns you have been studying above?

Rural Settlement

32.1 **In the beginning**

'Village' and 'town' are terms commonly used the world over. They trigger contrasting mental images, to the extent that one might think that there is a clear and easy distinction to be made between them. The popular perception is that a village is a relatively small, reasonably compact settlement made up of people primarily concerned with agriculture. In contrast, the town may be characterised as being larger, also compact, but with its population engaged in non-agricultural activities, especially the provision of a range of services from shops through to hospitals. But pause a moment – is the distinction that simple? The village also offers services, albeit of a low-order calibre, such as a general store, a pub and a surgery. Traditionally, village people have also been involved in basic secondary activities, albeit mainly linked to farming – milling, leather-working or spinning

and weaving. Processes of change, particularly in the developed world, are currently blurring the distinction between village and town to an even greater degree. The spread of commuting means that many town and city workers now live in what are termed 'villages'. Counterurbanisation is encouraging the flow from town to village not just of people, but also of what are customarily regarded as urban activities, such as information-based offices. In the developing world, processes of modernisation are also having an impact on rural settlements and in so doing are eroding the village–town distinction.

The first human settlements were those of hunters, fishers and gatherers and were probably natural shelters like caves, or tents and huts constructed from local vegetation and skins. Present-day hunters, gatherers and shifting cultivators live mainly in small but nucleated settlements like that in **32.1**, or sometimes in large communal dwellings like the long houses of the Dyaks in Indonesia. Though the individual settlements are small and usually occupied by an extended family, there are wider tribal groupings and strong similarities between settlements. Early pastoralists were often nomadic and, like today's nomadic peoples, probably lived in tented camps that they carried with them. However, once permanent cultivation became the norm, dispersed settlement of smaller family groups became more possible with people naturally living on or close to the land they tilled. Permanent structures were built and the remains of some of these have survived many thousands of years. How far these early settlements were simply extended family homes or housed wider social groups is difficult to say.

■ **32.1** An Amazon Indian settlement

Site: the actual land upon which the settlement is built.
Morphology, form: the type of buildings and the layout of the settlement.
Function: *of a building* – what it is used for.
　　　　　　 of a village – what it does, what activities take place there.
Nucleated settlement: buildings and farms in clusters.
Dispersed settlement: farms and houses spread across the landscape.

■ **32.2** Rural settlement vocabulary

32.2 Nucleation and dispersion

Some basic settlement vocabulary is given in **32.2**. Most rural landscapes today show skeins of dispersed settlement interspersed at intervals with larger, nucleated settlements. There is some argument in many areas as to whether the dispersed settlement came first or whether it infilled between the larger villages later. The spatial pattern or character is one aspect of rural settlement that particularly concerns the geographer.

The reason for the division of rural settlement into these two fundamentally contrasting types – nucleated and dispersed – was originally thought to be a cultural one. The village in Europe was seen as an essential part of the Germanic settlement tradition. Many, but not all, of the lands colonised and settled by the Saxons, are dominated by nucleated settlements. In contrast, the dispersion of settlement into single, isolated farmsteads was viewed as part of the Celtic cultural tradition.

32.3 gives some indication of how difficult it is to generalise about the distribution of these two contrasting types of settlement pattern within Britain. The map also suggests that other factors should be taken into account when attempting to explain their distribution. **32.4** lists some of the factors that ought to be considered. It might be argued that where water supply was limited and derived from springs or wells, where farming was concerned with crops rather than livestock, and where there was some division of labour within society, then settlement nucleation was to be expected. Alternatively, where water supply was ubiquitous and where farming was largely to do with livestock, then the isolated farmstead was to be expected as the settlement norm. In short, the character of settlement may be seen as a response to climate, the type of farming and social and economic organisation. On this last count, it is suggested that arable farmers do not need to tend their fields with the same frequency as pastoralists need to tend their livestock (for example, milking needs to be done twice a day). Thus the former do not incur serious costs as a result of living some distance from the fields, but the latter do. From this it follows that arable farming is more likely than livestock-rearing to be associated with nucleated settlement.

■ **32.3** Rural settlement in Great Britain

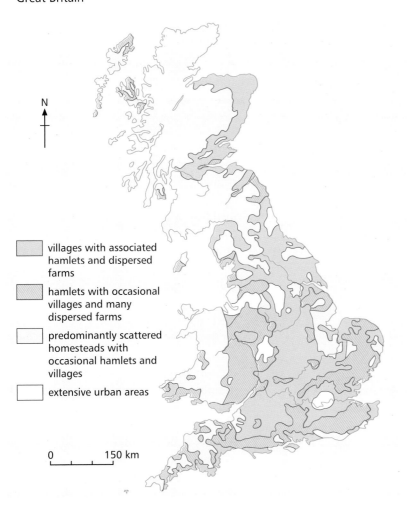

N

villages with associated hamlets and dispersed farms

hamlets with occasional villages and many dispersed farms

predominantly scattered homesteads with occasional hamlets and villages

extensive urban areas

0   150 km

Site availability and requirements – the need for a defensive site, and for a flat, dry site.

Resource availability – the difficulty of getting supplies of fuel, water and building materials at sites; the potential fertility of the land.

Land ownership and control of a large area by one person or organisation – planned building of settlements for workers and intentionally empty land.

Production methods – the number of people needed for rural activities, how frequently they need to visit specific areas, cooperative working of the land.

Technology – farming methods and their impact on agricultural productivity; ability to exploit other resources; available means of transport, the mobility of people and commodities.

Social organisation – the strength of the family and the way in which the local community is geared to farming and other rural activities.

■ **32.4** Some factors influencing the tendency to dispersion and nucleation

1 In rural areas, do you expect the density of population to be higher where the settlement is nucleated or where it is dispersed?

2 a Look at **32.5** and **32.6**. The average density of population in the Mulbagal District is 160 people/km². For comparison, look at an OS 1:50 000 map of an area of British upland where the settlement is dispersed. Make a map of 1 km² like that of the Kisumu area (**32.6**). Assess the density of population.

  b Write a statement about the relationship between rural settlement pattern and population density.

3 Taking each factor in **32.4** in turn:
  a Describe a situation for each that would tend to produce a nucleated rural settlement pattern.
  b Would the opposite in each case lead to a dispersed pattern?
  c In your study of a British upland in activity 2, which of these factors played a strong part?

4 From the information on the Kisumu area (**32.6** and **32.7**), what factors may have influenced the settlement pattern there?

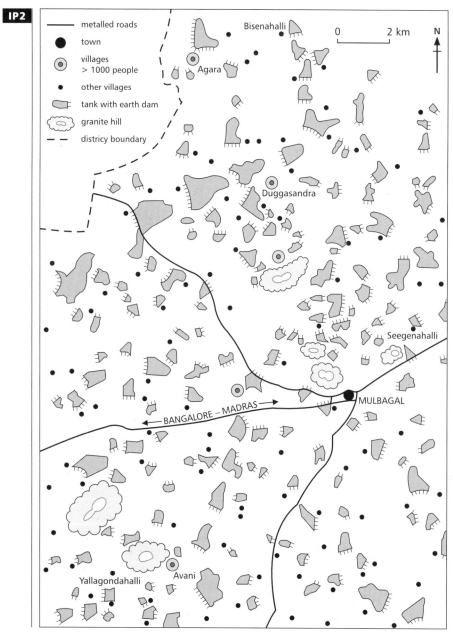

■ 32.5 The Deccan area of India

IP2

Legend:
— metalled roads
● town
◉ villages > 1000 people
• other villages
tank with earth dam
granite hill
- - - distric boundary

0 — 2 km   N

Bisenahalli
Agara
Duggasandra
Seegenahalli
MULBAGAL
BANGALORE – MADRAS
Avani
Yallagondahalli

Land ownership has also been a significant influence on the pattern of rural settlement. In many places, a ruling class of large landowners has emerged as a high caste or aristocracy, or invading conquerors have assumed control of large areas. In England, the manorial system of huge estates often involved the lord of the manor building and organising a settlement to house his workers in one place. There is similar nucleation in other parts of the world, for example on the latifundia of Latin America, and the cooperative farms of the former Soviet Union. It has also been promoted by various elite groups such as the high-caste Hindu landowners in India, the Asantehene and chiefs of Asante in Ghana, and so on.

The history of an area may often involve a succession of changing cultures, with each making an indelible mark on settlement and economy in particular, and the landscape in general. In England, successive waves of invaders – Romans, Saxons, Vikings, Normans – have all left their imprint on rural settlement, sometimes creating new villages, or taking over established ones, or introducing wholly new ideas about the organisation and layout of settlement. They have all been part of a **sequent occupance** of the landscape (**32.8**).

Once initiated, nucleated settlement would seem to generate is own multiplier effect. Assuming that farming methods improve and output per unit

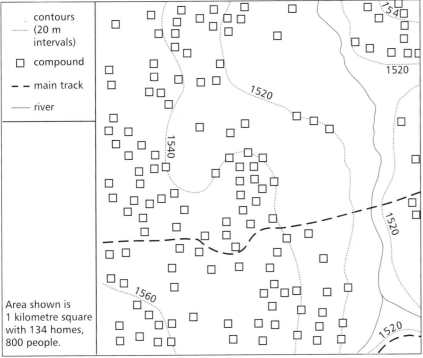

32.6 The Kisumu area in Kenya

Legend:
- contours (20 m intervals)
- □ compound
- – – main track
- —— river

Area shown is 1 kilometre square with 134 homes, 800 people.

32.7 A Sunday morning visitor joins in with the tree cutting near Kisumu – most compounds include a *shamba* (smallholding)

32.8 Lake District place names

area increases, then population growth may be anticipated and the support of higher population densities made possible. Established villages become larger, new villages may be established and there might be some dispersal of farmsteads spread across intervening areas. Other factors reinforce the nucleation tendency. Specialisation in crafts like metal-working and basket-weaving, and into tasks like sheep-shearing, gradually develop, with the workers usually living in the larger villages. Goods and services – food, fuel, seeds, markets, schools, etc. – would also be needed as rural population increased, and increased transport needs would have to be met. All these processes of change would interact in such as way as to encourage some villages, particularly those in favoured locations and with good accessibility, to grow into sizeable nucleated settlements.

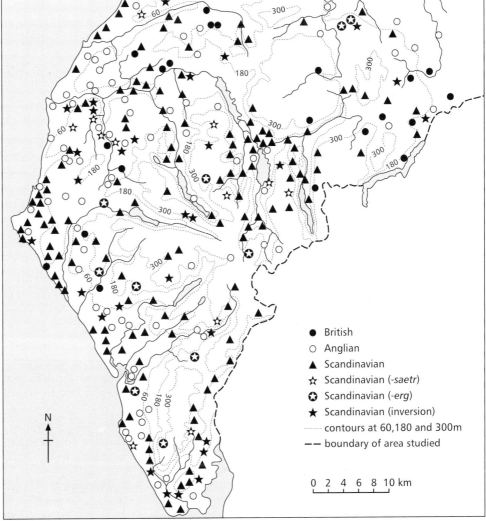

Legend:
- ● British
- ○ Anglian
- ▲ Scandinavian
- ☆ Scandinavian (*-saetr*)
- ✪ Scandinavian (*-erg*)
- ★ Scandinavian (inversion)
- ······ contours at 60,180 and 300m
- – – boundary of area studied

0 2 4 6 8 10 km

5 a What were the characteristics and distribution patterns of villages founded by:

   i the British and Romano-British

   ii the Anglo-Saxons

   iii the Scandinavian settlers in the Lake District (**32.8**)?

b What are the main differences? Suggest some reasons for these.

The model outlined above perhaps implies that with the passage of time, the nucleation tendency in the settlement pattern is reinforced. It is important that such a generalisation is qualified, for it is quite clear that in many parts of the world forces of dispersion have been, and still are, at work. A classic study by the French geographer, Demangeon, identified four types of dispersion:

- *primary dispersion* – long-established and an essential feature of original colonisation and settlement, as in the Celtic areas of Western Europe

- *intercalated dispersion* – where there is a mixture of villages and isolated farmsteads, with the latter interspersed between the former, as in many areas of England (see **32.3**)

- *secondary dispersal* – a gradual break-up of nucleated settlements as a result of economic, social and technological change, as occurred in England following the enclosure movement and the abandonment of the open-field system of farming

- *recent primary dispersal* – a contemporary phenomenon associated with the colonisation of less favoured terrain or the occupation of new territories, as on the island of Hokkaido, Japan.

We will return to the dispersal of settlement in sections 32.5 and 32.6, when discussion focuses on the processes of change currently affecting rural settlement.

32.3 **Morphology**

Homesteads and houses

The key ingredient in settlement morphology is the buildings themselves. Their design (architectural styles and building materials), together with their spatial layout and functions, profoundly affect the visual appearance and general 'feel' of all settlements. **32.9** identifies some of the factors influencing the design of homesteads.

Most rural dwellings around the world reflect the needs of an extended farming family living and working together communally, often with a patriarchal head of household. Hence we see surviving to this day the compound in Africa, the courtyard house of China, the *bari* in Bangladesh, and to a lesser extent the farm and farmyard in England. Of course, not all residences in rural settlements are like this. Many farm labourers not owning or renting land, and people involved with services and specialisation, live in houses without agricultural functions.

■ **32.9** Some influences on the design of homesteads   **IP2**

Cultural and religious traditions – how many people live together; what the matrimonial arrangements are; when younger people leave to set up new homes; how separate are the lives of different subsections of the family.

The local physical environment – what building materials are available; what weather-proofing is needed; how water is made available; what special site requirements there are (e.g. steep slopes for defence, river bank for water and access, etc.).

The economic activities of the family – what animals have to be housed; what fodder and crop storage is required; what machinery has to be stored; what space is needed for non-agricultural activities.

Affluence and availability of resources – will affect sanitation facilities, repair and upkeep, quality of construction, size of homestead.

Local tradition – can strongly influence the architecture and design.

Often small houses are built for landless farmworkers and poorer families. In India, for example, a village typically has an area of poorer housing for Harijan people, whilst in England the affluent village has its council estate.

But rural settlements are organic, living things. They are subject to the processes of change. Change may be an expansion of functions, as new activities (such as fishing or a craft industry) are taken on in order to supplement the livelihood derived from farming. Those new activities may well require purpose-built structures, such as a quay, warehouses and workshops, which add to the fabric of the settlement. Similarly, changes in lifestyles, like those for Bangladeshi rural women, can cause change in homestead design and layout (**32.10**).

The role of women in Muslim society varies from country to country in the Islamic world, depending on their housing and culture.

In rural areas of Bangladesh, women traditionally keep to their own family area. For most daily activities they are confined to their *bari*; if not that, then they undertake tasks nearby like collecting water and tending animals. Men work in the fields and do the shopping.

Women from the poorest families have always had to work for wages or help in the fields. Recently, more people have become landless, and divorce is becoming more common. So now more women, not just from the most deprived household, are seeking employment outside their neighbourhoods. That work may not be connected in any way with farming, and may be in a small factory in a nearby town or in some form of service.

As women find work outside the home, so this may be expected to bring about changes in the design and equipment of homesteads. Equally, the breakdown of the extended family often associated with divorce increases the overall demand for housing, and changes the type of housing in demand. The demand will be for smaller dwellings, not necessarily with any land attached.

■ **32.10** Women's space is expanding in Bangladesh

6 What evidence is there of the influence of each of the factors in **32.9** on the design of the Malinke compound (**32.11**)?

7 How does **32.10** help to explain the design of a *bari* in Bangladesh (**32.12**)? What changes may modernisation be bringing to Bangladeshi homestead design?

8 Annotate a sketch of **32.13** with questions about the reasons for the design of the settlement.

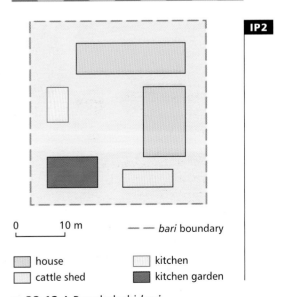

Plan and section of a Malinke compound:

△	well
◯	grain stores and other stores
Ⓚ	kitchens
Ⓗ	halls
▢	terraces
° °	hearth
—	high walls
🌳	tree
◯	round huts with conical thatched roofs

living rooms:

W	wife
B1–B6	brothers
M	mother
U	uncle
Y	young people
G	guests
S	servant

Section from A to B

■ **32.11** Plan and section of a Malinke compound: Dialakhoto in Mali

0   10 m   — — *bari* boundary

▦ house		▢ kitchen
▢ cattle shed		▣ kitchen garden

■ **32.12** A Bangladeshi *bari*

32.13 A typical scene in a Bangladeshi village

some 'home-based' cottage industry, a warehouse or a mill. In many parts of the developing world, the additional new structures may be a video cinema or a workshop for the repair of motor vehicles and agricultural machinery.

The social divisions and economic structure of the society, and the culture, religion and history of the people, make all the difference to the style and patterning of these buildings. Great variety is possible not just from region to region, but within a small area.

IP2

Three villages in the Mulbagal District of southern India show this cultural variety (**32.5**). Bisenahalli is the most isolated (**32.14** and **32.15**). Yallagondahalli is a high-caste Brahmin village, home to priests, teachers and university graduates as well as farmers, but also has a large Harijan ('untouchable') community (**32.16** and **32.17**). Seegenahalli is nearest to the town of Mulbagal, and part of its community is Muslim (**32.18** and **32.19**).

Village form and shape

Villages are essentially clusters of homesteads and take their character from them. But gradually additional buildings are drawn into the agglomeration as the growing and changing needs of the local people are met. It may be a church or temple, a school, a meeting place, a shop or market hall, premises to accommodate

32.14 Bisenahalli, Mulbagal District, Karnataka in south India: population 350

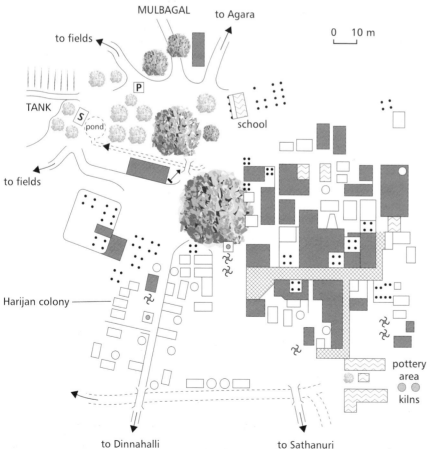

key to **32.14, 32.16, 32.18**

	Housing
	stone
	tile/brick
	thatch/mud
○	thatch/mud kitchens
⠒	open-sided barns
	paved area
—	walls
⊙	wells
P	water pump
S	shrine
▬	earth track
	banyan trees
∿	palm trees
	other trees
---	water courses
➤	photo viewpoint

IP2

Bisenahalli – same place, different story

Bisenahalli is a small village on the Deccan Plateau. The local farming relies on monsoon rains and irrigation from water saved in tanks. These are often dry from January to May. It is about three hours' journey from Mulbagal. About 300 people live here, including 70 primary school age children.

Description A

The buildings are all single-storied, many roughly thatched with reeds, and mostly built from sun-baked mud bricks. Some better, larger, houses are of stone – granite is quarried locally.

The houses have few windows, and the rooms are usually low and dark. The floors are made of cow dung. There is no furniture. The animals (cows, bullocks, goats, sheep) sleep in, or close to, the houses.

Electricity has not reached Bisenahalli, and there is no piped water or sanitation. Human excrement is found in the fields near the village, and the use of water in the home is limited because it has to be carried from the central village pump. Very few adults are literate and only 30 per cent of the children attend school – although there is a building and a teacher. The villagers have poorly-balanced diets and little understanding of nutrition or medicine.

There are one or two well-off farming families, but most villagers are only labourers and have no permanent employment. They labour all day with implements that have not changed for years. The economy is very inefficient and production per person is low.

Description B

We bought our house 15 years ago for the equivalent of a year's wages (which we borrowed from the owner), and since then I have replaced the thatched roof with granite slabs and strengthened the walls with granite pillars. It is a very sound house. We have added a separate kitchen and have no trouble with smoke in the main room.

The village pump provides clean water. We have no bathroom, but we all know where to go in the fields. Scavenging animals, especially pigs, clean up a lot, and the hot sun quickly sterilises any dung left. Personal cleanliness is very important and we are glad of a good water supply.

The house and patio are kept washed and swept. We sit cross-legged on the floor to relax, and sleep outside on reed mats for much of the year. We spend a lot of time outside – after work we eat and chat in front of the house. We farm a share of my family's land, but it only provides about half our needs. In the dry season there is no farm work and we must look for coolie work. This year there is work digging a well at a neighbouring village, and I, my wife, and eldest daughter (14 years old) work there most days. We are lucky to have a few animals which my 10-year old son looks after, so we have some milk each day.

9 Information about the small village of Bisenahalli is given in **32.14** and **32.15**, whilst the case study provides alternative descriptions of the village.
   a Which of the descriptions do think comes nearer to 'the truth'?
   b Who do you think may have written each piece?

10 Yallagondahalli and Seegenahalli are quite close to Bisenahalli (all are marked on **32.5**). What are the main differences in their locations?

11 Make copies of **32.14–32.19**, and present an annotated display to describe and, where possible, explain the differences and similarities between the three villages.

12 Using large-scale maps and/or fieldwork, complete a study of an English village. From interviews or your own ideas, complete two accounts of the village from contrasting viewpoints.

■ **32.15** A general view of Bisenahalli

■ **32.17** A Brahmin street in Yallagondahalli

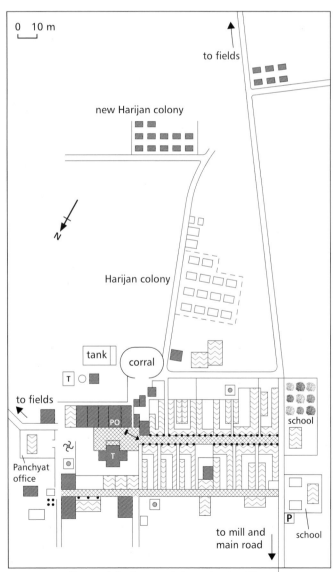

■ **32.16** Yallagondahalli, a mainly Brahmin village: 350 people, 70 houses (30 Harijan). For key see **32.14**

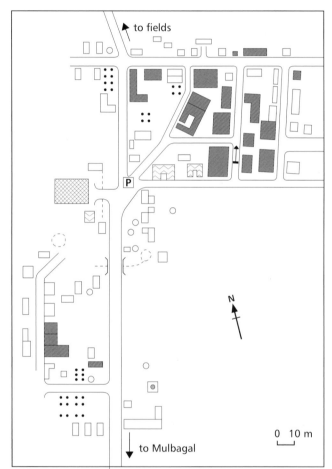

■ **32.18** Seegenahalli: 160 families (70 Muslim)

■ **32.19** Early morning on a Seegenahalli street

The shapes of villages are closely related to the physical environments in which they are located. For example, a narrow valley floor or ridge could only accommodate a linear settlement unless efforts are made to build on hill slopes – often costly and difficult in engineering terms. In lowland and plateau areas, where physical conditions are less constraining, villages may be expected to be reasonably compact and rounded, but possibly with some extensions along better roads. Often a focal point will be provided by a pond or an open space, particularly if the watering, grazing and security of livestock are important considerations. The origins of the village ponds and village greens that survive in many parts of England may be explained in this way.

Classifications of village form in Western Europe have been derived on the basis of three characteristics: shape, regularity, and the presence or absence of a village green. Two basic shapes are recognised – linear and agglomerated – whilst regularity refers to the spacing and strictness of alignment of rows of buildings.

13 a Consider the relevance of the three criteria to a classification of rural settlement in any area of the developing world of which you have some detailed knowledge.
b What other criteria might you introduce into the classification?

32.4 **Function and community**

So far in this chapter, the emphasis has been on the physical aspects of rural settlement. There are two other, equally dynamic aspects that should now be brought into focus. The first is the general role of the individual rural settlement – the functions that it perfoms. The second concerns the social relationships which develop between inhabitants – in other words, the way in which the individual settlement constitutes a community. These two dimensions of function and community are interrelated. This might be illustrated where the prime function of a settlement is farming. In this activity, there is mutual benefit to be derived from a degree of give-and-take, of cooperation, between farmers, whether it is pooling labour or machinery or just helping out in times of difficulty. All this generates neighbourliness which is a powerful bond that spills over into the social realm. Outside work, inhabitants of the settlement will gather together for entertainment and relaxation. Worship in the context of a common religion will also help this process of welding individuals into a cohesive community.

Although villages and other rural settlements are to be seen as being concerned first and foremost with agriculture, it should be recognised that villages in particular also function as central places. They provide a varying range of goods and services, not just to the villagers, but also to people living in outlying, often dispersed settlements. Four types of service are conspicuous:

- *commercial* – shops, a post office, possibly a bank, money lender
- *social* (public) – a doctor's surgery or health post, a primary school, a hall
- *social* (private) – voluntary societies, such as a youth club, a women's group, a young farmers' club
- *service industry* – a garage, or agricultural machinery workshop.

It is common for rural settlements gradually to broaden their economic base from an initial preoccupation with farming and food production. The most common pathway is for settlements to enter the secondary sector by beginning to process local agricultural produce. The textile, leather and milling industries

■ **32.20** Many of the compounds in Wonoo, Ghana, have their own weaving loom

now famous for certain crafts such as weaving, gold and silver-working, and wood carving, were encouraged in the 19th century to supply the Asantehene and his palace with these particular craft goods. Clearly, not only were they successful in meeting those particular demands, but as a result of doing so the economic momentum and skills gained have been sufficient to maintain their specialisation to the present day. Of course, they now sell to a wider market, which might include overseas tourists in search of ethnic souvenirs.

Clearly, any expansion of the economic base of a village is likely to have social repercussions; the community and its institutions may well be forced to make adjustments. An obvious example from Europe are the so-called **dormitory villages** which have emerged as part of the commuting revolution. This has permitted a growing body of people with town-based jobs to live in villages and the countryside. Socially, such villages can all too easily become polarised. The existence of two factions – the newcomers and the 'natives' – threatens the cohesion of the community. The newcomers may well bring different values, different codes of behaviour and have different social needs.

were generally launched in this manner. Alternatively, a special skill or craft may develop for some reason, and ultimately become the main function of that place, bringing to it a special reputation and status within the settlement system of the region. For instance, in south India, in Mulbagal Talug, there is a village known as 'the minstrel village', from which come many musicians and travelling singers. Less attractively, there is also 'a thieves' village'! These villages probably developed their specialities through generations, but some villages have become specialised by decree. In Asante in Ghana, some villages around Kumasi, like Wonoo (**32.20**), which are

32.5 **Change**

Villages in South Asia and Africa, like Bisenahalli in India and Dialakhoto in Mali, are traditional rural settlements, but even they are now responding to global forces of modernisation. The integration of their economy into regional and national systems, better communication with urbanised areas and easier movement of people and goods, mean that change is more likely and faster (**32.21**). Capital investment is a vital part of modernisation, making higher agricultural productivity possible, which in turn can make more investment available. So a multiplier is initiated, in that the additional capital can be used for a diversity of purposes. It might be used to

further improve agricultural practices and therefore productivity. It might be invested to launch secondary activities, either related to farming (milling, food processing and canning, etc.) or wholly new. Equally, it might be invested in the provision of more and better services.

As early as the 1950s, many villages in the UK and Europe already enjoyed a modern infrastructure of roads, water, sanitation, electricity, telephone and good commercial and social services. Since then, modernisation has meant something quite different and the changes involved have been no less profound than in the developing world

A In Africa and South Asia	B In the UK and Western Europe
Clean water made available	Already supplied
Proper sanitation installed	Already installed
Electricity supply provided	Already provided
Telephone connection	Already available
Primary school opened	Primary school closed
New place of worship	Reduction in church services
Shops and post office opened	Services withdrawn
More low-cost housing	More expensive housing
Houses improved/repaired	Farms/barns converted to dwellings
New agricultural schemes	Fewer working farms
More road traffic	More road traffic
Fewer young people	Fewer young people
New health centre	Doctor's surgery closed
New businesses	New leisure and tourist amenities

■ **32.21** A comparison of the typical features of village modernisation in different parts of the world

IT8

(**32.21**). Recent modernisation has gone hand in hand with a decline in the farming function, but has been compensated in part by new functions. For example, people are using the British countryside more and more for leisure and for other activities (**32.22**). At the same time, villages are becoming increasingly occupied by people who have taken the conscious decision to leave town. The growing volume of urban–rural migration is a key part of the process of counterurbanisation. Ironically, though, these and other changes may be seen collectively as effecting what might be described as 'urbanisation' of the whole countryside, not just its rural settlements. It is only in a superficial sense that the changes may be seen as a return to, or a revival of, grass

Farming
- Increasing use of factory-farming methods
- Large-scale arable mechanisation
- High output per worker and per unit area
- Fewer farms
- Land taken out of use because of surplus production

Recreation and leisure
- Controlled but open access to the countryside
- Provision of purpose-built facilities (car parks, information centres, hotels, etc.)

Settlement
- Planned villages as urban extensions
- Dwellings purchased as second homes

Land use
- Infrastructure to serve urban areas: water supply, sewage treatment and disposal, electricity generation, new roads and motorways, airports
- Decentralisation and delocalisation of industry and services
- Factories and warehouses built on greenfield sites near motorways
- Retail services located outside towns

■ **32.22** Characteristics of the 'urbanisation' of the countryside

roots. All that they are achieving is a blurring of the distinction between urban and rural, converting the urban–rural continuum concept into reality.

IT8

CASE STUDY

IP1, IT8

The urban–rural continuum in Japan

The interdependence of town and country in Japan today has become quite complex. Urbanising influences now affect rural settlements in ways other than labour recruitment through commuting. The permanent migration of members of rural households into towns and cities has gathered such momentum that there has been a breakdown of traditional family life. The outward diffusion of urban values and the urban lifestyle into rural settlements and the countryside has brought a more materialistic outlook.

The old values of mutual obligation and cooperation have become so diluted as to threaten the unity and stability of life in villages and hamlets. Improved transport, more leisure time and greater disposable income place other pressures on the countryside as increasing numbers of urban dwellers take weekend breaks and annual holidays in rural areas. These urbanising influences are most strongly felt in areas nearest to the largest cities and decrease with distance to give rise to an urban–rural continuum (**32.23**).

So important is this urban–rural interaction, particularly the former on the latter, that recent studies of Japan's rural geography have sought to analyse the character of the remaining rural space in terms of the type and scale of the urban elements that it contains. Thus **32.23** covers the transition from rural areas and settlements distinguished by varying levels of commuting to nearby towns and cities, through areas marked by different degrees of reliance on farming and different types of self-employment, to really remote rural areas almost wholly devoid of people and employment opportunities.

a) Types of rural space

U = dominant urban element
R = dominant rural element
u = minor urban element
r = minor rural element

b) Model of the urban–rural continuum and the distribution of different types of rural space around a metropolis

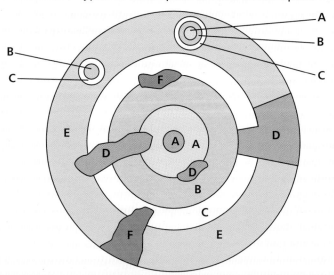

Type of space	A Urban	A Suburban	B Urban shadow	C Peripheral	D Highly agricultural	E Remote	F Self-employment
Landscape	U + r	U + R	u + R	R	R	R	U + R
Employment structure	U + r	U + r	U + R	U + R	u + R	U + R	U + r
Type of off-farm employment	←————— commuting to city jobs —————→ ←—— daily wage labour ——→ ←seasonal→ ←—self-—→ migratory employment work						
	highest – degree of intensity – lowest						

■ **32.23** The urban–rural continuum in Japan

---

14 Modernisation in rural Africa and South Asia maintains the village as a centre of agricultural activity and a focus for development and income generation.
  a Draw a diagram to show how the features in column A, **32.21** are related to agricultural improvements, business developments and improved living conditions.
  b Take each group of changes from your diagram. Who will benefit in a village like Bisenahalli?

15 The typical English village has almost lost its agricultural function and is a dormitory settlement for urban workers, a home for retired people, and a rural recreation centre. Put the features in column B, **32.21** into groups on a venn diagram showing social, economic and environmental changes.

16 Draw an annotated map of the village you studied in activity 13 to identify features like those in **32.21**, and comment on their effect on the people of the village.

17 a Using OS maps and/or fieldwork, investigate a rural area near to a British conurbation. The information in **32.22** may help you to assess the importance and impact of the urbanisation of the countryside in that area.
  b How far does the area you studied show the characteristics of urban–rural continuum suggested by the study of Japan (**32.23**)?

18 In what way is the urban–rural continuum (**32.23**) related to urban model A (**31.10**)?

32.6 Planning rural settlements

IT4

In many peripheral regions, there is a long-established force for change in rural areas. It relates to the loss of population, particularly of younger, more go-ahead people, attracted by the better opportunities and lifestyle perceived to exist in nearby towns and cities and repelled by the unemployment and poor services prevalent in remote, rural areas.

Mitchell (**32.24**) has suggested a fourfold classification of rural communities based on two criteria:

1 The extent to which the rural settlement and its community have been receptive to outside influences and to change.

2 The extent to which there is evidence of an integrated community feeling.

In the UK and other parts of Western Europe, there has been intervention in rural settlements and the countryside in two contrasting scenarios:

1 peripheral rural areas experiencing depopulation and economic decline

2 rural areas coming under particular pressure from such process changes as the spread of commuting, counter-urbanisation or the growth of recreation and tourism.

In the first, the aim is to halt the downward spiral and to create an environment that will retain people and businesses and perhaps even attract newcomers. A high priority has been to rationalise service provision, so that services are not withdrawn altogether, but are concentrated in **key settlements**. By concentrating services in fewer locations, service thresholds can be maintained and the benefits of scale economies reaped. In the longer term, the hope is that the key settlement becomes a growth centre, generating spread effects rippling out over larger areas of the periphery. Investment in transport infrastructure has been another common strategy, but there are concerns that improvements in accessibility can be double-edged – they do make rural settlements and the countryside more accessible, but they also make it easier for people and businesses to leave.

In the second scenario, the aim is generally to preserve the existing character of settlements and to ensure that they are not overrun by developments. Intervention is largely in the form of planning policies which seek to restrain. These can range from a complete restriction on growth through to the sanctioning of only limited growth. British planning devices in this context include green belts (wrapping a protective 'corset' around a village) and the designation of conservation and heritage areas within villages.

IT4

■ **32.24** A typology of rural communities

1

The open, integrated rural community

Usually large in size and diverse in occupational structure. In its institutional and organisational framework the community is able to adapt to changing conditions.

2

The closed, integrated rural community

Characteristic of the most isolated areas with little change in the population. Inward-looking, self-contained and traditional, maintaining firm boundaries against outside influences. Within the community, the roles of people are well defined and there are observed limits on the range of acceptable social behaviour.

3

The open, disintegrating rural community

There is a rapid rate of change which the community cannot assimilate. There are strong external linkages, and internal conflict is the result. This is the situation where greatest disagreement arises between local people and newcomers.

4

The closed, disintegrating rural community

Usually occurs where depopulation has undermined the standard village services and engendered a feeling of despair amongst the inhabitants as the established order progressively breaks up.

19 Find out about rural planning policy in your home county. What is the general thrust of that policy, and how is it being achieved?

20 Classify a village known to you, and identify what you consider to be its needs so far as planning is concerned.

33.1 **Is this a town?**

In the previous chapter, reference was made to the urban–rural continuum in Japan. Elsewhere, the differences between town and country are becoming blurred. The countryside is becoming urbanised, and efforts are being made by local authorities and their planners to make towns more environmentally friendly with open spaces, trees and vegetation. Indeed, planners in south-east England have begun to talk of the **spread city** as an emerging future settlement form. Spread city is not a sprawling metropolis, but a closely linked network of relatively self-contained towns that offer the best of urban and rural lifestyles. So far such areas house mainly affluent people in counties like Hertfordshire and Surrey.

In many parts of the world, however, the division between town and country remains clear enough. Here, the debate is not so much as to where 'urban' ends and 'rural' begins, but rather about the classification of settlements as 'villages' or 'towns'. Population can be used as a basis for differentiation, with an arbitrary population threshold, sometimes 1000 or 2500 inhabitants, defining villages. Use of this criterion implies that the distinction is purely a matter of size. Even if one does believe in the validity of this criterion, it must be conceded that the precise threshold value will vary from country to country, from region to region. It will do so according to the prevailing level of population density and the general scale of the settlement system. Simply put, the higher the level and scale, the higher the size threshold is likely to be. If on the other hand the view was that a town was in some way more 'important' than a village, then what the settlement does (i.e. function) should be the criterion for drawing the boundary between town and village.

Chainpur is a settlement of a few thousand inhabitants in the mountains of western Nepal (**33.1** and **33.3**). There are no roads to Chainpur, there is no wheeled transport in the region and all movement is on foot. Goods, and sometimes sheep, are carried by porters along narrow trails. The settlement itself has no paved roads.

IP2

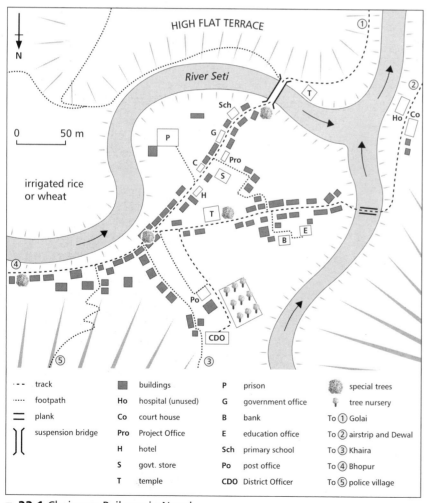

- - - track	**P** prison	special trees
····· footpath	**Ho** hospital (unused)	**G** government office	tree nursery
= plank	**Co** court house	**B** bank	To ① Golai
suspension bridge	**Pro** Project Office	**E** education office	To ② airstrip and Dewal
	H hotel	**Sch** primary school	To ③ Khaira
	S govt. store	**Po** post office	To ④ Bhopur
	T temple	**CDO** District Officer	To ⑤ police village

■ **33.1** Chainpur, Bajhang in Nepal

1 a Locate the photo **33.2a** on the map **33.1**.
  b Make a simple sketch of **33.2a** and annotate it to describe the site of Chainpur.

2 From the map **33.1** and photos **33.2**:
  a describe the morphology of Chainpur – its layout, the style and construction of its buildings, etc.
  b list the individual functions of Chainpur and describe its overall function.

3 'Chainpur is small, but definitely a town.' Explain why this may be so.

4 Find a settlement in your home region with about the same population as Chainpur (say around 2500). What functions does it perform? Is it a town?

5 Find a settlement in your home region with a similar range of functions as Chainpur. What is its population?

a) A general view

b) The main street

■ **33.2** Aspects of life in Chainpur

c) Most goods are carried by porters in Chainpur

d) Rice distribution from the government store

6 What is the difference between the pattern of the growth of Paris between 1857 and 1908, and the pattern since 1908 (**33.4**)? Look at the radial spurs and the outlying settlements for each stage. Why are there these differences?

7 From **33.5**, what seem to be the main constraints and stimuli for rebuilding in the central areas of a European city?

8 Study the growth of your home town or a town near you. Compare the boundaries of the town today with a map of, say, around 1960. Visit areas of recent growth: Are they all similar? What are the main land uses? Who owns the land? Does this make much difference to land use and the style of buildings? Who lives there? Does the area integrate with the older town? Generate more questions about the newer developments by talking to local residents. Evaluate the effect of recent changes.

33.2 **The nature of towns**

Modern towns and cities often seem to have little in common but their diversity. There are the mega-cities of the world, vast assemblages of people and concrete with their pockets of extreme wealth and extreme misery. There are still a few single-industry, working-class towns in poignant contrast, and there are opulent stockbroker-belt towns and villages, rural representatives of the new international financial system. There are desert retirement communities. There are heritage towns and cities pandering to the tourist dollar. There are cities which are centres of government and the military. The list goes on and on.

Nigel Thrift, 1989

Large towns, or cities, are very complex and very different places, but there are recurrent underlying processes at work. Urban model B shows one aspect of these processes linking the changes in the main functions of towns through history to specific parts of their form (**33.3**). Before we study these and other processes in detail, it is important to experience some of the variety and complexity mentioned by Thrift. The remainder of this section therefore presents five brief city case studies, each providing different kinds of information about process and form: Paris (age and growth); Dhaka (tourist information); Tokyo (urban structure); Birmingham (unemployment); and Kumasi (housing).

Outside Europe, urban growth patterns tend to be different. In Africa, South Asia and Latin America, for instance, many towns have either remained as compact indigenous settlements, or retained their European colonial mould until well into the 20th century. Now they are expanding very rapidly, leaving the old native or colonial town in the centre dwarfed by huge areas of recent growth. Dhaka, the capital of Bangladesh, is like this.

■ **33.3** Urban model B: Urban function and form through the ages

Function	→	Form
Trading	→	Market
Government, defence	→	Castle
Spiritual needs	→	Church, temple
	↓ 1600	
Services based on technology, science and social organisation	→	University Hospital Banks/brokers Entertainment
	↓ 1750	
Manufacturing – (Industrial Revolution)	→	Factories, warehouses, workers' housing
	↓ 1950	
Delocalisation of industry – back to services, information and advanced technology	→	Banks, insurance Entertainment Meeting places Suburban sprawl

IT7

Paris – city growth and the age of buildings

The growth of Paris since 1857 is fairly typical for a large European city (**33.4**). Many long-established towns were contained within their medieval defensive walls for centuries before the Industrial Revolution gave them the impetus to 'break out' through their gates and to expand along main routes. Once a town had spread beyond its walls, adjacent open spaces were infilled with buildings, and growth generally continued in concentric zones with 'legs' extending out along important radial routes. Surrounding settlements grew larger, but were progressively engulfed by the outward-spreading built-up area. New settlements might be built further out in the countryside, but they too stood the risk of subsequently being swallowed up by the relentless march of the built-up area.

Paris shows this process and pattern of growth; it is also very evident in the large extensions that have been added to the city in the 20th century. Not only has the population more than doubled since 1908, but in each new generation of suburbs, people have expected not only modern housing with up-to-date amenities, but also more living space than was available in the inner city. For this reason, residential densities generally decline with increasing distance from the city centre.

To some extent, the age of buildings in a city gives evidence of its growth. In many cities, concentric growth zones can be identified, especially when war or recession has caused breaks or stationary periods in construction activity. In Europe, the two World Wars slowed down construction in towns and cities, so that boundaries between pre-1914, 1918–39, and post-1945 building are often very obvious, and define recognisable inner, middle and outer zones.

The age of buildings need not correspond exactly to the urban growth stages. Buildings in towns and cities are constantly being replaced and updated, so even in the oldest parts towards the centre there are modern buildings and road patterns. **33.5** shows how much of central Paris was in fact rebuilt between 1954 and 1974. In this particular case, as in many European cities, the need to rebuild was increased by the need to rectify large-scale damage to the urban fabric suffered as a result of bombing and street fighting during the Second World War.

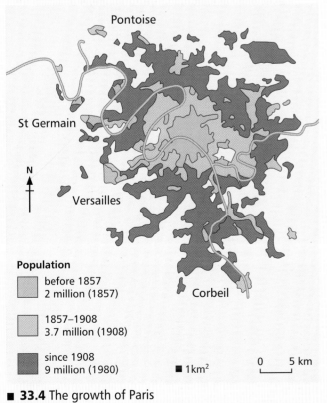

Population
- before 1857 / 2 million (1857)
- 1857–1908 / 3.7 million (1908)
- since 1908 / 9 million (1980)

1km² ⬛ 0 5 km

■ **33.4** The growth of Paris

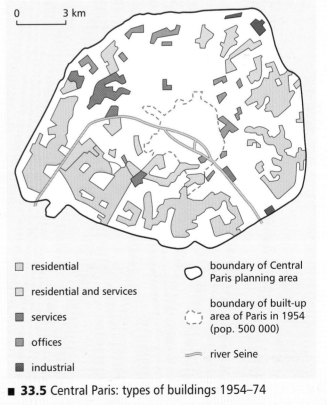

0 3 km

- ☐ residential
- ☐ residential and services
- ■ services
- ▨ offices
- ■ industrial
- ⬯ boundary of Central Paris planning area
- ⌇ boundary of built-up area of Paris in 1954 (pop. 500 000)
- ∼ river Seine

■ **33.5** Central Paris: types of buildings 1954–74

IP2, IT6

Dhaka – tourist information

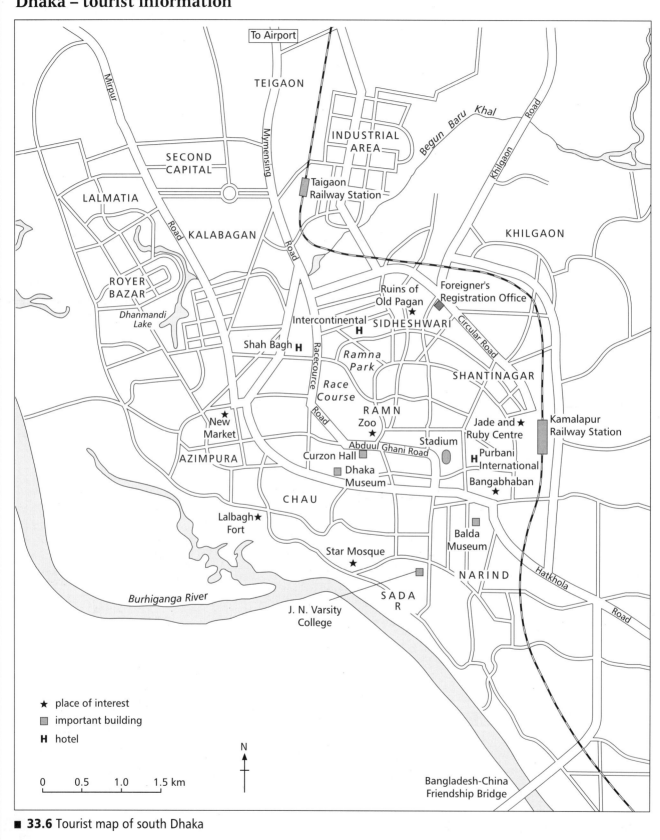

■ **33.6** Tourist map of south Dhaka

Mogul Dhaka was an important city in the 16th and 17th centuries, but was only 1 km by 2 km in area; it was centred on the area now occupied by J. N. Varsity College (**33.6**). In 1921, the population was still only 120 000; today it has risen to between 6 and 7 million and its built-up area extends to at least 340 km².

The tourist map of south Dhaka provides an excellent simplification of the road network and plenty of landmarks. In some of the streets (see for instance the scene in **36.8** on page 502) it may be more difficult to follow, but such a map gives basic information on the plan and structure of the city. Certainly, it shows the powerful influence which the main roads and railway have had on the northward extension of the city. Equally, the waterways of the delta area have made an impact, both attracting waterfront development in the south-east and repelling development to the west and south-west. In the latter case, it is the high risk of flooding which has deterred any building. There is no doubt that the demand for urban space has been such that in significant parts of the present built-up area, demand has outweighed the risk factor, so that large numbers of people have to live with the threat of regular inundation.

9 Use **33.6** to suggest some zones within south Dhaka that have a particular function.

10 Suggest a feasible itinerary for getting to know the parts of the city shown on the map.

CASE STUDY

IP1, IT7

Tokyo – land use zones

Urban land use maps like **33.7** are commonly used by planners and geographers to enable them to study the structure of cities and link to that structure the processes taking place. This map shows only the Ward Area of Tokyo (the equivalent of Central London), not the great metropolitan region of Tokyo–Kawasaki–Yokohama. You can see that maps of only one part of a metropolis could be misleading.

The vital point raised by **33.7** is that in all towns and cities there is a spatial sorting of

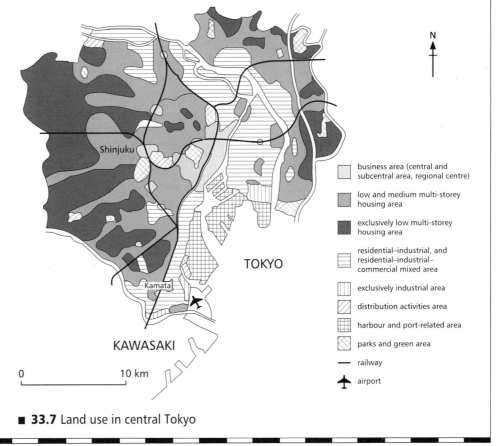

business area (central and subcentral area, regional centre)

low and medium multi-storey housing area

exclusively low multi-storey housing area

residential–industrial, and residential–industrial–commercial mixed area

exclusively industrial area

distribution activities area

harbour and port-related area

parks and green area

railway

airport

0   10 km

■ **33.7** Land use in central Tokyo

land uses. Similar activities tend to agglomerate; dissimilar activities tend to segregate. The result is that the land use or functional map of any town or city shows a mosaic of small regions, each specialising in a particular activity or group of related activities. Generally speaking, the larger the urban settlement, the finer and more clear-cut is this spatial sorting. As a process, it is initiated by the workings of the urban land market (see section 33.4), but it can also be enhanced and modified by the intervention of urban planners. Here in central Tokyo, the planners have **zoned** particular parts of the Ward Area for specific functions; in the case of housing areas they have indicated the type of residential development to be encouraged. The map is a kind of blueprint – it shows the sort of end-product that the planners are aiming at through the medium of development control and other intervention devices.

> **11** With reference to **33.7**, how would you describe the spatial distribution of:
> **a** high and low multi-storey housing
> **b** residential/industrial and residential/commercial/industrial mixed areas?

CASE STUDY

IT5

Birmingham – unemployment and deprivation

Social and environmental conditions are most important elements of city life. Mapping social information brings out the contrasts within cities and shows the concentrations of wealth and of deprivation that are typical of capitalist cities. **33.8** shows the dreadful unemployment situation for males in the inner city, a state of affairs in danger of being taken as 'normal' in Britain's economy and in many other industrialised 'rich' nations. Information like this is vital if the functioning of cities is to be understood and geographers are to contribute to improving the situation.

According to the 1991 census, in Birmingham as a whole, male unemployment was 17 per cent, but amongst ethnic minority people, many of whom live in the inner city, the rate was 27 per cent. Such figures expose the stupidity of the racist myth of 'people from abroad coming and taking all our jobs'. On the other hand, the opposite myth – 'they come here and refuse to work' (strangely enough often suggested in the same breath!) – is confounded by data from a place like Knowsley, Liverpool, where male unemployment was 27 per cent in a population classified as 99 per cent 'White'.

Concentration of deprivation is to be found around the centre of most European and North American cities, no matter who lives there. Needless to say, unemployment is but one of a whole series of deprivation indicators; others include housing conditions, personal health and education (see section 36.6). Geographers should study the political and economic power structures that create such situations, and must make judgements about the justice of such processes.

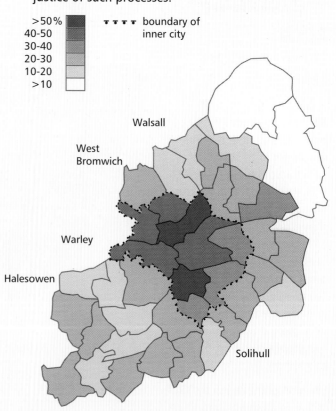

■ **33.8** Male unemployment in Birmingham, 1993

IT5

Kumasi – housing types and their distribution

Housing is an important factor in people's quality of life, and the distribution of different types provides an indication of the structure of a city and of social differentiation within it.

Kumasi is a city of over half a million inhabitants and the capital of the old Asante Kingdom in central Ghana. As in most rapidly growing cities, it is difficult to provide sufficient and adequate housing quickly enough, and the City Council is stretched to keep pace and provide a modern infrastructure. **33.9** provides information about the four main types of housing (see **33.10**).

	No. of people thousands	Population density per ha	Size metres	People per building
Tenements	140	350		40–100
Indigenous	320	200	30 × 30	20–50
Government	100	50	30 × 30	8–15
High-cost	40	10	30 × 30	5–10

■ **33.9** Housing areas in Kumasi

The tenements (see **31.1**) are typically two to four storeys high and often built around a central courtyard. The

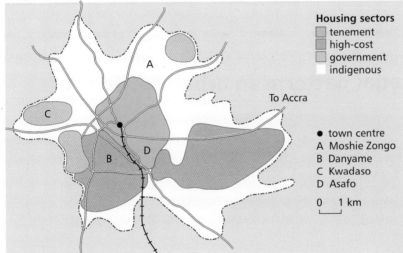

■ **33.10** Kumasi housing areas

Housing sectors
- tenement
- high-cost
- government
- indigenous

To Accra

● town centre
A Moshie Zongo
B Danyame
C Kwadaso
D Asafo

0   1 km

■ **33.11** High-cost housing in Kumasi

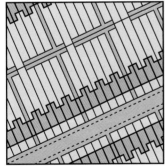

Terraced housing
Population density
140 persons/ha
Residential population density
140 persons/ha

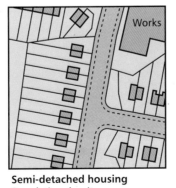

Semi-detached housing
Population density
80 persons/ha
Residential population density
100 persons/ha

0   100 metres

Detached housing
Population density
30 persons/ha
Residential population density
40 persons/ha

Each map shows one hectare of land.

■ **33.12** Housing types in England

indigenous housing comprises single-storey, traditional compounds with interior courtyards, shared by four to ten families. The new government areas are also single-storey buildings, but each is shared by one to three families. High-cost areas contain a variety of spacious single-family dwellings (**33.11**).

The distribution pattern in Kumasi shows that tenements dominate the central area of the city. A resort to vertical development is one way of increasing the housing capacity of the area. It is also a response to the relatively high cost of land in this most pressured part of the city. There are two distinct areas of high-cost housing to the south and east of the centre, taking advantage of some of the more physically attractive areas of the city's site. For comparison, **33.12** shows types of housing commonly found in British towns and cities.

12 In Birmingham, the spatial pattern of deprivation is fairly clear. Would you say the same is true for Kumasi?

13 Compare the main types of housing found in a city like Birmingham (**33.12**, and also multistorey flats) with those in Kumasi (**33.9**). What do you see as the advantages and disadvantages of each type?

14 Find out about the patterns of unemployment and housing in your local town or city, and discuss the implications of these patterns in the fight against deprivation.

33.3 Spatial patterns in urban settlements

Basic urban spatial patterns

- *Concentric zones with the CBD at the centre* Such zones tend to be related to town growth and to land values. In most towns, the highest land values are concentrated at the centre where accessibility and competition for land are greatest. Only certain types of land use are able to afford the most expensive rents.

- *Sectors radiating out from the centre* Usually related to physical features like valleys where land may be cheaper because of flooding, and to transport routes (which often follow physical features). The transport routes may be more or less attractive to certain land uses.

- *Patches (or 'multiple-nuclei') of varying size* Sometimes related to physical features like hilltops or terraces, or to areas engulfed by an expanding city, but frequently the result of decisions to segregate certain functions, types of housing, ethnic and religious groups from others. Also related to functions that require a large area.

Different criteria may be mapped to identify patterns, but the most widely used is generalised function (residential, industrial, services, open space, etc.) with some subdivision of residential into types of housing or social class. Analysis of spatial patterns of age of buildings, employment, wealth or quality of environment are just as rewarding.

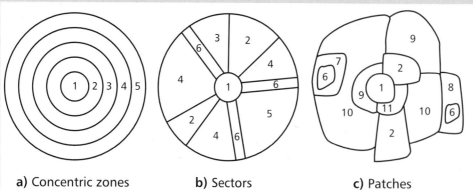

Key showing possible uses in each pattern

1 town centre (CBD) – shopping, offices, etc.
2 industry and warehousing
3 high-density housing
4 low-density housing
5 very low-density housing
6 shops, offices, etc. outside the town
7 ethnic quarter
8 colonial town
9 workers' housing
10 middle-class housing
11 government and administration

a) Concentric zones   b) Sectors   c) Patches

■ **33.13** Urban spatial patterns

■ **33.14** Mann's model of the British city

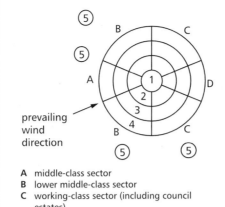

prevailing wind direction

A middle-class sector
B lower middle-class sector
C working-class sector (including council estates)
D industry and lowest working-class sector
1 CBD
2 transition zone
3 zone of small terraced houses in sectors C and D; larger by-law housing in sector B; large old houses in sector A
4 post-1918 residential areas; with post-1945 housing on the periphery
5 dormitory towns within commuting distance

IT7

The mapping of the information about each of the cities studied above reveals a spatial pattern. Such patterns have been used as the basis for the creation of urban models which might help the understanding of urban geography. Several of these models were developed in the USA and have since been found to be useful in understanding particular places, at particular times, rather than in understanding all towns and cities. The most famous is Burgess' concentric zone model based on Chicago in the 1930s. Others include Hoyt's sector model, the multiple nuclei model of Harris and Ullman, and Mann's model, the only one based on the British city (**33.13** and **33.14**).

It should be stressed that models are both generalisations and simplifications. They make certain simplifying assumptions, such as the prevalence of an isotropic surface, in order to bring into clearer focus those factors that have a major impact on the urban pattern. For example, the Burgess model stresses the importance of distance from the centre. The sector model draws attention to the significance of radial routes leading from the centre, providing important axes of urban growth. The multiple nuclei model simply underlines the tendency of similar activities and similar types of people to agglomerate within the built-up area (**33.13**). Mann's model is a compromise, for it combines the two factors highlighted by the concentric zone and sector models – that is, distance and direction from the centre (**33.14**).

It is generally agreed that the above models apply only to the towns and cities of the developed world, and that because of different circumstances the developing world merits its own model.

■ **33.15** Models of cities of the developing world

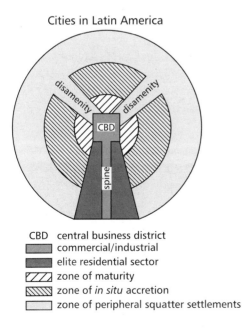

Cities in Latin America

CBD central business district
commercial/industrial
elite residential sector
zone of maturity
zone of *in situ* accretion
zone of peripheral squatter settlements

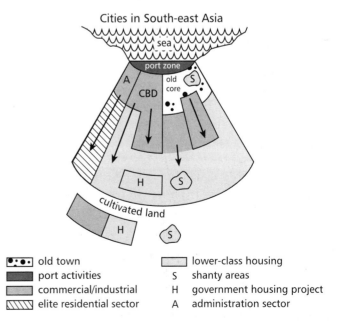

Cities in South-east Asia

old town
port activities
commercial/industrial
elite residential sector
lower-class housing
S shanty areas
H government housing project
A administration sector

Again, there are dangers of over-generalisation, but **33.15** is one suggestion. In a similar vein, although the 'Second World' is now in a state of collapse, socialist principles were applied for long enough to have a significant impact on the structure of towns and cities in Eastern Europe and the former Soviet Union. **33.16** shows Hamilton's model, which recognises at least seven different structural components inherited from the 'socialist period'. It is interesting to speculate what amendments will have to be made to the model as states move away from hard-line communism.

■ **33.16** Hamilton's model of the growth of a socialist city

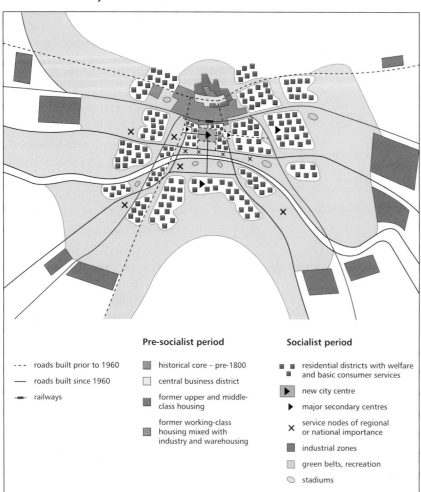

Pre-socialist period	
- - -	roads built prior to 1960
——	roads built since 1960
⊢⊣	railways

	historical core – pre-1800
☐	central business district
	former upper and middle-class housing
	former working-class housing mixed with industry and warehousing

Socialist period	
▪ ▪	residential districts with welfare and basic consumer services
▶	new city centre
▸	major secondary centres
×	service nodes of regional or national importance
	industrial zones
☐	green belts, recreation
⬭	stadiums

It is well worth identifying the spatial patterns of towns and cities. By studying the pattern, and in particular by comparing it with the models, it becomes possible to work out some of the reasons for the town or city being as it is. We can identify what have been the most powerful influences in moulding that particular urban pattern. Viewed in another way, it might be claimed that elements of the three different patterns shown in **33.13** can be detected, in an infinite number of different combinations, in the patterns of many towns and cities all over the world. However, it also has to be conceded that the pattern of each town and city has an element of uniqueness – the product of processes working on a unique inheritance from the past, moulded by a unique set of physical conditions and driven by a unique combination of activities and people. But such an admission of uniqueness is not to deny the existence of common processes operating the world over.

15 a Working in a group, compile a list of major functions common to towns in the UK (e.g. shops, factories, etc.). Break down each main category into a few subcategories. Write each function on a card. Arrange the cards into rank order (equals are possible) based on **i** their need to be accessible to the town's population as a whole, **ii** their need to be accessible to people living outside the town, and **iii** the willingness of owners/entrepreneurs to pay a high price or rent per m² of land to carry out the function. Make a note of your three rankings. To what extent do they coincide?

b Given a concentric pattern of land values in a town, with the most expensive land at the centre, what pattern of functions/land use would you expect from your rankings?

c How does this compare with the pattern of functions/land use in your local town?

16 Examine the maps of Paris (**33.4**), Tokyo (**33.7**), Birmingham (**33.8**) and Kumasi (**33.10**).

a What spatial patterns do you identify in each? Discuss possible explanations for the patterns you find.

b How do these compare with patterns in your local town?

17 Identify and try to explain the differences between Mann's model of the British city (**33.14**) and the model of the city in the developing world (**33.15**).

33.4 Urban land values, locational needs and spatial sorting

IT7

In most towns and cities of the world, the spatial patterns both of activities and people are conditioned above all by land values and the workings of the urban land market. At one time, notable exceptions would have been the urban settlements of the now largely defunct 'Second World', but as countries shake off communism, so their towns and cities will become more exposed to the market forces that characterise capitalism. **IT7**

All that is necessary here is to grasp two interrelated points. The first is that land values or rents vary within the built-up area, generally declining outwards from the centre, but also maintained at relatively high levels along major arterial and ring routes in the urban transport network, and particularly so at intersections (**33.17**). Like the town centre, these are places of enhanced accessibility and for this reason they command greater value. Secondly, the various urban land uses differ in terms of (1) their locational needs and (2) their bidding power on the urban land market and the degree to which this is affected by distance from the centre. Each urban land use has a distinct **bid-rent curve** (**33.18**). For example, retailing needs sites that are readily accessible both in terms of attracting customers and recruiting labour. Since retailing is a capital-intensive user of space, it commands considerable bidding power on the urban land market; it can afford the most expensive sites.

If we put these two observations together, we can begin to understand that similar activities come together within the built-up area because they have the same locational needs and can afford the same general level of land values or rent. Thus it is that retailing and other businesses (particularly offices) tend to cluster at the centre, and by so doing define a central business district (CBD). In contrast, although industry needs accessible locations for the assembly of raw materials and distribution of finished goods, this is a less capital-intensive use of space and therefore commands less bidding power. So industry tends

■ **33.17** The urban land-value surface

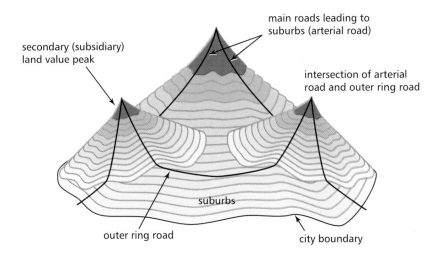

CBD
(peak land value intersection)

secondary (subsidiary) land value peak

main roads leading to suburbs (arterial road)

intersection of arterial road and outer ring road

suburbs

outer ring road

city boundary

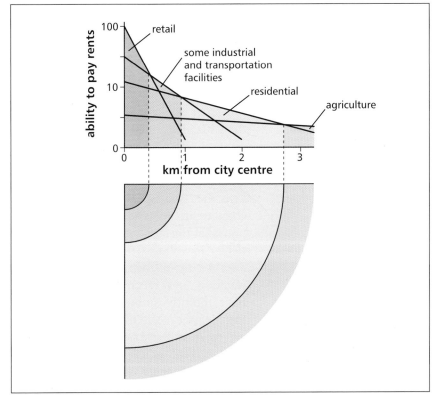

■ **33.18** Bid-rent model and urban land use zones

to be found outside the centre, often located along major arterial routeways (lines of enhanced accessibility).

As for residential development, this is even less competitive on the urban land market. For this reason, it tends to be pushed further away from the centre. But there is a paradox here, for in European and North American cities especially, poorer households rather than wealthy ones tend to be near the centre where land values and rents are higher. The paradox may be explained by low-cost housing being available in the form of:

■ small units of accommodation, for example flats in subdivided houses

■ dwellings that are obsolescent and often substandard

■ low-cost, purpose-built public housing, for example council houses, flats, tenements.

Within the residential areas of the town, there is a considerable amount of spatial sorting on the basis of wealth, social class and ethnicity. Although the sorting has a strong economic undertow, there is also a significant element of 'birds of the feather flocking together'. People feel most comfortable with neighbours whom they perceive as their peers.

Another general feature of spatial sort-

ing is that the larger the urban settlement, the finer is the sorting. This can be illustrated with reference to the CBD. In a sizeable city, not only is the CBD a reasonably clearly defined region, but within it there is a segregation of different types of business to form distinct quarters (**33.19**). Retailing tends to separate from commercial and professional offices to form a distinct **inner core**. Shops are surrounded by an **outer core** of entertainment and offices, whilst the margins of the CBD are marked by a **frame** containing wholesaling, car parks and some service industry. If, as is fairly common, the CBD is shifting its location within the growing built-up area, then to these three components will be added a **zone of assimilation** (often a residential area being invaded by the advancing front of the CBD) and a **zone of discard** (an area suffering from the progressive withdrawal of central businesses).

The above account has assumed the free play of market forces. Of course, in most towns and cities today, there are varying degrees of intervention, all of which pass under the very general heading of 'planning'. Obvious examples of that intervention in Britain include the council estates built on the urban fringe during the post-war period to provide low-cost housing, the strict zoning of land use within the CBD, the designation of industrial estates, and urban renewal programmes (see Chapter 35).

There are also other factors confusing the spatial pattern, such as changes in accessibility and a reappraisal of the costs and benefits of particular locations. Good examples here are the edge-of-town and out-of-town retailing and business parks which have recently sprung up in Western Europe (see section 29.5). No longer can town and city centres be regarded as points of prime accessibility; the balance of costs and benefits has shifted in favour of the urban periphery rather than the urban core.

■ **33.19** The internal structure of the CBD

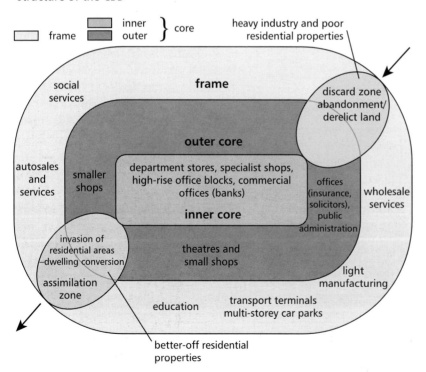

18 What would you define as the locational needs of:
   a an insurance office
   b high-class residential development
   c a secondary school?

19 With reference to **33.18**, describe and explain the difference in the bid-rent curves of retailing and industry.

20 Suggest reasons for the spatial sorting of central businesses shown in **33.19**.

33.5 **Synthesis – a process model**

Each of the maps you studied in section 33.2 presents a different way of looking at an urban area, and there are many more possibilities – type of building (style, materials), quality of buildings, amenities available, networks and flows, density of population, socio-economic characteristics of the resident population, ethnicity, perceptions of different individuals and groups of people, and so on. It is no easy matter to combine all of these and understand the structure and functioning of a city as a whole.

Some of the case studies, most notably those of Paris and central Tokyo, show that certain functions create distinct forms; these are illustrated in a historic context in **33.3**. For example, the character of a residential area is very different from that of an industrial estate. There are fundamental differences in the structures required to accommodate these two functions, and those differences have an impact on urban morphology. Equally, it becomes clear that the various urban functions involve certain recurrent processes; that is, there are underlying forces at work, such as the workings of the urban land market discussed in the previous section. These processes focus and interact with each other in such a way within all urban settlements as to both create and mould the town's functions, spatial structure and morphology.

Urban model C draws our attention to five processes (**33.20**). These are conceptually rather broader and more abstract than the bidding mechanism of the urban land market. None the less, they are vital in making some sense of the built-up area.

They do not work, as it were, on a clean slate, because they must interact with, and take account of, at least two pre-existing phenomena, namely (1) the built-up area and economic base inherited from yesterday, and (2) the local environment – that is, the physical conditions of the ground (i.e. the site) actually occupied by the built-up area. Perhaps it would be helpful to look at these five processes (**33.20**):

- **Commodity production** includes all those associated processes of packaging, marketing and transport that go with manufacturing and the production of consumer and capital goods. It is a process that is changing rapidly with new technologies and the global organisation of business. Transnational corporations (TNCs) dominate much of the world's production and can locate different parts of their process in different places to take advantage of labour skills and costs, capital available, tax systems, and so on. The significance of this process is that it is a vital component of the urban economic base and therefore provides much of the drive behind urban growth.

- **Consumption** includes food, consumer goods, entertainment and leisure as well as acquisition of public and private goods and services, like

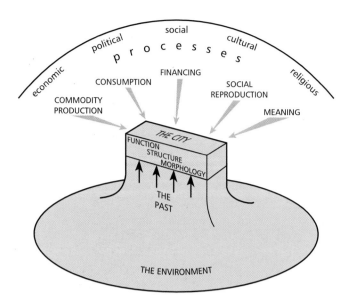

■ **33.20** Urban model C: Major processes in town and city

Generally speaking, the process of social reproduction is controlled by the more 'successful' members of society – 'upper and middle-class' people and 'the Establishment' in the UK; high-caste people in South Asia; elders in many African states; and party members in China.

This complex process includes the structuring of people in several ways:

■ by family tradition into households
■ by civil society into groups defined by gender, ethnicity and religion
■ by the state through law and education
■ by the economy through employment and class.

Often, especially in large cities, the mainstream of social reproduction has many subcurrents, with people with different value systems or life experiences creating their own process as communities. Examples include the ethnic groups in the Western city, squatter communities in the developing world, or 'outsiders' like the drug and criminal cultures of some city housing estates and of street dwellers in some cities of the developing world. A particularly significant aspect of the process is **social polarisation**, whereby people become segregated by social class and ethnicity.

The geographer is interested in all these aspects of social reproduction and uses them all to describe and analyse the social mosaic of towns and what is happening in urban society.

health, education and housing. Providing for consumption through the service sector is one of the basic reasons for the existence of towns and cities. Like commodity production, it too fuels urban growth.

■ **Financing** organises capital and credit via banking and commerce and is particularly linked with production and consumption. It is vital in the context of trade and provides the investment to support future expansion, be it of individual activities or of the town or city as a whole. In basic terms, finance might be seen as 'oiling the wheels' – keeping the urban settlement in running order.

■ **Social reproduction** ensures a supply of people suitable for the present and future needs of society. It can involve education, health, perceptions, attitudes and values, as well as standards of living and well-being. It may be a process you have not met often in geography. It is mainly studied by economists and sociologists, but it has far-reaching effects on urban settlements. Marxists would say its main aim is to produce a docile and effective workforce. On the other hand, it can be seen as a way to ensure that what is valued by society does survive.

■ **Meaning** refers to the images and symbols created in the minds of people as part of cultural understanding. Thus downtown São Paulo is an image of wealth and success, the new centre of Birmingham gives form to a culture of music and art, whilst the centre of Kathmandu is a symbol of religion. Meaning helps people to identify with, and feel part of, an urban settlement; it is a sort of bonding process.

Commodity production	→	light industrial estates
Consumption	→	shopping centres, car parks
Financing	→	city-centre offices
		construction and redevelopment
Social reproduction	→	council housing estates
		ethnic enclaves
Meaning	→	city-centre cultural developments
		gardens, statues

■ **33.21** Examples of urban form related to different processes

These five major urban processes constantly interact and combine, but some features of the city are strongly related to a particular process. Some examples are given in **33.21**.

21 Take each of the five cities described in section **33.2** in turn. Explain how each of the five processes described above contributes to the particular aspects of the city shown on the map. Suggest which processes are most important in each case.

22 Choose one of the cities, or use a map of a city known personally to you. Make an annotated diagram based on urban model C (**33.20**) to show the importance of processes in the creation of the city.

23 Compare the two urban models **33.3** and **33.20**. What are the links between them?

The Spread of Towns and Cities

34.1 **Historical perspectives, 1750 to 1950**

IT8

Before 1750, most towns and cities around the world were essentially non-industrial, compact and of 'walkable' dimensions. Workshops, trading places and offices mingled with rich and poor residences at the centre. **34.1** is a reminder that what was 'normal' in England between 1750 and 1950 was not necessarily so in other parts of the world. In England, town growth coincided with industrialisation.

By 1870, in cities like London and Birmingham, the rich had already moved to good housing areas 3–8 km from the centre. This pattern was partly a reflection of the social and environmental preferences of the rich, but it was made possible by the fact that large tracts of land in and around the cities were owned by the aristocracy, who developed their estates as desirable residential districts. The Calthorpe Estate in Edgbaston, Birmingham was a classic example of this residential segregation (**34.2**).

Around 1870, the transport revolution brought trains and trams to cities. The rich in English towns, already established in sectors of high-class residences, were seriously threatened by the movement of lower-middle and upper-working classes of people who could now afford to live at a distance from their place of work. After 1870, concentric waves of internal migration began to push the rich further and further out and to develop the endless miles of middle-class suburbia of the 20th century. This process tended to leave the poorest and the most recently arrived people around the centre of towns and cities in old and often poor-quality housing with few amenities. With investment priorities given to the construction of new housing on greenfield sites and to business and entertainment in the CBD, these 'inner rings' were seriously disadvantaged.

IT8

In most Continental countries and in Scotland, cultural and social norms led to the building of far more flats and tenements as urban settlements expanded, and cities like Paris, Rome and Vienna were far more compact than for example London or most North American cities. In the Soviet Union, from 1917 to 1990, socialist urban planning encouraged the mixing of all classes of people rather than the residential segregation of capitalism, and concentrated more on blocks of flats. Even so, high-ranking Party officials had their villas just outside town, a privilege that is still granted in China.

In many parts of the rest of the world, European colonial forces strongly influenced the development

■ **34.1** Urban growth and residential segregation, 1750–1950

		England	USA	Latin America	Rest of the world
1750 Industrial Revolution	}	Rich move to the edge of town to wealthy estates owned by aristocrats	Towns stay as 'walkable' settlements; any segregation is ethnic	Pre-industrial, colonial towns; slow growth	Pre-industrial, 'walkable' towns; rich living at centre
1870 Transport Revolution **1950**	}	Rich threatened by outward movement of middle and working classes; further outward ripples generated	Rich move to open countryside, the rest follow and the rich move even further out	Growth concentrated on a few large towns, where suburbs develop	Slow growth, often with Western colonial centres built in or alongside indigenous towns

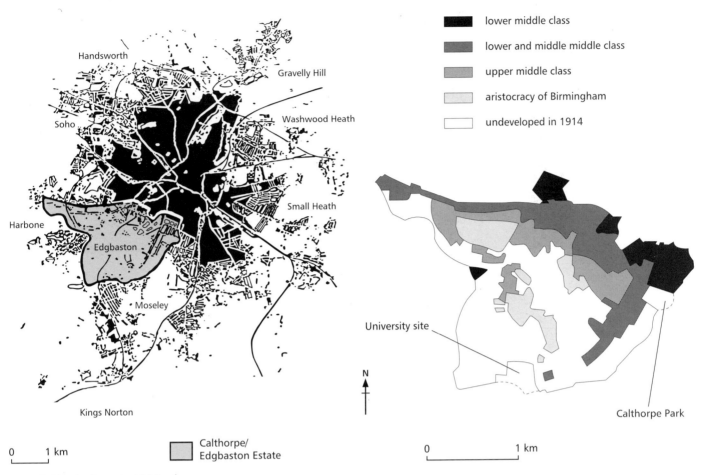

Built-up area of Greater Birmingham, c. 1914

Handsworth
Gravelly Hill
Soho
Washwood Heath
Harbone
Edgbaston
Small Heath
Moseley
Kings Norton

0   1 km

Calthorpe/
Edgbaston Estate

Edgbaston estate zoning pattern, c. 1914

- lower middle class
- lower and middle middle class
- upper middle class
- aristocracy of Birmingham
- undeveloped in 1914

University site

N

Calthorpe Park

0   1 km

■ **34.2** Birmingham in 1914

of towns. Well before 1750, the European conquests of North and South America had involved the establishment of colonial towns. Like most invaders' towns, their main function at first was to subdue local people and to establish law and order as well as safe trading conditions for the exploitation of resources for the benefit of the invading people and their country. In the Americas (and later in Australasia), there were relatively few indigenous people and they were soon subdued, almost exterminated, and their cultures decimated. Settlers were attracted from Europe in vast numbers and the colonial towns developed along lines familiar to Europeans, except that the streets were usually planned in grid patterns.

In the USA, residential segregation was far less marked before 1870 than it was in England, and the transport revolution often sent the first waves of rich people out to new developments on the edge of the city. Subsequently, outward waves of migration from the centres of towns produced effects similar to those in Britain, though the suburbs had lower densities of housing and the inner cities were if anything poorer than in Britain. Such areas increasingly functioned as

the reception areas for new immigrants from Europe and for Black people released from slavery. In Latin America, the colonial towns were of Spanish and Portuguese origin and grew only slowly before 1950. The exceptions were those few urban centres where industry and trade had become concentrated, such as Buenos Aires, Rio de Janeiro and São Paulo.

In Asia and Africa, many towns not exposed to industrialisation and commercial development remained as 'walkable' settlements to as late even as 1950, often with a new Western settlement built in or alongside the original town. In much of south and east Asia, colonial forces like the East India Company were faced before 1750 with sophisticated economies and cultures, often already urbanised, and a situation much less attractive to European settlers than the open territories of America and Australasia. So the colonial town tended to be built alongside the existing town and typically included the army and police barracks, the administration, the law courts, prison and customs houses. Later, banks, commercial offices and government buildings were added. Outside the centre, 'cantonments' of quality housing and clubs were developed for

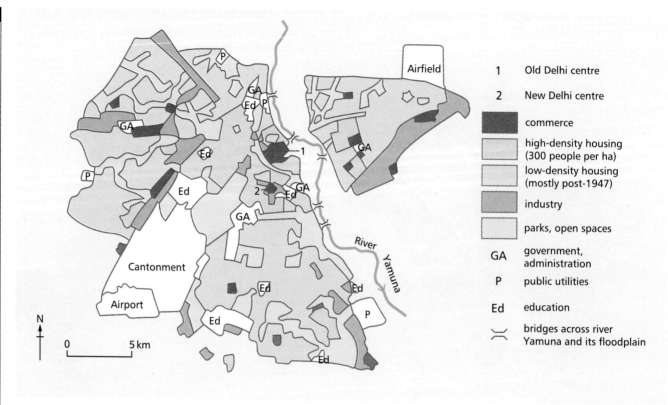

■ 34.3 The urban structure of Delhi

Legend for 34.3:

1   Old Delhi centre

2   New Delhi centre

commerce

high-density housing (300 people per ha)

low-density housing (mostly post-1947)

industry

parks, open spaces

GA   government, administration

P   public utilities

Ed   education

bridges across river Yamuna and its floodplain

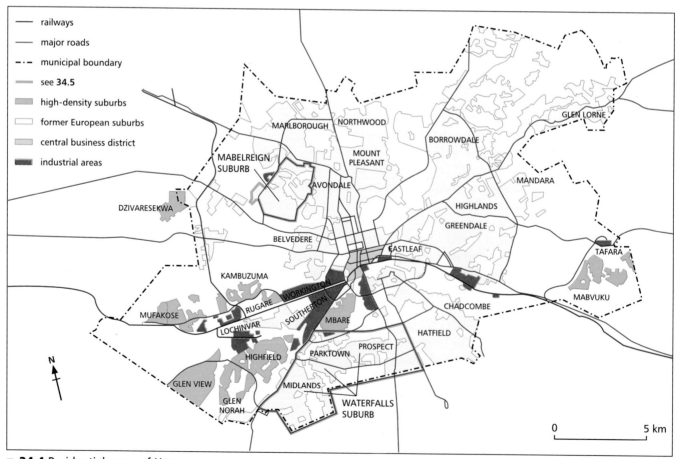

Legend for 34.4:

railways

major roads

municipal boundary

see **34.5**

high-density suburbs

former European suburbs

central business district

industrial areas

■ 34.4 Residential areas of Harare

Europeans. Delhi, a twin-centred city, shows these features, though the Western centre of New Delhi was not built until the 1920s. The British design displays wide streets and open space, with prestigious government buildings, offices and large shops. In contrast, Old Delhi is the original walled city, a maze of narrow streets lined with open small shops, services and workshops (**34.3**).

A similar pattern emerged during the 19th and early 20th centuries in those areas of Africa south of the Sahara that were settled by relatively small numbers of Europeans (mainly Central and West Africa). In East and South Africa, the more temperate climates and easier access attracted more settlers and the colonial towns were often more European in style, with high-density suburbs and townships built on the outskirts to house indigenous peoples at low cost with only basic amenities. Harare in Zimbabwe was such a colonial settlers' town (**34.4**); its ethnic residential structure has changed rapidly since its formal Independence in 1980 (**34.5**).

■ **34.5** Ethnic residential change in Harare

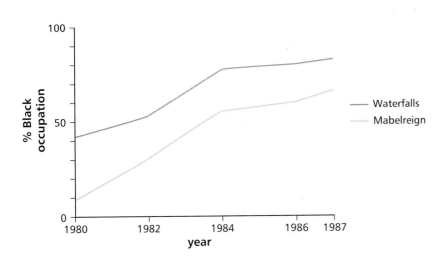

1 **Group discussion**. Imagine a family living in a large Victorian house near the centre of an English town in the 1920s. The head of the household is manager of a factory within walking distance. His wife runs the house and has four children to look after. The owner of the factory lives in a new house on the edge of town. Compile lists of reasons for the manager moving or not moving out into a new suburb. Group your reasons to provide a basis for discussing the proposition that 'English suburbia was the result of a male, middle-class dream'.

2 In 1870, the wealthy in Birmingham feared being **a** surrounded and **b** encroached upon by other people. Using the map showing Birmingham in 1914 (**34.2**), how far do you think these fears were realised?

3 Make a list of the most significant differences that had emerged by 1950 in the urban situation in North America, South America, Europe, Africa and South Asia. Organise these differences under headings such as 'economic', 'social', etc. What effects would you expect them to have on urban development after 1950?

34.2 **Urban growth in Africa, Asia and Latin America today**

Globally, urban growth since 1950 has been concentrated in Asia and Latin America, and to a lesser extent in Africa. Not only has urbanisation in its original sense been in full swing, with a continuously greater proportion of the population living in towns and cities, but the total population has been increasing at a faster rate than in the rest of the world. So high rates of natural increase in urban settlements (where health standards and economic production are almost always higher than in the surrounding countryside) compounded with large volumes of rural–urban migration have caused the fastest growth of towns and cities ever seen.

The fast-growing towns and cities of the developing world display a huge diversity, but do have some characteristics in common. These stem from their peripheral position in global capitalism.

Though they are often 'core' areas (see Chapter 31) of high income and economic development compared with their region or country, they are peripheral globally and have lower wages and less decision-making power than the cities of the USA, Europe or Japan. The move from a peripheral to a core role in the world economy can be accomplished, and indeed has been in the last 30 years by cities like Hong Kong, Seoul, Singapore and Taipei, and no doubt will be by many Chinese cities in the next 30 years. The new and ever stronger economic core of the Asian Pacific Rim may well force parts of Europe and North America into globally peripheral positions.

A major result of a peripheral position is that cities are relying almost entirely on capital and technology from outside their own country and beyond their control. Multinational or transnational corporations (TNCs), controlling most of the industrial investment available, choose locations based mainly on their evaluation of labour (cost, docility, skill, stamina, etc.), political stability and the friendliness of government to foreign business. Factors like trade and tax regulations are also very important.

As a result of these decisions, some cities receive much more investment than others. Some are used as 'off-shore' manufacturing and processing locations where raw materials or components are brought in, processed and packed, and exported all using local labour (see section 28.6). No taxes or tariffs are charged, and the work is often carried out in guarded enclaves where workers have no rights. Developments backed by multinational companies and capital make cities even more attractive to potential migrants from the countryside and smaller towns, and have led sometimes to what has been called **over-urbanisation** when the growth of population outstrips the economic growth of towns and cities.

The amazing variety of towns and cities in Asia, Africa and, to a lesser extent, Latin America reflects the characteristics of the pre-capitalist and pre-industrial settlements that have been overlain by modern development. On the economic side, particularly the flourishing **informal economy** of street-sellers, craftspeople and all kinds of services characteristic of cities in the developing world have directly descended from the pre-industrial city life. The informal economy not only gives colour and life to the towns and cities, but it is indispensable to the capitalist system, mopping up much of the surplus labour supply and transferring it into productive if unofficial employment.

Urban model D lists some of the characteristics of cities in the developing world, their relationship with a peripheral position in global capitalism, and their roots in pre-industrial life (**34.6**).

■ **34.6** Urban model D: Process links in cities of the developing world

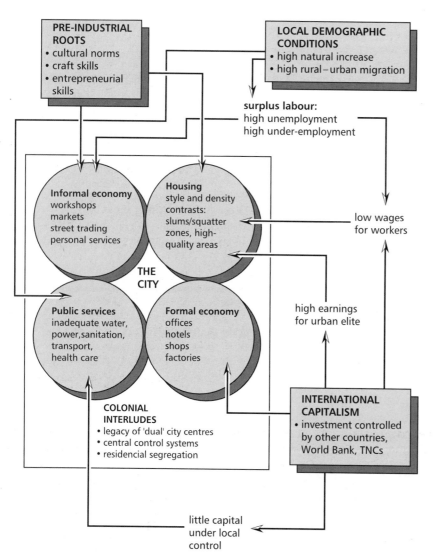

34.3 Three cities of the developing world

The next sections look at aspects of three cities, one each from Asia (Dhaka), Latin America (São Paulo) and Africa (Kumasi), and link their development to the model framework in **34.6**. Each illustrates a different facet of the housing problem which, it is no exaggeration to say, is the number one problem of towns and cities in developing countries. The study of Dhaka brings the issue of employment into focus – or to be more accurate, the problems of unemployment and underemployment and the poverty that ensues. In the case of São Paulo, the spotlight is put on the shanty towns and squatter settlements which are the material testimony of the housing problem, whilst the question of health in inadequately serviced housing is the issue to be investigated in Kumasi. In looking at these case studies, it is recommended that you refer to the model of the developing world city discussed in the previous chapter (**33.15**).

CASE STUDY

IP2, IT5

Dhaka, Bangladesh

Urban population in Bangladesh has grown at a rate of over 10 per cent per year during the last 25 years. Many of those migrating are the poorest of the rural people. They settle in slum dwellings in the worst parts of the towns and cities. It may seem strange to migrate to a slum from a village, but the city is the place of opportunity. In 1990, though only 16 per cent of the population lived in towns, already 25 per cent of the workforce of Bangladesh was urban. Even the average income of the bottom 40 per cent of urban

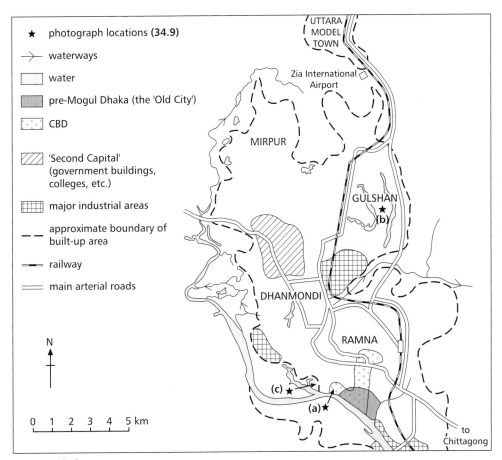

Key:
- ★ photograph locations (34.9)
- → waterways
- water
- pre-Mogul Dhaka (the 'Old City')
- CBD
- 'Second Capital' (government buildings, colleges, etc.)
- major industrial areas
- - - approximate boundary of built-up area
- railway
- main arterial roads

0 1 2 3 4 5 km

■ **34.8** Dhaka

	% population with safe drinking water		% population with sanitation		Death rate per 1000 people	
	1980	1988	1980	1988	Age 0–4	All ages
Urban areas	26	37	21	37	33	8
Rural areas	40	89	1	4	43	13

■ **34.7** Bangladesh: conditions in the town and country

■ **34.9** Scenes in Dhaka

households is half as much again as the bottom 40 per cent of rural households.

To begin with, migrants usually have a very hard life. Two-thirds of 'new migrants' are in low-paid jobs in construction, transport and domestic service. Only about 30 per cent of these newly-arrived people make an adequate living. After a few years, the average income increases. Less than half remain in lower-paid jobs; more set up as traders or in the garment industry or in better-paid services (see case study on page 460). Eventually, after some years, about 70 per cent of the rural immigrants are making an adequate living. As they do so, many move out of the slums. **34.7** shows other differences between urban and rural areas, fairly typical of Asia and Africa.

Dhaka is a city of contrasts. This can be illustrated by reference to four different locations in the city (**34.8** and **34.9**):

■ **Gulshan**. This is an exclusive suburb. Here the houses are large and well-appointed, and the population density is only 45 persons per ha. Affluent people live here, enjoying air-conditioning, an uninterrupted water supply and all modern conveniences. Dhanmondi and Ramna are similar suburbs.

■ **The Old City**. This is an area of acute overcrowding, with older buildings subdivided into flats, typical of the living conditions encountered near the city centre. A room may be

Rickshaw drivers   Owners of fleets of pedal rickshaws employ drivers who, after paying rent and repairs, earn about £1 sterling a day. They can work every day if they are fit.

Tempo boys   Tempos are small, often three-wheeled, petrol-driven buses. The boys act as conductors on the back step. There are around 18 000 tempo boys, mostly under 12. The Employment of Children Act makes employment of children under 15 illegal in the transport industry.

Handicrafts   Work is available on a project encouraged by overseas development workers, making wallhangings, bags and other articles from jute. Such projects function as small businesses and employees live an independent life in the city.

Prostitution and begging   Many women who cannot find employment are forced into 'rings' run by tough gang-leaders.

Garment factory workers   This is a boom industry, now providing 45 per cent of all exports. Factories are run by local managers relying on export contracts with retail outlets in the West.

■ **34.10** Employment in Dhaka

rented for the equivalent of a few pounds a month and may even be further subdivided to give accommodation for two parts of an extended family. Population densities reach as high as 5000 persons per ha.

■ **Narayanganj** This is an industrial suburb, a little way south of the city centre. It used to be a jute-milling and export centre, but now its industries include textiles, boatyards, electricity generation and engineering.

■ **Bustees and squatter areas** These are very poor areas of makeshift housing and are home mainly for recent immigrants from the countryside. They are often sited on land unsuitable for permanent building – next to railways, frequently flooded land, very small parcels of land left over from development, fringes of industrial sites or on the very edge of areas being developed.

Employment in Dhaka is as varied as the urban fabric. **34.10** gives a few examples of employment that might be available for a recent migrant.

---

4 Put a copy of the photograph of a street in central Dhaka (**34.9a**) in the middle of a large sheet of paper. Around the photo write as many questions as you can about the photo: what is going on, who, why, how, when? Some questions may be questions of fact, and you may know some of the answers; some may be about what people are thinking, what will happen next or about matters of opinion. Compare your 'poster' with those of other students. Discuss possible answers.

5 Put copies of the photographs of the bustee area (**34.9c**) in the middle of a piece of paper. Discuss the situation for the people living in this bustee.

Draw labelled arrows and describe and explain interesting and controversial features of the photograph.

6 The areas shown in **34.9** provide an example of housing contrasts in Dhaka. Explain how these contrasts are brought about by the factors and relationships outlined in **34.7**. How do the different kinds of employment described in **34.10** fit into the situation described in urban model D (**34.6**)?

7 Looking back through this case study of Dhaka, what evidence is there that, although Bangladesh is peripheral in global terms, Dhaka is a core area at the national scale?

CASE STUDY

IT5,7

São Paulo, Brazil

In 1930, a third of Brazilians lived in towns; now over three-quarters do. São Paulo grew from 1 million in 1930 to 5 million in 1967 and 17 million in 1990 (**34.11**). Rio de Janeiro, with a population of 11 million, is Brazil's second largest city, and there are seven other cities with populations over 2 million.

Before 1950, São Paulo developed in a similar way to European cities. The early growth was associated with the coffee trade, and redevelopment of the centre in 1911 made way for rail and road concentrations. In the early 20th century, industrialisation accompanied commercial and population growth. By 1950, the rich residents who had lived near the centre on the Avenida Paulista were moving out to attractive higher land a little further to the south-west, and Avenida Paulista was becoming a second CBD specialising in banking, commerce and business headquarters. Industry and workers' housing had developed quickly along transport corridors and along the valleys of the Tiete and Tamanduatei rivers, where large working-class residential districts emerged.

São Paulo was already a city of marked social segregation in 1956 when it was designated in the national development plan as the automobile centre for Brazil – what lobbying must have taken place

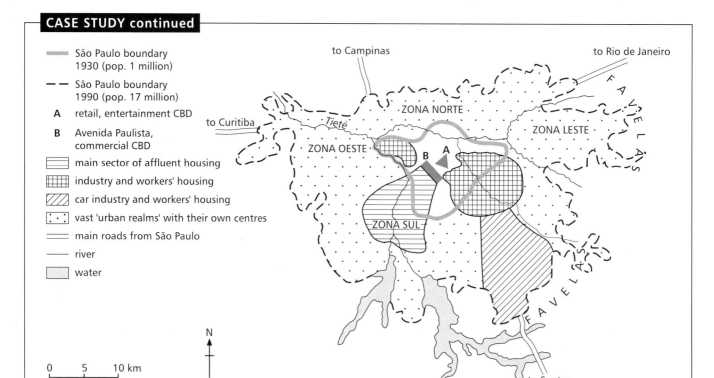

Legend:
- São Paulo boundary 1930 (pop. 1 million)
- São Paulo boundary 1990 (pop. 17 million)
- **A** retail, entertainment CBD
- **B** Avenida Paulista, commercial CBD
- main sector of affluent housing
- industry and workers' housing
- car industry and workers' housing
- vast 'urban realms' with their own centres
- main roads from São Paulo
- river
- water

0 5 10 km

N

to Campinas · to Rio de Janeiro · to Curitiba · ZONA NORTE · Tietê · ZONA LESTE · ZONA OESTE · B · A · ZONA SUL · FAVELAS · to Santos

■ **34.11** São Paulo

during that decision-making! The automobile multinationals sited themselves to the south-east and new working-class suburbs grew up. The enormous attraction of employment opportunities drew in people from all over Brazil to swell the well-established stream of foreign migrants from Europe. Shanty towns, already a feature on waste land inside the city, grew on the edges, especially to the south and east, and continue to grow to this day.

Since 1950, São Paulo has grown in a North American style, with huge urban realms or zones almost independent of each other. Today, there are five of these (**34.11**). Zona Sul is the most affluent, with its 'garden city' neighbourhoods. The Central Zone is the high-rise business and retail centre, but a decentralisation policy has led to 15 other important retail centres being located throughout the city (**34.12**). On the edge of the city, a mix of shanty towns, industrial estates and fenced, heavily guarded high-class residential enclaves exist side by side. The number of **favelas** (temporary housing, often illegal, on land awaiting development) inside the municipality has continued to increase; they now contain around 150 000 huts and houses. An even greater increase in favelas has taken place on the periphery, outside the municipal limits, with more and more people living in overcrowded self-built tenements and temporary buildings (**34.13**).

■ **34.12** São Paulo city centre skyline

It is difficult to keep pace with such rapid growth and huge numbers. Whilst the recent migrants often build their own houses on unoccupied land, as a stepping-stone to better things, it is not so easy to provide the urban infrastructure of roads, water, power, sewerage, schools, clinics, etc. In São Paulo, less than half the households have drains, and less than three-quarters have piped water. Many use polluted wells; the infant mortality rate has almost doubled in the last 15 years. **34.14** offers some comments on life in a 'mature' favela.

Housing type	Population
	thousands
Favelas	818
Tenements	2978
Temporary buildings	2420

■ **34.15** Vila Prudente

Conditions in squatter settlements
The main difficulties are:
- Clean water only supplied from a standpipe, shared by many households.
- No electricity; gas available in bottles but expensive.
- Shelter inadequate in rains; houses constructed cheaply.
- Hygienic sanitation very difficult; no sewerage system; pit latrines inadequate.
- Very difficult to maintain personal and food hygiene without plentiful clean water, sanitation and safe storage facilities.

■ **34.13** Housing in São Paulo

Vila Prudente began in the 1940s and its residents have fought many hard battles for land, water, sanitation and electricity. Dona Carmelita persuaded her husband and the other children to come to São Paulo and they moved into her son's two-roomed house in Vila Prudente. She worked as a cleaner in an office at night, and looked after favela children during the day. Seven years ago, she bought a house quite cheaply in the favela and she likes living there. She is involved with Catholic groups in the community where they try to understand the causes of their poverty and do something about it. She feels that when people come together many things are possible.

■ **34.14** Vila Prudente, a favela in São Paulo

8 Use the maps **34.11** and **33.4** to compare the growth of São Paulo between 1930 and 1990 with that of Paris between 1908 and 1980. What conclusions can be drawn about the increase in area, population and density of population in each case?

9 Study the photograph of Vila Prudente, a mature favela (**34.15**). Make lists of the things that surprise you, and those that you expected.

10 Suppose you were a recent migrant to a squatter settlement. What would you find most difficult? How could you cope with this?

11 Suppose a group of homeless people set up a squatter settlement on disused land near you. What should the police and council do? Evict them? Provide them with water and sanitiation? Let them have free electricity? Build them proper houses? Who should pay? Write out your recommendations.

12 What actions do you think the São Paulo authorities should take about squatter settlements? What would be the likely reactions of local residents?

CASE STUDY

IT5

Kumasi, Ghana

Kumasi is not a giant city like São Paulo, but it was already the capital of the Asante Kingdom in the 17th century. By the mid-19th century, the population was about 20 000, but in 1874 the town was attacked and burnt to the ground by British troops, and the population scattered. In 1896, Asante was added to the Gold Coast colony. The city was rebuilt during the period 1901 to 1910 and stayed part of a British colony until Ghana became independent in 1957. By

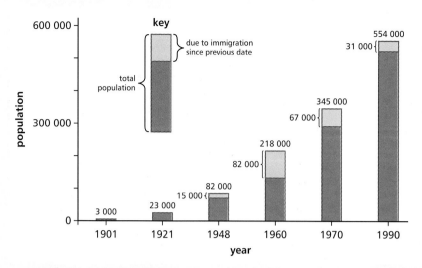

■ **34.16** Kumasi population

that time, Kumasi had become a transport centre as well as a political and trading focus, and had a

population of over 100 000. **34.16** shows the demographic changes, and **33.10** (page 463) the present extent of the town.

Kumasi does not have extensive squatter settlements, but the municipal authorities are fighting to keep pace with growth. In terms of public health, probably the most important aspect of infrastructure after clean water is sanitation. The Kumasi Metropolitan Assembly is developing a Sanitation Strategy for 1991–2000, and is currently fund-raising for the project. The UN and Britain are two important partners. The situation in Kumasi is summarised by **34.18** and **34.19** (and see also **33.10**), and **34.17** describes the sanitation options in Kumasi.

Ventilated improved pit latrines (VIP)

No water is required for flushing – all kinds of cleansing material can be used with no fear of blockage. The double-pit design allows one pit to be closed off after two years, and in 18 to 24 months the waste will be decomposed and disease-causing bacteria destroyed. The pit can then be emptied and the contents used for soil conditioning. The double pit needs controlled use, and the cabin should be cleaned daily. About 25 people are served per cabin.

Pour-flush (PF) toilets with seepage tank

Where water is used for cleansing, a squatting plate with a U-bend to seal off odours and insects is possible. The solids collect in a pit below, and water percolates into the ground. Internal plumbing is not necessary as household waste waters can be used for flushing. PF toilets cannot dispose of large amounts of water and clog easily. The seepage tank must be emptied after two to three years.

Septic tank and drain field systems

Flush toilets (WC) can drain to septic tanks, all household waste water flowing by gravity to a watertight concrete tank underground. Solids sink to the bottom and grease forms a scum: the liquid then flows to a drain field. The tanks require cleaning by suction after three to four years. The system requires plenty of household water and outside space for the tank and drain field.

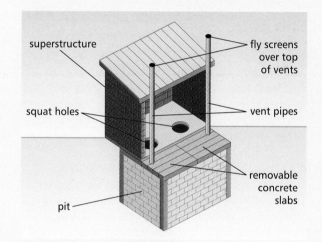

Simplified sewerage

This conveys all household waste water to an off-site treatment works. Small-diameter pipes are buried in shallow trenches with low gradients. It is cheaper than conventional urban sewerage but very expensive per person served. Individual houses are responsible for their own connection to sewers laid under alleyways and backyards. Septic and seepage tanks can be connected.

Public latrines

Multiple VIP latrines and/or WCs are possible. These need considerable space and are maintained by the authorities. The pits are emptied by suction hose. A charge of a few pence is made for each visit.

■ **34.17** Sanitation choices in Kumasi

Public latrines	38%	
Bucket latrines	25%	These are obsolete and are to be phased out
WC – septic tanks	24%	
Sewerage	1%	
Unimproved pit latrines	7%	Often leaky and overflowing, also to be phased out
Bush	5%	
VIP latrines	0%	

■ **34.18** Sanitation in Kumasi, 1990

---

13 Using the information in **34.17**, **34.18** and **34.19**, decide on the most appropriate sanitation for the indigenous area of Moshie Zongo (10 000 people) and the tenement area of Asafo (25 000 people).

14 What kind of sanitation may be appropriate for Vila Prudente (**34.14**) and for the bustee in Dhaka (**34.8** and **34.9**)?

Tenement areas
Nearly all have water, 25% have internal plumbing. 40% use septic tanks, 30% bucket latrines, 30% public latrines. Buckets often emptied into open street drains.

Indigenous areas
25% have a yard tap, most obtain water from neighbours. 40% use bucket latrines, the rest public latrines or *ad hoc* methods. Most is emptied into neighbours' drains.

New government areas
All have water and internal plumbing, WC flush toilets with septic tanks emptied by suction lorry, or to a sewer.

High-cost areas
All have water and internal plumbing, WC flush toilets draining to septic tanks with seepage pits and/or drain fields.

■ **34.19** Sanitation and water supply in Kumasi

34.4 **Hopes and expectations**

The statements in **34.20** show how different people perceive the city, both as regards its functions and its priorities. Most urban development policies are based on the perceptions of the urban elite, whose views are quite different to those of the urban poor. Hence the whole system is loaded against the best interests of the underprivileged and deprived.

It is both the scale and the speed of urbanisation that cause most stress in cities in the developing world. The shortage of financial resources means that there is a huge problem in providing homes, water, sewage disposal and power, as well as in providing public transport systems that would facilitate the movement from people between home and job opportunities. The difficulty of finding work is the root cause of much of the prevalent poverty.

The prevalence of the informal economy does not help in the accumulation of capital. Sections of this economy – sometimes called the 'bazaar economy' – involve the traditional system of sharing employment with other members of the family. This system results in lower wages, and the growth of 'shared poverty'. Also, goods and services are obtained through *ad hoc* exchange rather than through a formal, capital-based service sector. Thus saving and capital formation are more difficult, but this shared poverty may be seen as better than affluence for the few and absolute destitution for the many.

There are examples of encouraging initiatives being taken by city authorities to ease or improve the housing situation, but the position prevails that the majority of urban dwellers still have to make their own arrangements for shelter. The choices for new migrants include:

Urban poor

Functions The city is a tough place, but certainly better than the village of origin. It is the best opportunity for saving money to buy security (i.e. land) and to ensure children a better future and formal education.

Priorities Income opportunity, prices, schools, housing, transport. Emphasis on availability and affordability.

Affluent and semi-affluent national residents

Functions The city is the place to be. It provides the best services, easy access to government and business contacts, and a gateway to the external world.

Priorities Status, income, security, availability of cheap labour. Emphasis on quality of life and cost-quality trade-offs of goods and services.

Foreign business people and expatriates

Functions The city is a good place to extract the highest possible profit in the shortest possible time, to win 'brownie points' with headquarters, to save good money, and/or enjoy a privileged lifestyle while it lasts.

Priorities Political and social stability, security, urban services, schools, housing, amenities, labour markets. Emphasis on availability and reliability of services and quality of goods, with prices a marginal factor.

Visitors/Tourists

Functions The city has atmosphere, relaxation, a touch of the exotic, good shopping, and all the amenities for a good holiday.

Priorities Accommodation and transport, security, amenities, shopping, attractions, availability of 'essential' goods and services. Emphasis on trade-offs between price and quality of services.

■ **34.20** Functions and priorities in emergent developing cities: contrasting views

- if they have some resources, to rent a small room
- to lodge with friends or relatives
- to sleep 'rough' on the streets
- to build themselves a shelter on land which they do not own and for which they have no building permission.

Any long-term hope for the future must lie in achieving a better balance between labour and jobs. A two-pronged strategy is needed of population control (not just reducing the rate of natural increase, but stemming the flow of rural–urban migration), and employment growth. Both represent formidable challenges, possibly the latter even more so than the former. What chance is there of job creation when national resources are very limited, the global economy is in recession, and control of that economy is largely in the power of TNCs based in the developed world (see Chapter 30)? In the short term, perhaps city authorities should put as their priority the proper servicing of areas of spontaneous housing, and by so doing help upgrade such areas.

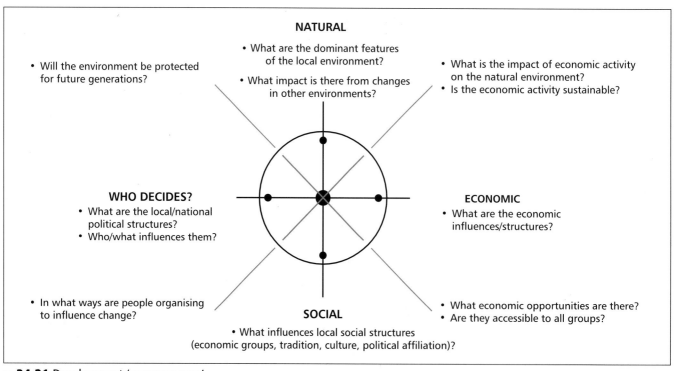

■ **34.21** Development 'compass rose'

15 Design some fieldwork to see how the views of different people in British cities compare with those in the developing world (**34.20**).

16 a Compile a list of the issues arising with rapid growth of cities in Africa, Latin America and Asia. Break these issues down to a manageable scale, e.g. not 'housing' – be more specific.
   b Put each issue on a card. Break into groups for discussion. Rank the issues by their importance and number the cards – equal ranks are possible.
   c Classify the issues as mainly local, national or international. Mark each card with a letter: L, N or I.

Conventionally, the issues could be classified by a planners' scheme under headings such as 'housing', 'transport', 'employment', etc., but the deeper causes can become clearer when the issue is looked at from different viewpoints, e.g 'economic', 'social', 'environmental', etc.

   d Draw a 'development compass rose' (**34.21**) on a large piece of paper. Place the cards in appropriate positions on the rose.
   e Synthesise your work by reviewing the issues and the relationship between their importance, scale and nature.
   f Look back at the sections on Dhaka, São Paulo and Kumasi. Do your general conclusions apply to these specific cities?

[Save your results for later.]

17 Look back at urban model D (**34.6**) and review your work in this chapter. How does the model help to explain the urban patterns and issues?

This chapter investigates some of the more important processes which are an integral part of urban growth and urbanisation. The processes to be examined may be seen as falling into three groups:

1 those processes that promote the outward spread of the built-up area – **development** and **suburbanisation**

2 the processes of **urban renewal** by which tired, obsolete urban fabric is subject to either **improvement** or **redevelopment**; that is adapted to new uses and generally modernised

3 the relatively new process of **counterurbanisation (35.1)**.

The first two groups involve processes which operate on the spatial patterns and structures examined in the previous chapter. The third is a process which affects the urban system as a whole rather than the structure of the individual urban settlement. This is quite distinct from the the **decentralisation** implicit in (1) and as yet has been experienced only in the developed world. However, it heralds a fundamental reversal of process direction within the urban system.

It is worth stressing at the outset that these different processes can and do operate at the same time and within the same town or city. For example, as the built-up area is being extended outwards, so older areas become subject to modernisation. Indeed, the processes may well be closely linked, with the renewal of inner areas often precipitating a displacement of people and activities to the urban fringe.

35.1 Development and suburbanisation

IT8

■ 35.1 Processes of change affecting the built-up area

Development in the present context simply means extension of the built-up area – the conversion of rural space into urban space to accommodate economic and demographic growth. Broadly speaking, up until the transport improvements of the late 19th century, the essential character of urban development was concentration and centralisation. In order to minimise the friction of distance, towns and cities were kept compact. Centripetal forces were paramount. However, the situation changed dramatically in the 20th century as a result of a number of interacting factors. **Suburbanisation** has become synonymous with urban growth. It represents decentralisation and deconcentration in action; it is the outcome of centrifugal forces.

Suburbanisation has its roots in the industrialisation of the 19th century. This resulted in the old areas of towns and cities becoming polluted, congested and less favoured for residence. At the same time, social fashions changed; the more affluent families sought new dwellings with all modern amenities, and open space in the form

IT8

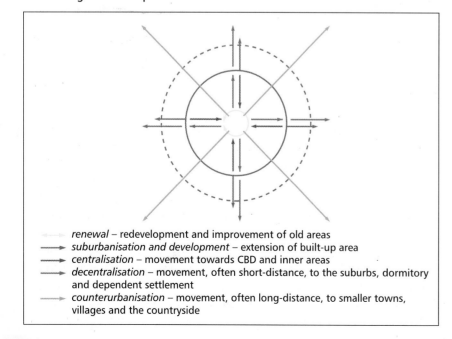

renewal – redevelopment and improvement of old areas
suburbanisation and development – extension of built-up area
centralisation – movement towards CBD and inner areas
decentralisation – movement, often short-distance, to the suburbs, dormitory and dependent settlement
counterurbanisation – movement, often long-distance, to smaller towns, villages and the countryside

35.2 A detached suburb in the Midlands

high-density 'urban' towards the centre to low-density 'suburban' towards the margins

3 an extension of commuting and the spawning of detached suburbs or dormitories in the countryside beyond (**35.2**).

However, residence is not the only land use involved in suburbanisation. Manufacturing industry has been shaken out of many inner-city areas whilst new, purpose-built industrial estates have been constructed in the suburbs. Other activities have followed. Retailing is to be found in suburban shopping parades and more recently in edge-of-town and out-of-town centres (see section 29.5). The everyday needs of local people have required the construction of schools, medical centres and sports halls, as well as the provision of public open space. Office parks are beginning to spring up (see section 29.4). Ironically, it would seem that suburbanisation today is gradually restoring the juxtaposition of workplace and home that characterised the 19th-century city – this time, hopefully, in an environmentally acceptable way.

of large gardens. The urban fringe became the 'in' place. But the accretion of new suburbs around the margins of the built-up area was only made possible on a large scale by improvements in transport. These allowed increasing distances to be inserted between places of work and service centres on the one hand, and home on the other. First, it was the extension of public transport systems – the tram and the train – that loosened the urban structure, then the bus and the private car. The net outcome of this transport revolution was threefold:

1 a massive outward spread of the built-up area

2 a fundamental change in the character of that built-up area from

1 Identify the push and pull factors involved in suburbanisation.

35.2 **Urban renewal**

The diagram of urban growth reminds us that whilst development takes place on the urban fringe and beyond, existing zones are continuously changing (**35.3**). Much of this change has involved shifts in function, the conversion of space and buildings from one use to another, and the replacement of old structures by new ones. This is urban renewal; it embraces what in morphological terms can be seen as two distinct processes. **Redevelopment**, sometimes referred to as the 'bull-

dozer treatment', involves demolition and rebuilding. It is an inescapable fact that buildings decay with age and that maintenance costs increase; old urban fabric can become unsuited to modern needs. In contrast, **improvement** is 'make do and mend' and seeks to adapt and modernise existing fabric to meet those same needs. At present, in a time of growing awareness of heritage, improvement is the preferred option in many instances of urban renewal.

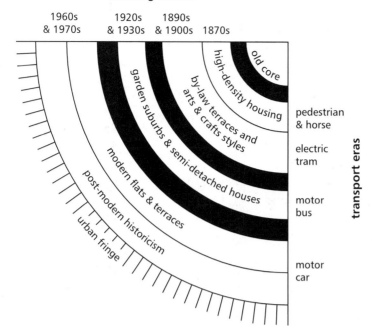

building booms

1960s & 1970s   1920s & 1930s   1890s & 1900s   1870s

old core

high-density housing

by-law terraces and arts & crafts styles

garden suburbs & semi-detached houses

modern flats & terraces

post-modern historicism

urban fringe

transport eras

pedestrian & horse

electric tram

motor bus

motor car

■ **35.3** A model of urban growth in the UK

IT8

2 Explain why the growing awareness of heritage should favour improvement rather than redevelopment.

3 Draw up a list of the advantages and disadvantages of redevelopment and improvement. Which does your appraisal favour?

At the end of the Second World War, the central areas of many cities in Europe and East Asia were devastated, and the rebuilding necessary gave the stimulus for large-scale planning and wholesale redevelopment. So new centres were designed and implemented for cities like Tokyo, Dresden and Birmingham. With the new age of mass-ownership of motor cars and large numbers of people to be rehoused, high-rise flats and wide, fast roads were the planners' solution in the city centre.

Even without the spur of wartime destruction, North America led the way

IT8

in these developments. In the UK, the rebuilding and new housing boom lasted through the 1960s. Planners and government, already worried by the congestion and overcrowding in large cities, encouraged a policy of dispersion away from major centres by creating new towns like Crawley, Basildon and Redditch, and later Milton Keynes and Telford. At first these towns were meant to be self-contained, with spacious sites set aside for light industrial development. In practice, however, the earlier schemes have tended to assume a dormitory function, as a significant proportion of their inhabitants have taken up employment in nearby established cities. This was particularly the case with the eight new towns ringing London. But subsequently, with the shift to longer projects involving the expansion of established freestanding towns, the second and third waves of new towns have been much more successful.

By the late 1970s, experience had revealed the weaknesses of the local authorities' high-rise developments and the planners' obedience to the needs of the motor car in city centres. In the 1980s and 1990s, redevelopments have been more piecemeal, with attempts to match new building to more traditional patterns with 'post-modern' designs. Many city-centre and suburban shopping centres have been pedestrianised and renewal plans have been more inclined to put people before cars. This leads to its own questions of priorities when most of the population are car-users as well as pedestrians.

4 Choose a large town near to you and compare the changes that have taken place in its built-up area since 1950 with those shown in the model (**35.3**).

35.3 A tale of urban renewal in two cities

In this section, the spotlight is put on two cities and the structural changes which have occurred as a result of urban renewal programmes.

CASE STUDY

IT4,7

Birmingham, England

Birmingham's Unitary Development Plan recognises that the City is home to a million citizens of diverse cultures, ethnic origins, skills and incomes. The Plan aims to:

– create a City which provides better facilities and opportunities for all its residents, and

– provide an attractive environment which will improve the quality of life for the City's residents as well as stimulating investment.

Birmingham City Council, 1993

This is a 1990s response of a city council to the challenges of changing economic and urban structures typified by high inner-city unemployment (see section 33.6). The map of Birmingham shows the growth of the south-east sector of the built-up area since 1950 (**35.4**). Several kinds of expansion are to be observed (examples are numbered on **35.4**):

(1) infilling and expansion into the countryside immediately bordering the built-up area

(2) creation of new estates (in this example Chelmsley Wood) on the edge of the city, including high-rise housing, to relocate people removed from city-centre redevelopment areas

(3) expansion of nearby small settlements into large dormitory settlements (in this example, Knowle and Dorridge)

(4) creating new small commuter 'villages' in the nearby countryside (this one is called Cheswick Green).

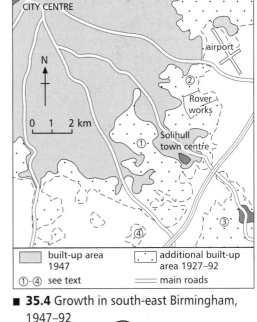

■ **35.4** Growth in south-east Birmingham, 1947–92

Key:
- major roads
- motorway
- O main shopping centres
- industrial developments
- housing regeneration and building
- commercial development
- open space
- **CC** city centre
- **C** convention centre
- **M** wholesale markets
- ▲ jewellery quarter
- ▼ gunsmiths quarter
- A see 35.6

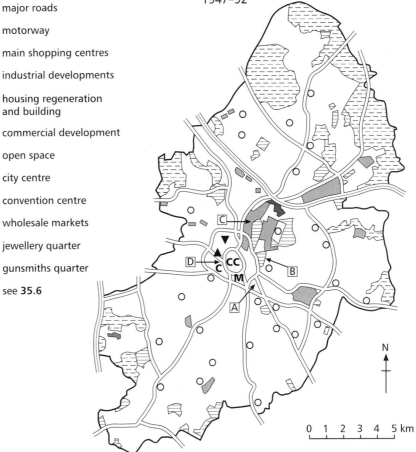

■ **35.5** City of Birmingham Structure Plan, 1993

A| *Birmingham's urban renewal*

21 years of urban renewal

When the last of Birmingham's slums were bulldozed in the 1960s, many privately owned homes remained in dire need of renovation.

In 1971, some 26,000 city households had no hot-water tap, and a further 28,000 had no fixed bath. A new solution had to be found.

The answer was renovation, to be achieved by allocating grants to owner-occupiers which would enable them to afford to improve their properties.

Since then, more than 80,000 homes have been made habitable by the team's various initiatives.

Many of the city's pioneering schemes have been adopted elsewhere, including 'enveloping', a major initiative which formed the backbone of urban renewal work in Birmingham for a decade. 'Enveloping' involved the external renovation of whole streets of terraced housing, in one fell swoop.

In this way, entire areas were transformed in a short space of time – in Birmingham, more than 11,000 homes were 'enveloped'. Birmingham has shared its expertise with many other cities throughout Britain and the rest of the world.

From *Birmingham Voice*, 16 September 1993

B| *Birmingham, urban village*

Village in the heart of a city

PUTTING a village – complete with its own village hall, shops and doctor's surgery – in the very heart of East Birmingham may, at first, sound bizarre.

But taking the facts that 300 new and 140 refurbished homes were sold even before they were finished and that this 'village' boasts a park, a children's nursery and new canal bridges, the idea begins to make sense.

It's all part of the realisation of a vision by the City Council for breathing new life and investment into Birmingham's Heartlands area, 2,350 acres in the east of the city which takes in districts like Nechells, Bordesley and Aston.

From *Birmingham City Council Annual Report 1992/93*

C| *Urban regeneration: the Heartlands Project*

New industrial, business and commercial developments and initiatives are proposed, including:

- the Star Project Site adjacent to the M6 motorway, which presents a unique opportunity for a development that will create a national profile for the Heartlands area and the City
- a major commercial area at Waterlinks with new high-quality business development and associated uses in a canalside setting
- the designation of a Simplified Planning Zone at Saltley, which will grant advance planning permission for a wide range of industrial developments.

From the Birmingham Structure Plan 1993

D| *Birmingham city centre regeneration*

Venues are good for city

report by
Joanne Barker

A CITY centre hotel boss has supported an independent study which shows prestige venues such as the Indoor Arena and International Convention Centre are good news for Birmingham.

Research carried out by accountants KPMG Peat Marwick has found that in Birmingham alone the NEC, ICC, Symphony Hall and NIA have generated £145 million and created 5,800 full-time jobs or equivalent, in the past year.

The report was commissioned by NEC Ltd to assess the benefits to Birmingham and the region of attracting 4.5 million visitors to 730 exhibitions, concerts, conferences and sporting events held at the four venues in the last 12 months.

It found more than two-thirds of the visitors to the venues come from outside the West Midlands region and spend more than one million nights at hotels in the region every year.

More than a third of the venues' international visitors – nearly 50,000 – were found to use Birmingham International Airport and around £2.2 billion of orders were placed at exhibitions.

In the West Midlands as a whole £438 million was generated for the local economy with almost 17,000 new jobs created.

From *Birmingham News*, 26 November 1993

NEC   National Exhibition Centre – on edge of city
ICC   International Convention Centre ⎤
NIA   National Indoor Arena   ⎬ – in city centre
         Symphony Hall   ⎦

Banning traffic from Victoria Square has created Birmingham's premiere civic piazza – the jewel in the crown of the city's pedestrianisation plans.

Giving the streets back to the people has been at the hub of the Council's policy to transform parts of the city centre into a traffic-free oasis of calm and pleasure amidst the bustle of busy city life.

Review
This £6.5 million transformation has taken place over the last two to three years.

From *BBC Annual Report 1992/93*

■ **35.6** Birmingham – change for the better

See **35.5** for locations of A – D.

The generalised map of the main features of the Structure Plan (**35.5**) and the selection of press releases and comments (**35.6**) relating to locations on it (marked A–D on **35.5**) provide further evidence of recent trends. The information on employment adds to the picture (**35.7** and **35.8**).

5 How do the developments in Birmingham shown on **35.4** and **35.6** reflect the general pattern described in **35.3**?

6 In a group, discuss Birmingham's approaches to restructuring. Make a list of the advantages and disadvantages of various approaches to comprehensive redevelopment, urban regeneration, environmental improvement, etc. How are different sections of the public affected?

	Inner city	Outer city
Energy and water	2928	1919
Automotive manufacture	8077	24926
Engineering	30302	17934
Rest of manufacturing	26129	20112
Construction	8745	8731
Transport & communications	19008	8096
Retail and wholesale	28349	27989
Tourism & leisure	10317	15758
Financial & professional	38770	23880
Other private services	4802	6187
Public & caring services	59248	71957
All services	160494	153867
Total employment	236675	227525

■ **35.7** Birmingham: inner and outer city employment, 1991

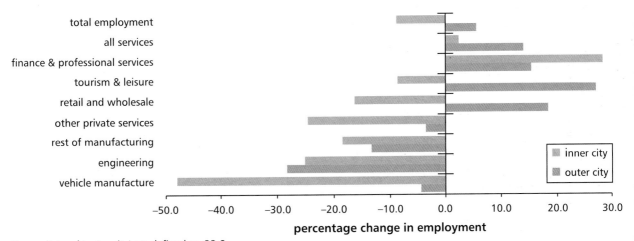

'Inner city' and 'outer city' are defined on **33.8**

■ **35.8** Employment changes in Birmingham, 1984–91

CASE STUDY

IP1, IT5,7

Tokyo, Japan

Tokyo is a much bigger city than Birmingham. With more than 12 million people, it dominates the greater metropolitan area which also embraces the cities of Yokohama (3 million) and Kawasaki (1 million). A feature of Japanese urban life is the very high residential densities of population (**35.9** and **35.10**). In Tokyo, these high values are matched in the central area by even higher densities of employment, causing daytime population figures to reach as high as 70000 people per km^2 – 15 times higher than the residential density.

■ **35.9** High-density housing in Tokyo

The centre of Tokyo was completely destroyed by US bombing in 1945. Today, however, the centre (known as the Ward Area) provides employment for over a million people and is a global centre of business (**35.11**). That employment is largely in the tertiary and quaternary sectors, being generated by Tokyo's role as a global business centre, its capital city function and the considerable personal affluence of its residents with plenty of spare cash to spend on expensive goods and services. But Tokyo is also a port city and one of the country's leading industrial centres. Its importance as a manufacturing centre derives from its waterfront industries and a great diversity of what are best labelled 'consumer industries'.

Tokyo has come to occupy an off-centre location within Tokaido megalopolis. This is Japan's core region, but it has an unusual linear shape as it stretches along the Pacific coastlands of the main island, Honshu.

Like so many that have achieved the status of global city, Tokyo has become a victim of its own success. The immense spread of its built-up area, fuelled by its booming economy, has given rise to a whole series of problems. The 'internal costs' range from acute traffic congestion to the shortage and great expense of housing, from environmental damage to great personal stress. Externally, the costs of Tokyo's

■ **35.11** Tokyo centre – from wartime devastation (top) to modern megalopolis

growth include loss of scarce farmland, great pressure on recreational resources and huge backwash effects, as well as environmental pollution on a wider spatial scale.

Attempts to achieve a planned reduction of those costs have been set in the wider spatial context of what is known as the National Capital Region (NCR) which reaches out to about 150 km from the centre of Tokyo. The history of planning here is a short one. For much of the time since the late 1960s, a three-pronged strategy has been pursued – one 'prong' for each of three major subdivisions of the NCR. **35.12** summarises the objectives for each area. More recently, although the overall strategy remains the same, namely to loosen the metropolitan structure, there has been some amendment to the detail. The aim now is to generate five 'self-sustained urban areas' some distance from Tokyo. The hope is that these these will prove powerfully attractive to employment, services and people currently located in Tokyo and thereby engender the required amount of decentralisation. Perhaps

	Distance ring from city centre km				
	0–10	10–20	20–30	30–40	40–50
Land area of ring km²	235	942	1978	4270	7065
Population million	4.8	7.8	4.1	4.3	2.8
Density persons per km²	20 400	8200	2100	1000	400

■ **35.10** Population densities around Tokyo

Subdivision	Objectives
The core	1 Selective decentralisation – removal of 'non-pivotal' functions (manufacturing, distribution, higher education, etc.) 2 Restructuring – creation of new business nodes to relieve pressure on downtown area 3 Improvement of accessibility 4 Public nuisance abatement 5 Residential renewal and lowering of densities
The surburban ring	1 Tighter control over location and standards of new housing 2 Provision of better infrastructure 3 Improving the quality of the residential environment
The outer development district	1 Development of reception area function 2 Concentration of new growth in 'urbanisation areas' 3 Protection and encouragement of agriculture 4 Promotion of recreation and tourism

■ **35.12** Tokyo – summary of planning objectives

working against all this is the fact that the planners have been successful in restructuring the very centre of Tokyo, creating new and relatively accessible business centres, such as Shinjuku, as well as creating much-needed urban space by reclaiming land from Tokyo Bay (**35.13**). These achievements seem set to keep Tokyo as a strong-centred metropolis.

Although the efficiency of the city and the quality of its built environment have been improved and the affluent of Tokyo enjoy a good standard of living, there are still some shortfalls in aspects of the lifestyle. Housing continues to be cramped and very expensive; there is much stress and pressure within a competitive society; and there are still strong elements of **uglification** in the built-up area (noise, poor drainage, lack of greenery, garish advertising, etc.).

On the plus side, however, as in all Japanese cities, there is a low crime rate and considerable personal security, with low unemployment, and there is much on offer in terms of entertainment. In a recent survey, a quarter of Tokyo residents who were questioned thought that Tokyo was not a comfortable place to live; **35.14** lists some of the good and the bad things respondents suggested about Tokyo.

7 Compare the population densities for Tokyo with those of typical English cities (**35.10**).

8 How would you account for the relative decline of Tokyo's importance as an international convention centre in the early 1980s (see **35.18** on page 497)?

9 Compare the recent changes in Birmingham and Tokyo. What common threads do you see?

10 Research recent developments in, and planning for London. Compare the strategy for London with that for Tokyo (**35.12**).

11 Question a few people on their views about life in your own home area. Compare the benefits and issues they raise with those raised by people in Tokyo (**35.14**). What similarities and differences would you say are mainly due to **a** environment, **b** social and cultural structure, **c** political organisation and planning, and **d** economic activities?

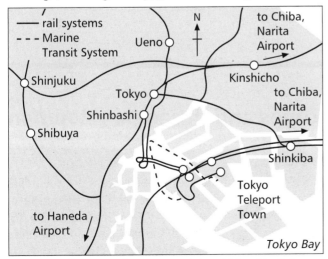

■ **35.13** Teleport project on a reclaimed island in Tokyo Bay

Q: What do you think are the good points of living in Tokyo? Please mention up to three points.

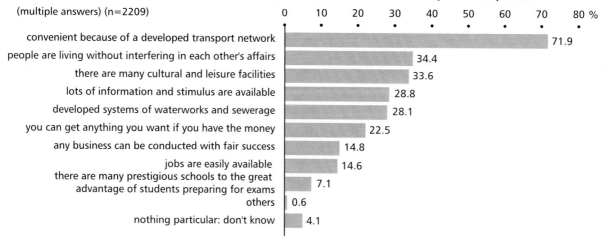

(multiple answers) (n=2209)

convenient because of a developed transport network — 71.9
people are living without interfering in each other's affairs — 34.4
there are many cultural and leisure facilities — 33.6
lots of information and stimulus are available — 28.8
developed systems of waterworks and sewerage — 28.1
you can get anything you want if you have the money — 22.5
any business can be conducted with fair success — 14.8
jobs are easily available — 14.6
there are many prestigious schools to the great advantage of students preparing for exams — 7.1
others — 0.6
nothing particular: don't know — 4.1

Q: What are the things you don't like about living in Tokyo? Please specify up to three things.

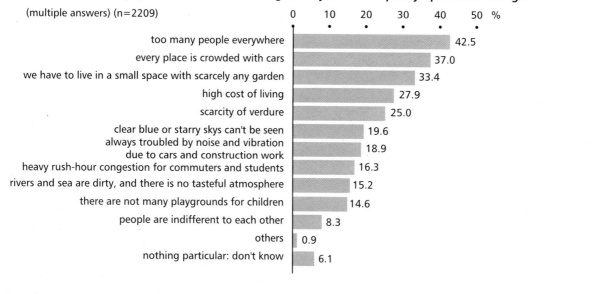

(multiple answers) (n=2209)

too many people everywhere — 42.5
every place is crowded with cars — 37.0
we have to live in a small space with scarcely any garden — 33.4
high cost of living — 27.9
scarcity of verdure — 25.0
clear blue or starry skys can't be seen — 19.6
always troubled by noise and vibration due to cars and construction work — 18.9
heavy rush-hour congestion for commuters and students — 16.3
rivers and sea are dirty, and there is no tasteful atmosphere — 15.2
there are not many playgrounds for children — 14.6
people are indifferent to each other — 8.3
others — 0.9
nothing particular: don't know — 6.1

■ **35.14** Tokyo opinion poll

35.4 **Enterprise Zones and Urban Development Corporations**

IT7, 8 It is clear that city initiatives such as those illustrated in the two case studies have been aimed at two broad objectives: to improve the working efficiency of the city, and to improve the quality of life and the environment. A major challenge has been the revival of inner-city areas. Three processes – the loss of employment oppor-tunities, the obsolescence of the urban fabric, and the outward migration of the people – are explored in **35.15**. The loss of jobs has been a major cause of the decline. Any revival of inner-city areas must include actions designed to regenerate local jobs. City authorities can do much, but the task is such as to **IT7, 8**

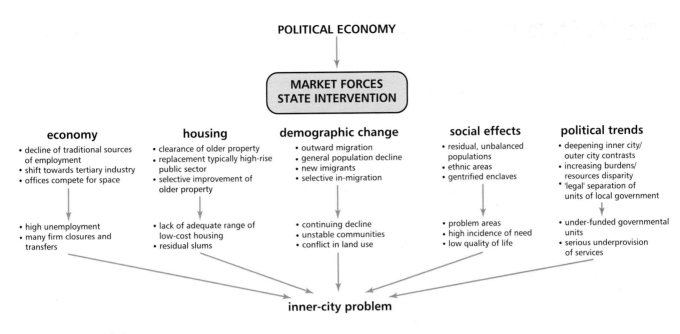

POLITICAL ECONOMY

↓

MARKET FORCES
STATE INTERVENTION

economy
- decline of traditional sources of employment
- shift towards tertiary industry
- offices compete for space

↓

- high unemployment
- many firm closures and transfers

housing
- clearance of older property
- replacement typically high-rise public sector
- selective improvement of older property

↓

- lack of adequate range of low-cost housing
- residual slums

demographic change
- outward migration
- general population decline
- new imigrants
- selective in-migration

↓

- continuing decline
- unstable communities
- conflict in land use

social effects
- residual, unbalanced populations
- ethnic areas
- gentrified enclaves

↓

- problem areas
- high incidence of need
- low quality of life

political trends
- deepening inner city/ outer city contrasts
- increasing burdens/ resources disparity
- 'legal' separation of units of local government

↓

- under-funded governmental units
- serious underprovision of services

inner-city problem

■ **35.15** Causes of the inner-city crisis

IT7, 8

■ **35.16** Distribution of Enterprise Zones and Assisted Areas in Great Britain

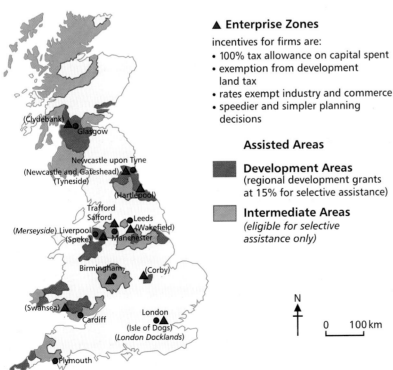

▲ **Enterprise Zones**

incentives for firms are:
- 100% tax allowance on capital spent
- exemption from development land tax
- rates exempt industry and commerce
- speedier and simpler planning decisions

Assisted Areas

Development Areas
(regional development grants at 15% for selective assistance)

Intermediate Areas
(*eligible for selective assistance only*)

N
↑

0   100 km

require the support of central government. In the UK there has been intervention in the form of two initiatives – Enterprise Zones (EZs), and Urban Development Corporations (UDCs). Both were launched in the 1980s in the wake of urban uprisings, as at Brixton, Handsworth and Toxteth, which had drawn attention to the simmering discontent within the ailing inner cities.

The declared purpose of the EZ scheme was to see how far commerical and industrial activity could be encouraged by the removal of certain tax burdens and local authority controls. EZs are relatively small, usually between 50 and 500 ha, and they are fairly widely distributed (**35.16**). Whilst there has been a fair record of job creation in many EZs, it has been an uphill struggle in recessionary times. Equally, the multiplier effects of those jobs have been disappointingly modest.

IT7, 8

It soon became apparent that, in some locations, regeneration programmes needed to be concerned with more than just employment. Thus the UDC scheme, which followed, represents a more comprehensive approach to inner-city regeneration. The first two UDCs to be established were in the Docklands district of east London, and in Liverpool. Subsequently, they have been established in many cities, and include the Heartlands Project in Birmingham (**35.6**) in 1992. The corporations have comprehensive powers of land acquisition and use public money as a 'pump primer' to create an attractive environment for investment, employment and residential development. The environmental improvements effected by such schemes have been impressive, but the record of job creation has been dismal, principally some would say because of the prevailing economic recession.

There are also instances of spontaneous, as opposed to planned, regeneration in the inner cities. **Gentrification** is a process of housing improvement associated with a change in neighbourhood composition involving the displacement of low-income by high-income households. It is widespread in urban USA, but it is only evident in a few British cities, such as Bristol and London. In essence, it is a process involving young, middle-income, well-educated households whose preference is to work and play in the central city. They have not been tempted by the pull of the suburbs. Rather, with the cooperation of estate agents, property developers and building societies, and with encouragement from the city authorities keen to increase their tax base, these people have caused an upturn in the fortunes of select areas of the inner city. They have invested in the rehabilitation of old houses and streets, often in areas developed during Georgian and early Victorian times. Clifton in Bristol and Chelsea and Islington in London are areas which have undergone gentrification.

35.5 **Global process, global change**

As we move towards the 21st century, urban development is seen to increasingly reflect global influences. The process of **globalisation**, or **internationalisation**, has transformed the economic world into one system (see section 30.7), and is influencing the social and cultural scenes as well. Of course, the physical environment has always been global, and awareness of this is mounting. Indicators of this globalisation include the rise in international travellers (from 25 million in 1950 to 325 million in 1986), the increase in international trade (a sixfold increase since 1965) and the rise of international banking, non-government organisations and multinational or transnational corporations (see Chapter 30).

Urban model E shows how global processes lead through to changed urban structures (**35.17**). Two most significant processes are the dematerialisation of production and the delocalisation of information. Technological changes have led to a marked reduction in the volume of raw material and energy needed in production, though more 'information' is needed. At the same time, global computer links, databases and rapid communication systems mean that information is available at any location that has the now widely available communications technology. Production is no longer tied to traditional locations.

These two important processes allow the delocalisation and dispersion of production to many places not necessarily in large urban settlements. Thus cities, especially those relying heavily on manufacturing, must change their function to ensure they stay at the centre of economic life. For most cities, this means a new emphasis on service industry.

The largest cities need even more fundamental change. Here two developments going hand in hand are the change to 'knowledge-based' cities, and

■ **35.17** Urban model E: Global processes and urban structure

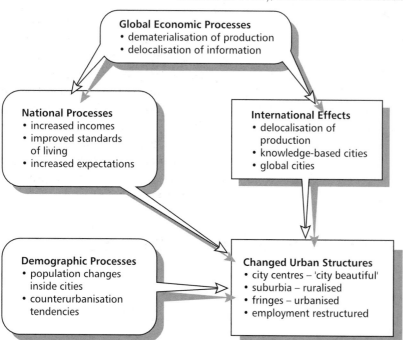

Global Economic Processes
• dematerialisation of production
• delocalisation of information

National Processes
• increased incomes
• improved standards of living
• increased expectations

International Effects
• delocalisation of production
• knowledge-based cities
• global cities

Demographic Processes
• population changes inside cities
• counterurbanisation tendencies

Changed Urban Structures
• city centres – 'city beautiful'
• suburbia – ruralised
• fringes – urbanised
• employment restructured

City	1986		1982	
	Rank	No.	Rank	No.
Paris	1	358	1	292
London	2	258	2	242
Geneva	3	180	3	147
Brussels	4	157	4	118
Madrid	5	118	33	22
Vienna	6	106	5	90
West Berlin	7	100	11	47
Singapore	8	100	14	44
Barcelona	9	96	–	8
Amsterdam	10	84	19	36
Seoul	11	84	19	36
Washington, DC	12	75	13	45
New York	13	72	6	70
Rome	14	69	8	69
Strasbourg	15	67	10	52
Munich	16	63	23	34
Copenhagen	17	63	6	70
Stockholm	18	63	27	28
Tokyo	19	56	9	55
Hong Kong	20	54	12	46
Budapest	21	53	18	37
Helsinki	22	52	23	34
Montreal	23	50	30	24
Bangkok	24	47	19	36
Buenos Aires	25	46	36	20
Total		6681		4353

■ **35.18** International conventions, 1982 and 1986

Metropolitan area	City centre	Suburbs
Brussels (1970–76)	0.2	–0.2	2.0
Montreal (1971–80)	0.2	–1.3	1.3
Toronto (1971–80)	0.7	–1.3	1.4
Copenhagen (1970–80)	0.0	–2.1	1.2
Helsinki (1970–78)	1.0	–0.5	4.7
Paris (1968–75)	0.5	–1.7	1.4
Lyon (1968–75)	1.0	–2.0	3.5
Hamburg (1970–78)	0.1	–0.9	1.8
Dublin (1971–79)	1.8	–0.5	5.6
Milan (1971–78)	0.6	–0.3	1.7
Tokyo (1970–75)	1.5	–0.4	4.6
Osaka (1970–75)	1.6	–1.4	3.1
Rotterdam (1970–76)	–0.3	–1.5	2.8
Amsterdam (1970–76)	–0.6	–1.5	1.6
Oslo (1970–80)	0.3	–0.6	1.4
Lisbon (1970–80)	3.2	1.4	4.6
Stockholm (1970–75)	0.2	–2.0	3.3
Zurich (1970–80)	–0.3	–1.4	1.1
London (1971–78)	–1.0	–1.6	–0.7
Manchester (1971–78)	–0.3	–1.6	–0.1
Chicago (1970–75)	0.1	–1.6	1.6
Detroit (1970–75)	0.0	–2.4	1.1

■ **35.19** Percentage population change in OECD cities in the 1970s

the attempt to obtain the status of a 'global city'. Knowledge-based cities treat knowledge as the basic resource that can make them attractive to a whole plethora of activities – science, technology, finance, marketing, insurance, education, logistics, cultural and international affairs – and to some areas of production. Such cities need a good quality of life to attract workers in these activities. The global city is typically the location of the headquarters of large international companies, a centre for international banking, insurance and finance, and a focus for international conferences and meetings. **35.18** shows the changing fortunes of the world's leading global cities by this last measure.

Other global trends are to be detected rather more at a national level, such as increases in income, standards of living and expectations. Their timing and scale vary from country to country, but for many people in Europe, North America, Japan and Australasia, these particular increases have intensified the outward movement to 'greener pastures' in new suburbs, dormitory settlements and retirement areas. **35.19** shows this trend in full swing in the 1970s. Subsequently, the decentralisation tendency has scaled up still further and to such an extent as to warrant recognition as a new process – **counterurbanisation**.

35.6 Counterurbanisation and the post-industrial city

IT8

Strictly speaking, counterurbanisation is a process of population decentralisation. Sometimes referred to as the **rural population turnaround**, it was first noted in the USA in the early 1970s. Census data began to show that the

IT8

metropolitan areas (i.e. the main cities) were losing population by net migration to non-metroplitan areas (i.e. lesser urban settlements and rural areas). Evidence of this process has now been found in most industrialised countries. Three specific traits are identified:

- a centrifugal tendency by which population is becoming more evenly distributed across national territory
- a downward redistribution of population from larger to smaller places within the urban system
- a negative correlation between settlement size and population growth (**35.20**).

Many explanations have been offered for these changes. The following merely lists what seem to be among the more plausible:

Technology
- Improvements in transport and communications technology.

Government intervention
- The availability of government subsidies for rural areas.
- The success of government policies designed to reduce spatial inequalities.

Movement
- The acceleration of retirement migration.
- The effects of economic recession on rural–urban migration.
- The expansion of commuting fields around employment centres.
- The shift of rural population to local urban centres.

Economic and social change
- The restructuring of manufacturing and the associated growth of branch plants.
- Change in the residential preferences of people of working age, and entrepreneurs.
- The improvement of education, health and other social services in rural areas.
- The emergence of scale diseconomies and social costs in large cities.

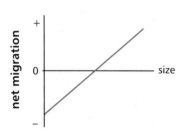

a) Urbanisation dominant

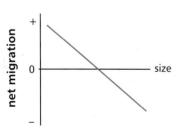

b) Counterurbanisation dominant

- **35.20** Models of urbanisation and counter-urbanisation

12 a Suggest how each of the items in the above list helps to explain the onset of counterurbanisation in the UK.
 b Can you think of any additional reasons for the process?

It is most likely that the explanation for counterurbanisation is to be found in a combination of reasons. But no matter the cause, it seems clear that a combination of global and national processes is leading to changed urban structures for the 21st century. The present urban system represents huge capital investment and 'plant', and will only be slowly modified and changed. The picture at the moment is confused. On the one hand, counterurbanisation seems to be above all else a reaction against large cities. On the other hand, globalisation appears to be calling for the emergence of a class of 'supercities'. Then there is the impact of new technologies, particularly in the realm of communications, which is clearly reducing the need for people and activities to agglomerate in towns and cities. Given this technology, shifts in the sectoral balance (from industry to services), reorganisation (internationalisation) of the global economy, and an accelerating counterurbanisation, one might be forgiven for wondering whether the post-industrial city has a future? Perhaps it will be that the urban system of the 21st century becomes increasingly polarised between the massed ranks of fairly prosperous small towns, and a 'super-league' of global cities.

13 Outline your own vision of the British urban system in the 21st century.

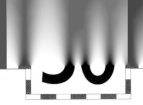

36.1 **Issues and personal investigative work**

The last chapter of this unit draws on your work in the preceding five chapters and gives you the opportunity to apply your knowledge, understanding and skills. A major function of your learning in this unit is to enable you to participate with understanding in the sorts of debate and discussion that lead to decisions on changes and issues in settlements now and in the future. The geographical skills you are developing here will help you to assimilate and critically analyse diverse

■ **36.1** Exploring issues

Issues should be discussed in groups and use made of techniques like brainstorming, questioning, ranking and presenting findings. A general approach to the study of issues should include:

1 Identification of the issue or issues involved. The choice of an issue to study.

2 Critical analysis of the information: Who wrote it? Is it reliable? What interest do the authors have in the outcomes? What is 'fact' and what is 'opinion'? Can the 'facts' be verified?

3 Assessment of the implications for quality of life, resource use and environment in the situation as it is.

4 Suggestion of alternative ways forward. Who is/may be suggesting them?

5 Analysis of what assumptions, beliefs, values and priorities underlie the alternatives and the views expressed.

6 Discussion on what decision-making process will decide the outcomes. Who has power to influence this process?

7 Re-assessment of the information – look for other evidence you need, and make your own response to the issue.

packages of information, and to consider the priorities and values that underlie the presentations and preferences.

The changes and developments taking place in settlements around the world today give rise to important issues and challenges. Many of these feature in the media; they are topical and 'relevant'; they are debated and different viewpoints are expressed. Often in tackling them, the distribution of power and access to decision-making become the major issue, and the quest for justice the mainspring of activity.

The suggestions in **36.1** offer a general approach to the analysis and discussion of issues; they offer an approach that can be used in each section of this chapter. Each section suggests a possible issue, and includes some questions about the specific resources to get you started. Each of the issues constitutes an excellent and challenging topic for project work, often involving fieldwork, as well as offering the opportunity for students to make a contribution to understanding spatial processes and patterns in their home area. All of the issues relate to urban rather than rural settlements, and most to the social dimension of towns and cities, thereby giving exposure to an aspect of settlement geography only touched on in earlier chapters.

36.2 **Urban ecology**

IT1, 3

Towns and cities are part of the global environment and are involved in the open system of life. An inputs–outputs approach shows up the massive impact of city life. The issues here involve the kind of project to which the work on Kumasi referred (Chapter 34).

The ecosystems outlined in **36.2** and **36.3** provide models of the living city, and **36.4** and **36.5** are examples of ecological problems.

IT1, 3

STARTER

Issue:

City waste disposal

Questions:

■ Why is 'circular metabolism' not already part of every city's plan?

■ Why do industrialists and business people pay so little attention to the environment and quality of life along the US –Mexican border?

The Mexican plants have thrived for more than 20 years on cheap labour, tax breaks and lax pollution laws. Much of the Mexican side of the 2000-mile border, that runs from Matamoros on the Gulf of Mexico to Tijuana on the Pacific, bears witness to environmental destruction.

Over the years the factories, mostly American owned subsidiaries, have been a magnet for hundreds of thousands of Mexicans in search of jobs. Mexico's headlong rush for development, however, has helped turn its cities along the border into cesspools. Environmentalists fear this could happen throughout Mexico if it signs a free-trade agreement with the United States and Canada.

To walk across the bridge from Brownsville to Matamoros is to step into an environmental nightmare. Municipal and industrial waste flows through the centre of town in open ditches that eventually empty into the Rio Grande and the Gulf of Mexico. Ramshackle huts have sprouted next to stinking canals full of fluorescent pink water from the toxic waste of chemical and electronic assembly plants nearby.

Across town from the Finsa Industrial Park, Matamoros's largest, plastics and highly toxic fibres smoulder at the landfill, producing a chemical cloud that often hangs over the city.

■ **36.4** On the US–Mexican border: from *The Independent*, 3 March 1992

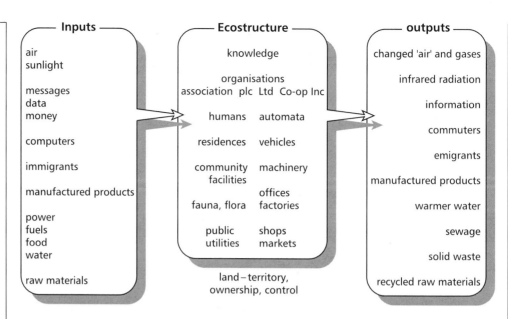

■ **36.2** An urban ecosystem

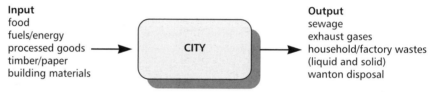

a) Present linear urban metabolism

Input
food
fuels/energy
processed goods
timber/paper
building materials

CITY

Output
sewage
exhaust gases
household/factory wastes
(liquid and solid)
wanton disposal

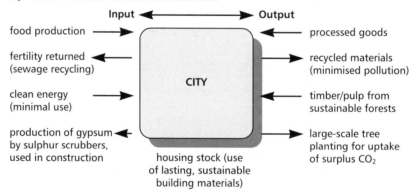

b) Future circular urban metabolism

Input ⟷ Output

food production →
← processed goods
fertility returned ←
(sewage recycling)
→ recycled materials
(minimised pollution)

CITY

clean energy →
(minimal use)
← timber/pulp from
sustainable forests

production of gypsum ←
by sulphur scrubbers,
used in construction
→ large-scale tree
planting for uptake
of surplus CO_2

housing stock (use
of lasting, sustainable
building materials)

■ **36.3** Present and future urban metabolism

City incinerator a 'disaster' – claim

■ **REPORT by JAMES DORAN**

BIRMINGHAM Friends of the Earth have released a report which they claim exposes the potential dangers involved in the proposed new incineration plant at Tysley.

The group fears the incinerator, which will turn household waste into energy, could become a gigantic white elephant within years, as well as an environmental disaster for decades to come.

Dangerous

They claim the furnace could emit dangerous toxic compounds into the atmosphere, increasing air pollution across the West Midlands and working against the growing international campaign to counter the causes of global warming.

The group also fears tens of thousands of tonnes of highly toxic ash will be produced and dumped in a landfill site, which could become a serious environmental hazard for many years.

Financial problems also bother the group, which is concerned that the new waste to energy process set to provide 25 megawatts of power per year, will jeopardise the recycling industry.

■ **36.5** Pollution threat from a city incinerator: from *Birmingham News*, 11 February 1994

36.3 **Children in cities**

IT5

Chapters 33, 34 and 35 provided discussion and several examples of the deprivation common in inner cities in the industrialised world and in the fast-growing cities of Africa, Asia and Latin America.

Children seem to take the brunt of the suffering caused by poverty, especially in large cities. And it is not only in the developing world – in Washington in the USA, for example, 51 under-18-year olds were murdered in 1993.

Two such sad events in different parts of the world are documented in **36.6**.

IT5

> **STARTER**
>
> **Issue:**
> The deprivation and ill-treatment of children in cities
>
> **Questions:**
> ■ Why are children forced into these situations?
> ■ How can ordinary people behave in these ways towards young children?
> ■ Who should take responsibility for this terrible state of affairs?
> ■ Who has the power to do something about these things?

■ **36.6** Children in cities

Colombia

Invited to their own funerals

In August last year, death notices were put up overnight in Colombia's capital, Bogota, inviting the local community to attend the funerals of street children. The posters were printed in large bold typeface, two feet square, and were plastered across the walls in one of the city's most deprived neighbourhoods. The message was clear.

"The industrialists, businessmen, civic groups, and community at large in the Zone of Martyrs invite you to the funerals of the delinquents of this sector, events that will commence immediately and will continue until they are exterminated."

Thousands of street children in Bogota and other cities in Colombia live in daily fear of being assassinated by armed vigilantes who work together in death squads. The planned murders of children on the street are commonly referred to as "social clean-up operations" and are being conducted with increasing regularity.

Every month, up to 40 children are simply wiped out. They are often shot, their bodies buried in unmarked mass graves.

The youngsters who live on the street – teenage prostitutes, beggars, petty thieves, drug addicts – are among the most vulnerable Colombians. They have often escaped from violent home lives, and now live in squalid conditions on the street where some spend their time sniffing glue or taking *basuco*, the highly addictive local variant on crack.

From *Amnesty International British Section Journal*, January/February 1994

Birmingham, England

Victims of neighbours' abuse

WHEN Jean (not her real name) moved into a predominantly white suburb in South Birmingham eight months ago, it wasn't long before her new neighbours made it clear she wasn't welcome.

Her six-year-old daughter was taunted at school, by children belonging to Jean's not-so-friendly new neighbours.

Their spiteful campaign was all down to the fact that Jean – who is white – was going out with a black man.

The eldest of Jean's three children, all of whom are white, has been beaten up by a gang of local girls.

Jean believes this was part of the campaign against her, because the ringleader of the gang – who is aged nine – has been among those hurling abuse at the family. The family' pet dog has also been stolen – and Jean suspects this is also down to the racial vendetta.

Ignorant

She says of her tormentors: "They are ignorant people – if that's the way they wish to lead their lives, let them. But why should I lead my life for other people?

"If I was on my own, I wouldn't move – but for the sake of the children, I will have to."

From *Birmingham Voice*, 11 November 1993

36.4 **Movement around towns and cities**

With the separation of workplace from residence, the journey to work has become a major issue in most large towns and cities. In cities in the developing world, like Dhaka, the rush-hour has to be seen to be believed, and is quite as bad

New bid to ease transport fears

BIRMINGHAM is getting ready to tackle transport headaches with an important new initiative aimed at focusing attention on the growing problem. With 500,000 people a day heading in and out of the city, continuing pressure is being placed on Birmingham's transport system.

"It's getting harder and harder to get in and out of the city. More traffic means more congestion and pollution, more pollution means poorer health. We need to look at better use of current transport systems and introduce cleaner travel methods."

Surveys carried out in 1985 predicted a 35 per cent increase in traffic on city roads by 2010. Traffic in Birmingham is currently increasing at a rate of 1.5 per cent a year.

■ **36.7** Getting to work in Birmingham: from *Birmingham Voice*, 26 January 1994

as that in Los Angeles or Tokyo (**36.8**). Dhaka is unusual in still having so many cycle-rickshaws. Local details vary, but in most South Asian cities the small, often three-wheeled, motorised enclosed taxi is more common. In Taipei, Taiwan, millions of scooters compete with buses, taxis and private cars, and in many African countries buses and shared taxis dominate the transport scene. But all major cities have their rush-hour problems.

There are at least three major components in the movement patterns of towns and cities. First, there is the great diurnal pulse of workers and goods generated by the high level of economic activity at the

■ **36.8** Rush-hour in Dhaka

centre, and accommodated by a converging radial network. Secondly, there are the circular movements within the city accommodated by ring roads. Thirdly, there are the motorway 'boxes' and 'orbital' roads which allow through traffic to by-pass whole towns and cities. Major hold-ups often occur where these components meet and/or intersect, where the radial routes converge at the centre, or where there are queues for parking spaces.

In Western cities, constant planning and adjustment are necessary to cope with increasing commuter needs. Heavy traffic is perhaps the most obvious polluter and degrader of the environment, from the blue-grey haze of diesel in Kathmandu to the petrol fumes belching from London's heavy road traffic.

Solutions tried vary from making traffic a priority and assigning public capital resources to the construction of multi-lane highways, flyovers, tunnels and giant parking areas, as in Los Angeles, to restricting or even banning cars from the city centre and giving priority to public transport systems of buses, trains and rapid transit.

The resources here give information on the situation in Birmingham, England (**36.7**) and in a city of the new Asian Pacific Rim economic core – Taipei.

■ **36.9** Taipei Rapid Transport System (RTS), Taiwan

The Taipei RTS

High capacity – 1600 people per train, 20–5 0000 people per hour

Short intervals – 1 to 10-minute intervals, depending on demand

High speed – 25–85 km per hour

High-quality service – well-equipped, stable, safe, secure and comfortable

Dept of Rapid Transit Systems,
Taipei Municipal Government

STARTER

Issue:
Journey to work

Questions:
■ Who moves, and who pays?
■ Why should inner and intermediate city residents suffer for the convenience of outer city commuters?
■ Can improvements be linked to a more equitable distribution of wealth from the city-centre activities?
■ What alternative solutions are there?
■ What is happening in your town?

36.5 Gender and equality

IT5

The issue of gender equality in urban design and morphology was mentioned in a historical context in Chapter 34. This and other issues of gender equality have if anything deepened as urbanisation has progressed. The change in employment patterns in the industrialised world, with many more part-time jobs available, and a more flexible view of career patterns becoming prevalent, is increasing the number of job opportunities available for women. Many of these, however, involve low rates of pay, few benefits and little security.

In Africa, women play a very important part in the informal economy (see section 34.3), especially dominating the trading scene. In Ghana, for instance, the market women are a very powerful economic and political group. In Latin America, and to a lesser extent in Asia, women's groups lead innovative work in self-help schemes, and their increased political awareness and activity are becoming a force in urban decision-making.

The resources in **36.10** look at three aspects of urban settlements where gender issues are especially relevant:

- the general development of residential suburbs well away from places of work

- the relative poverty experienced by women in cities, often compounded by ethnic prejudice

- the necessity for women to take part-time work, often in the informal sector.

■ **36.10** Women in cities

CHANGE
composition of households changing

CHANGE
increase in number of women in paid employment in the formal sector of the economy

cities have distinct areas of production and reproduction
workplace ||| residence

OK ?
single woman, high-paid job, gentrified city-centre residence

OK ?
married woman, children, suburban house, must commute to work

suburban woman lives in an out-of-date urban structure

STARTER

Issue:
The adjustment of settlement structure to provide gender equality

Questions:
- What adjustments should be made, and are they feasible?
- Is the city entirely 'a man's world'?
- Would there be striking improvements in economic and social position without radical political activity by women?

Women Working in Third World Cities

Much of the activity carried out by women in the informal sector of the large cities is in industrial subcontracting which produces commodities for the export market as in food processing, textiles, and clothing. The labour conditions are marked by exploitation through low wages, long hours, poor working conditions, non-payment of overhead costs, and the use of child labour. Moreover, low cash wages limit the purchasing power of the household with respect to food and other household necessities that require payment in money. Due to gender inequalities in family allocation of consumption items, urban women suffer from higher rates of malnutrition and morbidity. Women in the informal sector suffer not only from poverty through belonging to poor households but, in addition, they suffer from the gender subordination and sexual discrimination characteristic of the patriarchial values of the majority of Third World countries.

Lata Chatterjee, 1989

36.6 **Divided cities**

The contrasts between rich and poor in cities in the developing world are obvious, as are those between the inner and outer areas of Western cities. Chapters 33, 34 and 35 have described divisions within cities, and the issues raised are central to the future of urban life.

The American geographer Bunge has described the situation in the US city as follows:

> The people of the 'outer city of plenty' take benefit from investments in city centres, whilst the profits miss out the 'inner city of death' and only filter into the 'intermediate city of deprivation'.

Well-defined spatial inequalities have existed in European cities at least since the Industrial Revolution, and in North American cities since the Transport Revolution of the late 19th century, but recent worsening of the situation has given cause for added concern. Six main reasons have been put forward to explain this deterioration:

- increased unemployment
- less employment in manufacturing
- more single-parent households
- increase in paid jobs performed by married women
- earnings rising fastest in better-paid jobs
- state benefits rising more slowly than earnings.

36.11 outlines four different types of theory that have been put forward to explain the occurrence of urban poverty and deprivation. In reality, of course, it may well be that the actual explanation may involve elements of all four and that the mix of elements will vary from place to place.

Information based on research in New York and London is given in **36.12**. Both are global cities and have a population around the 7 million mark. They were both part of the 'urban revival' of the 1980s.

STARTER

Issue:
Inequality and segregation – the urban time-bomb?

Questions:
- How are Bunge's reasons interlinked?
- Why should these reasons affect the inner city in particular?
- What other 'reasons' lie behind Bunge's reasons?
- Should people be 'pigeon-holed' into classes?
- Is inequality and deprivation the inevitable result of the market economy in cities?
- Why has so little been done about this situation and the processes that lead to it?

- **36.11** Theories of urban poverty and deprivation

Theory	Source of problem	Characteristics of problem	Perpetuating features	Main outcome
Structural class conflict	social formation	• unequal distribution of power • maintenance of disparities	• organisation of labour • class distinctions	inequality
Institutional management	allocative system	• uneven distribution of resources • inefficient bureaucracies • weak communications/awareness	• maintenance of elitism • low welfare inputs • non-sharing of opportunities	disadvantage underprivilege
Cycle of deprivation	social group residential area	• few opportunities • limited access to social mobility • transmission of poor attitudes • disadvantaged environment	• subcultural norms • lack of positive interventions	deprivations low aspirations low achievement
Culture of poverty	individual inadequacies family background	• group apathy • inherited deficiencies	• fatalism • failure of welfare services	retardation poverty

a) Inequalities in household incomes

	Ratio of top to bottom quintile		
	1980	**1986**	**1988**
London	2.85	3.68	4.37
New York	3.50	3.81	NA

b) Changes in real household incomes

		% change in income	
		1980–86	**1986–88**
Top 10%	London	+25.8	+8.4
	New York	+22.0	NA
Bottom 10%	London	−7.6	−13.7
	New York	−8.3	NA

c) Classification of households according to control, ownership and marketability of occupational skills

[*Warning:* This classification is based on generalisations.]

I An upper class: owners, executives, the wealthy

II Middle classes:
  II a the new upper service class: professionals, administrators, officials, managers
  II b middle service class: lower grade, smaller businesses than (a)
  II c deskilled white-collar workers: clerical, technical, sales workers

III Working classes:
  III a skilled working class: in decline with loss of manufacturing industry
  III b semi-skilled and unskilled working class: many new jobs in consumer and producer services; insecurity and low wages

IV The underclass: long-term welfare-dependent households

d) Who lives where?

[*Warning:* These are also generalisations.]

1 Central luxury city of the wealthy – group I

2 Gentrified old inner-city housing – IIa and younger IIb

3 The suburban city: favoured areas – most of IIb
  less favoured areas – IIc and IIIa, especially older households

4 Inner tenement city (in New York) or public housing city (in London) – most of IIc and IIIa and b

5 The ghetto (in New York) or poorest inner city (in London) – many of IIIb and IV

6 Outside the city in 'stockbroker' commuter belts – I and IIa

■ **36.12** Information on poverty and wealth in London and New York

36.7 **Crime and delinquency**

IT5,7 One of the most common findings of analyses of crime and delinquency has been the correlation between crime rates and the growth of cities (**36.13**). There are many theories that seek to explain crime but none of these has found universal acceptance. Theories range from the **structural**, which see crime as being rooted in the inequalities that have been created by the capitalist system, to the **ecological**, which attach more importance to area characteristics and the nature of social groups. Certainly, many would agree that crime is probably one of the most overt symptoms of the inner-city crisis and of urban deprivation. IT5,7

There are two aspects of crime that come into focus in geographical studies, namely the spatial distributions of crime and of criminals. As regards the former, it is clearly necessary to distinguish between the type of offence. For example, shoplifting will show concentrations in the CBD and retailing parks, whilst burglary is most likely to

■ **36.13** City size and crime in the USA

City size	No. of reported crimes per 100 000 population
+ 5 million	4385
3–5 million	4186
2–3 million	3376
1–2 million	3543
0.75–1 million	3369
0.5–0.75 million	2927
0.25–0.5 million	2700
Rural areas	927

Sex & age	Council	Rented	Owner occupied	Mixed	Whole of city
Males 10–19	40	59	24	39	33
Females 10–19	11	13	6	12	9
Males 15–19	63	90	35	66	51

■ **36.14** Juvenile offender rates, by housing class in Cardiff IT5,7

the person (e.g. assault) and property (e.g. theft and vandalism). Conversely, the perpetrators of fraud and forgery may frequently be found living in middle-class areas. IT5,7

occur in the more wealthy residential areas. As for the residential locations of criminals, studies in Britain have indicated an association with what are termed 'problem housing estates', often located on the urban fringe, and with some of the most deprived parts of the inner city. This is illustrated by the data in **36.14**, which analyse juvenile delinquency by types of housing tenure. Again, the type of offence is significant, in that the sorts of crime likely to be committed by criminals in the two areas mentioned above are likely to be against

STARTER

Issue:
The spatial patterns of crimes and criminals in the city

Questions:
■ Why is crime widely regarded as a symptom of urban deprivation?
■ What are the possible links between environmental factors and the rise and distribution of crime?
■ Do the same possible explanations of urban poverty (**36.11**) apply to the incidence of crime?

36.8 Investigative topics and how to pursue them

One of the requirements of all the new A and AS Geography syllabuses is that they require all candidates to complete personal investigative work. In most cases, this means researching and reporting on a topic or issue. The worry for many candidates is finding a suitable topic for investigation.

Many of the topics touched on in this unit could certainly be further explored by wider reading and local investigation. For example, many projects are possible around the topics of retail patterns and shopping habits in any local area. They can be backed by some reading of Christaller's central-place theory and Reilly's retail gravitation laws. Journey-to-work patterns can provide fruitful topics for personal research, using tables in the 1991 Census Report as a starting point. Studies of both these topics can be put in the context of the spheres of influence of urban centres and the delimitation of urban fields and lead into one important dimension of rural–urban relationships.

In addition to the pursuit in your locality of the topics and issues indicated in this chapter or others raised elsewhere in the unit, there is a huge range of settlement topics awaiting exploration. These include: provision and access to leisure facilities; community projects; housing preferences and markets; local migration; the importance of boundaries to development and planning; perception and its part in urban decision-making; the spatial impacts of specific developments such as new shopping centres, industrial estates, motorways; or the re-organisation of the National Health Service.

Looking through local newspapers may well pay off in your search for a suitable topic or issue, by drawing your attention to some topical, perhaps contentious matter that has a spatial dimension. The sort of issue that might be revealed by your search could be the siting of a new sewage treatment works, the proposal to build a new road through an established residential area, or the incidence of crime.

Type of problem		Pollutants/ sources	Nature of damage	Indicators	Treatment	Recent trends
Human	Air pollution	sulphur oxides nitrogen oxides carbon oxides hydrocarbons	health hazard loss of amenity	indices show concentrations of pollutants	ban on fuels emission control	sources decline with more control on fuels and emission increase in small particulates
	Water pollution	industrial commercial waste: sewage	health hazard polluted waterways aesthetic problems	biological oxygen demand PDI index	emission control water processing	increasing sources stricter controls several irredeemable outcomes
	Solid waste	industrial domestic building rubble packaging	fire risk health hazard aesthetic deterioration disrupted ecosystem	visible environment weight collected	collection disposal recycling	increasing problem technology available recycling
	Noise and heat	highways industries airports	physical and mental property value	decibels noise exposure index	noise shield land-use planning	increasing problem more attemptel control
Natural	Fogs	particulates urban climates	traffic hazard safety, stress health	visibility		
	Floods	drainage condition floodplain	threat to life and property	water level frequency	channels flood control	greater control higher losses
	Special events: earthquake hurricane drought	geological or climatic conditions	life, property urban system	frequency vulnerability	basic precautions warning systems	greater disasters increased vulnerability

■ **36.15** Ecological hazards and cities

The integrative themes pursued in this book provide subject areas well worth searching for suitable topics. Set out below are some lines of thought relating to the settlement context of those themes:

IT1 **Systems** – the duality of settlements as components of systems and as systems in their own right; analysing the inputs and outputs of a suburb (**36.16** and **36.18**).

IT2 **Natural hazards** – the assessment of flooding risk and its impact on the location of rural settlements and the configuration of the urban built-up area; urban design in tectonically 'active' areas (**36.15**).

IT3 **Pollution** – the different types of pollution generated by urban growth, and their spatial variations within towns and cities; the relative success of remedial measures (**36.15**).

IT4 **Sustainability** – achieving a proper balance between urban population growth and the expansion of employment and service provision; types of planning intervention to achieve sustainability and a problem-free future (**36.16**).

IT5 **Health** – the incidence of illness as an indicator of urban deprivation; planning the optimum location of medical and welfare services provision within a city or in a peripheral rural area.

IT6 **Leisure and recreation** – the impact on rural settlements and their economies; the urban heritage as a tourist resource (**36.17**).

IT7 **Competition and conflict** – as between different land users and social groups within a built-up area.

IT8 **Environmental change** – brought about by the processes of urbanisation and counterurbanisation; the process of change within settlements.

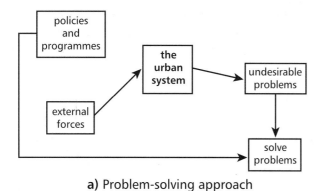

a) Problem-solving approach

b) Regulation of trends approach

■ **36.16** Achieving sustainability: two models of urban planning

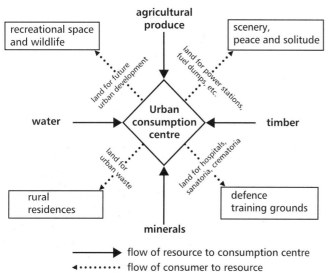

■ **36.17** The countryside as supplier, the town as consumer of rural resources

Having discovered a possible topic for your personal investigation, it is important that you approach it in a methodical and purposeful manner. As regards method, it is essentially a matter of progressing through a logical sequence – topic definition, background reading and investigative design, moving through data collection, analysis and evaluation, to presentation of your findings both verbally and with the aid of maps, diagrams, photos, etc. As regards maintaining a sense of purpose, a useful tip is to ensure that the matter for investigation is posed either as a question or as a hypothesis for testing. And go easy on the questions and hypotheses – one thoroughly answered or tested is

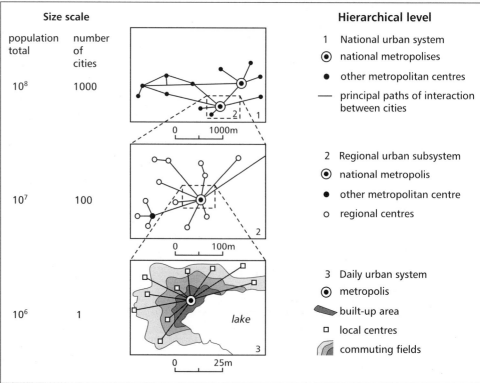

■ **36.18** Urban systems: hierarchical and spatial levels

infinitely preferable to a handful given superficial treatment.

Finally, to return to the task confronted in this section. The bottom line to any potential topic selected for personal investigation is this: Does the topic interest you sufficiently to provide much-needed motivation and enthusiasm? If the answer is 'no', then continue your search.

36.9 **Looking at future trends**

By 2025, if current trends continue, three-fifths of the world's population will live in or close to cities, most of them in the South. It will be in cities that new jobs, opportunities and investments will be concentrated.

Most cities of the South are growing far beyond the capacity of governments to plan the directions and nature of that growth and to provide their inhabitants with basic services.

The basic problem with Northern cities is that they are unsustainable. In general, most Northern city dwellers are adequately housed and fed, but they meet their needs by consuming at rates the planet cannot afford and polluting at rates the planet cannot tolerate. Most Southern city dwellers cannot meet their basic needs for food, clean water, clean air, fuel, transport, and an environment free of disease-causing microbes and worms.

Northern urban development will require less wasteful resource consumption, less fossil fuel use and less pollution; Southern urban development will require more provision of goods and services, but with less pollution and more efficient resource use.

The Human Settlements Programme at the IIED argues that 80% of housing, health and environmental problems can be solved in poor Southern cities, given appropriate approaches to housing, sanitation, water supply and health care. This will not be done by building concrete-block houses with flush toilets, but can be achieved by establishing programmes to help people build and improve their own housing using local materials, and with innovative schemes for water, sanitation and drainage which greatly reduce costs but still provide convenience and health benefits.

This Settlement unit has concentrated firmly on process as the key to understanding, and the five urban models A to E are the core of its theoretical basis. The statement on human settlements (**36.19**) sets out some of the parameters of the present global scene and suggests priorities for future development.

It is clear that the urban future is going to be a challenge for humanity, and there will continue to be tough battles for power between forces with different policies. At a national level, the choices can be polarised between extremes when political decisions are being made, though compromise is possible (**36.20**). Too often the victims of the power-struggles for priorities in development are the poor and powerless, and justice and equality are valued well below wealth creation and stability.

In the past 10 years there has been significant growth in community groups. This has happened both in industrialised cities and in the developing world. These grass-roots movements, whilst still largely impotent at a national or global scale, do influence local circumstances and often lead to improvements in the environment and the quality of life. As a result, they clearly point to one way in which individual participation is possible and effective.

ECONOMIC GROWTH POLICIES
economic growth, efficiency, centralisation, male values,
material wealth, large units, hard technologies,
expert steering, representative, democracy

LEFT-WING POLICIES
emphasis on public sector
public control with trades and
industries
-planning
strong unions
high wages
full employment
social security
-housing
cultural freedom
disarmaments
social experiments
socialist society

RIGHT-WING POLICIES
emphasis on private sector
private initiative and property
free enterprise
right to be unorganised
competitiveness
financial stability
low taxes
private housing
moral values
strong defence, law and order
capitalist society

GREEN POLICIES
ecology, environment, decentralisation, female values,
life qualities, small units, soft technologies,
public participation, direct local democracy, self-management

■ **36.20** Urban policy choices

Join a group to participate in these final activities:

1 What do you see as the main urban and/or rural issues arising in your home area?

2 Look back at the five urban models in this unit (**31.10**, **33.2**, **33.20**, **34.6** and **35.17**). If possible make a copy of each.
a What characteristics do they have in common?
b What perspective does each bring to the study and understanding of settlements?

c In what ways might the processes in each model be changed in order to improve the nature of urban development? Choose one model to explore in detail from this point of view.

3 What are your predictions for the future of settlements over the next 25 years? What will happen to your home settlement? What can you do about it?

The drive for sustainability

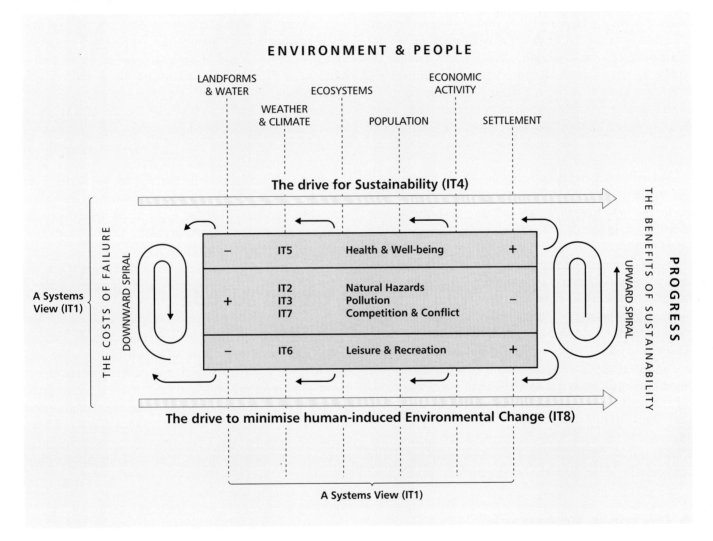

ENVIRONMENT & PEOPLE

LANDFORMS & WATER

WEATHER & CLIMATE

ECOSYSTEMS

POPULATION

ECONOMIC ACTIVITY

SETTLEMENT

The drive for Sustainability (IT4)

THE BENEFITS OF SUSTAINABILITY

PROGRESS

A Systems View (IT1)

THE COSTS OF FAILURE

DOWNWARD SPIRAL

UPWARD SPIRAL

−	IT5	Health & Well-being	+
+	IT2 IT3 IT7	Natural Hazards Pollution Competition & Conflict	−
−	IT6	Leisure & Recreation	+

The drive to minimise human-induced Environmental Change (IT8)

A Systems View (IT1)

The aim of this short conclusion is simply to revisit the eight integrating themes (ITs) threaded through the preceding six units. By finally drawing these themes together, the presentation of this integrated geography is made complete.

The diagram above attempts to show the relationships between the integrating themes and how they interact in a broader framework. Two of the themes – *Sustainability* (IT4) and *Environmental Change* (IT8) – are seen to be particularly significant in this respect. They provide two parallel axes within which all the other themes, with the possible exception of *Systems* (IT1), are located. They are represented as two goals or targets to be aimed at in the

general context of human progress and development.

Without doubt, the major challenge confronting human society at the dawn of the 21st century is to achieve a mode of development that is soundly based on a sustainable balance between population growth on the one hand and use of resources and the environment on the other. If this is achieved, then there is the prospect of reducing environmental abuse and minimising degenerative environmental change attributable to human as opposed to natural causes. A whole range of other benefits should ensue from the associated upward spiral. One has been singled out in this book, namely improved *Health & Well-being* (IT5). But even in pursuit of this one vital outcome, there is always the danger that the improvements being sought might be achieved by resorting to unsustainable practices. Hence the indication on the diagram of the consequent risk of being drawn into the downward spiral – a cumulative downturn involving more devastating *Natural Hazards* (IT2), increased levels of *Pollution* (IT3) and intensified *Competition & Conflict* (IT7) in the exploitation of the Earth's surface. The situation with regard to *Leisure & Recreation* (IT6) is similar in this respect. Whilst increases in both leisure and recreation may rightly be regarded as making a positive contribution to improved health and well-being, as well as generating economic growth (and for this reason are shown as being drawn into the virtuous upward spiral), it is quite clear that much provision today is currently unsustainable. Substantial environmental and social costs are being incurred, such as excessive disturbance of fragile ecosystems and traditional societies with their long-held customs and values.

Failure to achieve sustainable modes of progress and development certainly promises a vicious downward circle, the net effect of which will be a descent towards even more irreversible *Environmental Change* (IT8). Such is the scale of the pressure on the Earth and its resources, and such is the power of modern technology, that people now have the capability to trigger environmental change of an order equivalent to that of creating an Ice Age. The recent phenomenon of global warming serves clearly as a sinister global warning. Similarly, whilst it is people who convert natural events into hazards, there is now an additional and growing list of truly human hazards, from war to AIDS, from poverty to death on the roads. The case studies presented in this book, particularly those related to the two integrating places of Japan and the Indian subcontinent, clearly convey the stark message that the need for *Sustainability* (IT4) applies to the developed and developing worlds alike.

A systems approach

Providing further integrating sinew to this book is the theme of *Systems* (IT1). It is shown as applying to both dimensions of the diagram, namely across the six systematic units and across the other seven integrating themes. A systems approach is particularly appropriate and valuable in pursuit of an integrated geography. It helps in two ways. First, it facilitates a comprehensive view of what is undoubtedly the key focus of geography: the interrelationships of things as they occur in the spatial dimension of the Earth's surface. After all, the very essence of the systems approach is to identify interrelationships – what interacts with what, and how? The second way it helps is by allowing us to break down global complexity into smaller and more manageable, bite-sized morsels. Systems can be defined at a whole range of spatial scales, from a small woodland ecosystem or a single farm system, through drainage basins and regional systems of increasing scale and complexity, to the global systems of atmosphere, biosphere and hydrosphere.

However, whilst the use of a systems approach is invaluable in achieving an integrated geography, it is important to recognise the pitfalls of pursuing it to extremes. There is as much potential harm in an obsession with systems, as there is potential loss of insight from not following such an approach. As with all things, a sense of proportion is crucial.

A global agenda

Finally, the diagram might be seen as setting out a sort of global agenda, a programme of action for the 21st century so far as the environment and people are concerned. Two main objectives are clearly defined – achieving sustainability and minimising environmental change – and at either end of the diagram the upward and downward spirals of benefits and costs respectively are indicated. Perhaps as a last activity you might identify some examples of each. It is hoped that you, the reader of this integrated geography *Environment and People*, are now better informed as to the nature and complexity of today's world, the challenge embodied in the global agenda outlined in the diagram, and what might be required by way of appropriate action to ensure the survival of planet Earth and its peoples.

Index